THE MECHANISM OF ENZYME ACTION

Contribution No. 70 of the McCollum-Pratt Institute

A Symposium on

THE MECHANISM OF ENZYME ACTION

Sponsored by

THE

McCOLLUM–PRATT INSTITUTE

OF

THE JOHNS HOPKINS UNIVERSITY

Edited by

WILLIAM D. McELROY AND BENTLEY GLASS

BALTIMORE

THE JOHNS HOPKINS PRESS

1954

PREFACE

A Symposium on the Mechanism of Enzyme Action was held at The Johns Hopkins University, under the sponsorship of the McCollum-Pratt Institute, on June 16-19, 1953. This volume consists of the papers and discussions presented at these meetings.

During the past thirty years remarkable progress has been made in the isolation and identification of intermediates, necessary enzymes and coenzymes of a large number of biochemical reactions. The availability of isotopes and large quantities of purified enzyme has made it feasible to study in some detail the mechanisms involved in these processes. In recent years such studies have led to the idea that some enzymes enter as reactants, functioning to preserve bond energy. Contributions to the present symposium from the physical chemists, organic chemists, protein chemists, and enzymologists further emphasize the importance of the catalytic protein as a reactant in biochemical transformations. We hope that the exchange of ideas from these various disciplines will help stimulate further research on the mechanism of enzyme action.

Again, it is a pleasure to acknowledge the contributions of the participants and members of the Institute in the planning and conduct of the symposium. I would particularly like to acknowledge the valuable assistance of Dr. S. P. Colowick, in editing the transcription of the discussion and his helpful suggestions in the preparation of the review by Dr. Glass. Dr. Michael Heidelberger (Part 1), Dr. Frank Brink (Part 2), Dr. Leslie Hellerman (Part 3), Dr. Eric G. Ball (Part 4) and Dr. Fritz Lipmann (Part 5) acted as moderators of the symposium. The extensive discussions following the formal papers are evidence of the excellence with which they performed their task.

W. D. McELROY, Director
McCollum–Pratt Institute

v

CONTENTS

———

vii

CONTENTS

Part I

PROTEIN CONFIGURATION AND BIOLOGICAL ACTIVITY

INTRODUCTION

MICHAEL HEIDELBERGER

Professor of Immunochemistry,
College of Physicians and Surgeons, Columbia University;
and Chemist to the Presbyterian Hospital, New York

I ASSUME that I have been asked to act as moderator at this session because immunochemistry is immediately concerned with biological actions resulting from protein configuration. We are still at the beginning of our knowledge of the influence of the fine structure of proteins on their immunological reactivity, to single out, for the moment, but one of their manifold activities. We know something of the effects of size and shape, of the number and character of certain polar groups on the quantitative aspects of the reactivity of a few proteins as antigens with other proteins functioning as specific antibodies. But the effects remain obscure, for example, of the order of amino acids, of the influence of their arrangement in characteristic patterns or outcroppings on whatever functions as the surface of a protein.

Some of these immunochemical questions are of great importance to the understanding of the mechanisms of enzyme actions, our larger topic. To give an example, the activities of some enzymes are inhibited by combination with their homologous antibodies, whereas other enzymes remain active.

In expressing my eager anticipation and confidence that the papers read at this session will throw new light on immunochemical problems I cannot refrain from suggesting, as well, that immunochemistry with its biologically marked specific antigens and antibodies, offers powerful tools for penetration into some of the mysteries of protein configuration.

THE NATURE OF THE FORCES BETWEEN PROTEIN MOLECULES IN SOLUTION

JOHN G. KIRKWOOD

Sterling Chemistry Laboratory
Yale University

INTRODUCTION

THE PHYSICAL-CHEMICAL behavior of proteins in solution is determined, according to the principles of statistical mechanics, by the intermolecular forces which the protein molecules exert on each other, and by the forces which act between them and other solute molecules present in the solution, for example, the ions of electrolytes. These molecular interactions not only determine the thermodynamic properties of solutions in equilibrium, but they also play a decisive role in the kinetics of chemical reactions in which the protein molecules participate. In certain instances the forces between protein molecules and between proteins and the ions of an electrolyte manifest themselves as a general and non-specific thermodynamic interaction. In other instances, the forces exhibit high specificity, as in the antigen-antibody reaction and in the binding between enzyme and substrate. In an investigation of the nature of the forces between protein molecules, it is therefore necessary to consider the manner in which non-specific intermolecular forces may give rise to specific interactions, which are highly sensitive to the structural patterns of the interacting molecules.

The forces between protein molecules may be investigated experimentally by a variety of physical-chemical techniques. Measurements of the solubility of proteins in the presence of other solutes, such as proteins of a different species or electrolytes, provide a simple but important method for studying thermodynamic interaction, from which the magnitude of the intermolecular forces may be deduced. Light-scattering measurements in solutions of a single

4

protein or in solutions containing a protein and other solutes provide similar thermodynamic information. The scattering of light by solutions is determined by fluctuations in composition, which may be shown by the methods of statistical mechanics to be determined by the derivatives of the chemical potentials of the several solutes with respect to their concentrations. Measurements of osmotic pressure are particularly well adapted for the determination of the thermodynamic interaction of proteins and electrolytes. In the case of highly specific interactions leading to the formation of complexes between protein molecules of different species, the methods of electrophoresis and ultracentrifugation prove to be very useful. The complexes may be identified in the electrophoretic and sedimentation boundaries, their constituent mobilities determined, and their concentrations estimated by area analysis, in certain limiting cases. These techniques have been successfully applied to the study of the antigen-antibody complex in the antigen excess range, and to the study of such complexes as those formed between insulin and protamine and between serum albumin and nucleic acid. From such quantitative physical-chemical measurements important information may be obtained as the basis for the construction of a theory of interprotein forces.

THE THEORY OF INTERPROTEIN FORCES

There is no evidence that the forces between protein molecules differ fundamentally from those acting between simple molecules. At small intermolecular distances, quantum mechanical exchange produces a repulsion which determines the size and shape of the molecules. At larger distances, the dispersion forces act to produce a general Van der Waals attraction. Moreover, since the proteins are amphoteric polymers of the highly polar amino-acids, many of which possess acidic or basic side-chains, the molecules undoubtedly possess characteristic distributions of electric charge which give rise to strong electrostatic interactions. Strong evidence for the dominant role of electrostatic forces is provided by the sensitivity of the thermodynamic interaction of protein molecules to ionic strength. The commonly observed reduction in interaction with increasing ionic strength produced by the screening action of the statistical space of the ions of an electrolyte could only be effective on that part of the interaction which is electrostatic in origin, since the high frequency exchange forces and van der Waals forces would be unaffected by the screening action. Except for a class of macromolecules possessing a high degree of conjugation, into which most proteins do not fall, there is no a priori reason, as London has shown, to suppose that dispersion forces play a dominant role, either in strength or specificity of interaction. We shall therefore adopt the reasonable hypothesis that the forces of major importance are the electrostatic forces and the exchange repulsive forces determining the size and shape of protein molecules. By this hypothesis, we do not intend to exclude certain important special instances, in which covalent chemical forces play a role through the intermediate action of heavy metal ions and -SH groups, as in the mercury dimer of mercaptalbumin or through chelate complexes.

The interactions between protein molecules, although of the same origin as those between simple molecules, possess special features arising from their complex structural organization. These special features relate to the pattern of arrangement of the structural elements responsible for the specificity of interaction, and to the mobility of the charges, responsible for electrostatic interaction. The influence of the mobility of the charge distribution has hitherto been largely overlooked, and will be the special subject of this discussion. The electrostatic forces between molecules possessing permanent electric multipoles has been previously treated in some detail, and will not be reviewed here (1). While the theory of interaction of permanent electric multipoles is adequate to describe the interaction of simple ampholytes, such as that of the amino-acids with ions and with each other, it ignores certain important features of the interactions of protein molecules relating to the mobility of their charge distributions and attendant fluctuations in total charge and charge distribution (2). Proteins, considered as ampholytes, contain a large number of neutral and negatively charged basic groups, for example, $-NH_2$ and COO^-, to which protons are attached. Except in highly acid solutions, the number of basic sites generally exceeds the number of protons bound to the molecule, so that there exist many possible configurations of the protons, differing little in free energy, among which fluctuations, induced by thermal motion, may occur. Fluctuations in the number and configuration of the mobile protons impart to the molecules fluctuating charges and fluctuating electric multipole moments. When two protein molecules are separated by a distance R, the electric field of the fluctuating charge distribution of each molecule alters the distribution of fluctuations in the charge and constellations of the mobile protons of the other in such a manner as to produce at the isoionic point a long-range attractive force between them with a potential diminishing asymptotically as $1/R^2$, in the absence of screening by the statistical space charge of an electrolytic environment. With screening, the range is reduced by a factor $e^{-2\mathcal{H}R}$, depending upon ionic strength through the Debye-Hückel parameter $\mathcal{H}$. Fluctuations in charge and charge configuration associated with bound ions other than protons also make a contribution to the intermolecular force.

At sufficiently large distances of separation, the potential $W(R)$ of the fluctuating force between two protein molecules may be expressed as a function of the intermolecular distance R in the following manner,

$$W(R) = -\frac{\overline{\Delta q_1{}^2}\,\overline{\Delta q_2{}^2}}{2D^2kTR^2}\frac{e^{-2\mathcal{H}(R-a_{12})}}{(1+\mathcal{H}a_{12})^2} \tag{1}$$

where $\overline{\Delta q_1{}^2}$ and $\overline{\Delta q_2{}^2}$ are the total charge fluctuations of the two molecules, D is the dielectric constant of the solvent, k Boltzmann's constant, T the absolute temperature and a_{12} the sum of the radii of the two molecules. The Debye-Hückel parameter $\mathcal{H}$ is given by the usual expression,

$$\mathcal{H}^2 = \frac{4\pi Ne^2}{1000DkT}\sum_j C_j Z_j{}^2 \tag{2}$$

where e is the protonic charge and the sum extends over all ionic species j, of molar concentration C_j and valence Z_j, present in the solution. If the interacting protein molecules possess ν_1 and ν_2 basic groups respectively, the conjugate acids of which have dissociation constants $K_i^{(1)}$ and $K_k^{(2)}$, the charge fluctuations of the two molecules are determined by the following relations,

$$\overline{\Delta q_1{}^2} = e^2 \sum_{i=1}^{\nu_1} [2 + K_i^{(1)}/[H^+] + [H^+]/K_i^{(1)}]^{-1}$$

$$\overline{\Delta q_2{}^2} = e^2 \sum_{k=1}^{\nu_2} [2 + K_k^{(2)}/[H^+] + [H^+]/K_k^{(2)}]^{-1} \tag{3}$$

as functions of the hydrogen ion activity $[H^+]$, with the neglect of intramolecular electrostatic interaction between the proteins. A more refined calculation of the charge fluctuations with allowance for intramolecular electrostatic interaction of the protons may be carried out numerically by the methods of Linderstrøm-Lang (3) and Kirkwood (4).

The influence of the fluctuating force on the thermodynamic properties of a solution of a single protein at its isoelectric point in an aqueous electrolyte solution of total ionic strength large in comparison with that of the protein is illustrated by the following expression for the osmotic pressure, Π,

$$\Pi = \frac{RTC_1}{100M_1}\{1 + BC_1 + \cdots\}$$

$$B = \frac{1}{100M_1}\{B_0 - \frac{\pi N \overline{\Delta q_1{}^2}^{\,2}}{2DkT\mathscr{H}(1 + \mathscr{H}a)^2}\} \tag{4}$$

where B_0 is the co-volume contribution to the osmotic coefficient and C_1 is the protein concentration in grams per 100 ml. of solution. For serum albumin in water at $25°C$, the coefficient B is estimated from its dielectric constant increment and molecular size to be

$$B = (4.3 - \frac{1.2}{\sqrt{\Gamma}})/1000 \tag{5}$$

where Γ is the ionic strength of other electrolytes present in the solution. At ionic strengths of the order of 10^{-3}, the fluctuation term is approximately ten times as large as the co-volume term and gives rise to values of the osmotic coefficient substantially less than unity at protein concentrations of the order of several per cent, and reflecting a strong intermolecular attraction.

The estimates which have been presented demonstrate the magnitude of the fluctuation force. However, since they are based upon the artificial assumption of random distribution of basic groups on the surface of the protein molecule, they exhibit no specificity. It is nevertheless clear that highly specific interactions might well arise from the fluctuation mechanism, if one invokes the concept of complementary patterns. In favorable orientations, steric matching of a constellation of basic groups on one molecule with a complementary constellation on the other could conceivably produce a redistribution of protons leading to a strong specific interaction depending upon local structural details of the complementary constellations. Considerations relating to specificity of the fluctuation force, as in the case of other types of interaction, must necessarily remain speculative until detailed knowledge of the fine structure of proteins is available. It is nevertheless important to emphasize that the existence of the fluctuation force makes it necessary to consider the mobility of the charge distributions an important factor in determining the interactions between protein molecules. This implies that relatively distant groups may influence local interactions of complementary sites on two protein molecules by serving as sources or sinks of mobile charges supplied or withdrawn from the interacting sites.

REFERENCES

1. Kirkwood, J. G., *J. Chem. Phys.*, 2, 351 (1934).
2. Kirkwood, J. G., and J. B. Shumaker, *Proc. Nat. Acad. Sci. U. S.*, 38, 863 (1952).
3. Linderstrøm-Lang, K., *Compt. Rend. trav. lab. Carlsberg*, 15, 7 (1924).
4. Kirkwood, J. G. (Cohn and Edsall, eds.), in *Proteins, Amino Acids, and Peptides*, Chapter 12, Reinhold, New York (1943).

DISCUSSION

DR. HEIDELBERGER: I think you will all agree with me that this fine example of rigorous thinking is going to influence work in protein chemistry for a long time to come. To an organic chemist like myself it's a little disturbing at first thought to consider fluctuating charges, but we all know that proton charges are not the only things that fluctuate in a protein. And the idea of still another quicksand is not necessarily too disturbing on reflection.

With my difficulties in following the rigorous mathematics I will probably take refuge in what I think Dr. Kirkwood would call the occupational therapy variable. To continue with the serious discussion: Dr. Eyring, would you like to comment on Dr. Kirkwood's presentation?

DR. EYRING: The forces that Dr. Kirkwood specifically neglects often seem to me to be very important, particularly with reference to the shape of the molecules. I am sure Dr. Kirkwood would agree with this especially when dealing with enzyme action, where levo and dextro rotatory substrates usually react with greatly differing rates. A close estimate of this effect may be made. To introduce a hole into a liquid the size of a molecule costs energetically the heat of vaporization. When two molecular surfaces come next to each other they may fail to fit, by a certain volume. Activated complexes involving such holes will have correspondingly greater activation energies. Each 1.3 calories increase in activation energy means a decrease by a factor of 10 in the rate of reaction. Thus activated complexes involving really badly fitting molecules will fail to react. A hole the size of a water molecule would increase the activation energy by about 10 calories and decrease the rate by a factor of 10^7. Big inhibitions will thus accompany bad fits between enzyme and substrate. An entirely different effect can introduce large inhibitions. Thus if an oil surface is in contact with a water surface there is a difference in surface energy of about 50 ergs per square cm. A cube 25 square Å on a side with one face water-like and the other five oil-like will lower its free energy 9,000 calories per mole in passing from pure water to an interface where the one face remains in water and the other five are immersed in oil. Thus, reversible denaturation of the enzyme luciferase by three alcohol molecules may well occur as a molecular rearrangement designed to surround the oily parts of the alcohols with compatible surroundings. Such forces, I am sure Dr. Kirkwood will agree, are very large.

DR. KIRKWOOD: I agree thoroughly. When I used the word matching constellations I wanted to include such things as this, but when one does have this favorable matching one must have a mechanism for this binding.

DR. EYRING: If I understand Dr. Kirkwood, the effects he is talking about are probably going to be small additional things on top of these of which I have spoken.

DR. KIRKWOOD: Not necessarily small additional things. With appropriate matching groups you can get strong binding with the forces that I was talking about.

DR. KLOTZ: May I ask one or two questions in connection with your picture? You mentioned at the outset in connection with your dielectric constant calculations that you can account for the dielectric increments largely by these fluctuations. Although you looked at the moments which have been interpreted as dipole moments previously as rather large, in a sense one can also look at them as rather small. If you have a molecule about 100 Å long with a net charge of only one, then you have a dipole moment of about 400 Debye units.

DR. KIRKWOOD: Yes; that is correct.

DR. KLOTZ: That in itself is rather surprising, because for a large molecule 400 Debye units is a rather small asymmetry in charge, considering the total distribution. If you can show that even this value can be cut down in certain cases, that would mean these molecules are even more symmetrical with respect to charge. Does that imply that these proteins are a good deal more spherical than we have ordinarily thought?

DR. KIRKWOOD: I don't think it necessarily implies a spherical shape, although that, again, is possible.

DR. KLOTZ: Can you visualize a simple case like insulin where perhaps there are only two chains? Can we visualize a distribution in the chains which would cancel out the charges so well that you would get almost zero dipole moments?

DR. KIRKWOOD: Well, I think that this is something which should be looked into. On the basis of our present provisional knowledge of the structure of insulin one could attempt a calculation.

DR. KLOTZ: It is a little harder to see how a spiral or helical model could average out to a very tiny net moment.

DR. KIRKWOOD: Unless, of course, you have two spirals in opposite directions which cancel each other.

DR. KLOTZ: If insulin has a weight of only 6,000 and consists of only an A and a B chain of quite different composition, it would be rather remarkable if this coincidence could happen.

DR. KIRKWOOD: I don't think there has been a measurement of the dielectric increment with insulin. Under conditions of successfully measuring the increment, the measurement of 6,000, I think, would be a low estimate. Certainly 12,000 would be closer to a correct estimate of the molecular weight.

DR. KLOTZ: There is another question I should like to raise with respect to the mechanism of enzyme action. You pointed out that there was an analogy, roughly speaking, between these electrical fluctuations and van der Waals forces. Would that also be carried over to a point where you could speak of a charge affecting this polarization, in your case, so that one might visualize, let us say, a succinate ion coming in which might so affect these fluctuations that with a suitable constellation on the protein it might induce a suitable enzyme configuration?

DR. KIRKWOOD: Yes. That is certainly correct. This mechanism gives rise to the possibility of the rise of interaction of small ions such as succinate with proteins, so that we can get highly specific effects.

DR. KLOTZ: In a highly specific case.

DR. KAUZMANN: I wonder if there might not be even more specificity than this in Dr. Kirkwood's model. Suppose that we had a mixture of two proteins, one having large fluctuations and the other small ones. Wouldn't the protein molecules with the large fluctuations tend to attract each other in spite of the presence of the other ones?

DR. KIRKWOOD: Yes, I think that's right.

DR. KAUZMANN: Many people are looking very hard to find reasons why in biological systems like molecules attract one another—as in the pairing of chromosomes, for instance. An effect such as this might be involved in these systems. Suppose that a very elongated protein (or nucleoprotein) molecule contained localized regions with large charge fluctuations arranged at irregular intervals along its length. Two identical molecules of this type would attract one another much more strongly than two molecules which did not have the same spatial arrangements of fluctuating regions. The attraction would not be spoiled by the presence of other kinds of molecules in the solution. Dr. Kirkwood's mechanism seems much more reasonable in this kind of situation than the more old fashioned intermolecular forces, such as hydrogen bonds and van der Waals forces.

DR. GUTFREUND: Dr. Eyring mentioned the possible importance of forces at oil-water interphases. I should like to give some sub-unit dissociation-association phenomena in protein systems as a possible example for such interaction.

We now know a large number of cases where crystalline proteins can exist in solution in varying degrees of aggregation of, probably identical, sub-units. From the evidence so far available one can suggest, in some cases at least, that these sub-units are bound together along closely fitting hydrophobic surfaces. In some such systems complete dissociation into sub-units occurs in acid solutions when the repulsion between the highly charged units become greater than the cohesive forces. This is similar to the model used by Debye for his theory and calculation on the aggregation of soap into micelles.

It may well be that further dissociation phenomena could be discovered by the addition of organic solvents to solutions of proteins. Incidentally this could possibly be an explanation for the discrepancy between the size of the repeating sub-unit of insulin found to be $M = 12000$ from physical measurements in aqueous solution and $M = 6000$ by Dr. Craig's partition in organic solvents.

I should like to add that this is of course not the only possible mechanism by which such sub-unit aggregations could take place. It is very likely that in some cases the mechanism consists of salt bridges between properly spaced acid and basic groups on the sub-units. Examples could be given as to how the conditions of dissociation allow one to decide between the two types of mechanisms as the responsible one in different systems.

Next I should like to ask Dr. Kirkwood whether he has calculated the contribution of his forces to the activity coefficients for some protein models like serum albumin assuming random distribution of the known positive and negative charges (a) for the case of isoionic solutions and (b) as a function of ionic strength?

DR. KIRKWOOD: Only a very rough calculation has been made, neglecting intramolecular electrostatic interactions. And this expression for (b) is subject to revision of the numerical values of the constants. I may have given that to you before.

DR. GUTFREUND: No. I should like to see those, because I have been using one of the methods which Dr. Kirkwood has described—namely, the osmotic pressure procedure — for measuring protein-protein interaction. If one studies the osmotic activity of serum albumin under isoionic conditions one observes a negative deviation from the ideal solution, indicating the attractive force, which is predicted from the existence of a dipolar force. There are three types of protein systems for which this has been done. Firstly, for the case of serum albumin, where we only worked under isoionic conditions since small amounts of salt appear to suppress the effect. In the case of gamma globulin the effect is much stronger and it can still be measured at low, but finite ionic strength, but there the difficulty is that gamma globulin might not be pure and you have a distribution of isoelectric constants. Attraction might be due to the interaction of protein molecules with different charge. Lactoglobulin, which has a very large dipole moment can't be studied under isoionic conditions because it is insoluble in the absence of salt, but it can be studied in the presence of increasing salt concentration, and you can show that the attractive forces decrease as the salt concentration increases.

DR. KIRKWOOD: I think it might be interesting to use the gamma globulin fractions prepared by electrophoresis-convection.

DR. GUTFREUND: Yes. I should like to do that. On gamma globulin fractions and also on gamma globulin-serum albumin mixtures at the isoelectric point in between the two, where one also gets these attractive forces.

DR. WESTHEIMER: I should like to ask Professor Kirkwood whether his proton redistribution model will account for the known relaxation time of proteins.

DR. KIRKWOOD: A quantitative theory of dielectric dispersion on the basis of the present ideas has not yet been developed. If one imagines that the relaxation is due to a redistribution of protons, this means redistribution by diffusion. For simplicity let us say protons moving over the surface of the proteins. One can calculate the order of magnitude of the relaxation time by taking the square of the linear dimensions divided by the translational diffusion constant for the protons. If one makes a very crude assumption that the self-diffusion of protons in water is such then one gets the right order of magnitude for the relaxation time. Oncley has been attempting to discuss relaxation using model systems similar to this but somewhat simplified. If one ignores the discrete distribution of protons at basic sites and assigns to the molecule certain conductivity associated with the mobility of the proton, then one can use the Maxwell-Wagner theory for the complex conductance of the medium, to obtain a qualitatively correct description of dispersion. An experiment which one might make in order to test this hypothesis suggested by Dr. Singer at Yale is to measure the dielectric dispersion in heavy water, because one expects on general grounds that the mobility of the deuteron will be less than the proton. Recently Oncley and Dintzis have started these experiments, and in a preliminary run it could either correspond to a rotatory relaxation time shifted according to the changes in viscosity or it could be somewhat greater corresponding to the lower mobility of the deutrons.

DR. NEURATH: I should like to come back to the question of the specificity, because after all the proteins do not only interact with sodium chloride, methyl orange, and other ions and molecules which lend themselves readily to quantitative studies, but also with coenzymes and substrates. I should like to emphasize in particular the coenzymes since they are restricted to relatively few structural units of rather unique size, shape and chemical characteristics, and yet capable of interacting with varying avidities with a number of proteins, that is, with enzymes. The question arises, therefore, whether these enzymes do have common constellations which predispose them for interactions with the same coenzyme or whether, conversely, there may be something peculiar to fluctuating charges within the coenzymes which make them particularly predisposed to interact with the enzymes. I think that this is one of the most important aspects of the problem of specificity and mode of enzyme action, and I think that the simple lock and key picture on one hand and the rather rigid model of the structure of proteins as described by Pauling and Corey on the other create a rather unhappy conflict in the thinking of the specificity-minded biochemist. I should be very much interested to hear Dr. Kirkwood discuss this particular aspect of the problem.

DR. KIRKWOOD: Again this is a question which can be analyzed only in terms of detail of fine structure. I can say that because of the influence of side chains even when one does have common structural features of the Pauling-Corey helices the variety of side chains of the amino acids which enter into the structure of proteins is sufficiently great to give you an extraordinary multiplicity of patterns which still allow one to obtain the matching constellation picture.

DR. CHANCE: I would like to bring up the question of the kinetic aspects that Dr. Kirkwood mentioned in his introduction as being relevant to molecular interactions especially with respect to the particulate enzyme systems in which some of us are interested. These consist of insoluble particles for example for mitochondrial fragments which may contain several electron transporting enzymes. One of the theories of these electron transporting systems requires a sufficiently close relationship of the enzymes so that they collide by thermal vibrations. The enzyme surfaces would be held nearly in contact, corresponding to a very high effective concentration in the soluble particles. I would like to ask what sorts of interactions you would expect to dominate under these conditions and how they would alter the kinetic aspects of this particulate system as compared to what one would expect to obtain if the enzymes were in solution. According to the fluctuating charge theory would one expect a big difference in the kinetics of such soluble and insoluble systems?

DR. KIRKWOOD: That, again, is a question which depends on structural details. I would not like to maintain that the fluctuating charge mechanism is one which simply has to be brought into account for all kinds of binding. I wanted specifically to exclude that impression. I wanted to emphasize, however, that it is one of the possible mechanisms of binding and one which can give rise to very strong binding. Now, it would still be possible, if one is considering the interaction between either a protein molecule or a small molecule and a surface that has a possibility of fluctuation in charge, that this mechanism could make an essential contribution to the binding.

DR. HAMMETT: I should like to ask just a couple questions for clarification. Does the picture of a fixed charge distribution give the right order of magnitude for relaxation time? In other words, can you get any distinction between these possible theories?

DR. KIRKWOOD: It would be necessary to have a theory of relaxation upon a mobile distribution.

DR. HAMMETT: I mean just the rotation of protein molecules with fixed charges.

DR. KIRKWOOD: Yes, I know. There is a well worked out theory for that based upon arbitrary assumptions concerning shape. I am not at all convinced that our obsession with the ellipsoid of revolution is a justifiable one at all. But if one accepts a simple model as to shape—say, an oblate or prolate ellipsoid of revolution—as you know, one can work out relaxation times which are of the right order of magnitude and will account for Oncley's dispersion measurements. On the other hand, as I pointed out, one would expect relaxation times of the same order of magnitude on the basis of the charge fluctuation theory.

DR. HAMMETT: So there's no distinction.

DR. KIRKWOOD: No. One cannot distinguish on the basis of a semi-quantitative comparison of orders of magnitude. It would be necessary to work out a theory of relaxation of mobile charges of the same mathematical exactness as that for the rotatory relaxation of the ellipsoid in order to decide.

DR. HAMMETT: Is there really any contradiction between what Dr. Kirkwood and Dr. Eyring have said? Dr. Kirkwood said that he didn't think that van der Waals forces were of any great significance in interaction between molecules of this sort, and I think I understood Dr. Eyring when talking about this oil droplet picture to say that if you can have enough interaction the van der Waals forces can accumulate to quite a large magnitude. Is there a conflict or not?

DR. KIRKWOOD: What would you say, Dr. Eyring?

DR. EYRING: It seems to me that you can have very large forces if you have oily patches that don't like to be exposed to the water and if two large molecules fit particularly well to the order of magnitude of whether a water molecule can go in or out. As indicated earlier a misfit leaving a hole half the size of a water molecule corresponds to five kilocalories per mole higher energy. The differences we see where an enzyme can react with a substrate which is levo but not with one that is dextro although both have the same primary bonds must be purely a matter of fitting and even with small molecules the effects on rate can be extremely large. The juxtaposition of polar surfaces with oily ones has similar dire consequences. These effects are specific and of great importance.

DR. KIRKWOOD: I think that one might say that the average attraction between the aliphatic group in a polar solvent is not so much due to their direct van der Waals attraction as to the fact that the displaced water molecules may interact more effectively with themselves when the aliphatic groups are in contact. I think that attention should be called to the role of water molecules which has been far too much oversimplified in electrostatic theory. It is certain that in order to get a clear quantitative picture it would be necessary to take into account the discrete structure of the water in the immediate neighborhood of the interacting protein molecules. I think we might take an example of a case in which we know the binding — that is, the case of Dr. Hughes's mercury dimer of serum albumin. We are not very much in the dark but that the binding is there but we know that the contribution of the chemical bond would certainly be exothermic just from any sort of reasonable model, and yet the reaction is endothermic or nearly so. I think that we can find other examples in which that is true. This must mean that the ensemble of processes participating in the interaction is a very complicated one in which a large number of water molecules participate, and that somehow one must release rotational degrees of freedom of neighboring water molecules, bringing the serum albumin molecules together in such a manner as to release a considerable amount of entropy to give a negative free energy increment. At the same time, there results an increase in energy more than sufficient to compensate for the free energy of the mercury sulphur bond. I think Dr. Sturtevant has other thermochemical examples of this kind of thing.

DR. STURTEVANT: Yes. For example, as nearly as we can make out, the combination of soybean trypsin inhibitor with trypsin is accompanied by a negligible change in heat content but probably by quite a large decrease in free energy since there seems to be a very tight bonding in aqueous solution.

DR. GUTFREUND: Another example of such thermodynamic behavior in protein interaction is the association of insulin, which is very slightly affected by temperature, thus giving a very small heat of binding.

DR. E. SMITH: It doesn't seem to me that these considerations can express, at least to the complete satisfaction of the biochemists, the tremendous number of variations in binding that one observes in biological systems. When we look at the different kinds of compounds that interact with proteins, it would appear that all of the types of interactions already mentioned are possible. To take one of the more striking examples, for the interaction of a steroid with the steroid-oxidizing enzyme, it is very unlikely that electrostatic forces are involved. It is more likely to involve van der Waals forces, and they are strong forces possibly by exclusion of water or possibly because they like to get together on the surface of the enzyme. Similar types of oily forces must be involved in the interaction of many other kinds of substrates with enzymes. I don't want to go into any detail now, since I will give some examples of this tomorrow. If we consider the peptidases, for example, we find that these substrates have alkyl side chains which are highly important in relation to the effect on hydrolytic rate. They must be concerned enormously in the specificity of the system even though they are very weak forces by themselves.

DR. KIRKWOOD: This would be an example of forces to which Dr. Eyring is referring.

DR. CALVIN: I am afraid I must confess that I did not follow to the point at which the approximations were introduced into the quantitative calculations. I would like to ask just how these approximations depend upon the relative values of the distances between the centers of the protein molecules and the distances between the basic points on the protein molecules. Is there some specificity in the approximations of that relationship?

DR. KIRKWOOD: Yes, and I should have mentioned an important simplifying structural assumption made in the calculations, which were designed to be order of magnitude calculations. Each type of basic group was assumed to be randomly distributed on the surface of the protein molecule. We used for the molecule itself the conventional ellipsoidal model and took the axial ratio as given by other types of physical measurements. This, as I more or less implied, means that we renounce in this order of magnitude calculation taking into account the very important specific effects of constellation.

DR. CALVIN: So this treatment, then, does not take into account the important question of enzyme specificity; it would not be applicable as it stands to such problems?

DR. KIRKWOOD: It would be possible if one were to give me a detailed structure for two proteins which interact. Say that protein A has a definite constellation of basic groups of a given type matching a complementary constellation of basic groups of another type in molecule B; it would be possible to make the calculation of the fluctuation force on the basis of the same principles. The general calculation, however, gives us a good idea of the magnitude and suggests that the magnitude is important.

DR. ANFINSEN: I have a few comments to make that may not have any direct bearing on this subject of protein interaction, but do relate to some of the comments of other discussers. It has to do with some recent observations made in our laboratory by Dr. Gordon and others on the role of serum albumin in the so-called clearing reaction. The clearing factor reaction is one in which a heparin-protein complex catalytically converts beta lipoproteins into alpha lipoproteins. In the course of studying this reaction it has been found that there is a second protein involved, which hitherto we called, very loosely, "coprotein." Recently it has been found that highly purified clearing factor can carry out this conversion when serum albumin is added to the reaction mixture, and that the system can carry out the splitting of triglycerides in oil-water emulsions to form fatty acids and glycerol. It appears that the reaction will proceed only so long as there are free sites on the albumin molecule for accepting the fatty acids. The albumin supports the clearing reaction as long as there are free sites, and the reaction stops when approximately 6-7 mols of fatty acid have been added per mol of albumin at pH 7.2. Although the discussion so far has dealt mainly with protein — protein interactions, it is perhaps pertinent to mention this phenomenon since it is a striking example of small molecule-protein interaction and indicates the importance of protein surface structure on enzymatic processes.

DR. KOSHLAND: To follow up what Dr. Calvin said, I would like to ask Dr. Kirkwood whether his theory really doesn't apply to cases where there are solvent molecules—namely, water molecules—between the two proteins or between the protein and the substrate. When the substrate is directly on the protein or when the two proteins are in direct contact, we really just have hydrogen bonding.

DR. KIRKWOOD: No, it's not as simple as that. I think I would have to illustrate this by a picture. Suppose that we ignore the effect of orientation and that we bring two molecules together. Assume that we plot on the ordinate the potential of the average forces and on the abscissa the distance the molecules are from one another. Then the simple electrostatic theory, which ignores the structural features of the water and possibly—although it couldn't be proved—the local effects of fixed distribution, which is essentially what you are saying—hydrogen bonds are electrostatic. The theory, as we have used it and as you have described it, using water as the dielectric continuum would give a curve in which the $VV(R)$ value will become more and more negative as the molecules come closer to one another. The effects that you are talking about would, I believe, cause small deviations when the molecules come very close to one another. This would not necessarily, however, amount to very large corrections in the dissociation energy. In certain special instances the difference may not be negligible, but where one knows the magnitude of the potential of the average forces this doesn't seem to be a big factor. The other very short-range effects could enhance this by an arbitrary magnitude, which in certain instances might be comparable. That does not mean that the short-range effects would swamp the effects of which we have spoken.

DR. BALLENTINE: There are other various forces that might contribute to specificity, and I would like Dr. Kirkwood's and Dr. Eyring's viewpoints on this. I would like to get their views on another force which, although very small, might be very important in determining stress and strains. Normally we think of chemical reactions as involving electron shifts, but in recent years studies have indicated that so-called isotope effects and particularly nuclear magnetic resonance have become of some importance, and I am wondering whether or not nuclear resonance effects are not important, particularly where you have protons as the important component in the reaction.

DR. EYRING: I think the forces are much too small. The frequencies correspond to the resonance far down in the microwave range, and this would represent a very low energy. They are much too small to enter here.

DR. KIRKWOOD: I agree.

DR. BALLENTINE: They are in the megacycle range.

DR. EYRING: Yes, and that is a range in which their contribution would be insignificant. For example, a frequency of 10^{10} vibrations per second corresponds to a wave length of 3 centimeters and an energy of .92 small calories per mole.

DR. E. SMITH: There is one important example which should be brought up in connection with Dr. Kirkwood's theory, and that is the case of seed globulins, which are very insoluble in water at the isoelectric point and which require tremendous concentrations of salt in order to dissolve them. In such cases one might expect very large electrostatic forces to be involved in the binding.   There are examples of this kind by the dozens which we could give in which ionic strength is an important factor in solubility.

DR. KIRKWOOD: I would like to answer Dr. Smith in this way: I would not accept his comment if he wishes to say that the electrostatic mechanism—either the fluctuating one or the fixed dipole one—is important only in these very special cases.   You mentioned earlier an extreme case involving binding of steroids to protein, in which I think it is necessary to consider that extreme case in which van der Waals interactions with participation of solvent are very important in binding, but I would say that we have a good experimental test whenever a given interaction is observed experimentally to be sensitive to ionic strength and we can be quite certain that it is electrostatic in origin—that's a good test—would you not agree?

DR. E. SMITH: Yes.   The only thing I would like to emphasize is that there must be multiple sites of binding in order to explain enzyme specificity, and the different sites may involve different types of forces.   With small substrates one can identify at least the sites on the substrate which are concerned in the binding to the protein.   If we consider a special case—for example, carboxypeptidase—there must be some sort of electrostatic interaction, since there is a big effect of ionic strength.   However, one must also postulate some sort of van der Waals effect, because the nature of the side chain determines the rate of the reaction.   You get variations in rate of something like 10,000 fold with acyl dipeptides that have different terminal amino acids.   This difference in rate depends on the nature of the non-ionic side chains; yet with aliphatic and aromatic side chains it is very unlikely that any ionic effects are involved in the differences observed.   Thus it must be due to something like van der Waals forces. So we have both electrostatic and van der Waals forces interacting.

DR. KIRKWOOD: It may depend—and this is a small point—on what you wish to call van der Waals forces. If you wish to call all forces other than electrostatic van der Waals forces, then one would have to agree. I would make a deliberate distinction between van der Waals attraction of the London type and the quantum mechanical repulsive forces at short range which are responsible, I think, for the steric effects which we see.   It was not my intention at any time to minimize the importance of steric effects in allowing matching of constellations of groups, which is necessary to bring into action the attractive mechanism.

DR. MAYER: There are antigen-antibody reactions which are highly sensitive in their response to salt concentrations; others are not.   For example, egg albumin reacting with rabbit antibody is very little influenced by increase in ionic strength, whereas the polysaccharide antigens interacting with specific antibodies are strongly influenced by ionic strength. Would you comment on that, Dr. Kirkwood?

DR. KIRKWOOD: I would like to ask Dr. Heidelberger to comment concerning the facts. I am not familiar with the range of ionic strength which was used in these studies. But I am under the impression from Dr. Singer's findings of a very marked effect of ionic strength on precisely the same systems in which you say they do not occur. Again, this is a matter of fact, and I don't have all the details to marshal here. This would depend upon the range of ionic strength. Possibly if the ionic strength were very high and one increased it some more one might observe very small effects, whereas if one investigated it in a sensitive region of low enough ionic strength one might find an effect.

DR. STURTEVANT: I would like to ask Dr. Kirkwood a question. You mentioned at the start of your talk that there was in some cases an inverse effect of ionic strength. Do you have any theoretical interpretation of this?

DR. KIRKWOOD: Again, I think one would have to come to specific examples. I think that one can certainly imagine systems which are not too preposterous, say where a multivalent anion was binding two proteins together through interaction with positive sites, one on one protein and one on the other; or several multivalent anions might be binding constellations of sites of positive charge. Then I think that one would get the inverse effect of ionic strength.

DR. STURTEVANT: So it is not an ionic strength effect.

DR. KIRKWOOD: No, it is not the general screening effect. It may be possible to conceive of a general screening effect giving rise to an inverse effect of ionic strength. I don't know of any examples where one gets the inverse ionic strength which cannot be attributed to some special mechanism, but there may be.

DR. GUTFREUND: The following is one type of special mechanism which one might get: If you have a large fitting surface with favorable geometry for a large van der Waal's interaction, which is held apart by positive charges in acid solution. When this repulsion between charges is suppressed, either by titration of the charge or by sheltering them with Gegen ions, the binding takes over and one does get increasing attractive interaction with increase in ionic strength. This is an elaboration of the type of mechanism which I have quoted earlier in support of Dr. Eyring's hydrophobic forces.

DR. KIRKWOOD: Yes. Perhaps this is similar to what you are saying, but another plausible model is this. Suppose both proteins are similarly charged —that is, have a charge of the same sign—but that the centers of charges are so located that they can be bound specifically at some point. We won't say what the specific mechanism of binding is. It might be in itself electrostatic, and it might be of a different origin. Then the total binding will have a negative contribution due to coulomb repulsion and a positive binding due to the specific interaction. Then, in that case one gets an inverse ionic strength effect because increasing ionic strength weakens the repulsion. I think that's probably the best example.

DR. GUTFREUND: That was the reason I brought up the point.

DR. HEIDELBERGER: I would like to get back to two previous comments. I was glad to hear Dr. Smith talk about multiple reactive groups in enzyme reactions. It is gratifying to know that enzymological theory and immunological theory are approaching each other in that respect. With regard to Dr. Mayer's comment about some immune reactions being sensitive to electrolytes and others less sensitive, the example of the sensitive reactions which has been most carefully worked out is that between the specific polysaccharide of type III pneumococcus and homologous antibody. The antigen is probably a linear polymer with only one kind of polar group. It is possible that structural considerations enter in that the salt-sensitive aggregates may be quite extended, whereas amphoteric electrolytes like egg albumin in a more compact form may render the large aggregates of antigen-antibody sensitive to electrolyte action; but I think that is pure speculation.

DR. KIRKWOOD: What about the experimental facts? What is the range of ionic strength in this investigation?

DR. HEIDELBERGER: In the same range in which the type III reaction is extremely sensitive. The amount of precipitate obtained at the equilibrium zone in the egg albumin system is almost entirely insensitive.

DR. KIRKWOOD: Would the order of magnitude be a tenth or a hundredth?

DR. HEIDELBERGER: Well, that was between about one-tenth and 2 or 3. Not a very large range.

DR. KIRKWOOD: I think it is possible for such systems to become much more—if one were to go to other ionic strengths one might observe a more marked effect.

DR. HEIDELBERGER: That has been done in some recent work on the egg albumin system, and the only significant differences that were found at very low ionic strengths were in the region of antigen excess, where the molecules are probably linear and stretched out and more accessible to the action of electrolytes.

DR. WILSON: There is another manner in which salts may affect interaction —that is, salts may change the shapes of proteins, affecting the intramolecular forces rather than just the intermolecular forces.

DR. KIRKWOOD: Yes. I think, again, we have a very wide variety of things that can occur—and this is something which has not been explicitly mentioned by any of us—certainly something which one must be prepared to encounter. Even with the globular protein system, which one is inclined to regard as rigid and not very deformable structures, one may have changes in shape and changes in internal structure produced by the environment, and one might even get contributions to the interaction changes associated with distribution of a molecule between several internal states.

DR. BOYER: I would like to return to the question of hydrogen bonds. If my suspicion is right, ionic strength variation should have little effect on hydrogen bonding as compared to its effect on ionic interactions. It may be that in the egg albumin-antibody system it is the hydrogen bonding type of interaction which plays a prominent role.

DR. KIRKWOOD: I do not think that I would agree that hydrogen bonding interaction would be insensitive to ionic strength, but here is a case in which no quantitative calculations have been made, and they are rather difficult. About all one can do in a quantitative way is to surmise orders of magnitude from the strength of the hydrogen-hydrogen bonds in liquid water, but since hydrogen bonding is in essence an electrostatic interaction it should be sensitive to ionic strength. It might not be very sensitive if the important bonds are well buried in the surface contacts, but again this is a quantitative question which has not been answered.

DR. HAMMETT: Isn't this really a question not of the type of interaction but of the range of forces? I don't want to quibble, but the London dispersion forces are electrostatic but they are very short range. The hydrogen bond is still a short-range force, and therefore one would have very small ionic strength contributions.

DR. KIRKWOOD: I think it is worthwhile to distinguish, however, between the quantum microchemical forces—that is, the high frequency London dispersion forces and what I have been referring to as electrostatic forces—between fixed charges and low frequency fluctuating charges. It would probably confuse the issue if we extend the term electrostatic to include all forces.

DR. HAMMETT: I agree.

DR. KIRKWOOD: The low frequency electrostatic forces, and I would include in that category hydrogen bonding (I would be willing to argue with anyone who wishes to on that)—will be ionic strength sensitive, whereas van der Waal's forces and the exchange repulsive forces will not.

DR. HAMMETT: If your hydrogen bonding force drops off with distance fast enough so that it has become negligible by the time you get an ion or two in between, then would you have an ionic strength effect?

DR. KIRKWOOD: I think you would still have this effect, because, although the hydrogen bonding force cannot be described in terms of a simple dipole-dipole interaction, one can get the right order of magnitude if one supposes that it is an electrostatic interaction between two molecules—say, water with two static charges supplemented by some polarization of the molecules by the other. Such an interaction, I feel, would be sensitive to ionic strength.

ESSENTIAL CHEMICAL STRUCTURES OF CHYMOTRYPSIN AND PEPSIN

ROGER M. HERRIOTT

Department of Biochemistry, Johns Hopkins University,
School of Hygiene and Public Health, Baltimore

OBSERVATIONS THAT the activation energy of certain substrate reactions is lowered by appropriate enzymes (1) and the accumulating evidence that in general enzymes and substrates probably form intermediate complexes (2, 3, 4, 5) as predicted by the Michaelis-Menten theory (6) have led several workers (7, 8, 9, 10) to suggest an operational explanation for enzyme action. Thus, when the enzyme and substrate come into close proximity, the substrate bond is probably put under a strain, thereby weakening it and permitting a greater number of bonds to be broken per unit of time. In this connection it should be noted that it is not always enough that the enzyme combine with the substrate, though this appears to be essential, but there may be a labilizing influence in addition (11).

It is not the purpose of this paper to present data in support of this general idea, for it is not new, and others on this program will have considerable to say on this and related subjects. This concept may prove valuable, however, as evidence of the essential nature of certain structures in enzymes is presented.

While it is not strictly correct to attribute to a particular structure a property of the whole molecule, yet there is ample evidence that certain structures bear a closer relationship to the catalytic property of an enzyme than do others. It has been demonstrated in a few instances and generally assumed in the others that the coenzyme is the essential structure of the enzyme that needs it, although it may have no measurable catalytic action in the absence of the proteinous apoenzyme.

The problem of the nature of the structures which confer enzymatic properties upon certain proteins has interested enzyme workers for a long time, but progress toward its solution has been relatively slow. Perhaps the first contribution to our knowledge of this subject was the discovery of Harden and Young in 1906 that two or more dissociable components were necessary for activity of some enzymes and that at least one of the components was heat-stable and dialyzable. In recent years great progress has been made in the chemical identification of many of these cofactors. There are, however, many enzymes which show no tendency to dissociate or for which no evidence of a prosthetic group is known, and for them purification is almost a prerequisite to a study of their essential structure. That brings up the next important milestone along our road, namely, the crystallization of urease by Sumner (12). This discovery and the reports that followed by Northrop and Kunitz (13, 14, 15) on the crystallization of several proteolytic enzymes, plus their correlation of the enzyme activity with protein concentration throughout fractionation by a variety of physical-chemical procedures, went far to establish the protein nature of enzymes. With the exception of one brief unconfirmed report (16) nothing has altered this conclusion.

With the isolation in quantity of essentially pure enzyme preparations an attack on the specific catalytic structures became feasible. Studies were made using relatively specific chemical reagents under conditions which kept to a minimum the secondary effects, such as denaturation. Deductions were made regarding the essentiality of certain structures only after experiments were performed in which a complete balance sheet was kept (82, 83). This included the structures modified, the number of reagent molecules attached, and these correlated to the changes in catalytic property. In certain instances, reversal of the changes with a recovery of catalytic function strengthened the interpretations (83).

The isolation of precursors (15, 17, 18, 19) and determination of the conditions for conversion to the enzymes provided a unique approach to the problem. When accompanied by an analysis of the chemical changes paralleling activation, this approach has great attraction, for in some instances the chemical changes are small and are therefore subject to closer correlation. Yet another attack has developed from studies of various substrate analogues which either serve as substrates or inhibitors of the enzymes. From an examination of the essential structures of these synthetic substrates and inhibitors certain limitations may be suggested for the enzyme structure.

TABLE 1

AMINO ACID ANALYSES

Amino Acid	α-Chymotrypsinogen * (Brand, 27)	Pepsin (Brand, 27)	Pepsin Inhibitor (Van Vunakis, 78)
Mol. wt.	37,000	34,300	2,533
	Number of residues per mole protein		
Glycine	26.2	29.3	1
Alanine		1	2
Valine	32.0	20.8 ⎫	
Leucine	29.4	27.2 ⎬	8
Isoleucine	16.1	28.3 ⎭	
Proline	19.0	14.9	
Phenylalanine	8.1	13.3	1
Cysteine	3.95	1.4	
Half cystine	10.2	4.7	
Methionine	3.03	3.9	
Tryptophane	10.1	3.97	
Arginine	6.0	1.97	1
Histidine	2.94	1.99	
Lysine	20.3	2.11	4
Aspartic acid	31.4	41.2	2
Glutamic acid	22.7	27.8	2
Serine	39.8	39.5	
Threonine	35.4	27.6	
Tyrosine	6.05	16.1	1
Amide N	40.5	32.3	2 (?)
Total no. of amino acids	321.	306.	22
Total amino acid N as % of total N	97.7	99.2	

* These values are similar to those reported more recently by Lewis, et al. (52).

Finally, the use of specific enzymes as reagents to modify the protein structure of other enzymes has recently been employed in a number of instances (20, 21, 24) and holds some promise for the future. The use of infrared (25, 26) and similar techniques have not yielded significant results yet, but improvements in techniques or the choice of other enzyme systems may show this to be the powerful tool that it is with smaller molecules.

In place of making a general review of the field of enzymes, a more detailed discussion from many angles will be presented on just two enzymes which have received more attention than the others, namely, chymotrypsin and pepsin. Although these enzymes consist almost entirely of amino acids (27) (see Table 1), Price (28) found that after acid hydrolysis they both contained a factor favoring bacteriophage formation which was not replaced by a mixture of the known amino acids nor acid hydrolysates of certain other purified proteins. More work is needed to bring out the relationship of this unknown component to the enzyme activity, but it might be noted that amino acid analyses are not precise enough to exclude the presence of as much as 1 to 2 per cent non-amino-acid components.

CHYMOTRYPSIN

Preliminary remarks

Unfortunately we shall have to initiate this phase of the discussion on a discordant note by admitting that rather important differences have been reported by competent workers regarding what are ordinarily considered simple properties of the precursor and enzyme of this system. In the first place, it is known that there are two different chymotrypsinogens, designated respectively α (15) and B (29). Most of the present discussion deals with the α precursor and the enzymes derived from it. Next, the isoelectric point of α-chymotrypsinogen has been reported to have values ranging from pH 5.5 (15, 30) to pH 9.5 (31, 32). Finally, there is considerable evidence to indicate that the molecular weights of some preparations of α-chymotrypsinogen and the enzymes from it are in the region of 37,000 (15, 27, 33), whereas others appear to have a value closer to 23,000 (34-37). One method of analysis produced a value of 80,000 (38). It is not possible to resolve these differences at this time, but it is probable that they will be reflected to some degree in the analytical results to be reviewed.

Conversion from α-chymotrypsinogen

A number of different enzymes are obtainable following the

initial tryptic action on α-chymotrypsinogen. Jacobsen (39) found that rapid activation at 0°C. resulted in an enzyme with two and a half times the activity of the usual α enzyme originally described by Kunitz and Northrop (15). He designated this as π-chymotrypsin. On continued contact with trypsin the π enzyme changed to a product with one and a half times the milk clotting activity of α, and this was designated as δ (see Table 2). Autolysis of δ led to the α enzyme. The δ enzyme was shown to be more active than α on synthetic esters as well as on amide bonds of similar synthetic substrates (40). Kunitz had described earlier the autolytic conversion of α-chymotrypsin to two other forms which were crystallized. They were designated as β and γ and were distinguished from α by their crystalline form, solubility, and molecular weight, though the last property has been questioned recently (36).

While this series of degraded enzymes is of considerable interest, it complicates the problem we are considering at this time. The structural changes that accompany the formation of π-chymotrypsin are of primary interest, not the succeeding degradative changes. Since some of the structural studies on this system were performed before π-chymotrypsin was discovered and before all these degradative changes were appreciated, new interpretations will be necessary in some instances.

It is clear from their original report that Kunitz and Northrop (15) recognized that an independent proteolysis accompanied the tryptic conversion of chymotrypsinogen to chymotrypsin. They suggested that the conversion *per se* involved the separation of no nitrogenous products and that in such a case an internal rearrangement would account for the formation of enzyme. This work was later confirmed by a more thorough study by Butler (41).

Jacobsen's study is particularly interesting in this connection. He followed the peptide bonds split during enzyme formation. His results are shown in Fig. 1, where the formation of enzyme is plotted against the number of peptide bonds split per molecule of 36,000 (mol. wt.). During formation of the first half of the total enzyme activity, there was an average of approximately 0.35 peptide bonds split. Had there been only one product formed, namely π-chymotrypsin, full activity would have required the splitting of only one peptide bond. However, the peptide bonds per molecule were calculated on the basis of 36,000 molecular weight protein. If the molecular weight of the precursor and enzyme is 23,000, there may be some question about the relationship between enzyme formation and peptide cleavage. An over-all view of this work is given in Table 2.

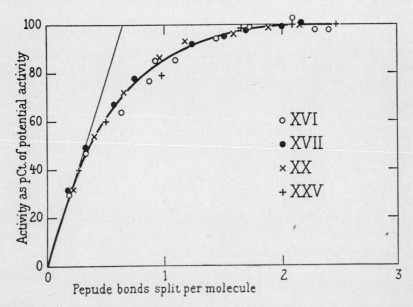

FIG. 1.   Conversion of α-chymotrypsinogen by trypsin at 0° C. to π and δ-chymotrypsin (Jacobsen, 39).

The possibility that conversion of the precursor to enzyme by trypsin involves the splitting of an ester bond should be given consideration, since these bonds are now known to be opened by trypsin (53). In this connection it might be noted that acetylation of trypsin results in no loss of esterase activity while half of the protease action is destroyed (72, 48). Use of the acetylated trypsin to activate chymotrypsinogen might be useful in indicating which type of bond is opened upon formation of the enzyme.

TABLE 2

Chymotrypsins Formed from α-Chymotrypsinogen

(Jacobsen, 39)

Enzyme Symbol	Milk clotting * Activity/mg. N	No. of peptide bonds split in formation	Catalyst †
π	21	0–1	Trypsin
δ	13	2	Trypsin
α	8.5	4	Trypsin + Autolysis
β	8.5	?	Autolysis
γ	8.5	?	Autolysis

* The milk clotting activity per mg. N was calculated from Jacobsen's factors (39) and Kunitz's data (42).

† Each succeeding enzyme is presumably formed from the preceding one.

Ionization and activity

The pH-activity curves of α-chymotrypsin vary somewhat depending on the substrate and on whether synthesis or hydrolysis is being studied (64, 43). In general, however, the activity rises abruptly between pH 5.5 and pH 7 (15). This may be interpreted as meaning that over this region of pH certain structures in the enzyme having pKs in this region are important for the active functioning of the enzyme. Titration curves (42) over this same region of pH reveal that only 0.15 millimoles of ionizable structures were involved per gram of enzyme, or 3 groups per particle of 23,000 molecular weight. This should not be regarded as a very precise value, but it may represent an upper limit. From thermodynamic measurements (3) it has been found that the enthalpy values of -5000 cals. per mole of enzyme coincide quantitatively with those of the imidazole of histidine (44, 45). The pH range where this value was observed is also that expected of this structure. Preliminary results from a study which was initiated to compare the titration curves of the precursor and α enzyme over the pH range of 5.4 to 7.4 revealed that the enzyme has one more titratable structure per 23,000 molecular weight, with a midpoint near pH 6.8 (78). This is close to the pK' of 7.0 for the histidine imidazole (45). The titrations were not extended beyond pH 7.4 because of the complication introduced by the overlap from known α-amino groups of the enzyme which are not present in the precursor (60). Neurath (46) has also given some consideration to imidazole structures in chymotryptic activity. The nature of this structure will come up for consideration again later.

Chemical modification of certain protein groups

Considering its availability, purity, and ease of study, surprisingly little interest has been shown until recently in the chemical modification of this enzyme and, of course, the resulting effect on enzymic action. Sizer's (47) failure to observe a change in proteolytic activity following treatment with formaldehyde or phenylisocyanate suggests that the amino structures of this enzyme are not essential to its catalytic activity. Ketene, which is known to react with the phenol group of tyrosine in proteins, and nitrous acid, which introduces nitroso or diazo structures ortho to the phenol group (85), reduce the activity. Although the conclusion is a tenuous one, the tyrosine phenol group of this enzyme seems to be implicated in the active structure. Oxidation as well as acetylation have also been reported (48), but it is difficult to assign the activity changes to structural modification. These workers crystallized the oxidation product which had lower activity but the same amino nitrogen as the unmodified enzyme.

Perhaps the most interesting and important aspect of the problem was uncovered by Jansen, Nutting, Jang, and Balls (49). Their series of reports (50, 51, 36) followed the important discovery of the esterase activity of crystalline chymotrypsin and trypsin (53). As is now well known, Jansen et al. (49) found that di-isopropyl-fluorophosphate (DFP), a chemical previously shown to inactivate choline esterase (54, 55), destroyed the proteolytic and esterolytic activity of both trypsin and chymotrypsin. Extremely small quantities were required, as may be seen in Fig. 2, which was taken from their paper (49). From this curve, a 50 per cent inhibition of 0.4 mg. of α-chymotrypsin per ml. required 1×10^{-5} molar DFP. For complete inactivation, double this quantity was assumed to be needed or 1 mole of DFP for 25,000 g. of enzyme. The inactive product was crystallized and contained 0.125 per cent bound phosphorus, which is only 10 per cent more than expected on a mole for mole basis. The authors noted that the reaction is not instantaneous and results in the formation of HF as a byproduct. Chymotrypsinogen mixed with a one hundred-fold greater relative concentration of DFP did not result in any phosphorus being bound to the protein. DFP does not react with amino acids nor with an acid hydrolysate of chymotrypsinogen (36). One wonders if proteolytic hydrolysates of the chymotrypsin would also fail to bind the reagent.

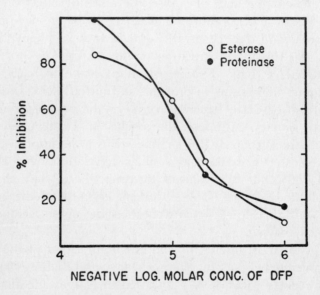

Fig. 2.   Inactivation of 0.4 mg./ml. α-chymotrypsin by di-isopropylfluorophosphate. (From Jansen et al., 49).

It is hoped that all these negative experiments were accompanied by tests for fluoride ion or changes in hydrogen ion. Otherwise unambiguous interpretations are not possible.

We may conclude tentatively that there is some single structure in the active enzyme that is not present in amino acids nor in the precursor. Electrophoretic studies of the active enzyme and inactive DFP derivative showed no difference, a result suggesting that the reaction of DFP is not with an ionizable structure. Heat denaturation of the chymotrypsin blocks the site of reaction with DFP, yet the same denaturing procedure when applied to DFP-chymotrypsin failed to liberate the phosphorus (36).

Digestion of the inactive DFP-derivative can be brought about with pepsin, trypsin, or acid (36, 56) without liberation of all the phosphorus. Thus, Schaeffer, May, and Summerson (56) have presented strong evidence that the combination of DFP is with the hydroxyl group of serine. Although they isolated serine phosphate, they showed appropriate caution in suggesting that in the breakdown of the protein the DP radical might have moved from its original site to the serine hydroxyl. Similar movements of other radicals are known (57, 58). It has been observed that the di-isopropyl derivative (DP) of the imidazole structure is very labile in aqueous solution (59, 97), a behavior which is in sharp contrast to the relative stability of the oxy-DP-serine derivative (56). Since the DP-imidazole structure is very labile (97), then it must be supposed that in the protein the linkage is more stable, or one must explain why the enzyme remains inactive.

Use of Sanger's dinitrofluorobenzene reagent to make dinitrophenyl (DNP) derivatives of these enzymes has led to some important observations. Thus, Desnuelle and associates (60) using this method concluded that chymotrypsinogen contained no α-amino groups, a conclusion which indicated that this protein is a cyclic peptide. In contrast to the precursor, the α enzyme was found to contain two end amino groups, one belonging to the amino acid alanine and the other to isoleucine. This suggests that this enzyme is a branched peptide chain or two parellel chains. More recently these same workers reported the same N-terminal amino acids for β- and γ-chymotrypsins (61), a result which suggests that their formation resulted from cleavage near the carboxyl end of the proteinous peptide chain. The use of carboxypeptidase (21) on these two products should prove very interesting.

An interesting, if preliminary, experiment was described by Weil and Buchert (62) in which α-chymotrypsin was photo-oxidized by visible light with the aid of traces of methylene blue. This resulted in a loss of enzyme activity, and the authors note that 4 moles of oxygen were consumed per mole of enzyme. This action resulted in the destruction of one of the two histidine residues of this enzyme and two of the six tryptophanes. In a personal communication noted elsewhere (56), these same workers found that this oxidized product did not combine with DFP. Once again the histidine imidazole is implicated. However, recent work in the writer's laboratory by Van Vunakis (95) suggests that both the imidazole structures of this protein are free in the precursor as well as in the enzyme itself. It is known (96) that dinitrofluorobenzene (DNFB) reacts with the imidazole nitrogen of histidine in proteins but that this substituted amino acid is destroyed upon acid hydrolysis. Treatment of both precursor and enzyme with DNFB, followed by acid hydrolysis, destroyed both histidines of these two proteins, as determined by microbiological techniques and paper chromatography. If further work substantiates these results, this will suggest that while the imidazole structure may be involved in union with the substrate it is probably not liberated upon formation of the enzyme from the precursor and does not react with DFP. While the presumption has been made that appearance or acquisition of a new property depends upon the formation of a structure or group which was previously masked, there may be an alternative explanation. Thus, a structure may be potentiated by alteration of its structural environment. In the present instance, although the imidazole structures may both be free in the precursor, it is possible that conversion to the enzyme alters the structural environment of one of the two groups and it then takes on a qualitatively new property. There is not sufficient information to suggest this as more than a possibility.

Substrates

Several groups of workers have studied the influence of substituents of the substrate on behavior with respect to the enzyme (63-65). Neurath and Schwert (64) have reviewed this subject recently, and only a few pertinent points will be noted at this time. It has been suggested (64) that for rapid hydrolysis the substrate should contain the four structures shown on p. 35.

Replacement of I, the secondary peptide, by another electro-negative constituent greatly decreased the rate of chymotryptic action. The primary peptide or ester bond, II, is of course the susceptible or labile bond. Its replacement by a carboxylate ion or methyl ketone makes the compound an excellent inhibitor. The methylene structure, III, separating the aromatic structure from the peptide chain appears to be important. Structure IV can be any of the several aromatic structures or the " electronic equivalents " found in amino acids. It may also be replaced by methionine. The results obtained by Sanger (66, 67) in studying the chymotryptic digestion of A and B chains of oxidized insulin will necessitate some broadening of these requirements, for the bond between threonine and tyrosine was found to be a major site of chymotryptic digestion.

Kaufman and Neurath (68) have suggested that the active centers of the enzyme are complementary to the substrate and consist of peptide linkages.

In an interesting experiment, Sprinson and Rittenberg (69) have shown that the carboxyl-oxygen exchange of carbobenzoxy-L-phenylalanine with H_2O^{18} is catalyzed by chymotrypsin. This was essentially confirmed by Doherty and Vaslow (3), who found that chymotrypsin catalyzes the exchange of oxygen from water to the carboxyl group of N-acetyl-3, 5-dibromo-L-tyrosine. The authors note that this makes this compound a substrate. They also found that one mole of this substrate was bound to the enzyme. In a follow-up of this work, these authors (11) showed that the precursor chymotrypsinogen also bound the substrate but failed to catalyze the exchange.

They suggest that there are two structural requirements for catalysis: one used for substrate binding, and another structure for activating or labilizing the bond.

Enzymatic modification

Recently enzymes have been used to modify or determine protein structure. Sizer (70) has reported oxidation of the tyrosine of chymotrypsin and other enzymes without loss of enzyme activity, but this was seriously questioned (71). For details, see a recent review (20). A preliminary report without data (24) indicates that others are using this technique.

Another use of enzymes which has been proposed recently is to determine the terminal carboxyl amino acids of proteins (21). Use is made of the pancreatic enzyme carboxypeptidase, which is commercially available as a crystalline product. In the case of α-chymotrypsin, it has been found (22) that two amino acids, tyrosine and leucine or isoleucine, occupy the C-terminal positions of this enzyme. A more detailed discussion of this work will be given by Dr. Hans Neurath in the following paper. It might be noted that the parallel peptide chain which this result suggests is in agreement with the results described earlier in the N-terminal amino acid analyses.

Summary of the Work on Chymotrypsin

1. Formation of the essential catalytic structure of this enzyme on activation of the precursor does not require the liberation of any nitrogenous fragments. It is not certain that the cleavage of a peptide bond is even necessary. It could be an ester bond. Peptide bonds are split in the degradative process of forming δ- and α-chymotrypsins, but the important step is the formation of the first active product, π-chymotrypsin.

2. One molecule of N-acetyl-3, 5-dibromotyrosine is bound to both the precursor and enzyme, but only the enzyme catalyzes the exchange of isotopic water with the carboxylate oxygen, a fact suggesting that the labilizing structure is formed on activation.

3. The ionization of only a few groups in the region of pH 5-7 is essential for the chymotryptic activity. The pK of the imidazole

structure of histidine falls in this region. The present evidence suggests that in this region the enzyme has one more titratable group than the precursor.

4. DFP binds to the enzyme but not to the precursor. Although DP serine has been isolated from the inactivated enzyme, the obvious conclusion should not be made prematurely. No amino acid reacts with DFP, although the oxy-DP serine isolated from the enzyme derivative is relatively stable.

The serine hydroxyl structure is implicated in the activity of this enzyme by virtue of its isolation in combination with the di-isopropyl phosphate. In the precursor it might be a component of an ester linkage and be liberated by the esterase activity of trypsin.

The evidence suggesting the participation of a histidine imidazole is more indirect and less well established. The photo-oxidation experiments and the pH-activity curve can be placed in this category. It appears unlikely that the imidazole structure is liberated upon formation of the enzyme from the precursor. This group may be important, however, in binding the substrate.

PEPSIN

Preliminary remarks

The peculiar pH-stability range of pepsin and pepsinogen has restricted the studies that might otherwise have been made on these materials. Pepsinogen is stable for only short periods below pH 6, while pepsin is equally unstable above this pH. Whereas pepsinogen is unstable because it is converted to pepsin, the latter above pH 6 is rapidly and irreversibly denatured (13). The description of yet another property of pepsin will help to explain some of the aberrations in the experimental results in the literature. Pepsin, being a protease, digests denatured protein, so that if in the process of chemical treatment denaturation of the enzyme occurs, products of hydrolysis will be formed which may obscure the small structural changes that are being studied in the enzyme.

Several different pepsins and pepsinogens are known to exist (73-76). The specific activity may vary on particular substrates as much as three-fold. This has its disturbing aspects, but it does not mar the general conclusions that have been made in this review.

Formation from pepsinogen

The autocatalytic conversion of pepsinogen to pepsin (18) is shown diagrammatically below:

$$P'g \xrightarrow{\text{(P)}} X \text{ peptides} + PI \underset{\text{pH 5.4}}{\rightleftharpoons} P + I \longrightarrow P + Y \text{ peptides}$$

where $P'g$ = pepsinogen; P = pepsin; PI is an inactive pepsin-inhibitor complex; I = the inhibitor. X and Y are peptide products.

In this system pepsin catalyzes the initial change in pepsinogen, but since this reaction does not yield pepsin immediately, but rather the inactive pepsin-inhibitor compound (PI), the reaction is not strictly autocatalytic. However, the over-all reaction is autocatalytic, as can be demonstrated by adding pepsin to the reaction mixture (77). The enzyme inhibitor compound dissociates below pH 5 into enzyme (P) and free inhibitor (I).[1]

The formation of pepsin from its precursor is accompanied by an increase in the trichloroacetic acid-soluble nitrogen to the extent of 15 to 20 per cent of the nitrogen of pepsinogen. Fig. 3 shows that the increase in non-protein nitrogen is a linear function of the enzyme formed and appears to be independent of pH and temperature. Such a close correlation might not be expected were the non-protein nitrogen arising from the digestion of a protein impurity.

Table 3 contains the results of some experiments designed by Van Vunakis (78) to determine by means of the DNP technique (79, 80) the size and number of products appearing during the formation of pepsin. It may be seen from this experiment and others to be described later that pepsinogen and pepsin are single peptide chains, since they have but one terminal α-amino nitrogen per mole of protein. This suggests that in spite of the nine bonds that are broken during conversion to the precursor to active enzyme, only one of

---

[1] This inhibitor blocks the milk clotting action of pepsin as measured between pH 5 and 6. It is not effective in the region of pH 2.

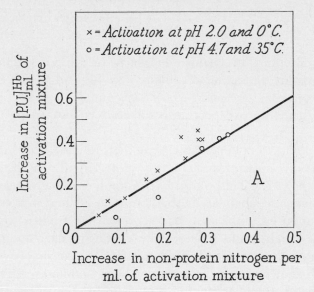

FIG. 3. Formation of non-protein nitrogen and enzyme activity during conversion of swine pepsinogen to pepsin (18).

TABLE 3

ANALYSES OF PEPSINOGEN ACTIVATION MIXTURE BY DNP METHODS

(Van Vunakis and Herriott)

Mol. Wt. Pepsinogen   42,500 (Os. press., light scattering, P analysis)
Mol. Wt. Pepsin   34,500 (Os. press., centrifugation, amino acids, S and P
                      _____   analyses)
     Difference   8,000 = 19% of Pepsinogen

Net increase in NH_2-N (Van Slyke) on activation = 9 groups/mole pepsinogen.
Activation of 4 g. Pepsinogen at pH 2 for 1 min., then fractionated.

Fraction	Percentage of P'gen N	NH_2 as Percentage of Total N	Minimum mol. wt.	No. of α-NH_2 peptides	Total mol. wt.
Pepsinogen (before activation)	100.0			1	42,500
Soluble in 2½% TCA					
Basic (inhibitor)	6.3		3,100	1	3,100
acidic	3.9	0.5	20,000 (?)	0	0
neutral	11.9	10.0	1,000	5	5,000
Total TCA–soluble	22.1			6	8,100
Pepsin	77.8			1	34,500
Total in activation mixture	100.0			7	42,600

them may be essential. The other amino groups probably arise from a breakdown of the non-enzymatic fragment. Lest the wrong impression be gotten, let it be noted that there is no information at present concerning the manner in which the various fragments are liberated from the precursor. They may be broken off randomly or in a particular sequence. The main point is, however, that it is possible that only one peptide bond need be broken to form the enzyme.

Other points to note in Table 3 are that the inhibitor is the entire basic fraction and has a molecular weight value derived from DNP analyses of 3100. This compares favorably with a value of 2533 from amino acid analyses (Table 1). The acidic fraction appears to be an impurity, if the analyses are correct, for a particle of 20,000 molecular weight could arise only by a cleavage near the middle of the chain of the protein. The neutral fraction consists of five peptides with an average size of 10 amino acids and an average molecular weight of 1000. Excluding the acidic fraction, it was possible to account for seven of the nine bonds broken.

TABLE 4

NITROGEN TERMINAL AMINO ACID SEQUENCE

Material	N-terminal amino acid	Second amino acid in chain
Pepsinogen	Leucine	Isoleucine or leucine
Inhibitor	Leucine	Glutamic acid
Pepsin	Isoleucine	Glycine

The DNP procedure is also useful in determining the nature of the N-terminal amino acids of proteins. These are shown in Table 4 for pepsinogen, pepsin, and the inhibitor. For those not acquainted with this technique it may be briefly indicated. The dinitrophenylamino acid linkage is relatively resistant to the acid hydrolysis used in hydrolyzing proteins, and the amino acid derivatives can be separated on a silica-gel column. Most of these amino acid derivatives are colored, which facilitates their location on the column. Following elution, they may be determined quantitatively in a spectrophotometer (79, 81). The second amino acid in a peptide sequence is obtained by incomplete acid·hydrolysis of the DNP protein and a fractionation of the DNP products on a silica-gel column. Complete acid hydrolysis of these fractions, followed by paper chromatography for the amino acids, reveals which amino acid(s) is/are associated with the one carrying the DNP residue.

It may be seen from Table 4 that it was essential to determine the second amino acid in the peptide chain of each of these compounds to decide how they were arranged in the original pepsinogen molecule. Without this information it would be difficult to know whether the end amino acid of pepsinogen was the same as that of the inhibitor, since they were both leucine.

Williamson and Passmann (98) have reported that the one N terminal amino acid of pepsin is leucine. They based this conclusion on a two dimensional papergram using m-cresol saturated with 0.3 per cent NH₄OH and collidine. Tertiary amyl alcohol (99) provides a much greater separation of leucine from isoleucine and led us to favor the latter amino acid in the case of pepsin.

An analysis of the c-terminal amino acids of pepsin and pepsinogen using crystalline carboxypeptidase (21) showed both these enzymes to contain alanine (78). It will be necessary to obtain the second amino acid in the two proteins to know whether pepsin occupies the carboxyl end position in the pepsinogen chain.[2]

Chemical derivatives of pepsin

The amino acid composition of pepsin is shown in Table 1 along with that of chymotrypsinogen and the pepsin inhibitor. In considering pepsin, it may be noted that it contains 16 tyrosine residues and 2 or 3 disulfide bonds, about which more will be said. There is a preponderance of acidic amino acids over the basic ones, a relation which was to be expected from the known acid properties of the protein.

Acetylation (82-84) and deamination (85) of the three free

---

[2] Van Vunakis (78) has found that the second and third amino acids from the C-terminal end of the chain in pepsin are one of the leucines and valine, respectively. Since the same sequence was observed in pepsinogen, it is very probable that pepsin occupies the C-terminal segment of pepsinogen. Others (Passmann, J. M., and Williamson, M. B., *Am. Chem. Soc.* abstrs. Sept. 1953, p. 47 C) have similarly reported that alanine occupies the terminal position in pepsin.

amino groups of pepsin, which can now be assigned to two lysine and one isoleucine residues, had no measurable effect on the peptic activity, though other properties such as solubility were markedly changed. Further acetylation at pH 5-6 resulted in a decrease of activity. There was a correlation in the change in number or re-activity of tyrosine phenol groups and the alkali-labile acetyl radicals introduced, and of these to the loss in activity. A comparable cor-relation was obtained upon acid hydrolysis of the acetyl groups (83). This suggests that in some manner the phenol groups of tyrosine in the enzyme are associated with its catalytic activity. This received support from studies in which iodine (86) and nitrous acid (85) were used to modify the tyrosine residues, although these agents substitute at positions ortho to the phenol group. With both re-actions there was a decrease in activity, but whereas complete iodina-tion destroyed all the activity, diazotization left the product half active. Philpot and Small (85) suggested that some of the tyrosine moieties may be in a different state of reactivity or availability, since only half of the tyrosine had been diazotized in spite of the excess nitrous acid. Kinetic studies of the rate of iodination (87) also indicated that the tyrosine residues of pepsin were not equally reactive. Thus, Li (87) reported that about twelve of the tyrosine residues were as reactive as free tyrosine, while five became avail-able only on denaturing the protein.

As a result of work done during the war, it was found that sulfur mustard reacts relatively specifically with protein carboxyl groups when the reaction medium is maintained at pH 5.5-6 (88). Except for the one on the end amino acid (alanine), the majority of the 36 carboxyl groups (89, 88) belong to either aspartic or glutamic acids. The reaction of mustard with pepsin (88) produced a drop in activity.

Fig. 4 depicts the chemical studies on pepsin in an unusual form. In this figure the logarithm of the peptic activity is plotted against the number of reagent residues bound per mole enzyme. All three reactions follow this logarithmic plot, and their slopes were the same within a factor of two. The iodine reaction is plotted two ways, one as the iodine atoms and the other as the number of tyrosines iodinated. The latter has twice the slope of the former, since the tyrosine in this protein has been shown to form di-iodotyrosine (86). These results mean that for each protein structure modified there is a constant fractional decrease in the remaining activity. The course of the reaction can be expressed in a simple exponential form such as $y = e^{-N}$, where y is the surviving activity and N is the number of groups bound per mole protein. The usual "dosage"

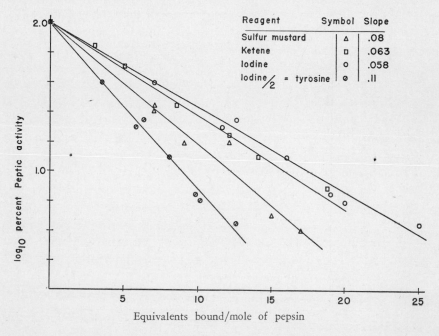

Reagent	Symbol	Slope
Sulfur mustard	△	.08
Ketene	□	.063
Iodine	o	.058
Iodine$/2$ = tyrosine	⊘	.11

FIG. 4.   Effect of various chemical reactions on the enzymic activity of pepsin.

formula, which at first glance this appears to resemble, is not applicable, since the number of absorbing structures does not remain constant in the present system. If several assumptions are made regarding the number of structures affecting the enzyme activity and the relative chemical reactivity of these groups compared to the similar but enzymically inert ones, a general expression can probably be made.

Another chemical attack on the general problem has recently been made in the writer's laboratory by Kern (90), who studied the effect of mercaptan reduction of the cystine disulfide bonds of pepsin and pepsinogen on their biological action, shape, and molecular weight. He found that one disulfide bond could be reduced in either precursor or enzyme without a measurable change being reflected in

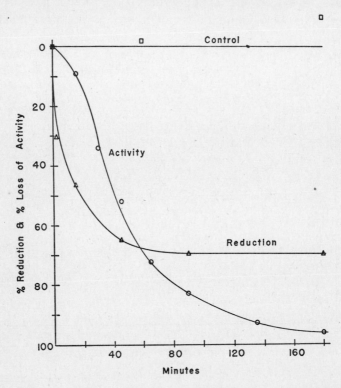

FIG. 5. Effect of thioglycol reduction of disulfide bonds of pepsinogen on the potential peptic activity.

any of the three properties. Further reduction introduced certain complications which are better seen in Fig. 5, where the various changes during the reaction are plotted against time. It may be observed that at the time when there had been 33 per cent reduction, equivalent to one of the three disulfide bonds, the activity change was slight. Further reduction to 67 per cent, beyond which this system did not change,[3] was accompanied by a drop in activity, but it should be noticed that the activity was still 50 per cent at a time when the reduction had apparently ceased. Following this, the activity continued to drop with time, suggesting that a secondary change was responsible for the loss of activity. A study of the temperature coefficient of enzyme inactivation revealed a Q_{10} of about 100, which is strongly suggestive of denaturation. Since inactivation by denaturation of the protein probably occurred before the reduction reached 67 per cent, the question may be raised whether the reduction *per se* of the second disulfide bond of pepsinogen had any direct effect on the enzymatic activity of pepsin derived from it. It is clear, however, that the reduced protein appears to have a lower temperature-stability threshold than the original enzyme.

It may be noted in passing that complete reduction of denatured pepsin (90) did not change the molecular weight of this protein, as judged from osmotic pressure measurements. This indicates that pepsin is a single peptide crosslinked by cystine disulfide bonds.

Direct action of enzymes

It was mentioned earlier that carboxypeptidase has been used on pepsinogen to liberate the terminal carboxyl amino acid. In this experiment it was found that there was no measurable change in activity of the protein over a period of many hours, during which time strong alanine spots were detectable on the paper chromatogram, an observation suggesting that this amino acid is not important to the peptic activity (78). Additional quantitative correlations are necessary to establish this suggestion.

The use of tyrosinase on pepsin (62) has been described, but definitive proof of action on the tyrosine of the protein has not appeared.

Recently Perlmann (23) has shown that the single atom of phosphorus in pepsin and pepsinogen can be hydrolyzed with the aid

[3] Sullivan and Goldberg (91) have reported that pepsin contains only 1.35 per cent cystine, as measured by 3 different procedures. Since this is only 2 cystine residues per mole of enzyme, the other disulfide bond may be different, even though it apparently can be reduced under certain conditions (90).

of potato phosphatase without producing any measurable change in the peptic activity.[4]

Summary of the Work on Pepsin

1. Pepsinogen is a single peptide chain, and although nine peptide bonds are split in its conversion to pepsin, only one may be important in the activation. The fact that the pepsin-inhibitor compound dissociates more slowly than the splitting of the bonds interferes with critical studies on this point.

2. Chemical studies on the enzyme reveal that primary amino groups, two disulfide bonds, and the phosphate ester can be altered without producing measurable changes in the catalytic power. Several different reactions involving the tyrosine residues of the enzyme lowered the catalytic properties. Esterification of the free carboxyl groups with sulfur mustard produced a similar effect. The decrease in activity was logarithmic with increased binding of reagent residues.

GENERAL CONCLUSIONS

Studies on chymotrypsin suggest that one structure of this enzyme is essential for its activity. Much of the evidence bearing on the nature of this structure is not in a very satisfactory state at present, and no firm conclusion is justified.

Carboxyl and tyrosine phenol groups appear to be important for peptic activity.

The possibility that both these proteases may contain prosthetic groups cannot be dismissed.

PROTEASE SPECIFICITY

One additional point should be brought up at this time, for it is particularly pertinent in discussing enzyme specificity. Johnson, in the writer's laboratory, has repeated and extended the work of

---

[4] Further studies by Van Vunakis (78) have shown that carboxypeptidase will split as many as four amino acids from pepsinogen without a measurable change in rennet activity of the enzyme.

Behrens and Bergmann (92) in which they showed that a peptide, resistant to papain, was made susceptible by the addition of certain resistant acylated peptides. Johnson (93) found that using crystalline papain and naturally occurring peptides he could duplicate the earlier results. This work shows that the specificity of this enzyme is sometimes altered by a change in the environment. That this is not peculiar to papain is suggested by a recent report (94) in which crystalline trypsin and crystalline pepsin were studied.

It follows, therefore, that the extent of digestion and the nature of the bonds split in a large peptide or protein may vary considerably, depending on the presence of peptides that can serve as cofactors for the splitting of otherwise resistant ones. These results may require a revision of some of the prevailing ideas of protease specificity.

REFERENCES

1. Moelwyn-Hughes, E. A., *The Enzymes*, Chapter 2, Vol. 1, Part 1 (J. B. Sumner and K. Myrbäck, eds.), Academic Press, New York (1950).
2. Stern, K., *J. Biol. Chem.*, 114, 473 (1936).
3. Doherty, D. G., and F. Vaslow, *J. Am. Chem. Soc.*, 74, 931 (1952).
4. Keilin, D., and T. Mann, *Proc. Roy. Soc.* (London), B, 122, 119 (1936).
5. Chance, B., *Advances in Enzymol.*, 12, 153 (1951).
6. Michaelis, L., and M. Menten, *Biochem. Z.*, 49, 333 (1913).
7. Stearn, A. E., *Ergeb. Enzymforsch.*, 7, 1 (1938).
8. Neurath, H., and G. W. Schwert, *Chem. Rev.*, 46, 69 (1950).
9. Fruton, J. S., and S. Simmonds, *General Biochemistry*. Wiley, New York (1953).
10. Holley, R. W., *Science*, 117, 23 (1953).
11. Doherty, D. G., and F. Vaslow, *J. Am. Chem. Soc.*, 75, 928 (1953).
12. Sumner, J. B., *J. Biol. Chem.*, 69, 435 (1926).
13. Northrop, J. H., *J. Gen. Physiol.*, 13, 739 (1930).
14. Northrop, J. H., and M. Kunitz, *J. Gen. Physiol.*, 16, 267 (1932).
15. Kunitz, M., and J. H. Northrop, *J. Gen. Physiol.*, 18, 433 (1935).
16. Binkley, F., *Nature*, 167, 888 (1951).
17. Kunitz, M., and J. H. Northrop, *J. Gen Physiol.*, 19, 991 (1936).
18. Herriott, R. M., *J. Gen. Physiol.*, 21, 501 (1938).
19. Elliott, S. D., *J. Exp. Med.*, 92, 201 (1950).
20. Sizer, I. W., *Advances in Enzymol.*, 14, 129 (1953).
21. Lens, J., *Biochim. et Biophys. Acta*, 3, 367 (1949).
22. Gladner, J. A., and H. Neurath, *Biochim. et Biophys. Acta*, 9, 335 (1950).
23. Perlmann, G., *J. Am. Chem. Soc.*, 74, 6308 (1952).
24. Klein, R. M., J. A. Gladner, and H. Neurath, quoted in (87).
25. Uzman, L. L., and E. R. Blout, *Nature*, 166, 862 (1950).
26. Herriott, R. M. (unpub.).
27. Northrop, J. H., M. Kunitz, and R. M. Herriott, *Crystalline Enzymes*, 2nd ed. Columbia Univ. Press, New York (1948).

28. Price, W. H., *J. Gen. Physiol.*, 31, 233 (1948).
29. Keith, C. K., A. Kazenko, and M. Laskowski, *J. Biol. Chem.*, 170, 227 (1947).
30. Ingram, V. M., *Nature*, 170, 250 (1952).
31. Anderson, E. A., and R. A. Alberty, *J. Phys. & Coll. Chem.*, 52, 1345 (1948).
32. Kubacki, V., K. D. Brown, and M. Laskowski, *J. Biol. Chem.*, 180, 73 (1949).
33. Mallette, M. F. (unpub.).
34. Schwert, G. W., *J. Biol. Chem.*, 179, 655 (1949).
35. Smith, E. L., D. M. Brown, and M. Laskowski, *J. Biol. Chem.*, 191, 639 (1951).
36. Balls, A. K., and E. F. Jansen, *Advances in Enzymol.*, 13, 321 (1952).
37. Tietze, F., and H. Neurath, *J. Biol. Chem.*, 194, 1 (1952).
38. Bull, H. B., *J. Biol. Chem.*, 185, 27 (1950).
39. Jacobsen, C. F., *Compt. rend. trav. lab. Carlsberg.*, *Ser. chim.*, 25, 325 (1947).
40. Schwert, G. W., and S. Kaufman, *J. Biol. Chem.*, 180, 517 (1949).
41. Butler, J. A. V., *J. Am. Chem. Soc.*, 63, 2968 (1941).
42. Kunitz, M., *J. Gen. Physiol.*, 22, 207 (1938).
43. Schuller, W. H., and C. Nieman, *J. Am. Chem. Soc.*, 74, 4630 (1952).
44. Wyman, J. J., *J. Biol. Chem.*, 127, 1 (1939).
45. Cannan, R. K., *Chem. Rev.*, 30, 395 (1942).
46. Neurath, H., *Trends in Physiology and Biochemistry* (E. S. G. Barron, ed.), Academic Press, New York (1952).
47. Sizer, I. W., *J. Biol. Chem.*, 160, 547 (1945).
48. Jansen, E. F., A. L. Curl, and A. K. Balls, *J. Biol. Chem.*, 189, 671 (1951).
49. Jansen, E. F., M. D. F. Nutting, R. Jang, and A. K. Balls, *J. Biol. Chem.*, 179, 189 (1949).
50. Jansen, E. F., M. D. F. Nutting, and A. K. Balls, *J. Biol. Chem.*, 179, 201 (1949).
51. Jansen, E. F., M. D. F. Nutting, R. Jang and A. K. Balls, *J. Biol. Chem.*, 185, 209 (1950).
52. Lewis, J. C., N. S. Snell, D. J. Hirschmann, and H. Fraenkel-Conrat, *J. Biol. Chem.*, 186, 23 (1950).
53. Schwert, G. W., H. Neurath, S. Kaufman, and J. E. Snoke, *J. Biol. Chem.*, 172, 221 (1948).
54. Mackworth, J. F. (1942), quoted by A. Mazur, and O. Bodansky, *J. Biol. Chem.*, 163, 261 (1946).
55. Adrian, E. D., W. Feldberg, and B. A. Kilby, *Brit. J. Pharmacol.*, 2, 56 (1947).
56. Schaeffer, N. K., C. May, and W. H. Summerson, *Federation Proc.*, 11, 282 (1952).
57. Bergman, M., and A. Miekeley, *Z. physiol. Chem.*, 140, 128 (1924); *Naturwissenschaften*, 12, 1155 (1924); *Z. physiol. Chem.*, 143, 108 (1925); *Z. physiol. Chem.*, 146, 247 (1925).
58. Herriott, R. M., *J. Gen. Physiol.*, 19, 283 (1935).
59. Hackley, B. E., Jr., and T. Wagner-Jauregg, *Federation Proc.*, 11, 224 (1952).
60. Desnuelle, P., M. Rovery, and C. Fabre, *Compt. rend.*, 233, 1496 (1951); *Biochim. et Biophys. Acta*, 9, 109 (1952).
61. Rovery, M., C. Fabre, and P. Desnuelle, *Biochim. et Biophys. Acta*, 10, 481 (1953).
62. Weil, L., and A. R. Buchert, *Federation Proc.*, 11, 307 (1952).
63. Bergmann, M., and J. S. Fruton, *Advances in Enzymol.*, 1, 63 (1941).
64. Neurath, H., and G. W. Schwert, *Chem. Rev.*, 46, 69 (1950).
65. Nieman, C., *Record Chem. Progr.* (*Kresge-Hooker Sci. Lib.*), 12, 107 (1951).
66. Sanger, F., and H. Tuppy, *Biochem. J.*, 49, 481 (1951).

67. Sanger, F., and E. O. P. Thompson, *Biochem. J.*, 53, 366 (1953).
68. Kaufman, S., and H. Neurath, *J. Biol. Chem.*, 181, 623 (1949).
69. Sprinson, D. B., and D. Rittenberg, *Nature*, 167, 484 (1951).
70. Sizer, I. W., *J. Biol. Chem.*, 163, 145 (1946).
71. Edman, P., *J. Biol. Chem.*, 168, 367 (1947).
72. Fraenkel-Conrat, H., R. S. Bean, and H. Lineweaver, *J. Biol. Chem.*, 177, 385 (1949).
73. Desreux, V., and R. M. Herriott, *Nature*, 144, 287 (1939).
74. Herriott, R. M., V. Desreux, and J. H. Northrop, *J. Gen. Physiol.*, 24, 213 (1940).
75. Borgstrom, E., and F. C. Koch, *Proc. Soc. Exp. Biol. Med.*, 52, 131 (1943).
76. Hoch, H., *Nature*, 165, 278 (1950).
77. Herriott, R. M., *J. Gen. Physiol.*, 22, 65 (1938).
78. Van Vunakis, H., and R. M. Herriott, unpub.
79. Sanger, F., *Biochem. J.*, 39, 507 (1945).
80. Porter, R. R., in *Methods in Medical Research*, Vol. 3 (J. H. Comroe, Jr., ed.). Year Book Publishers, Chicago (1950).
81. Van Vunakis, H., Doctorate Dissertation, Columbia University, Department of Biochemistry, New York (1951).
82. Herriott, R. M., and J. H. Northrop, *J. Gen. Physiol.*, 18, 35 (1934).
83. Herriott, R. M., *J. Gen. Physiol.*, 19, 283 (1935).
84. Hollander, V., *Proc. Soc. Exp. Biol. Med.*, 53, 179 (1943).
85. Philpot, St. J. L., and P. A. Small, *Biochem. J.*, 32, 542 (1938).
86. Herriott, R. M., *J. Gen. Physiol.*, 20, 335 (1937); *J. Gen. Physiol.*, 31, 19 (1947).
87. Li, C. H., *J. Am. Chem. Soc.*, 67, 1065 (1945).
88. Herriott, R. M., M. L. Anson, and J. H. Northrop, *J. Gen. Physiol.*, 30, 185 (1946).
89. Mears, W. H., and H. Sobotka, *J. Am. Chem. Soc.*, 61, 880 (1939).
90. Kern, H. L., Doctorate Dissertation, Johns Hopkins University, School of Hygiene and Public Health, Department of Biochemistry (1953).
91. Sullivan, M. X., and Goldberg, *Proc. Biochem. Soc., Biochem. J.*, 35, CXXIX (1941).
92. Bergmann, M., and O. Behrens, *J. Biol. Chem.*, 129, 587 (1939).
93. Johnson, A. C., Doctorate Dissertation, Johns Hopkins University, School of Hygiene and Public Health, Department of Biochemistry (1952).
94. Brady, E. M., *J. Biol. Chem.*, 198, 607 (1952).
95. Van Vunakis, H., unpub.
96. Porter, R. R., *Biochem. J.*, 46, 304 (1950).
97. Wagner-Jauregg, T., and B. E. Hackley, Jr., *J. Am. Chem. Soc.*, 75, 2125 (1953).
98. Williamson, M. B., and J. M. Passmann, *J. Biol. Chem.*, 199, 121 (1952).
99. Miettineu, J. K., and A. I. Virtaneu, *Acta Chem. Scand.*, 3, 459 (1949).

THE ACTIVATION OF CHYMOTRYPSINOGEN AND TRYPSINOGEN AS VIEWED BY ENZYMATIC END-GROUP ANALYSIS *

HANS NEURATH, JULES A. GLADNER,† and EARL W. DAVIE

Department of Biochemistry, University of Washington, Seattle

REACTIONS INVOLVING the conversion of an enzyme precursor to the active form may be regarded as model systems for the study of the relation between the chemical structure and biological activity of enzymes. Such reactions involving the crystalline proteolytic enzymes have been the subject of classical investigations by Northrop, Kunitz, and Herriott (1) and have since been followed by comparative molecular-kinetic analyses of zymogens and active enzymes, using the methods of sedimentation in the ultracentrifuge and free diffusion (2–7). The more recent developments in chemical and enzymatic protein analysis and in chromatographic technics have paved the way for a more detailed elucidation of the comparative properties of proteolytic enzymes and their respective zymogens. One such system, namely, pepsinogen and pepsin, has been elegantly studied by Herriott and coworkers (8), as described in a preceding paper of this volume. In the present paper, the results of an analogous investigation of the activation of chymotrypsinogen and trypsinogen are presented in brief.

Since during the enzymatic activation of chymotrypsinogen and trypsinogen one or more peptide bonds are presumably opened (1, 9), it was to be expected that the zymogen differed from the active form in the number and nature of terminal groups; and since

* Investigations conducted in this laboratory, referred to in this paper, were supported in part by the United States Public Health Service, by funds made available by the people of the State of Washington, Initiative 171, and by the Office of Naval Research, Department of the Navy, under contract No. nonr-477-04 with the University of Washington.

† Predoctorate Fellow of the United States Public Health Service.

50

the activation is enzyme-specific, being mediated by trypsin at least in the initial stage, the newly created terminal groups should conform to the specificity requirements of the mediating enzymes. The determination of C-terminal groups with the aid of carboxypeptidase was, therefore, chosen as the first objective of a general program dealing with proteolytic enzymes and their zymogens, currently under way in this laboratory.

END-GROUP ANALYSIS WITH THE AID OF CARBOXYPEPTIDASE

While it would be beyond the scope of this contribution to the Symposium to discuss in detail the theoretical and experimental aspects of the use of carboxypeptidase as an analytical tool, a few explanatory comments on both aspects appear essential.

Experimental procedure. The experimental procedure involved incubation of protein substrate with carboxypeptidase in solution at pH 7.8, the course and extent of the reaction being followed quantitatively by colorimetric analysis with a ninhydrin reagent (10, 11) after precipitation of the proteins with 5 per cent trichloracetic acid. Qualitative and semi-quantitative analysis of liberated amino acids was carried out by adsorption of amino acids onto and elution from Dowex 50 ion exchange resin (hydrogen form, 8 to 12 per cent crosslinked) (12, 13, 14), followed by one- or two-dimensional paper chromatography. Unknown spots were identified, and estimated in amount, by comparison with R_f values and color intensities of graded dilutions of known amino acids. For quantitative work, the eluate was subjected to column chromatography (15).

It is imperative that the protein substrate be devoid of adventitious impurities of free amino acids or peptides. The conventional methods of crystallization, dialysis, and column chromatography using ion exchange resins (15), when applied with scrutiny and care, have been found to be adequate to remove these trace impurities. Perhaps even more important is the complete absence from protein substrates and carboxypeptidase of catalytic amounts of endopeptidase, which otherwise would continuously create new terminal groups. This experimental precaution is of particular importance when proteolytic enzymes or their zymogens are used as substrates.

Diisopropylfluorophosphate, which is without effect on carboxypeptidase, proved effective in inactivating residual endopeptidase activity (6, 16), as tested by the sensitive and specific assay methods involving the use of synthetic substrates for trypsin and chymotrypsin (2).

Substrate specificity and reaction rates. End-group analysis with carboxypeptidase is based upon the primary assumption that the specificity requirements of this enzyme toward synthetic peptide and protein substrates are the same. This is equivalent to postulating that the length of a polypeptide chain is not a contributing factor in the enzymatic hydrolysis of the C-terminal bond. Consequently, carboxypeptidase may be expected to hydrolyze proteins provided (1) that the protein substrate is composed of one or more open polypeptide chains; (2) that the C-terminal peptide bond and other points of interaction with the enzyme (e. g., "secondary peptide bond" and the C-terminal side-chain (2)) are accessible to the enzyme; and (3) that the C-terminal side-chain conforms to the specificity requirements of carboxypeptidase (2, 17). Following hydrolysis of the C-terminal bond, enzymatic cleavage may then continue along the polypeptide chain in a sequential one-by-one process until a structural situation is created which fails to conform to the above requirements. It is worthy of note that in every case examined, hydrolysis of the protein substrate has been found to be restricted to the liberation of relatively few amino acids, even though the enzyme-substrate mole ratio exceeded by one or more orders of magnitude that which usually prevails in the hydrolysis of synthetic substrates (13, 14, 18–20). However, if protein substrates are considered as a group, every amino acid with the exception of proline, hydroxyproline, cystine, cysteine, and possibly glutamine has been obtained as a reaction product, a fact suggesting that the side-chain specificity of carboxypeptidase is wider than was inferred from studies with synthetic substrates (2, 17).

Since the intrinsic rate of hydrolysis of a peptide bond depends largely on the nature of the side chain which contributes the peptide nitrogen, the sequence of amino acids in the polypeptide chain is a prime rate-determining factor. A general formulation of the under-lying kinetic problem has been recently given by Linderstrøm-Lang (21), but a solution of the equation could be found only for the specific, and practically unlikely, case that the intrinsic kinetic con-stants (k_3/K_m), for the hydrolysis of adjacent bonds are identical. Couched in more descriptive terms, it is evident that the relative rates of liberation of amino acids will be directly related to their sequence along the peptide chain if they are arranged in order of decreasing rates of hydrolysis, the C-terminal bond being hydrolyzed fastest. At any point of inversion of this sequence, the rate of hydrolysis of the preceding bond will become the rate-determining step for the hydrolysis of the succeeding one, and the constituent amino acids will be liberated at the same rate. While side-chain specificity is probably a dominant rate-determining factor, it is entirely possible that other structural details, such as hydrogen bond-ing, involving either the susceptible or the "secondary" (adjacent) peptide bond, also influence the rate of liberation of amino acids, particularly if the Pauling-Corey helical structure is accepted as a model for the configuration of polypeptide chains in proteins.

If the enzymatic reaction proceeds to completion, one equivalent of every C-terminal amino acid per mole of substrate should be liberated by carboxypeptidase. In practice, however, fractional stoichiometric relations have sometimes been found, and have neces-sitated a decision between alternative interpretations: (1) fractional quantities are due to substrate impurities, or (2) the enzymatic reac-tion has failed to reach completion. No generally applicable ex-planation of this phenomenon, which is being investigated further, can yet be offered.

Effect of carboxypeptidase on β-lactoglobulin and insulin. As illustrative examples of the use of carboxypeptidase for end-group analysis, the results obtained with β-lactoglobulin and insulin are presented below. These proteins were chosen since β-lactoglobulin has been reported (22) to contain three N-terminal groups of leucine

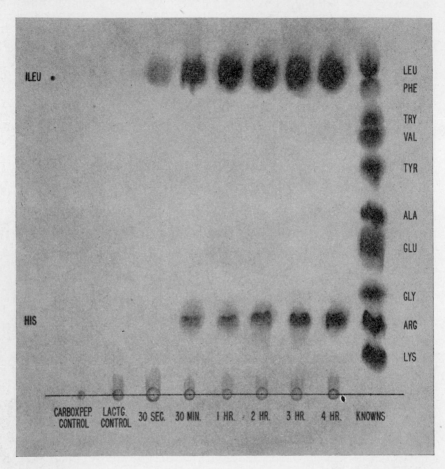

Fig. 1. Paper chromatogram (butanol : acetic acid : water, 4: 1: 5) of the reaction products resulting from incubation of β-lactoglobulin with carboxypeptidase (substrate/enzyme mole ratio of 25) in the presence of DFP. The vertical columns, from left to right, correspond to: carboxypeptidase control; lactoglobulin control; reaction products after 30 seconds, 30 minutes, 1, 2, 3, and 4 hours of incubation at 25° C; mixture of known amino acids. The known amino acids are identified on the right margin and the unknown ones (identified by R_f values, colors and color intensities) on the left margin. Not shown are graded dilutions of the known amino acids. Figs. 1 and 2 were made from an artist's drawing using the original paper chromatogram to record R_f values and spot areas, and using colored photographs of the chromatogram to judge spot intensities.

per molecule (molecular weight 40,000), whereas only two equivalents of amino acids per mole of protein substrate, viz., isoleucine and histidine, could be maximally detected when β-lactoglobulin and carboxypeptidase were incubated in a substrate/enzyme mole ratio of 25 (see Fig. 1). As seen from the paper chromatogram shown

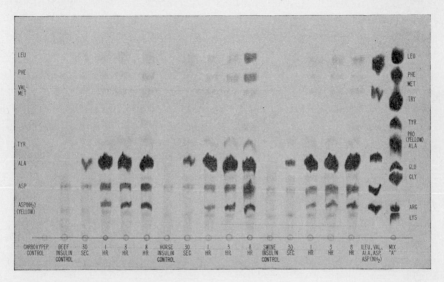

FIG. 2. Paper chromatogram (butanol : acetic acid : water, 4: 1: 5) of the reaction products resulting from incubation of beef, horse, and swine insulin with carboxypeptidase (substrate/enzyme mole ratio of 50), in the presence of DFP. The first column shows the carboxypeptidase control; the following group of five columns represents the beef insulin control and the amino acids liberated after incubation of substrate and enzyme for periods up to 8 hours. The following two groups of five columns each show the analogous results for horse and swine insulin. The last two columns show spots corresponding to known mixtures of amino acids. Unknown amino acids were identified by comparison of R$_f$ values, colors and color intensities with those of graded dilutions (not shown) of the known amino acids. Asparagine does not appear in this photograph with full intensity because it yields a yellow spot with ninhydrin, and moreover, some of the amide is decomposed by the resin into aspartic acid.

in Fig. 1, the reaction was essentially completed in 2 hours. While it is evident from these results and those of N-terminal group analysis, that the three polypeptide chains of β-lactoglobulin cannot be identical, additional analytical data are needed for a more complete elucidation of the structural implications of these findings.

Insulin was selected as another representative protein substrate because the amino acid sequence of both constituent polypeptide chains is known (23, 24), alanine and asparagine occupying the C-terminal positions (beef insulin). The same amino acids were shown by Harris (19) to be among the products of hydrolysis by carboxypeptidase. In the analyses illustrated in Fig. 2, crystalline insulin from three species, namely, pork, beef, and horse,[1] were subjected to hydrolysis by carboxypeptidase under strictly identical experimental conditions (substrate/enzyme mole ratio of 50, up to 8 hours of incubation). While alanine and asparagine are indeed the main products, traces of other amino acids, viz., aspartic acid, glutamic acid, tyrosine, and leucine, are also apparent. All of these are known to occupy positions adjacent to the C-terminal group of the A chain of beef insulin. Differences among the three species exist with respect to phenylalanine, which is definitely present as a reaction product of horse insulin, but is of questionable occurrence in the enzymatic hydrolysate of beef insulin, and which cannot be accounted for by the amino acid sequence of either the A or B chains of beef insulin.

THE ACTIVATION OF CHYMOTRYPSINOGEN

The action of carboxypeptidase on chymotrypsinogen and DFP-α-chymotrypsin has been recently investigated in detail (14, 25), and since the results of this work are being published elsewhere (26) it will suffice to summarize herein the final results and their interpretation. In this work, as in the companion investigation of the activation of trypsinogen (vide infra) it was necessary to substitute for the active enzymes their inactive diisopropylphosphoryl derivatives (DFP-enzymes) in order to avoid general proteolysis of protein substrate and carboxypeptidase. This substitution involves the tacit assumption that the active enzyme and its respective DFP-deriva-

---

[1] We are indebted to Dr. H. C. Hagedorn of the Nordisk Insulin Laboratory, Gentofte, Denmark, for a generous supply of crystalline horse and pork insulin. Crystalline beef insulin (lot 2842) was obtained through the courtesy of the Lilly Research Laboratories, Eli Lilly and Company, Indianapolis.

tive are structurally identical and that the diisopropylphosphate group is not attached to a C-terminal side chain (16, 27).

Carboxypeptidase fails to liberate from seven or eleven times recrystallized chymotrypsinogen stoichiometrically significant quantities of free amino acids. The protein remains also resistant to hydrolysis after reversible denaturation by heat or by acid (1, 28). These findings, together with the absence of α-amino groups reactive toward dinitrofluorobenzene (29), suggest that the zymogen consists of one or more cyclic polypeptide chains. In contrast, incubation of carboxypeptidase with DFP-α-chymotrypsin gives rise to one mole each of leucine and tyrosine per mole of substrate (molecular weight 21,500) in addition to 0.4 moles of glycine and 0.12 moles of serine. Additional quantities of glycine, serine, and leucine (about 0.4 moles of each) are liberated during a second cycle of enzymatic hydrolysis. Since DFP-α-chymotrypsin contains two N-terminal groups, i. e., isoleucine and alanine (29), a like number of C-terminal groups has been tentatively identified with tyrosine and leucine. A comparison of characteristic molecular properties of chymotrypsinogen and DFP-α-chymotrypsin is given in Table 1.

TABLE 1

COMPARISON OF SOME CHARACTERISTIC PROPERTIES OF CHYMOTRYPSINOGEN
AND α–CHYMOTRYPSIN (OR DFP–α–CHYMOTRYPSIN)

Property	Author	Chymotrypsinogen	α-Chymotrypsin or DFP-α-Chymotrypsin
Molecular Weight (Sed. and Diff.)	Schwert et al. (3, 4)	23,000	21,500 (monomer)
N-Terminals	Desnuelle et al. (29)	0	2 Isoleucine Alanine
C-Terminals	Gladner and Neurath (14, 25, 26)	0	2 Tyrosine Leucine
Isoelectric Point	Anderson and Alberty (30)	9.5	8.6
Free Amino Groups	Wilcox * (unpub.)	13	14
$E_{280}^{1\%}$	Wilcox * (unpub.)	20.0	21.5

* Private communication from Dr. P. E. Wilcox.

The results obtained from end-group analysis are in accord with all known aspects of the activation process if it is assumed that the activating enzymes, trypsin and chymotrypsin, have the same specificities toward proteins as they do toward synthetic substrates. A tentative scheme which is based essentially on Jacobsen's interpretation of kinetic data (9) and which takes into consideration all relevant data of Table 1, is shown in Fig. 3. According to this

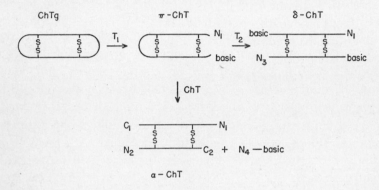

ACTIVATION SCHEME OF CHYMOTRYPSINOGEN (HYPOTHETICAL)

$N_{1,2}$-terminal A.A. (Desnuelle): Ileu, Ala

$C_{1,2}$-terminal A.A. (this work): Leu, Tyr.

FIG. 3. Hypothetical scheme of the activation process of chymotrypsinogen. *ChTg*, chymotrypsinogen; *ChT*, chymotrypsin; *Ileu*, isoleucine; *Ala*, alanine; *Leu*, leucine; *Tyr*, tyrosine. For further details see the text.

scheme, one peptide bond is opened during the tryptic activation, T_1, with the liberation of one basic C-terminal group (arginine or lysine). Since the second stage, i. e., the conversion of π-chymotrypsin to the α-form, is catalyzed by chymotrypsin, C-terminal groups conforming to the specificity requirements of chymotrypsin must be expected; and since presumably there are only two C-terminal groups (leucine and tyrosine), it follows that the basic C-terminal group formed in the first stage must have been split off in the second. The conversion of π-chymotrypsin to the δ form, also indicated in Fig. 3, will not be considered herein, since a paucity of experimental data precludes a test of this hypothesis.

The basic group, N₄-basic, is probably attached to a peptide which, in fact, has been identified by chromatographic methods. Some of the properties of this peptide may be inferred from the analytical data of Table 1. Thus, according to the most reliable molecular weight analyses of chymotrypsinogen and α-chymotrypsin, the molecular weight of the peptide should be of the order of 1000 to 1500. This value also agrees with the difference in extinction coefficients listed in the last row of Table 1, on the assumption that the zymogen and the active enzyme have identical tyrosine and tryptophane contents. According to the isoelectric points of the two proteins, the peptide should be predominantly basic. The difference in free amino groups is compatible with the presence of 2 α-amino groups in α-chymotrypsin if one ε-group of lysine had been removed with the peptide.

Chromatographic analysis of the protein-free filtrate of activation mixtures of chymotrypsinogen prepared according to Kunitz (1) (chymotrypsinogen/trypsin mole ratios of 10,000) revealed the presence of one or more peptides which, upon acid hydrolysis, yielded 8 or possibly 9 amino acids, i. e., lysine, arginine, serine, glycine, aspartic acid, glutamic acid, leucine, alanine, and possibly valine. Assuming for the present that the peptide contains one of each amino acid, the molecular weight would be about 1200, as expected, and the peptide would be predominantly basic. Further studies on the identification of the peptide are in progress (26).

THE CONVERSION OF α-CHYMOTRYPSIN TO THE β- AND γ-FORMS

Kunitz (31) has described the preparation of crystalline β- and γ-chymotrypsin, presumably resulting from limited autolysis of the α-form. β- and γ-Chymotrypsin exhibit the same substrate specificities as does the α-form (31), and γ- and α-chymotrypsin have the same sedimentation characteristics (3).

When crystalline DFP-β- and γ-chymotrypsin are subjected to the action of carboxypeptidase (25, 26), much the same spectrum of amino acids is obtained as with DFP-α-chymotrypsin, but some significant differences are apparent. Leucine and tyrosine are the main reaction products in all three cases, one mole of each amino acid being maximally liberated per mole of substrate. However, the β- and γ-forms, which gave practically identical results, yielded in addition, aspartic acid, asparagine, and phenylalanine, and more serine and less glycine than did DFP-α-chymotrypsin. While all three forms of DFP-chymotrypsin thus appear to have identical C-terminal groups (leucine and tyrosine) and identical N-terminal groups (32), it remains to be decided whether the present findings reflect differences in the amino acid sequence or in configurational details, or in both, of the C terminal portions of the constituent polypeptide chains of β and γ chymotrypsin as compared to the α form.

The Activation of Trypsinogen

Using the same experimental approach previously described (vide supra), an analysis of the C-terminal groups of trypsinogen and DFP-trypsin was attempted. Contemporary studies by Desnuelle and coworkers (33) had shown that these proteins contain approximately one N-terminal group each per molecule (molecular weight 24,000 (6, 7)), and the presence of a like number of C-terminal groups was, therefore, expected.

Effect of carboxypeptidase on trypsinogen and DFP-trypsin (34, 35). As judged by chromatographic analysis, carboxypeptidase is essentially without effect on trypsinogen or DFP-trypsin when these proteins are in the native form. Even in substrate/enzyme mole ratios as low as 10:1 no free amino acids could be detected. After denaturation by acid (48 hours at pH 1 at 4° C, followed by exhaustive dialysis at pH 3), not more than 0.05 moles of lysine per mole of trypsinogen were maximally liberated by carboxypeptidase, in addition to traces of several amino acids (aspartic acid, alanine, tyrosine, methionine). The same amino acids were liberated from acid-denatured DFP-trypsin except that 0.3 moles of lysine per mole of substrate were found. The action of carboxypeptidase thus suggests that the carboxyl end of the polypeptide chain of trypsinogen may remain unaffected during activation, but that the product of the activation process is more susceptible to acid denaturation than its precursor.

Trypsin-soybean inhibitor compound and soybean inhibitor. In order further to substantiate the absence of a reactive C-terminal group in native trypsin, the enzymatically inactive, crystalline, trypsin-soybean inhibitor compound (36) was subjected to hydrolysis by carboxypeptidase and compared to the hydrolysis of the soybean inhibitor (37) alone.

Using inhibitor/enzyme mole ratios of 8, in each case, identical results were obtained when the trypsin-inhibitor compound and the inhibitor, respectively, were compared to one another and the results were corrected to the concentration of the inhibitor present in the substrate-enzyme system. One mole of leucine per mole of inhibitor (molecular weight 24,000) was maximally liberated in each case, in addition to fractional stoichiometric quantities of aspartic acid and alanine. These results thus demonstrate that trypsin, in combination with soybean inhibitor or as a diisopropylphosphoryl derivative, is devoid of a free C-terminal group, and that soybean trypsin inhibitor contains a single C-terminal group which is reactive toward carboxypeptidase, and which does not seem to be involved in the interaction with trypsin.

The peptide resulting from activation of trypsinogen (35). As viewed by chemical and enzymatic end-group analysis, trypsinogen and DFP-trypsin each appear to consist of a single polypeptide chain with a free and reactive amino end-group (33), the carboxyl end being unreactive either because of ring closure or because it is sterically inaccessible. As judged from measurements with acid-denatured DFP-trypsin as substrate, the C-terminal amino acid is probably lysine.

The fact, however, that the N-terminal group in trypsinogen is different from that in DFP-trypsin, viz., valine, and isoleucine, respectively (33), suggests that during the activation of trypsinogen a peptide is split from the open amino end. This single peptide has been identified by paper chromatography and paper electrophoresis, and following acid hydrolysis (24 hours and 48 hours at 110° C, 6 N HCl, in a sealed tube) was found to contain three amino acids in stoichiometrically significant amounts, namely, valine, aspartic acid, and lysine.

The experimental procedure consisted essentially in activating crystalline trypsinogen by the addition of trypsin (0.7 mg. of trypsin per 120 mg. of trypsinogen), in the presence of 0.05 M CaCl$_2$, pH 8.0, 0° C, removing aliquots at various time intervals corresponding to known degrees of activation, and removing peptides of free amino acids on Dowex 50 resin (hydrogen form, 4 or 12 per cent cross-linked). Chromatographic analysis of the eluate on paper, and by paper electrophoresis, revealed a single spot which was eluted, hydrolyzed, and subjected to semi-quantitative analysis on paper.

The three constituent amino acids were found to occur in mole ratios of valine : aspartic acid : lysine $= 1 : (5$ or $6) : 1$. Since the C-terminal position of lysine in the peptide is suggested by the specificity requirements of the activating enzyme, trypsin, and the N-terminal position of valine by comparison of the N-terminal groups of trypsinogen and DFP-trypsin (vide supra), the tentative structure of val-(asp)$_{5 \text{ or } 6}$ – lys, with a minimum molecular weight of about 1000, may be assigned to this peptide. Though the presence of amide groups in the peptide has not yet been investigated, the peptide has acidic properties, as judged by paper electrophoresis. These are to be expected also from a comparison of the isoionic points of trypsinogen and DFP-trypsin, 9.3 and 10.1 respectively (38).

CONCLUSIONS

The experimental evidence available to date points toward a common feature of the activation of the zymogens of proteolytic enzymes, namely the splitting of a peptide from the constituent polypeptide chains. While it is inviting to conjecture that the function of the peptide is to shield the enzymatically active center of the molecule, thus supressing catalytic activity, the structural relations underlying the process of activation are probably more complex. It is significant, however, that the peptide liberated during activation appears to occupy structurally different regions in trypsinogen and in chymotrypsinogen, and has a different composition in each case. The activation process seems to be a simpler one in the case of trypsinogen, in that a portion of the open amino end of the single polypeptide chain is split off, the carboxyl end remaining shielded by ring closure, or being otherwise resistant to hydrolysis by carboxypeptidase. The peptide is more acidic in character than the zymogen or the active enzyme.

In the more complex sequence of reactions attending the enzymatic conversion of chymotrypsinogen to α-chymotrypsin, a predominantly basic peptide is split off from the carboxyl end of one of the two polypeptide chains which are formed after the cyclic polypeptide chain of chymotrypsinogen is opened in the tryptic phase of the activation process. The liberation of the peptide appears to be under chymotryptic control.

It is to be emphasized that these interpretations remain tentative until the results of enzymatic end-group analysis are confirmed by chemical methods.

REFERENCES

1. Northrop, J. H., M. Kunitz, and R. M. Herriott, *Crystalline Enzymes*, 2nd edition, Columbia Univ. Press, New York (1948).
2. Neurath, H., and G. W. Schwert, *Chem. Rev.*, 46, 69 (1950).
3. Schwert, G. W., *J. Biol. Chem.*, 179, 655 (1949); 190, 799 (1951).
4. Schwert, G. W., and S. Kaufman, *J. Biol. Chem.*, 190, 807 (1951).
5. Smith, E. L., and D. M. Brown, *J. Biol. Chem.*, 195, 525 (1952).
6. Cunningham, L. W., Jr., F. Tietze, N. M. Green, and H. Neurath, *Discussions Faraday Soc.*, 13, 58 (1953).
7. Tietze, F., *J. Biol. Chem.*, 204, 1 (1953).
8. Herriott, R. M., this Volume.
9. Jacobsen, C. F., *Compt. rend. trav. lab. Carlsberg, Sér. chim.*, 25, 325 (1947).
10. Moore, S., and W. H. Stein, *J. Biol. Chem.*, 176, 367 (1948).
11. Troll, W., and R. K. Cannan, *J. Biol. Chem.*, 200, 803 (1953).
12. Partridge, S. M., *Nature*, 169, 496 (1952).
13. Thompson, A. R., *Nature*, 169, 495 (1952).
14. Gladner, J. A., and H. Neurath, *Biochim. et Biophys. Acta*, 9, 335 (1952).
15. Moore, S., and W. H. Stein, *J. Biol. Chem.*, 192, 663 (1951).
16. Balls, A. K., and E. F. Jansen, *Advances in Enzymol.*, 13, 321 (1952).
17. Smith, E. L., *Advances in Enzymol.*, 12, 191 (1951).
18. Lens, J., *Biochim. et Biophys. Acta*, 3, 367 (1948).
19. Harris, J. I., *J. Am. Chem. Soc.*, 74, 2944 (1952).
20. Harris, J. I., and C. A. Knight, *Nature*, 170, 613 (1952).
21. Linderstrøm-Lang, K. U., *Discussions Solvay Conf. on Proteins*, in press.
22. Porter, R. R., *Biochim. et Biophys. Acta*, 2, 105 (1948).
23. Sanger, F., and H. Tuppy, *Biochem. J.*, 49, 481 (1951).
24. Sanger, F., and E. O. P. Thompson, *Biochem. J.*, 53, 366 (1953).
25. Neurath, H., and J. A. Gladner, *Federation Proc.*, 12, 251 (1953).
26. Gladner, J. A., and H. Neurath, *J. Biol. Chem.*, in press and in prep.

27. Schaffer, N. K., S. C. May, Jr., and W. H. Summerson, *J. Biol. Chem.*, **202**, 67 (1953).
28. Eisenberg, M. A., and G. W. Schwert, *J. Gen. Physiol.*, **34**, 583 (1951).
29. Desnuelle, P., M. Rovery, and C. Fabre, *Biochim. et Biophys. Acta*, **9**, 109 (1952).
30. Anderson, E. A., and R. A. Alberty, *Phys. & Colloid Chem.*, **52**, 1345 (1948).
31. Kunitz, M., *J. Gen. Physiol.*, **22**, 207 (1938).
32. Rovery, M., C. Fabre, and P. Desnuelle, *Biochim. et Biophys. Acta*, **10**, 481 (1953).
33. Rovery, M., C. Fabre, and P. Desnuelle, *Biochim. et Biophys. Acta*, **9**, 702 (1952).
34. Davie, E. W., and H. Neurath, *J. Am. Chem. Soc.*, **74**, 6305 (1952).
35. Davie, E. W., and H. Neurath, *Biochim. et Biophys. Acta*, **11**, 442 (1953).
36. Kunitz, M., *J. Gen. Physiol.*, **30**, 311 (1947).
37. Kunitz, M., *J. Gen. Physiol.*, **30**, 291 (1947).
38. Green, N. M., unpub.

DISCUSSION

DR. EYRING: I don't know whether I understand well enough to ask an intelligent question but as I do understand Dr. Herriott's results he found that the logarithm of the K of his reaction is linearly proportional to the number of groups removed whether this be one, two or more, a result somewhat like Hammett has found for other types of reactions. Is this the correct idea, that is, in pepsin if you are removing groups the number of groups removed is proportional to the change in the logarithm of the rate process?

DR. HERRIOTT: Yes; that is correct if you mean enzymic rate.

DR. EYRING: If the group is some distance from the reaction site, irrespective of whether you are substituting one group or changing another you would expect to find the logarithm of the rate proportional to how many things you acted on. It isn't hard to see why it shouldn't be quite linear if these groups are at somewhat different distances. One would expect also to get different free energy changes when one takes different groups off. If at any time one finds an effect on the logarithm of a rate constant, that is to say on the free energy of activation, one expects it to be an effect on the activation energy itself. This is a very familiar result in organic chemistry.

DR. KAUZMANN: Suppose that we have a solution of enzyme molecules each of which contains groups which can react with a reagent. Suppose that the enzymatic activity is only affected if the reagent reacts with a particular one of the groups in each molecule (call it type A), but that if it reacts with this group the enzymatic activity of that molecule is destroyed. Call the remaining groups type B and suppose that there is no effect on the activity if any or all of them react with the reagent. Would this not lead to a relation such as you found?

DR. HERRIOTT: No, that is the dosage experiment that I mentioned, and it doesn't fit.   I think that the dosage experiment assumes that the structure which has reacted is still able to absorb reacting reagent molecules. And what we have plotted here is the number of reactive sites that remain.

DR. KAUZMANN: We must then assume that the type B groups react more slowly with the reagent but that there are many more of them in each molecule. This is best discussed mathematically. Let n_A and n_B be the numbers of the two types of groups present in the solution and let k_A and k_B be their specific rate constants for reaction with the reagent.   Then

$$\frac{dn_A}{dn_B} = \frac{k_A n_A}{k_B n_B}$$

or

$$d \ln n_A = (k_A/k_B n_B) \quad dn_B.$$

If k_A is much greater than k_B but $k_A n_A$ is much less than $k_B n_B$, then most of the reagent will react with type B groups but the type A groups (and the enzymatic activity) will disappear before an appreciable fraction of the type B groups will have reacted. As long as there is any activity n_B can be treated as a constant and we find

$$\log\left(\frac{activity}{initial\ activity}\right) = \ln(n_A/n_{AO}) = (k_A/k_B n_B) N$$

where N is the number of reagent molecules bound.   This is the law that you found.

DR. CALVIN: I don't know how the experiment was done—but, assuming that you put in the reagent all at once and took out samples at different times—that is, different contact periods between the enzyme and the reagent was the only thing that was determined.   After determining the number of reagent molecules that were left, from this one calculated the number of reagent molecules that are bound.

DR. HERRIOTT: The actual experiment was done by determining the number of reagent molecules bound to the protein molecule.

DR. CALVIN: From your plot you found five bound groups per mol. Thus this would indicate that each molecule will be inactivated when it has taken up five reagent molecules on the average.

DR. KAUZMANN: It seems to me that if it took five there would be an induction period, which was not observed.

DR. STADTMAN: The only thing that is demanded here is that all of these reactive sites will react with the same facility.

DR. HERRIOTT: Well, that's the dosage experiment, and that doesn't satisfy these results, unless one introduces at least two additional assumptions.

DR. E. SMITH: I would like to ask Dr. Neurath a question, if I may. Before we get into too much of a hurry to ascribe our failure to find C-terminal amino acids to the presence of peptide chains shaped as 0's 9's and 6's, wouldn't it be desirable to check the absence of C-terminal residues by chemical methods, such as the lithium aluminum hydride reagent or lithium borohydride? As a footnote to Dr. Neurath's discussion, I would like to point out that not only will terminal proline block the action of the enzyme but also proline adjacent to the terminal residue. For example, if there is a C-terminal sequence — prolylphenylalanine, then the terminal phenylalanine will be liberated slowly or not at all.

DR. NEURATH: It is evident, and we have stated it also in the manuscript, that all the experiments involving enzymatic end group analysis will have to be ultimately repeated once a wholly satisfactory chemical method for determining C-terminal groups is available. We have recognized the fact that only in the most favorable case, can the rate of liberation of amino acids by carboxypeptidase be related to the sequence of occurrence of amino acid residues along the polypeptide chain, and that the absence of any reaction does not necessarily indicate the absence of a C-terminal group. Looped chains or closed chains are something which we should be open minded about and which, for the time being, is primarily an operational concept.

Having the floor, I should like to dispel some of the doubts which Dr. Herriott may have conveyed in his discussion of the characterization of the proteolytic enzymes. First of all there is little question that the molecular weight of chymotrypsinogen is approximately 23,000 rather than 36,000, and that of α-chymotrypsin is somewhat less. Molecular weight determinations involving the ultracentrifuge and the diffusion method carried out in two independent laboratories are in accord on this point. Chymotrypsinogen is indeed perhaps the only protein which satisfies all criteria of purity, the latest proof being the column chromatography in the hands of Hirs and Stein. While the question of the isoelectric point is perhaps the most debatable one yet, I think that electrophoresis by the moving boundary method does give us the best answer, namely the higher isoelectric points which I quoted in our paper. So in all, and I don't want to go into too many details, I think that we can feel rather confident that in the case of the enzymes considered by Dr. Herriott, we are dealing with well-defined proteins and well-characterized enzymes.

DR. BESSMAN: Dr. Herriott mentioned the question of two resistant peptides, one potentiating the hydrolysis of the other. Is this effect specific for glutathione, or is it given by other thiol peptides?

DR. HERRIOTT: It is not specific for glutathione. In the instances which we have studied, if one either blocks the alpha amino structure of the peptide, as Bergmann did, or if you remove the alpha amino to the gamma position, glutamyl peptides will carry out this effect; but the SH group as far as I can tell is not essential. Incidentally, I didn't mention that Brady has reported a somewhat similar study with crystalline pepsin and crystalline trypsin; so this is not peculiar to papain. She found that a non-protein extract, the nature of which she does not fully understand yet, would facilitate complete digestion of hemoglobulin with either trypsin or pepsin, whereas normally they carry the digestion to the extent of only about 20 per cent to 25 per cent.

Dr. HEIDELBERGER: Is there any theoretical explanation for this effect?

Dr. HERRIOTT: There probably are many explanations, but I prefer to suggest only one, namely that the second or catalytic peptide combines with the enzyme much as a coenzyme does and gives it a new or extended specificity. Bergmann had suggested as an explanation of the observations, that a tetrapeptide was synthesized from the two peptides and then a cleavage of the C-end amino acids of this tetrapeptide occurred until there remained the dipeptide cofactor and the amino acids of the originally resistant peptide. In our studies we used a sensitive biuret test to detect the formation of such a tetrapeptide, and if it is formed, it is present free in solution at any one time to the extent of less than 0.1 per cent of the original dipeptide. Another possibility is that once the tetrapeptide is formed it is so rapidly split by the enzyme that its concentration never reaches a detectable level.

Dr. HEIDELBERGER: Would that be a kind of transpeptidation?

Dr. HERRIOTT: We looked very carefully for evidence of transpeptidation but obtained none. We chromatographed the digestion mixtures and looked for new peptides as would be expected from a transpeptidation mechanism and no new spots were observed. It is possible that the splitting of the tetrapeptide is so fast that we couldn't detect its formation. This study was initiated to determine whether Bergmann's theory of peptide synthesis during hydrolysis is correct, for if it is, the use of enzymes for determining protein structure would be virtually meaningless.

Dr. MALLETTE: It might be worth pointing out in this connection that synthetically prepared tri- and tetrapeptides were split at a reasonable speed—more rapidly than the reaction occurred with the mixtures of peptides.

Dr. RACKER: There is another possibility to be considered—namely, that the co-substrate is converted to a tripeptide by transpeptidation and that the tri-peptide is then rapidly hydrolyzed to regenerate the original dipeptide. If this occurred rapidly, perhaps the tripeptide would not be detectable. I wonder whether any experiments have been done to rule out the possibility of a tripeptide?

Dr. MALLETTE: That was also studied.

Dr. RACKER: It was studied and tripeptides were found to be inactive?

Dr. MALLETTE: The synthetic tripeptide was studied and found not to be very reactive.

DR. GREENSTEIN: Are you able to recover the original co-substrate intact at the end of the reaction?

DR. HERRIOTT: Not with glutathione as co-substrate. With one co-substrate it was recovered in high yield — that is, there was a very high percentage of the original material still present.

DR. NEURATH: I do not know of any real evidence, nor any necessity, for assuming that the enzyme unfolds during its action on the substrates. As far as the other questions are concerned, we have been dealing with the DFP-inhibited chymotrypsin and trypsin, and since it is difficult to reactivate these inhibited enzymes, I cannot give you a direct answer as far as these protein substrates are concerned. However, we are now trying to reactivate other forms of inhibited chymotrypsin, after enzymatic cleavage by carboxypeptidase, and Dr. Dowmont in our laboratory has found that yeast triosephosphate dehydrogenase can be degraded quite appreciably with carboxypeptidase and yet retain its enzymatic activity. Let me remind you, too, that Knight and Harris have shown that some 3,400 threonine residues can be removed from tobacco mosaic virus with carboxypeptidase, but that the degraded virus is still capable of causing infection and incidentally gives rise to a progeny of the original, undegraded composition.

DR. E. SMITH: I think I can help to answer the questions. There have been several other cases which have been reported, for example, carboxypeptidase will split the C-terminal peptide bond of lysozyme. Mrs. Adrienne Thompson has found that lysozyme can be recovered afterwards and is still enzymatically active, so that this would be against the view that denaturation preceded the digestion. One other curious thing discovered by Dr. E. Thompson in our laboratory is that carboxypeptidase can be cannibalistic in the presence of denatured carboxypeptidase. It will start taking end groups off itself. Native carboxypeptidase will not attack itself. If you have a solution of completely native carboxypeptidase no free amino acids are liberated, but if you denature some of the carboxypeptidase and add native carboxypeptidase free amino acids appear, which means that it is the active enzyme which liberates groups from the denatured protein.

DR. DOUDOROFF: May I ask about this glutathione business? Do you need large amounts, or does this act more or less catalytically to change the specificity? Have you tried to see whether a complex with the enzyme may be formed in this reaction?

DR. HERRIOTT: I think the concentration of glutathione was of the order of .05 molar, the same concentration as was used of the acylated peptides that Bergmann had described as bringing about this effect. As to the combination of the enzyme, we have not gotten around to deciding that. It happens that the papain is an SH enzyme; but when we found that both pepsin and trypsin were having a somewhat similar reaction as was described by Brady we thought that the SH was probably of secondary importance, especially since we could also bring this reaction about with glutamyl peptide which did not contain the SH group.

DR. DOUDOROFF: You have never really studied the effect of concentration?

DR. HERRIOTT: No.

DR. HEIDELBERGER: Before our own enzymes get too cannibalistic we had better take advantage of a 15-minute recess.

DENATURATION OF PROTEINS AND ENZYMES

WALTER KAUZMANN

Frick Chemical Laboratory, Princeton University, Princeton

ENZYMATIC ACTION is one of the many unusual properties which appear among the proteins and in no other class of substances. These properties seem to depend in some way on the manner in which the polypeptide chain and its attached amino acid residues are arranged within and on the surface of the molecule, the whole structural pattern presumably being stabilized by a great number of weak secondary intramolecular bonds, such as hydrogen bonds and van der Waals' forces. These bonds are fairly well understood, but only in a general way. It is safe to say that the most important and perhaps the toughest problem in protein chemistry is to find out in detail what these structural patterns are, how they are stabilized, and how they make it possible for proteins to do the things that they do. We may have to wait for the organic chemists and the x-ray experts to provide us with the most important ingredients for the solution of this problem. But it will be a fairly long wait, and meanwhile it is possible to make some progress along other routes.

When the structural pattern of a protein is disturbed the protein loses some or all of its characteristic properties. Careful observation of all kinds of alterations may provide a way of learning something about these patterns and the mechanism by which they function. For instance, the functional groups of a protein can be changed by making them react with appropriate chemical reagents. Dr. Herriott has told us about the results of such experiments. Another approach is to break up the pattern by rupturing the secondary intramolecular bonds which maintain it—a few at a time if possible. This process is what many, if not most, people would agree to call denaturation, and it is this that I propose to discuss here. What can we learn about protein structure from the study of denaturation? Before considering this question, however, let us review some pertinent information on intramolecular bonding and denaturing agents.

70

INTRAMOLECULAR BONDS RESPONSIBLE FOR PROTEIN FOLDING

The known types of intramolecular bonds which might be important in maintaining the native protein in its unique folded state are these:

1. *Hydrogen bonds* (74), especially those between the carboxyl oxygens and the amide hydrogens of the peptide bonds, which play a prominent part in the most recent proposals of protein structure (8, 46, 81).

2. What might be termed *hydrophobic bonds*, referring to the tendency of the more hydrophobic amino acid residues (valine, the leucines, phenylalanine, tryptophane, and possibly alanine and proline) to avoid the aqueous phase and adhere to one another in a sort of intramolecular " micelle " analogous to those occurring in soap and detergent solutions (64). In a sense, hydrophobic bonds also represent a kind of hydrogen bond (or " anti-hydrogen bond ") because they arise by being unable to participate in the strong hydrogen bonding of the water molecules; that is, they are stabilized by the rather strong hydrogen bonds of water. They may therefore make a very large contribution to the stability of the native protein.

Hydrophobic bonds are the same as what many writers have called " van der Waals bonds," but this term does not seem to be appropriate because the forces ordinarily called van der Waals forces probably contribute only a small fraction to the total energy of hydrophobic bonds.

3. *Salt bridges.* These are ionic bonds which might be expected to form between positively charged (lysine and arginine) and negatively charged (glutamic and aspartic acids) amino acid residues. Jacobsen and Linderstrøm-Lang (49) have, however, given strong reasons for doubting that these links are important in most proteins. (These reasons may not apply in the case of carboxyhemoglobin and methemoglobin, for which Steinhardt and Zaiser (91, 92, 98) have recently found that a considerable fraction of the carboxyl ions do not combine with hydrogen ions until the protein has been denatured.)

4. *London dispersion forces* (*" van der Waals forces "*). In each of the other bond types mentioned above dispersion forces should help to increase the stability, but it is not likely that bonds exist in proteins which owe a major part of their stability to dispersion forces.

5. *Intramolecular chemical bonds.* Aside from the ubiquitous alpha peptide linkage, the cystine disulfide bond is the first to come to mind in this connection. According to the review of the situation by Haurowitz (41), there is as yet little evidence that other types of chemical linkage are important in helping to maintain the native protein structure. The role of cystine will be discussed below.

DENATURING AGENTS

In their comprehensive review of denaturation, Neurath, Greenstein, Putnam, and Erickson (76) have summarized the more important agents capable of causing denaturation in typical proteins, and the following is a slight modification of their list.

1. *Physical agents*: heat; pressure; freezing; surface forces; irradiation; sound.

2. *Chemical agents*: hydrogen ions and hydroxyl ions; organic solvents (acetone, alcohols, etc.); amides and related compounds (urea, formamide, guanidinium ion, etc.); detergents.

3. *Biological agents*: enzymes.

The great diversity of denaturing agents is one of the most striking features of the phenomenon of denaturation. Let us see what can be said about the mechanisms by which these agents operate.

SPECULATIONS ON THE MODES OF ACTION OF DENATURING AGENTS

1. *Urea.* It seems fairly obvious that urea denatures proteins by rupturing the hydrogen bonds that are among the important stabilizers of the native molecular pattern, since urea is itself essentially a pure peptide bond and can presumably form hydrogen bonds similar to those believed to occur intramolecularly in proteins. But as Aten et al. have pointed out (4), we should not forget that water

is itself also able to form, and therefore to break, hydrogen bonds. The fact that proteins do not denature so readily in pure water implies that water is not as effective as urea in rupturing the important hydrogen bonds. This must mean that the equilibrium,

$$\begin{array}{c} \diagup \\ C=O \cdots H-N \diagdown \end{array} + \begin{array}{c} H \diagdown \\ H \diagup O \cdots H-O \diagdown \\ H \end{array} \rightleftharpoons \begin{array}{c} \diagup \\ C=O \cdots H-O \diagdown \\ H \end{array} + \begin{array}{c} H \diagdown \\ H \diagup O \cdots H-N \diagdown \end{array}$$

tends toward the left, a conclusion which is consistent with the fact that the deviations of aqueous urea solutions from ideality indicate a tendency of urea molecules to associate in water (Schellman, as reported in 87). Furthermore, anyone who has dissolved urea in water will have noticed the strong absorption of heat that accompanies this process, showing that the members of the left-hand side of the above equation are lower in energy than those on the right.

The concept of the hydrogen bond has been injected into proteins on one occasion or another to explain almost everything that proteins can do. It is important to realize, however, that because of the presence of water around proteins, this concept has very definite limitations. We must remember, for instance, that the energies involved in the rupture of the interpeptide hydrogen bonds by water are rather small—probably less than one thousand calories and perhaps as little as a few hundred. Obviously bonds which are as weak as this can contribute significantly to the stability only because there are a great many of them (two per amino acid residue, or as many as several hundred bonds in even the smallest protein molecule). Other types of hydrogen bonds, involving for instance the hydroxyls of serine, threonine, and tyrosine, and the amino and carboxyl groups of lysine and glutamic and aspartic acids, cannot occur in anything like these numbers, so it seems doubtful that they can be very important in holding most native proteins together.[1]

We thus seem to have in interpeptide hydrogen bonding a reason-

[1] Note, however, that the stability of each hydrophobic bond depends in effect on the entire dissociation energy of several hydrogen bonds of the type occurring in water, and not merely on the much smaller difference in the energies of two different types of hydrogen bonds. Therefore the number of hydrophobic bonds needed to confer a given degree of stability on a protein may be much smaller (perhaps one-fifth or one-tenth) than the number of interpeptide hydrogen bonds.

able basis for understanding the action of urea on proteins. The case for this kind of hydrogen bonding is strengthened when one tries to find an alternative property of urea that might account for its activity. For instance, urea solutions have a higher dielectric constant than water. Is it possible that this is in some way responsible for urea denaturation? Since glycine, which also gives a solution having a high dielectric constant, is not a denaturing agent, the answer to this question seems to be in the negative. Other reasons for rejecting this possibility, which has importance in the interpretation of the kinetics of urea denaturation, are discussed elsewhere (87).

As will be mentioned below, the kinetics of the urea denaturation of ovalbumin and some other proteins is rather remarkable. The denaturation of ovalbumin by guanidinium chloride shows the same remarkable behavior, and since there is also a close similarity in their chemical structure, the two substances undoubtedly act on ovalbumin in the same way. The same is probably true of formamide (90) and the methylated urea and guanidine derivatives studied by Hopkins and by Greenstein (37, 44). It is interesting that glycine (87), which is isomeric with O-methyl and N-methyl ureas (both denaturants), and arginine, which is a monosubstituted guanidine, are not denaturants.

2. *Heat.* There is a strong temptation to suggest that the heat denaturation of aqueous protein solutions occurs by a mechanism similar to that of urea denaturation, the role of the urea molecules being assumed by water (59). Heat is necessary because, as we have seen, water is somewhat less effective than urea in breaking inter-peptide hydrogen bonds. Starting with this point of view it is possible to develop equations for the rate of denaturation as a function of temperature and urea concentration which are in complete agreement with the observed kinetics of both the urea and the heat denaturation of ovalbumin (87). Unfortunately some of the numbers which have to be introduced in order to make these equations fit the facts are a bit unreasonable, however, so it is by no means proven that urea and heat denaturation occur by essentially the same mechanism. Furthermore, the heat denaturation of ovalbumin

seems to be somewhat more sensitive to pH than is urea denaturation, and the interesting results of Christensen and Jacobsen (17, 48) on the urea denaturation of β-lactoglobulin indicate that in this protein there is a difference in the denaturation product at low and high temperatures. Neither of these observations are consistent with the simple picture mentioned above.

3. *Organic solvents, detergents, and surfaces.* These denaturants would all have an affinity for the non-polar residues of the protein. We should, therefore, expect that they operate by rupturing the " hydrophobic bonds," since they provide a more favorable environment for these residues than that existing in water.

Small quantities of surface active agents stabilize serum albumin (7, 23) and β-lactoglobulin (39) (but *not* ovalbumin (87) or fibrinogen (73)) against denaturation by urea and heat. Luck has suggested (66) that this effect may be caused by the stabilization of the intramolecular " micelles " (see above) through the adsorption of one or two non-polar molecules. Soap micelles are similarly stabilized by the addition of non-polar substances such as hydrocarbons.

4. *Hydrogen ions and hydroxide ions.* The denaturing action of acids and bases has usually been explained by supposing that certain of the ionized forms of a protein are particularly unstable (34, 35, 60, 76, 89). It is assumed that proteins are capable of the following reactions:

$$\left. \begin{array}{l} P_0 = P* + nH^+ \\ \text{or } P_0 + nH^+ = P* \end{array} \right\} \text{(rapidly established equilibria)}$$

followed by

$$P* \longrightarrow \text{denatured protein (rate-controlling step)}.$$

$P*$ represents the unstable form of the protein. Starting with this hypothesis and a very thorough investigation of the pH and temperature dependence of the denaturation rate of the protein, ricin, Levy and Benaglia (60) have proposed that the native protein is held together by a few " proton sensitive hydrogen bonds." The identity of these bonds is not known. Other workers have suggested that acids and bases rupture a few strategically located salt linkages by neutralizing the electric charge on the carboxyl and amino groups, respectively (26, 42).

There is, however, another, much simpler factor which may account equally well for acid and alkali denaturation, at least in some instances. This is the very large electrostatic repulsion which exists within typical protein molecules at extremes of pH. Wu (97) in 1931 suggested that these forces might be responsible for denaturation by acids and bases, and McLarin and Lewis (71) have also considered them. We shall now show that a reasonable semi-quantitative theory can be constructed on the basis of this effect.

Assume that the protein molecule has M amino groups and N carboxyl groups arranged uniformly over its surface. Let the dissociation constant of an isolated carboxyl group be K. Then if P_M represents the species for which all charged groups are present as NH_3^+ and $COOH$ (net charge $= M$), there is a series of equilibria at acid pH[2] in which varying numbers of protons dissociate from the carboxyls:

$$P_M = P_Z + nH \qquad\qquad (n \leq M),$$

the species P_Z having a net charge $Z = M - n$. The corresponding dissociation constant is

$$K_n = (P_Z)(H^+)^n / (P_M), \qquad\qquad (1)$$

where, according to Linderstrøm-Lang (62)

$$K_n = K_{no} \exp[w(M^2 - Z^2)] \qquad\qquad (2)$$

$$K_{no} = K^n N! / n! (N - n)! \qquad\qquad (3)$$

The exponential factor is meant to take account of the electrostatic interactions of the charged groups. The constant, w, is given by E/kT, where E is proportional to the energy arising from these electrostatic interactions. For a spherical molecule of radius a immersed in a medium of dielectric constant D, $E = e^2/2Da$, where e is the electronic charge. In general, w can be expected to be inversely proportional to some molecular dimension, r.

Now suppose that when a molecule denatures the activated com-

---

[2] The argument is readily extended to the dissociation of protons from the amino groups at alkaline pH.

plex is swollen because the intramolecular bonds are loosened, so that the molecular dimension is increased from r to $r + \Delta r$. This swelling will reduce the electrostatic repulsion energy in the activated complexes of all species having a net charge. Obviously those species with the largest charge should therefore denature most rapidly. If k_0 is the denaturation rate for the species with no net charge $(Z = 0)$, then the Linderstrøm-Lang theory leads to a denaturation rate for the species with charge Z given by

$$k_Z = k_0 \exp(xZ^2) \tag{4}$$

where

$$x/w = \Delta r / (r + \Delta r). \tag{5}$$

The over-all denaturation rate will be the weighted average rate for all species,

$$k = \sum_Z k_Z (P_Z) / \sum_Z (P_Z) \tag{6}$$

If we set

$$S' = \sum_n K_n (H^+)^{-n} \exp(xZ^2) \tag{7}$$

and

$$S = \sum_n K_n (H^+)^{-n} \tag{8}$$

then

$$k = k_0 S'/S. \tag{9}$$

Expand the exponential in S', giving

$$S' = \sum_n K_n (H)^{-n} (1 + xZ^2 + 1/2x^2Z^4 + 1/6x^3Z^6 + \cdots) \tag{10}$$

$$= S(1 + x\overline{Z^2} + 1/2x^2\overline{Z^4} + 1/6x^3\overline{Z^6} + \cdots) \tag{11}$$

where

$$\overline{Z^m} = \sum_n Z^m K_n (H^+)^{-n}/S \tag{12}$$

Let us make the assumption that

$$\overline{Z^m} = (\bar{Z})^m \tag{13}$$

making it possible to replace the sum in (11) by $\exp(x\bar{Z}^2)$, giving

$$k = k_0 \exp(x\bar{Z}^2) \tag{14}$$

or

$$\frac{d \log_{10} k}{d \, \text{pH}} = \frac{2x\bar{Z}}{2.303} \frac{d\bar{Z}}{d \, \text{pH}} \tag{15}$$

In fact, however, $\overline{Z^m}$ will always tend to be greater than $(\overline{Z})^m$, and the more so, the greater the value of $\overline{Z}$ and m. As a result, the assumption (13) leads to a variation of k with $\overline{Z}$ which should be less than the true variation. That is, equation (15) should under-estimate the variation of denaturation rate with pH.

For the denaturation of ovalbumin by acid, Lewis (61), Cubin (20), and Gibbs, Bier, and Nord (35) found that $d \log_{10}k/d\text{pH} =$ approximately 2 in the vicinity of pH 2. At this pH Cannan, Kibrick, and Palmer (13) found $d\overline{Z}/d\text{pH} =$ about 15 and $\overline{Z} =$ about 40. When substituted in equation (15), these values give

$$x = \text{about } 0.004.$$

Because of the approximation (13), the correct value of x may be somewhat less than this.

Cannan, Kibrick, and Palmer (13) found $w =$ about 0.05 for ovalbumin. Using this value in equation (5) we find as an upper limit,

$$\Delta r/r = \text{about } 0.08.$$

That is, the electrostatic repulsions alone can account for the observed effect of pH on the denaturation rate of ovalbumin if the mechanism is the same as that for heat denaturation and if the activated com-plex is "swollen" in its linear dimensions by less than 8 per cent as compared with the native molecule. Since this is not an unreason-able figure, the above theory seems to deserve serious consideration.

We may mention in addition that salts should, according to this theory, reduce the rate of acid denaturation because they reduce the electrical interactions (62).

The existence of considerable electrostatic repulsions at acid pH is shown by the fact that serum albumin seems to swell reversibly at acid pH, giving a considerably higher intrinsic viscosity than at the isoelectric point (82, 31).

Another point in favor of the above theory is the fact that pepsin denatures readily at neutral pH, where most proteins are stable. If a "proton sensitive hydrogen bond" played any part in stabilizing pepsin, it would therefore probably have to be different from those occurring in other proteins. On the other hand, because of the small number of basic amino acids and large number of acidic amino acids in pepsin, this protein has a low charge at acid pH's (where it is stable) and a high charge at neutral pH's (where it is unstable). Therefore, the present theory requires no unusual properties in the pepsin molecule beyond those already known to be present, viz., an unusually high ratio of acidic to basic amino acids.

The detailed theory outlined above presents, of course, a much over-simplified picture. It is merely intended to show that the postulated effect can be of the correct order of magnitude. Other factors undoubtedly operate, as shown by the fact that proteins do not generally show their maximum stability at exactly their isoelectric points. This could be a result of local electrostatic interactions, for instance, which do not pass through a minimum when the net charge is a minimum. That is, it is only a first approximation to treat the energy of the electrostatic interactions as proportional to Z^2, where Z is the net charge. Therefore it would be surprising if equation (14), or even equation (6), gave quantitative agreement over the entire pH range for all proteins.

5. *Pressure.* The mechanism of denaturation by pressure appears to be complex. Very high pressures (above about 5000 atmospheres) seem to cause denaturation (70), but Johnson and Campbell (51) found that 700 atm. inhibited the coagulation of ovalbumin and serum globulin by heat. Tongur (93, 94) has recently confirmed these opposing effects of pressures above and below 5000 atm. on the development of turbidity in serum albumin and ovalbumin.

On the other hand, 600 atm. accelerate the denaturation of ovalbumin by urea at 0° C, though it has no effect at 40° C (87). Pressure also has no effect on the rate of urea denaturation of staphylococcus antitoxin at 25° C (96).

Eyring and Johnson (25) suggest that the denaturing effect of very high pressure is caused by a change in the structure of water, which is apparently thereby converted into a stronger denaturing agent.

The effect of pressure on denaturation should be closely related to the volume change which accompanies the reaction (principle of

LeChatelier). Dilatometer studies (17, 63, 65, 87) show that urea denaturation is accompanied by a decrease in volume for ovalbumin and β-lactoglobulin. If the activated complex is intermediate in volume between the native protein and the urea-denatured one, this would account for the acceleration of urea denaturation at low temperatures. Accurate information is not available on the relative volumes of native and heat-denatured proteins,[3] but the work of Johnson and Campbell would seem to indicate that in the absence of urea, the formation of the activated state in the heat denaturation of ovalbumin is accompanied by an increase in volume. The absence of a pressure effect in the urea denaturation of ovalbumin at 40° C may therefore be a result of the opposite and competing effects of pressure on two different mechanisms.

6. *Radiation.* High-energy particles, ultraviolet light, and x-rays, as well as intense sound waves, probably rupture chemical bonds, but nothing is known of the extent to which this affects the secondary intramolecular bonds of proteins, so we shall not speculate any further at this time. This would seem to be a fruitful problem for further research.

7. *Enzymes.* Proteolytic enzymes may " cause " denaturation by merely shifting an equilibrium between the native and the denatured forms of a protein as a result of attack by the enzyme on the denatured form and not on the native form, according to the following sequence:

$$\text{Native protein} \rightleftharpoons \text{Denatured protein}$$

$$\text{Denatured protein} \xrightarrow[\text{Enzyme}]{} \text{Hydrolysis products.}$$

The interesting experiments of Christensen (17), however, do not exclude the possibility that in some instances enzymes may also exert a more direct denaturing effect, perhaps by hydrolysing critical peptide links. The situation is very clearly summarized in the third of Linderstrøm-Lang's Lane lectures (64).

---

[3] Dilatometer measurements by Heymann (43) indicate an expansion of the order of 0.2 ml. per 100 g. protein in the heat denaturation of ovalbumin, serum albumin, and serum globulin near their isoelectric points.

8. *Inhibitors of denaturation.* A number of substances exist which are very effective in slowing down the urea denaturation of ovalbumin (87). Among them are sulfate and phosphate ions, sucrose, glycerol, and glycine. Sulfate is such a potent inhibitor that guanidinium sulfate does not denature ovalbumin in spite of the fact that guanidinium ion is an even stronger denaturant than urea (11). There is no point in speculating on the cause (or causes) of the inhibition by this very diverse group of substances until we have more information.

The stabilizing action of surface active substances on serum albumin has been discussed above.

9. *The complexity of the denaturation reaction.* Do all denaturing agents cause essentially the same change in structure? Is there one chemical individual, " the denatured protein," which is produced by all denaturing agents? Or do different denaturing agents act on different parts of the molecule, producing chemically different species?

Much work has been done to detect differences between the denatured proteins produced in different ways from a given native protein (e. g., 6, 68). Although differences are detectable, their significance is not clear because it is always possible that they arise from changes subsequent to " true " denaturation. As might be expected, the answer to these questions therefore depends very much on just what changes are to be included in the term " denaturation." In spite of the fact that there is no general universal agreement on this, a significant problem with a definite answer does exist here, as will now be shown.

Two alternative modes of behavior are conceivable in proteins: (a) One portion of the native molecule might be held folded by one type of bond (say interpeptide hydrogen bonds) and another portion might depend for its stability on another type of bond (say hydrophobic bonds). With one reagent one portion of the molecule would unfold, and with another reagent another portion would unfold. Thus different types of reagents would act independently of one another in bringing about denaturation.

(b) The native protein might be kept folded by all kinds of

bonds which work together, in that if all bonds of one type are ruptured, the remaining types of bonds are not strong enough to hold the protein together so that the entire molecule unfolds. In this case different types of reagents would help one another in bringing about denaturation.

Because of the fact that hydrophobic reagents (alcohol, detergents, dioxane, acetone) strongly accelerate the denaturation of ovalbumin in urea (87), it would seem that situation (b) exists in this protein as far as interpeptide hydrogen bonds and hydrophobic bonds are concerned. Of course, this is not necessarily true of all proteins, though it does not seem unlikely.

This aspect of the question has some bearing on the controversy over the "all or none" character of denaturation (1). It would seem that if denaturation were always an "all or none" phenomenon, situation (b) would have to exist in all proteins. Situation (b) is not, however, a guarantee that denaturation is an "all or none" phenomenon.

The Structure of the Denatured Protein

So far we have discussed the mechanisms of denaturation without saying anything about the appearance of the protein molecule after it has been denatured. The picture implicit in these mechanisms was clearly presented by Wu in 1931: "The compact and crystalline structure of the natural protein molecule, being formed by virtue of secondary valences, is easily destroyed by physical as well as chemical forces. Denaturation is disorganization of the natural protein molecule, the change from the regular arrangement of a rigid structure to the irregular, diffuse arrangement of the flexible open chain" (97).

Disorganization seems to be the most important feature of the denaturation process, and we shall now try to obtain a more explicit description of it. But before doing this we must mention that there is another rather widely accepted interpretation according to which the essential feature of denaturation is the aggregation of globular and more or less unaltered native molecules. At the end of this section, however, we shall see that there are good reasons for thinking that this view is incorrect.

Two different types of disorganization seem to take place when proteins are denatured. In many of the common proteins (ovalbumin, serum albumin) denaturation in urea seems to consist of the *unfolding of the peptide chain.*[4] But in some instances it appears that denaturation is brought about by another form of disorganization, namely, *dissociation* into smaller units which may or may not be unfolded. Dissociation seems to be the predominant feature of the denaturation of tobacco mosaic virus by urea, alkali, and detergents (30, 59, 84). Other proteins which dissociate on denaturation are mentioned by Neurath et al. in their review (p. 215, ref. 76).

The case of tobacco mosaic virus is especially interesting because the viscosities of TMV solutions in urea decrease with time, showing that disaggregation of the very elongated virus molecule has a greater influence than any subsequent unfolding of the subunits (30, 85). Yet the kinetics of the disaggregation by urea (59) shows the same unusual features as the urea denaturation of ovalbumin (87), in which unfolding takes place without dissociation. Evidently the mechanism of the rupture of the intramolecular hydrogen bonds by urea is very similar in the two proteins, in spite of the very different structural changes which result. This is not at all unreasonable; whether a protein dissociates or merely unfolds when its secondary intramolecular bonds are ruptured depends on the continuity of the polypeptide chain. The native TMV molecule must be constructed of subunits which are not chemically linked to one another, whereas the ovalbumin molecule is probably a continuous polypeptide chain.

Let us now consider in more detail the structures of those proteins which unfold when they are denatured. The shapes of these proteins have in the past been interpreted in terms of the shapes of

[4] Some workers (21, 22, 53, 86) prefer to use the word *swelling* instead of unfolding or uncoiling for this phenomenon. This does not represent a very important difference in viewpoint, however. According to the interpretation of Scheraga and Mandelkern (86), the serum albumin molecule in 6.66 M urea is swollen to eight times the volume of the native molecule in water. Obviously the polypeptide chain must have undergone some rather large readjustments in order to accommodate itself to this change in the over-all size of the molecule, and these readjustments are the sort of thing that we call unfolding or uncoiling.

ellipsoids having the same hydrodynamic properties (9, 76, 77, 86). There is, however, another way of interpreting these structures which emphasizes other aspects of the structure. Is it not possible that in some of these proteins the amount of disorganization approaches that found in a typical randomly coiled linear polymer such as polystyrene? This question is best answered by comparing the intrinsic viscosities and friction constants of denatured proteins with those of linear high polymers of similar molecular weights or similar degrees of polymerization.

TABLE 1

INTRINSIC VISCOSITIES OF SOME HIGH POLYMERS

Polymer	Solvent	$[\eta]$ * for Mol. Wt.		$[\eta]$ * for extended chain length of		Reference
		45,000	70,000	1500 Å	2200 Å	
Rubber	Benzene	42	64	20	29	(33)
Polyvinyl chloride	Various	63	98	52	76	(72)
Polyiso- butylene	Cyclo- hexane	40	54	33	43	(69)
Polymethyl methacrylate	Benzene	27	38	30	40	(36)
Polystyrene	Toluene	31	41	37	48	(79)
Polydimethyl siloxane	Toluene	23	31	23	30	(36)

* In units of ml. solvent per ml. polymer rather than the more common units of $(g./100 ml.)^{-1}$.

It is well known that the intrinsic viscosity of a polymer depends on the solvent in which it is dissolved, being much greater in good solvents than in poor ones. The reason for this is the tendency of the molecules to contract or roll up into balls when in a poor solvent because different parts of the molecule tend to " stick " to one another under these conditions. Therefore the comparison of viscosities should be made in good solvents, where the randomness of the coiling is not restricted by " stickiness." For denatured proteins strong urea solutions are the best solvents for which suitable data are available. Table 1 shows the intrinsic viscosities of some typical polymers in good solvents, and Table 2 gives the values for denatured ovalbumin and serum albumin in strong urea solutions.

When the differences in chain length and molecular weights are taken into account, there is obviously a similarity in magnitude. (Serum albumin has a large number of intramolecular disulfide cross links due to cystine. As we shall mention later, these links can be broken by adding cysteine to the solution, giving a molecule more nearly comparable to a random coil. Therefore the comparison of

TABLE 2

INTRINSIC VISCOSITIES OF DENATURED PROTEINS

Solvent	$[\eta]$ (ml. per ml.)	Reference
Ovalbumin (mol. wt. 45,000, extended chain length 1500 Å.)		
10 M urea, 0.05 M borate buffer, pH 10	51	(31)
10 M urea, 0.05 M phosphate buffer, pH 7.6	45	(31)
7.5 M urea, 0.05 M phosphate buffer, pH 7.3	33	(31)
Strongly diluted with 0.2 M phosphate buffer after denaturing with 9.5 M urea	12.3	(9)
Native protein	5.5	(9)
Serum albumin (mol. wt. 70,000, extended chain length 2200 Å.)		
8 M urea, 0.05 M borate buffer, pH 10	29	(31)
8 M urea, 0.05 M borate buffer, pH 10, 0.02 M cysteine	71	(31)
6.66 M urea, 0.2 M acetate buffer, pH 5.2, 0.2 M NaCl	23	(77)
Native protein	6.7	(77)

intrinsic viscosities in the case of serum albumin should be made using the value measured in the presence of cysteine). Table 3 gives a comparison of the friction constants, corrected for differences in solvent viscosities, of some high polymers (obtained from sedimentation constants) with those of serum albumin in urea (obtained from the diffusion constants measured by Neurath and Saum, 77). When allowance is made for the fact that the disulfide cross linkages are present in the serum albumin, the trend of the values with increasing urea concentration falls into line with those of the polymers.

When denatured proteins are dissolved in poorer solvents (more dilute urea solutions and water) there is a considerable reduction in viscosity, just as is observed with other polymers. This is seen by comparing the intrinsic viscosity of ovalbumin which has been denatured in urea and then dissolved in water with its intrinsic viscosity when dissolved in strong urea (Table 2). Of course the same " stickiness " which leads to the contraction of the denatured molecule can cause two or more denatured molecules to stick together in poorer solvents; where we had intramolecular bonding in the

TABLE 3

COMPARISON OF FRICTION CONSTANTS OF POLYMERS AND UREA-DENATURED SERUM ALBUMIN

Substance	Mol. Wt.	Extended Chain Length in Å	$f/\eta \times 10^5$	Reference
Polystyrene in toluene	70,000	1820	1.18 *	(78)
	93,000	2200	1.41 *	(78)
Polyisobutylene in cyclohexane	70,000	3100	1.38	(69)
	50,000	2200	1.14	(69)
Polysarcosine in water	70,000	3700	1.95 **	(27)
	42,500	2200	1.45 **	(27)
Serum albumin in				
0 M urea			0.67	
0.5 M			0.74	
1.5 M			0.76	
3.0 M	70,000	2200	0.81	(77)
4.5 M			1.03	
6.0 M			1.08	
6.66 M			1.11	

* Extrapolated from values for molecular weights between 250,000 and 1,300,000.
** Extrapolated from values for molecular weights between 6700 and 16,200.

native protein we can have intermolecular bonding in the denatured protein. If the solvent is poor enough and electrostatic repulsions are not high (water at the isoelectric pH), aggregation goes to the point of precipitation and we have insolubility—often the most obvious consequence of denaturation. Under some conditions, however, aggregation leads to gel formation rather than to precipitation (31).

This picture of a denatured protein as a random coil is, of course, to be taken as only a first approximation in the same sense that the shapes of native proteins are generally interpreted in terms of rigid ellipsoids of revolution. Several effects (electrostatic interactions, intramolecular chemical cross-linkages, exclusion of certain configurations because of overlapping of different parts of the molecule, restriction of rotation about bonds) can, and as we shall see, apparently do cause some rigidity in the denatured molecule which must result in deviations from complete randomness even in good solvents. The random coil is, however, probably much closer to the truth for the denatured protein in good solvents than any model based on a rigid ellipsoid.[5] In poor solvents, the ellipsoid may become a useful first approximation, however.

Foster and Samsa (29) have recently reported measurements of the flow birefringence of urea-denatured ovalbumin which are inconsistent with the random-coil picture. They found that the molecule behaved like a rod 500 to 600 Å. long—far greater than the value of about 60 Å. calculated for the root mean square separation of the chain ends, assuming a completely random coil containing 400 amino acid residues in a single chain.[6] The measurements of birefringence were made in a rather poor solvent at low pH (3 M urea, 60% glycerol, pH 2.5). If the denatured ovalbumin molecule were an unhydrated prolate ellipsoid 500 Å. in length it would have to have an axial ratio of nearly 100 and an intrinsic viscosity of 4.4 (g./100 cc.)$^{-1}$. This is many times the observed intrinsic viscosity in strong urea near neutral pH, so it is obvious that the length measured by Foster and Samsa does not occur under the conditions with which we have been concerned. It would be desirable to have both viscosity and birefringence measurements in a better solvent at a higher pH, with precautions to avoid aggregation through the sulfhydryl reactions which will be discussed below.

[5] As is pointed out by Scheraga and Mandelkern (footnote 41 of ref. 86), the hydrodynamic properties of randomly coiled chains are not equivalent to those of any rigid ellipsoid.

[6] Whether or not a random coil would show any flow birefringence (other than that imposed by the molecule's being stretched out as a result of the shear gradient) depends on the rate at which the molecule changes its configuration as compared with the rate of rotation due to Brownian motions. Many of the random configurations would be rather extended, so if the configurations changed slowly one might find inherent birefringence even in a randomly coiled molecule. The fact that birefringence was observed is therefore of itself not proof that the molecule was not a random coil.

The theory mentioned at the beginning of this section, that an aggregation of unaltered native molecules is the essential reaction in denaturation, is also inconsistent with the picture of a random coil presented above. We shall now try to show that this theory is inadequate. There is no doubt that aggregation often accompanies denaturation, and many examples can be given (5). (Some of the causes of aggregation have just been mentioned and others will be given later.) On the other hand there are a number of examples in which what must be recognized as denaturation takes place without aggregation. Serum albumin, ovalbumin, and many other proteins undergo a marked increase in intrisic viscosity and decrease in solubility when they are exposed to guanidine and strong urea, yet osmotic pressure, diffusion, and sedimentation measurements show that their molecular weight is unchanged (76). Numerous measurements of the kinetics of denaturation by many different agents show that the rate-controlling step is in most instances independent of the protein concentration. Even in one of the few clear-cut examples for which the denaturation rate constant does vary with the protein concentration (the heat denaturation of pepsin, 14), it does so over only a limited range of protein concentrations. In another example (the urea denaturation of tobacco mosaic virus, 59) the rate constant is smaller, the greater the protein concentration, i. e., under conditions favoring aggregation. The bulk of the kinetic evidence therefore indicates that the basic change underlying denaturation occurs in the isolated protein molecules and does not require the collision of two or more protein molecules. This would hardly be expected if aggregation were the essential step leading to denaturation.

Eisenberg and Schwert (24) showed that in the reversible heat denaturation of chymotrypsinogen the equilibrium constant (determined from the fraction of protein which had become insoluble at the isoelectric point) for the reaction

$$\text{native protein} \rightleftharpoons \text{reversibly denatured protein}$$

was independent of the protein concentration. Anson and Mirsky (2) found the same for the equilibrium between native and reversibly denatured trypsin (measured by means of the enzymatic activity). This shows that the essential change responsible for the loss of solubility and activity of these materials has nothing to do with aggregation.

The considerable change which takes place in the optical rotation (6, 50, 80, 87) and in the x-ray diffraction pattern (3) of proteins upon denaturation by heat as well as by urea provides strong evidence that denaturation is accompanied by a reorganization of the internal structure. That is, even if aggregation does occur, the elements that aggregate must have a different structure from that of the native protein. Finally, there is the problem of accounting for the increase in entropy which accompanies the known examples of reversible denaturation, since aggregation would lead to a decrease in entropy.

In the light of evidence of this type one must conclude that aggregation, when it occurs, must be a consequence of an earlier, more drastic change in the structure of the protein, and therefore plays no essential part in the denaturation process.

THE THERMODYNAMICS OF DENATURATION

Available information on the entropy and enthalpy changes which occur with different proteins in the reaction

$$\text{native protein} \rightarrow \text{denatured protein}$$

is summarized in Table 4. One striking feature of these results is the large positive value of ΔH found in all instances but pepsin at high pH values. Because of the exponential dependence of the equilibrium constant on $\Delta H/T$,

$$(\text{denatured})/(\text{native}) = K = \exp(-\Delta H/RT)\exp(\Delta S/R).$$

the equilibrium between the two forms of the protein is shifted from one side to the other within a narrow temperature range. (For soybean trypsin inhibitor, K changes from 0.1 at 38° C to 10 at 55° C, a variation by a factor of 100 in a temperature interval of only 17° C. For chymotrypsinogen at pH 3, K changes by the same amount in a temperature interval of 5.7° C). This rapid shift in equilibrium with

TABLE 4

THERMODYNAMIC DATA FOR DENATURATION

Protein and Denaturation Conditions	Mol. Wt.	ΔH cal/mole	ΔS e. u.	Reference
From equilibrium constants				
Trypsin (heat denaturation in 0.01 N HCl)	34,000	67,600	213	(2)
Soybean trypsin inhibitor (heat denaturation at pH 3.0)	24,000	57,300	180	(57)
Chymotrypsinogen (heat denaturation at pH 2.0)	38,000	99,600	316	(24)
(Heat denaturation at pH 3.0)		143,000	432	(24)
From calorimetric measurements				
Pepsin (pH 6.7–7.5, 15° C)	36,000	10,000–20,000	—	(12)
(pH 5.1–6.5, 35° C)		20,000–70,000	—	(12)
(pH 6.95–4.3, 30° C)		0–85,000	—	(19)
Methemoglobin (alkali denaturation, 25° C)	68,000	138,000	—	(18)

temperature is unique among chemical reactions and begins to resemble a phase transition in which an equilibrium, say

$$\text{solid} \rightleftharpoons \text{liquid},$$

shifts from one side to the other over an infinitesimal temperature interval. In this respect denaturation can be described as a sort of "melting" process. The "melting point" is not sharp merely because the "crystal size" is so small. (Ordinary crystals would also melt over an appreciable range of temperature if their particle size were of the order of a few tens or hundreds of angstroms.)

The large values of ΔH have generally (26, 42, 74, 76) been explained in terms of the energy required to break large numbers of weak secondary intramolecular bonds, and there seems to be no reason to doubt the validity of this suggestion. The number of bonds broken in denaturation could be estimated by dividing the observed value of ΔH for denaturation by the energy change per bond, but unfortunately not enough is known about the changes in bond energy to make such a calculation worthwhile. It should be remembered, as Aten et al. have pointed out (4), that although intramolecular bonds may be broken on denaturation, new bonds are also formed between the protein and the solvent. Furthermore, many of the intramolecular bonds are probably merely rearranged with no change in enthalpy, especially if the solvent is a poor one, as is the case in the examples listed in Table 4.

The thermodynamic criterion for a spontaneous isothermal reaction is that the quantity $\Delta F = \Delta H - T\Delta S$ be negative. It is obvious that denaturation could not occur at all if the positive value of ΔH were not compensated by an increase in the entropy. In those examples for which values of ΔS are available it has indeed an enormous positive value. (Normal chemical reactions rarely result in entropy changes of more than 20 or 30 entropy units, and the values given in Table 4 are about ten times as large as this.) This entropy increase must be regarded as the driving force that makes denaturation possible. Since entropy represents disorganization, this is one of the chief reasons for believing that, as has already been stated, disorganization is the essential feature of denaturation.

For both chymotrypsinogen and trypsin the fraction of denatured protein present at equilibrium is not affected by varying the total protein concentration. Therefore the disorganization cannot be ascribed to disaggregation in these two substances. Nor can it be ascribed to dissociation of hydrogen ions in the manner suggested for pepsin by Steinhardt (89) and LaMer (58), since the pH dependence of the equilibrium shows that chymotrypsinogen (24) and trypsin [7] *combine*, respectively, with 3 and 2.5 hydrogen ions when

---

[7] Anson and Mirsky (2) found that the temperature at which the equilibrium concentrations of native and denatured trypsin are equal is shifted from 44° C. to 61.3° C.

they denature. Therefore for these two substances the entropy increase must be caused by some process taking place within the protein molecule, i. e., the unfolding of the polypeptide chain.

The magnitude of the entropy change, large though it seems, can be readily accounted for according to the theory that denaturation consists of unfolding into a more or less randomly coiled molecule. According to the Boltzmann relation,

$$\Delta S = R \log_e C_2/C_1,$$

where R is the gas constant, and ΔS is the entropy change which results when one mole of a substance undergoes a change from a state in which its molecules can have C_1 configurations to a state in which they can have C_2 configurations. If the native molecule has a rigid structure, C_1 can be taken as unity. If in the denatured molecule there are n single chemical bonds, and if it is possible for the polypeptide chain and its attached side groups to twist about with p positions available on the average for each single chemical bond, then the total number of configurations available to the denatured protein is $C_2 = p^n$. Thus

$$\Delta S = nR \log_e p.$$

In a protein with a molecular weight of 35,000 there are about 300 amino acid residues, each contributing three single bonds to the polypeptide chain, plus some other single bonds in the side chains. Let us say that $n = 1000$ and $p = 2$, corresponding to a fairly large amount of flexibility about each single bond. Then $\Delta S = 1000\ R \log_e 2 = 1400$ e.u., which is considerably larger than the observed values listed in Table 4. Evidently proteins which have been reversibly denatured in water (a rather poor solvent, as we have seen) retain a considerable amount of rigidity. Either a small portion of the molecule is unfolded, or the chain has comparatively little flexibility.

---

when the concentration of hydrochloric acid is reduced from 0.01 N to 0.001 N. Taking $\Delta H = 67,600$ cal., this corresponds to a decrease in the equilibrium constant at constant temperature by a factor of $10^{2.5}$ when the hydrogen ion concentration is decreased by a factor of 10. (This calculation is only a rough one since ΔH probably varies with pH.)

The Kinetics of Denaturation

The resistance of different proteins to denaturation varies over wide limits. For instance, many proteins, including ovalbumin, are stable in water at pH 7 at room temperature, yet pepsin denatures rapidly in water at pH values more alkaline than about 6. β-lacto-globulin can be heated in a boiling water bath without affecting its ability to crystallize on cooling, yet ovalbumin is rapidly and per-manently denatured on warming above 70° C. Pepsin, trypsin, and papain are able to hydrolyse peptide bonds in strong urea solu-tions which rapidly denature many other proteins, including oval-bumin. Evidently one cannot simply say that some proteins are inherently more stable than others, because the relative stability depends on the denaturing agent which is employed (cf. ovalbumin, which is more stable than pepsin in neutral aqueous solution and less stable than pepsin in urea).

This difference in stability is primarily a result of differences in the rates of denaturation of proteins. For this reason alone the study of the rates of denaturation is of some importance. But even more important is the insight that such a study may provide into the larger problem of why different proteins, in spite of many funda-mental structural similarities, can perform such a great variety of functions.

To the physical chemist the kinetics of protein denaturation has the additional attraction of having many unusual characteristics not commonly found in ordinary chemical reactions; the subject is of interest for its own sake, quite aside from any possibly more im-portant biological implications. We shall now review some of these peculiarities, returning in due course to the problem of differences in protein stability.

1. *The temperature coefficient of heat denaturation.* One of the most striking characteristics of the kinetics of heat denaturation in many proteins (but not all!) is the very large temperature coefficient of the rate. For instance, the rate of heat denaturation of ovalbumin increases by a factor of several hundred when the temperature is

raised 10° C. (16, 61). This is to be compared with the factor of two or three found in ordinary chemical reactions for a similar interval of temperature. The reason for this is, of course, the large activation energy of the process. Large positive entropies of activation are also observed.

Interesting and important kinetic and equilibrium studies have been made on the reversible denaturation of soy-bean trypsin inhibitor by Kunitz (57) and of chymotrypsinogen by Eisenberg and Schwert (24). The rates of both the forward and backward reactions have been measured as a function of the temperature, and it has been found that the activated states in these particular reactions have thermodynamic properties intermediate between those of the native and reversibly denatured proteins. We can therefore infer that the structures of the activated states are also intermediate, and all that has been said about the over-all ΔH and ΔS of reversible denaturation applies to the energy and entropy of activation.

2. *The urea denaturation of ovalbumin.* Some interesting results have been obtained recently in a study of the kinetics of the urea denaturation of ovalbumin (87). When urea is added to ovalbumin solutions the levorotation increases with time by as much as a factor of two or three, the rate and amount of increase depending on the urea concentration, temperature, pH, and other factors. Even in strong urea the initial rotation is, however, the same as that of the native protein in water. Urea therefore imposes its influence in some other way than simply by being in the general vicinity of the folded protein molecule. We may presume that the change in rotation is due to the drastic changes in conformation and solvation which accompany the unfolding of the molecule. This assumption is supported by kinetic studies of viscosity and solubility changes.

The increase in the levorotation does not follow a simple first order law. The half-time of the increase is, however, practically independent of the initial protein concentration, showing that a number of reactions must be going on, each of which is of the first order in the protein. These probably represent stages in the unfolding, though it is difficult to be entirely sure that they do not result in part from inhomogeneity in the native protein, some of the molecules possibly being more resistant to denaturation than others. The different reactions seem to be affected in about the same way by the temperature, urea concentration, and many other variables, since the shape of the rotation vs. time curve is fairly constant under many different conditions. This presumably means that if there are stages in the unfolding of ovalbumin they are not dissimilar.

The half-time of this change is extremely sensitive to the urea concentration, especially at low temperatures, the half-time at 0° C. being proportional to the 15th power of the urea concentration. The reaction therefore appears to be of a very high order in urea. If the thermodynamic activity of urea is used instead of the concentration, the apparent reaction order tends, if anything, to be slightly higher, so this behavior has nothing to do with the deviations of urea solutions from ideality at the high urea concentrations used in these experiments. Arguments which are presented in detail elsewhere (87) make it difficult to avoid the conclusion that the simultaneous attack on the protein by 15 or more molecules of urea is necessary to cause the unfolding of the ovalbumin molecule at 0° C. The reaction order with respect to urea is smaller at higher temperatures (15 at 0°, 12.5 at 30°, 8.3 at 45°, and about 3 at 65° C.).

The high reaction order with respect to urea probably means that the folds in the polypeptide chain cannot be opened unless several hydrogen bonds are broken simultaneously. This conclusion has some interesting connotations. If the folds contained free chain ends exposed to attack by urea we should expect that the chains could be unwound by breaking one hydrogen bond at a time, in the fashion of a zipper. Since this does not seem to be the mechanism of unfolding, we must conclude that the ends of the polypeptide chains in ovalbumin are buried inside the molecule or are inaccessible to the urea for some other reason.[8] Instead, the folds must be attacked in the middle of the chains, and they can apparently only be opened up if several bonds are first broken simultaneously. A possible reason for this is shown schematically in Fig. 1. The process

[8] This conclusion is interesting in connection with Porter's finding (83) that no chain ends could be detected in ovalbumin with 2, 4-dinitrofluorobenzene; Steinberg (88), however, has found that terminal amino acids can be hydrolysed from ovalbumin by carboxypeptidase.

of going from state A to state B in this figure obviously cannot occur without breaking about eight bonds at the same time, and if two urea molecules were required to rupture each bond we should have a reaction of the sixteenth order in urea. Once a single loop of a fold has been pried loose in this way, the rest of the fold can be opened by breaking single hydrogen bonds one after the other, as in a zipper. In this way state C is reached.

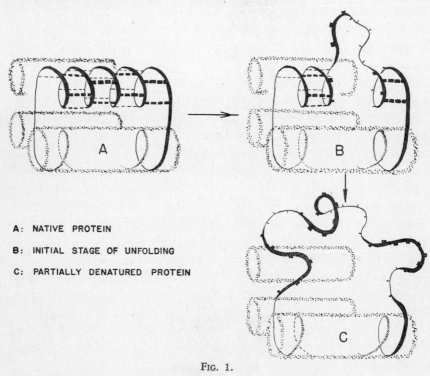

A: NATIVE PROTEIN

B: INITIAL STAGE OF UNFOLDING

C: PARTIALLY DENATURED PROTEIN

Fig. 1.

At higher temperatures water molecules (which are less effective than urea in breaking hydrogen bonds) should be able to replace more and more of the urea molecules; this may account for the decrease in reaction order with temperature. If neither water nor urea are present it should be much more difficult to unfold the molecule, which probably accounts for the stability of dried proteins.

The temperature dependence of the half-time at constant urea concentration is also unusual. In 7.3 M urea at pH 7.6 the rate passes through a strong minimum, being ten times slower at 20° than at either 0° or 40° C. This behavior is almost quantitatively the same as that found by Lauffer in the urea denaturation of tobacco mosaic virus (59). It differs somewhat from the rather rough observations by Hopkins (44) on the urea denaturation of ovalbumin at more acid pH, since Hopkins found only a negative temperature coefficient, with no minimum in the rate between 0° and 37° C. in 6.9 M urea at pH 6. We find on repeating Hopkin's experiments under our conditions, however, that a strong minimum in rate at 20° C. is observed.

Hopkins suggested that urea might form an easily denatured complex with ovalbumin which decomposes on raising the temperature, giving the negative temperature coefficient. Lauffer further suggested that the mechanism of denaturation is essentially the same at low temperatures as at high ones, but that each adsorbed urea molecule merely low rs the activation energy for denaturation by a fixed increment. In this way he was able to account for the change in sign of the temperature coefficient at 20° C. It is not clear, however, that this explanation can be placed on an entirely satisfactory quantitative basis.

The high reaction order and strong minimum in rate at 20° C. are also found with guanidine hydrochloride, but the concentration required to attain a given rate is only about one-third that required with urea.

The effects of salts and other substances on the rate of change of rotation in urea have also been studied. Some substances ($MgCl_2$, $CaCl_2$, $BaCl_2$, KCNS, KI, $NaNO_3$, ethanol, acetone, veronal, p-nitrophenol, guanidine hydrochloride, dioxane) accelerate the change. Other substances (Na_2SO_4, Na_2HPO_4, glycerol, glucose, sucrose) inhibit it. Still others (NaCl, borate buffers, glycine, potassium oxalate, sodium citrate, sodium acetate, ethylene glycol) have only slight effects on the rate. Detergents and iodine produce relatively complicated changes. On a molar basis many of these substances are far more potent than urea in their effect on the rate of denaturation. For instance, in 7 M urea at 30° C. and pH 8, 0.1 M Na_2SO_4

decreases the rate by a factor of two, while 0.1 M KI, $CaCl_2$, $MgCl_2$, $BaCl_2$, or KCNS increase the rate by a factor of about four. Addition of 0.1 M urea to the same solution would increase the rate by only 22 per cent. Most of these effects are very difficult to explain. They are mentioned here because they show that many things remain to be explained about denaturation.

The levorotation finally attained in urea is greater the higher the urea concentration, and it decreases strongly with increasing temperature. At 0° C. in saturated urea the specific rotation of ovalbumin is — 110°, a rather high value for an open-chain compound. What might this mean in terms of protein structure? Because of the rather primitive state of the theory of optical rotatory power very little can be said about this, but we do know that high optical rotations in open-chain compounds generally indicate steric restrictions on the freedom of orientation about the bonds in the chain (54). (The converse of this statement is, however, not necessarily true, so it cannot be said that the increase in optical rotation upon denaturation indicates that the denatured protein molecule is more rigid than the native molecule). These steric restrictions therefore seem to be large in the unfolded protein, especially in the presence of urea, though the effect of thermal motions in reducing them also seems to be evident in the large negative temperature coefficient of the rotation. It is interesting that synthetic polypeptides also tend to have rather large optical rotations (32, 54).

The existence of these steric restrictions is interesting in the light of the discussion of the entropy change accompanying denaturation, since this also seemed to show that the polypeptide chain in a denatured protein is not completely flexible.

3. *The effect of protein concentration on the denaturation rate.* In most instances denaturation is of the first order with respect to the protein concentration. (That is, the half-time of the change is independent of the initial protein concentration.) This shows that the process usually occurs independently in different protein molecules, as one would expect from the point of view being taken in this paper. In two instances, however, the protein concentration seems to have a significant effect on the half-time. Lauffer (59) found

that the urea denaturation of tobacco mosaic virus has a longer half-time the more concentrated the solution of virus, and Case and Laidler (14) found that the half-time for the denaturation of pepsin is less, the higher the protein concentration. Lauffer explained his results by postulating the presence of an inhibitor of denaturation in his tobacco mosaic virus preparations. This inhibitor reversibly forms a complex with the virus, the complex being resistant to denaturation and its formation being favored at high virus concentrations in accordance with the law of mass action. A similar explanation might be given for the results of Casey and Laidler, except that here it is necessary to assume that the complexed protein denatures more readily than the uncomplexed one. That is, pepsin may contain dissociable fragments which promote denaturation.

4. *Differences in the susceptibility of proteins to denaturation by urea.* Urea increases the optical rotation of serum albumin, but at all urea concentrations these changes are completed before the first reading of the optical rotation can be made (i. e., in less than one minute), and the observed rotations undergo no further change with time (87). The rotations obtained are similar in magnitude and in their dependence on the temperature and urea concentration to those ultimately reached with ovalbumin, indicating a similarity in the conformations and flexibility of the denatured forms of the two proteins. The very much greater rate of change of the optical rotation of serum albumin at all urea concentrations tells us that the native serum albumin molecule must be much less firmly coiled than the native ovalbumin molecule.

β-lactoglobulin seems to be intermediate in its behavior between ovalbumin and serum albumin. There is an instantaneous increase in rotation at all urea concentrations, but in 3 to 5 M urea at pH 7 this is followed by a further change whose rate is strongly dependent on the urea concentration (17, 87). This might be taken to indicate that part of the β-lactoglobulin molecule is built on the pattern of serum albumin, while another part of it resembles ovalbumin.

Pepsin is quite inert to the action of urea, and unless the pH is high enough to cause alkali denaturation, even saturated urea has little effect on its optical rotation (87). This agrees with the observations of Steinhart (90), who found that urea has no effect on the proteo-lytic activity of pepsin. Pepsin is thus in a class by itself.

From a few preliminary experiments edestin seems to behave in urea in about the same way as ovalbumin.

The differences in behavior of these globular proteins in the presence of urea are indications that they are not all folded in exactly the same way, but it is difficult to say at this time just how great are the structural differences which this result implies. Is the basic pattern of folding in ovalbumin entirely different from that in serum albumin, or can the difference in behavior of the two proteins be accounted for by other relatively minor differences, such as the num-ber of free ends of polypeptide chains, or a different amount or kind of intramolecular chemical cross-linking? We shall have to know more about the mechanism of unfolding before this can be decided, but perhaps a more important point arises in the next paragraph, where we shall show that the tendency of proteins to adsorb dyes may be related to the ease of unfolding. This suggests that, be the *structural* connotations what they may, the *functions* of pro-teins may be closely related to the phenomena which we have just discussed. More will also be said about this question later in the paper.

It is interesting that serum albumin stands alone among native proteins in its ability to adsorb dyes and other compounds of low molecular weight. Klotz and Urquhart found that at a given con-centration of methyl orange, serum albumin adsorbed about three times as much of the dye as did the same weight of β-lactoglobulin (56). No adsorption of methyl orange by ovalbumin and pepsin could be detected. This affinity for dyes parallels the ease with which the optical rotation is changed by exposure to urea, which in turn is an indication of how firmly the folds of a protein are held together. Could it be that "looseness" in folding is favorable for the adsorption of dyes by native proteins? It is easy to believe that if there were a certain amount of flexibility in the protein molecule, this might permit substances of low molecular weight to penetrate into the molecule and thereby become more strongly adsorbed. Just this kind of behavior has in fact been postulated by Karush (52) for entirely different reasons. He has remarked that the adsorption sites of serum albumin are quite non-specific as compared with those involved in, say, antibody-antigen reactions. He has therefore suggested that serum albumin molecules possess what he aptly calls " configurational adaptability " — that is, the ability to change the conformation of their adsorption sites to fit the contours of whatever molecules are available for adsorption. This notion is entirely consistent with the properties of serum albumin which we have found in our work.

5. *The reversible and irreversible denaturation of proteins.* Many examples are known in which proteins recover all or most of their native properties after having been denatured by exposure to various denaturing agents (1, 76). We have, in fact, already made use of the reversibility of denaturation in discussing the thermodynamics of the process. But there are also many instances in which denatured proteins cannot be returned to the native state, in which case the protein is said to be irreversibly denatured. Furthermore, reversible denaturation is almost always accompanied by irreversible denaturation.

The relationship of these two types of change is not clear. Lundgren and Williams (67) proposed a sequence of reactions having the form

| Native protein | ⇌ | Reversibly denatured protein | ⟶ | Irreversibly denatured protein |

but there is also definite evidence in some instances (15, 95, 96) for the sequence

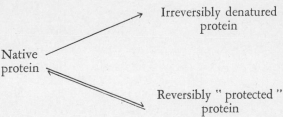

the " protected " form being possibly the reversibly denatured protein. Jacobsen and Christensen's (17, 48) results with the urea denaturation of β-lactoglobulin at different temperatures also seems to fit the second sequence.

The general relationship, if any, of reversible and irreversible denaturation is not known. In the next section, however, we shall see that for serum albumin irreversible denaturation in urea seems to involve changes in the intramolecular disulfide cross-linkages.

The existence of a reversibly denatured state in some proteins complicates the question of the relative stabilities of proteins. This is best shown by means of an example. We have mentioned above that the rate of change of the optical rotation reveals that serum albumin is much more rapidly unfolded by urea than is ovalbumin. (Viscosity measurements show the same thing). Yet if the rates of denaturation of serum albumin and ovalbumin are compared by exposing both proteins to concentrated urea and observing the amount of insoluble protein that is formed when the urea is diluted with buffer at the isoelectric pH, ovalbumin will seem to be denatured much more rapidly than serum albumin. Thus, depending on the type of measurement one uses to detect denaturation in urea, serum albumin can be made to appear highly stable or highly unstable in comparison with ovalbumin. The reason for this is simply that the denaturation of serum albumin is very easily reversed, whereas that of ovalbumin is highly irreversible. When the urea solution is diluted with buffer, serum albumin rapidly refolds to give a soluble " renatured " protein similar to, if not identical with, the original protein. Ovalbumin, once it is unfolded, cannot regain its native state. The reason for this difference in the ease of reversal of denaturation of ovalbumin and serum albumin will be discussed in the next section.

The Role of Sulfhydryl and Disulfide Groups in the Denaturation of Ovalbumin and Serum Albumin

The increase in the reactivity of sulfhydryl and disulfide groups which often accompanies denaturation has been thoroughly discussed elsewhere (1, 76) and will not concern us here. Instead we shall describe entirely different and probably quite unrelated phenomena which result from changes in these groups (31).

When ovalbumin and serum albumin are denatured in urea, the viscosities of their solutions at first increase in very much the same manner as does the optical rotation. Thus the intrinsic viscosity of ovalbumin immediately after addition of urea is the same as that of the native protein, and the rate of the subsequent change is extremely sensitive to the urea concentration, while with serum albumin there is an immediate increase in the viscosity upon exposure to urea. In the later stages of the denaturation process, however, there is a difference in that the viscosity continues to change long after the optical rotation has reached a more or less steady value. This subsequent change in viscosity is more marked the higher the protein concentration and the more alkaline the pH. If the protein concentration is sufficiently high the viscosity eventually becomes infinite and the solution forms a gel. At very low protein concentrations, on the other hand, the viscosity tends to change only when the optical rotation changes.

The increase in viscosity which accompanies the change in optical rotation is undoubtedly a manifestation of the unfolding of the molecules, and it was this part of the change that was interpreted in terms of random coiling in an earlier section of this paper. The change in viscosity that occurs after the change in optical rotation must be attributed to aggregation of the unfolded protein molecules.

Huggins, Tapley, and Jensen (45) have shown that gel formation in urea solutions of ovalbumin and serum albumin can be prevented by blocking the sulfhydryl groups, and they have suggested that the aggregation which is responsible for gelling is caused by formation of intermolecular disulfide linkages through the exchange reaction diagrammed below.

Halwer (40) has also found evidence from light-scattering for such a reaction in heat-denatured ovalbumin. The reaction probably occurs through the mercaptide ion, formed by the equilibrium,

$$RSH \rightleftharpoons RS^- + H^+,$$

and this accounts for the acceleration of gelling in alkaline solutions.

In agreement with this suggestion it is found that the addition of a reagent which combines with or destroys the sulfhydryl groups of ovalbumin (parachlormercuribenzoate is most convenient for this purpose) eliminates the change in viscosity which occurs in this protein after the optical rotation has levelled off. The effects of changes in the urea and electrolyte concentrations show, however, that hydrogen bonds and electrostatic interactions also have some influence on aggregation. Furthermore, exposure of urea-denatured ovalbumin to air accelerates aggregation, presumably by forming new intermolecular disulfide links through the oxidation of the sulfhydryl groups. It is interesting to note that in accordance with these views, oxidation of the sulfhydryl groups with iodine before denaturation prevents gelation in urea, whereas oxidation after denaturation results in immediate gelation.

The effects of sulfhydryl reagents on the time-dependent viscosity changes of serum albumin in urea resemble those observed with ovalbumin, so apparently a similar sulfhydryl-disulfide exchange reaction occurs here. There are, however, some interesting differences between the two proteins. The ovalbumin molecule contains five cysteine residues and two cystines (28). Serum albumin, on the other hand, contains one cysteine and eighteen cystines (47). Because of the very low cysteine concentration of serum albumin, air oxidation stops aggregation by removing the group necessary for the exchange reaction (45). Furthermore, the serum albumin molecule is much more extensively cross-linked by disulfide groups than is ovalbumin, and the cross-links are distributed in such a way that they hold the denatured serum albumin molecule in a somewhat compact configuration, because when they are broken by the addition of an excess of cysteine the intrinsic viscosity is more than doubled (see Table 2). This shows that the two halves of some or all of the cystine residues must be located in the polypeptide chain at fairly widely separated points.[9]

The intramolecular disulfide cross-links of serum albumin appear to be very important in permitting its reversible denaturation. If these bonds are broken by adding cysteine at pH 10, the solubility of the protein in water is immediately and permanently lowered (i. e., the protein is irreversibly denatured) (54a). If they are re-arranged via the exchange reaction with sulfhydryl groups through the exposure of the protein to urea at a pH more alkaline than 6 or 7 (higher pH requiring shorter times of exposure), the protein's solu-bility in sodium sulfate solutions is also permanently reduced, though it is still soluble in water. The decrease in solubility is more marked if the rearrangement takes place at a high protein concentration so that intermolecular disulfide bond formation is encouraged. Para-chlormercuribenzoate inhibits the irreversible loss of solubility even at pH 10 because it prevents the exchange reaction by blocking the sulfhydryl group.

[9] The findings of Katz and Doty (21, 22, 53) must be interpreted in the light of these results. These workers found that the light scattering of serum albumin in urea at pH 8 was much greater than would be expected from a molecular weight of 68,000 and the observed refractive index increment. They assumed that the molecular weight was unchanged and ascribed their results to an adsorption of upwards of 2000 urea molecules (which in effect increases the refractive index increment). Aggregation leading to an approximately threefold increase in the molecular weight is also con-sistent with their results.

Their serum albumin solutions in urea were allowed to stand for several weeks at a pH of 7 to 8 and a protein concentration of around 0.8 per cent. Turbidity measure-ments were then made on successive dilutions of these solutions. Our viscosity measure-ments show, however, that under these conditions there is a good deal of aggregation because of the sulfhydryl-disulfide exchange reaction, so it is unlikely that the assump-tion of a normal molecular weight is correct. The fact that the apparent adsorption of urea was eliminated by adding thioglycolate (which should suppress aggregation through disulfide linkages) supports this interpretation. There is no contradiction with the results of Burk (10) and Neurath, Cooper, and Erickson (75), who found no change of the molecular weight of serum albumin in urea, because their measurements were extrapolated to infinite dilution of the protein and were made at a lower pH, where aggregation is less likely to occur.

In acid urea solutions (0.1 N HCl in 8 M urea) Katz and Doty found that the turbidity produced by serum albumin after standing for several weeks was *less* than that expected from the normal molecular weight and refractive index increment. The magnitude of the effect can be accounted for if the protein had dissociated into about two fragments or if it had preferentially adsorbed about 3000 water molecules. Until other measurements show that dissociation does not occur under these conditions, it is not possible to say which is the actual cause of the discrepancy.

It would appear that the cystine cross-links, as long as they are unaltered, are able to prevent complete unfolding of serum albumin in urea; upon dilution of the urea the molecule is still able to find its way back to the native state (or to something fairly close to it). Thus in Figure 2 the change A → B would be reversible, but once stage C had been reached it would be impossible to return to stage A.

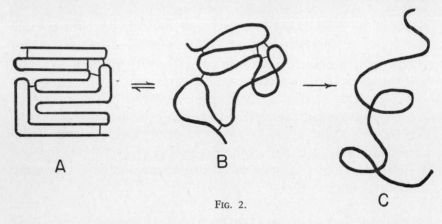

A   B

Fig. 2.   C

The ease of the reversal of the denaturation of serum albumin as compared with ovalbumin is readily accounted for because ovalbumin contains far fewer disulfide cross-linkages.

The large number of cross-links in serum albumin might also be the reason for the great ease with which this protein is unfolded. The abundant cross-links must place constraints on the folding of the polypeptide chain; surely the chain cannot fold into a structure which is as stable as would be possible if these cross-links were absent. Ovalbumin, with only two cross-linkages, is hardly subject to this constraint, so can assume a more stable configuration.[10]

[10] Klotz and Ayers (55) have given another explanation of the instability of serum albumin. They suggest that proteins are normally stabilized by hydrogen bonds which form between hydroxy amino acids and — COO^- and $\equiv NH^+$ groups. Because of the somewhat smaller number of hydroxy amino acids present in serum albumin, it would be more easily unfolded than other proteins. But this explanation runs into the same difficulties as those raised by Jacobsen and Linderstrøm-Lang (49) against salt linkages. Furthermore, as we have mentioned earlier in this paper, hydrogen bonding through groups other than peptide bonds and hydrophobic bonds probably does not contribute very much to the stability of native proteins.

It is possible that the rather large optical rotation of native serum albumin is a reflection of a certain amount of disorder in the native serum albumin molecule, which would be expected if the folding were imperfect. ($[a]_D = -60°$ as compared with $-20°$ to $-40°$ for many other native proteins having a similar amino acid composition, and denaturation invariably results in an increase in the levorotation of proteins (50, 80)). The high optical rotation of cystine and cystine-containing peptides (32) may, however, also be involved. The phenomenon of configurational adaptability (52) mentioned earlier in this paper would also be readily understandable according to this picture of the serum albumin molecule.

One wonders to what extent these findings can be generalized to other proteins. Is intramolecular disulfide cross-linking a necessary or sufficient condition for the reversibility of denaturation? Is the irreversible denaturation of proteins which can be reversibly denatured always a result of the rearrangement of disulfide links, and particularly the formation of intermolecular disulfide links? It is too early to give the answers to these questions, but there are several observations which have some bearing on them. Neurath et al. (76) have noted that " a cursory inspection of analytical data reveals that many proteins which are capable of regeneration have a notably high cystine content." Kunitz (57) has found that the amount of irreversible denaturation of soy-bean trypsin inhibitor increases considerably as the protein concentration is increased, and Eisenberg and Schwert (24) have observed the same thing in the irreversible denaturation of chymotrypsinogen. Steinhardt and Zaiser (92), however, have found that the irreversible denaturation of methemoglobin is favored by low protein concentrations.

REFERENCES

1. Anson, M. L., *Advances in Protein Chem.*, **2**, 361 (1945).
2. Anson, M. L., and A. E. Mirsky, *J. Gen. Physiol.*, **17**, 393 (1933).
3. Astbury, W. T., S. Dickenson, and K. Bailey, *Biochem. J.*, **29**, 2351 (1935).
4. Aten, A., C. Dippel, K. Keuning, and J. van Dreven, *J. Colloid Sci.*, **3**, 65 (1948).
5. Barbu, E., and M. Joly, *Discussions Faraday Soc.*, **13**, 77 (1953).
6. Barker, H. A., *J. Biol. Chem.*, **103**, 1 (1933).
7. Boyer, P. D., G. A. Ballou, and J. M. Luck, *J. Biol. Chem.*, **162**, 199 (1946).

8. Bragg, L., J. C. Kendrew, and M. F. Perutz, *Proc. Roy. Soc. (London)*, **A 203**, 321 (1950)

9. Bull. H., *J. Biol. Chem.*, **133**, 39 (1940).

10. Burk, N. F., *J. Biol. Chem.*, **98**, 353 (1932).

11. Burk, N. F., *J. Phys. Chem.*, **47**, 164 (1943).

12. Buzzell, A., and J. Sturtevant, *J. Am. Chem. Soc.*, **74**, 1983 (1952).

13. Cannan, R. K., A. Kibrick, and A. H. Palmer, *Ann. N. Y. Acad. Sci.*, **41**, 243 (1941).

14. Casey, E. J., and K. J. Laidler, *J. Am. Chem. Soc.*, **73**, 1455 (1951).

15. Chase, A., *J. Gen. Physiol.*, **33**, 535 (1950).

16. Chick, H., and C. J. Martin, *J. Physiol. (London)*, **40**, 404 (1910); **43**, 1 (1911).

17. Christensen, L. K., *Compt. rend. trav. lab. Carlsberg, Sér. chim.*, **28**, 37 (1952).

18. Conn, J. B., D. C. Gregg, G. B. Kistiakowsky, and R. M. Roberts, *J. Am. Chem. Soc.*, **63**, 2080 (1941).

19. Conn, J. B., G. B. Kistiakowsky, and R. M. Roberts, *J. Am. Chem. Soc.*, **62**, 1895 (1940).

20. Cubin, H. K., *Biochem. J.*, **23**, 25 (1929).

21. Doty, P., and J. T. Edsall, *Advances in Protein Chem.*, **6**, 72 (1951).

22. Doty, P., and S. Katz, *Abstr. 118th Meet. Amer. Chem. Soc., Chicago*, p. 14C (1950).

23. Duggan, E. L., and J. M. Luck, *J. Biol. Chem.*, **172**, 205 (1948).

24. Eisenberg, M. A., and G. W. Schwert, *J. Gen. Physiol.*, **34**, 583 (1951).

25. Eyring, H., and F. H. Johnson, pers. com.

26. Eyring, H., and A. E. Stearn, *Chem. Rev.*, **24**, 253 (1939).

27. Fessler, J. H., and A. G. Ogston, *Trans. Faraday Soc.*, **47**, 667 (1951).

28. Fevold, H. L., *Advances in Protein Chem.*, **5**, 1 (1951).

29. Foster, J., and E. G. Samsa, *J. Am. Chem. Soc.*, **73**, 5388 (1951).

30. Frampton, V. L., *J. Biol. Chem.*, **129**, 240 (1939).

31. Frensdorff, H. K., M. T. Watson, and W. Kauzmann, *J. Am. Chem. Soc.*, to be published.

32. Fruton, J. S., *Advances in Protein Chem.*, **6**, 188 (1951).

33. Gee, G., *Trans. Faraday Soc.*, **40**, 264 (1940).

34. Gibbs, R. J., *Arch. Biochem. and Biophys.*, **35**, 229 (1952).

35. Gibbs, R. J., M. Bier, and F. F. Nord, *Arch. Biochem. and Biophys.*, **35**, 216 (1952).

36. Goldberg, A. E., W. P. Hohenstein, and H. Mark, *J. Polymer Sci.*, **2**, 503 (1947).

37. Greenstein, J. P., *J. Biol. Chem.*, **125**, 501 (1938).

38. Greenstein, J. P., *J. Biol. Chem.*, **130**, 519 (1939).

39. Groves, M. L., N. J. Hipp, and T. L. McMeekin, *J. Am. Chem. Soc.*, **73**, 2790 (1951).

40. Halwer, M., Abstr. *122nd Meet. Amer. Chem. Soc., Atlantic City*, p. 19C (1952).

41. Haurowitz, F., *Experientia*, **5**, 347 (1949).

42. Haurowitz, F., *Chemistry and Biology of Proteins*, New York (1950).

43. Heymann, E., *Biochem. J.*, **30**, 127 (1936).

44. Hopkins, F. G., *Nature*, **126**, 328, 383 (1930).

45. Huggins, C., D. F. Tapley, and E. V. Jensen, *Nature*, **167**, 592 (1951).

46. Huggins, M. L., *Chem. Rev.*, **32**, 195 (1943).

47. Hughes, W. L., Jr., H. A. Saroff, and A. L. Carney, *J. Am. Chem. Soc.*, **71**, 2479 (1949).

48. Jacobsen, C. F., and L. K. Christensen, *Nature*, 161, 30 (1948).
49. Jacobsen, C. F., and K. U. Linderstrøm-Lang, *Nature*, 164, 411 (1949).
50. Jirgensons, B., *Arch. Biochem. and Biophys.*, 41, 333 (1952).
51. Johnson, F. H., and D. H. Campbell, *J. Biol. Chem.*, 163, 689 (1946).
52. Karush, F., *J. Am. Chem. Soc.*, 72, 2705 (1950).
53. Katz, S., Ph. D. Thesis, Harvard University (1950).
54. Kauzmann, W., and H. Eyring, *J. Chem. Phys.*, 9, 41 (1941).
54a. Kauzmann, W., unpublished results.
55. Klotz, I. M., and J. Ayers, *Discussions Faraday Soc.*, 13, 189 (1953).
56. Klotz, I. M., and J. M. Urquhart, *J. Am. Chem. Soc.*, 71, 1597 (1949).
57. Kunitz, M., *J. Gen. Physiol.*, 32, 241 (1948).
58. LaMer, V. K., *Science*, 86, 614 (1937).
59. Lauffer, M., *J. Am. Chem. Soc.*, 65, 1793 (1943).
60. Levy, M., and A. E. Benaglia, *J. Biol. Chem.*, 186, 829 (1950).
61. Lewis, P. S., *Biochem. J.*, 20, 965, 978 (1926).
62. Linderstrøm-Lang, K. U., *Compt. rend. trav. lab. Carlsberg*, 15, No. 7 (1924).
63. Linderstrøm-Lang, K. U., *Cold Spring Harbor Symposia Quant. Biol.*, 14, 117 (1950).
64. Linderstrøm-Lang, K. U., Lane Medical Lectures, Stanford University Press, Stanford, Calif. (1952).
65. Linderstrøm-Lang, K. U., and C. F. Jacobsen, *Compt. rend. trav. lab. Carlsberg*, 24, No. 1 (1941).
66. Luck, J. M., *Discussions Faraday Soc.*, 13, 235 (1953).
67. Lundgren, H. P., and J. W. Williams, *J. Phys. Chem.*, 43, 989 (1939).
68. MacPherson, C. F. C., M. Heidelberger, and D. H. Moore, *J. Am. Chem. Soc.*, 67, 574, 578, 585 (1945).
69. Mandelkern, L., W. R. Krigbaum, H. A. Scheraga, and P. J. Flory, *J. Chem. Phys.*, 20, 1392 (1952).
70. Matthews, J. E., Jr., R. B. Dow, and A. K. Anderson, *J. Biol. Chem.*, 135, 697 (1940).
71. McLarin, A. D., and C. Lewis, *J. Polymer Sci.*, 5, 379 (1950).
72. Mead, D. F., and R. M. Fuoss, *J. Am. Chem. Soc.*, 64, 277 (1942).
73. Mihályi, E., *Acta Chem. Scand.*, 4, 334 (1950).
74. Mirsky, A. E., and L. Pauling, *Proc. Nat. Acad. Sci. U. S.*, 22, 439 (1936).
75. Neurath, H., G. P. Cooper, and J. O. Erickson, *J. Biol. Chem.*, 142, 249 (1942).
76. Neurath, H., J. P. Greenstein, F. W. Putnam, and J. O. Erickson, *Chem. Rev.*, 34, 157 (1944).
77. Neurath, H., and A. M. Saum, *J. Biol. Chem.*, 128, 347 (1939).
78. Newman, S., and F. Eirich, *J. Colloid Sci.*, 5, 541 (1950).
79. Outer, P., C. I. Carr, and B. Zimm., *J. Chem. Phys.*, 18, 830 (1950).
80. Pauli, W., and L. Hoffmann, *Kolloid-Beih.*, 42, 34 (1935).
81. Pauling, L., R. B. Corey, and H. R. Branson, *Proc. Nat. Acad. Sci. U. S.*, 37, 205, 235 (1951).
82. Pedersen, K. O., *Discussions Faraday Soc.*, 13, 49 (1953).
83. Porter, R., *Biochem. J.*, 46, 304 (1950).
84. Schachman, H. K., *J. Am. Chem. Soc.*, 73, 4808 (1951).
85. Schachman, H. K., pers. com.
86. Scheraga, H. A., and L. Mandelkern, *J. Am. Chem. Soc.*, 75, 179 (1953).
87. Simpson, R. B., and W. Kauzmann, *J. Am. Chem. Soc.*, unpub.
88. Steinberg, P., *J. Am. Chem. Soc.*, 74, 4217 (1952).
89. Steinhardt, J., *Kgl. Danske Videnskab. Selskab., Mat.-fys. Medd.*, 14, No. 11 (1937).

90. Steinhardt, J., *J. Biol. Chem.*, **123**, 543 (1938).
91. Steinhardt, J., and E. M. Zaiser, *J. Am. Chem. Soc.*, **73**, 5568 (1951).
92. Steinhardt, J., and E. M. Zaiser, *J. Am. Chem. Soc.*, **75**, 1599 (1953).
93. Tongur, V. S., *Kolloid, Zhur.*, **11**, 274 (1949) [*Chem. Abstr.*, **44**, 176 (1950)].
94. Tongur, V. S., and V. I. Kasotochkin, *Doklady Akad. Nauk. S.S.S.R.*, **74**, 553 (1950) [*Chem. Abstr.*, **45**, 2039 (1951)].
95. Wright, G. G., and V. Schomaker, *J. Am. Chem. Soc.*, **70**, 356 (1948).
96. Wright, G. G., and V. Schomaker, *J. Biol. Chem.*, **175**, 169 (1948).
97. Wu, H., *Chinese J. Physiol.*, **5**, 321 (1931).
98. Zaiser, E. M., and J. Steinhardt, *J. Biol. Chem.*, **190**, 197 (1951).

DISCUSSION

DR. HEIDELBERGER: Dr. Kauzmann has touched on so many aspects of protein denaturation that I am sure that there will be a great many questions. I would like to start with a relatively minor one and ask whether in the case of serum albumin the addition of cysteine or thioglycolic acid produces a further change in optical activity. I notice in your reaction you get an immediate change, followed by a slow change in the optical activity when you break your S–S bonds.

DR. KAUZMANN: I don't remember whether we have tried that or not, but I rather doubt whether we find much of a change, because of the large number of amino acid residues which would be unaffected by the breaking of S–S. The optical rotation will depend upon the environment immediately around the asymmetric center, and that is not going to be greatly affected by disulfide-splitting agents. But this is something that should be tried.

DR. E. SMITH: I would like to call attention to a possible complementary mechanism involved in acid-base denaturation, and that is the suggestion that Max Bergmann made some 25 years ago regarding the acyl shift that occurs in the serine peptide linkage. You may remember that Bergmann and coworkers made N-acetyl serine which in acid solution is converted into O-acetyl serine and, therefore, postulated the existence of an intermediate oxazoline ring. Elliott in London has recently done some very beautiful studies which show that this serine acyl shift occurs with intact proteins. This was done by taking a protein, such as casein or silk fibroin, treating with acid, then formylating the liberated free amino groups with formic acetic anhydride. When the unsubstituted protein is brought to pH 8 or so, the reverse acyl shift occurs to form an N-peptide bond. When the formylated protein is brought to alkaline pH values, the reverse acyl shift cannot take place and there are present ester bonds which are susceptible to base catalysis. The peptide chain will then fragment to give N-terminal serine and threonine residues. Elliot and Crawhall have been able to achieve hydrolysis of about 80 per cent of the susceptible threonine and serine linkages. This is in agreement with the experience of those doing sequence work on peptide or protein chains that the weak links in these chains are at the serine and threonine bonds. There is considerable evidence indicating that the acyl shift can occur at pH 4 or higher. Steinhart found a large uptake of hydrogen ions 20 seconds after pH 5 is reached; this is in line with the acyl shift mentioned. Such an acyl shift would provide an alternative mechanism for acid denaturation from that suggested by Dr. Kauzmann, or would provide a supplementary mechanism, since for each serine or threonine bond which undergoes an acyl shift, additional protons are going to be taken up as free amino groups are liberated. I think it perhaps also ought to be mentioned that a protein like pepsin, for example, which has its optimal action near pH 2, probably exists in the native state with ester bonds at the serine and threonine residues present.

DR. STURTEVANT: I would like to emphasize one point which I think Dr. Kauzmann went over rather rapidly. This has to do with the change of the ΔH for denaturation with pH. Just two systems have been measured over a range of pH. In the case of chymotrypsinogen, equilibrium measurements were made at pH 2 and 3 by Eisenberg and Schwert. At one pH the ΔH is 99 Kilocalories per mol; at the other pH the ΔH is 143. In the case of the pepsin, measured calorimetrically there is a much more dramatic heat change in ΔH as a function of pH. Thus in the two cases where ΔH versus pH has been observed, very drastic changes in ΔH take place over short pH ranges. It seems to me that one has to be very careful in interpreting entropy values, etc., that have been obtained at a single pH.

DR. E. SMITH: This would be in line with Elliott's work. From the measurements of Steinhardt and Zaiser on hemoglobin, there were a large number of protons bound or removed under conditions that may be interpreted as due to the acyl shift.

DR. STURTEVANT: There were 36 acid binding groups which became available which were not available in the native protein. The liberation of these groups appeared to be controlled by a triggering ionization involving, on the average, 2.5 protons.

DR. KAUZMANN: I merely wanted to emphasize the large numerical values of ΔH. ΔH is positive and very large in many cases, so ΔS must be positive and very large. It has been known for a long time, having first been pointed out by Pauling and Corey, that this is consistent with random uncoiling. It has also been pointed out that if the denatured protein is a random coil it is not very random, at least in water. I wouldn't want to take the exact values too seriously, but use them only as an indication of their order of magnitude. ΔS is of the order of a couple of hundred entropy units and it couldn't be very much less.

DR. STURTEVANT: Incidentally, I suppose that one must speak of a ΔS per atom.

DR. KAUZMANN: Oh, that would be very low, but why can't we use ΔS per mole?

DR. HAMMETT: In connection with your hypothesis of the heat denaturation involving the freezing out of water molecules around the charged groups, the net result is that you have lost a lot of entropy from the water molecules. The degrees of freedom in the protein molecule itself is considerably larger than one would think.

DR. KAUZMANN: Well, there is considerable question as to whether the charged groups are not already exposed to the water in native proteins. I made no hypotheses about changes in the hydration of charged groups on denaturation.

DR. HAMMETT: I am just using your hypothesis about the heat denaturation.

DR. KAUZMANN: You mean concerning the entropy?

DR. HAMMETT: Yes. I understood you to say that you could account for heat denaturation as a competition of the water molecules for the intramolecular hydrogen binding—that is, hydrogen binding of the water molecules. This means you have to tie up more water molecules to lose more entropy.

DR. KAUZMANN: Of course the water molecules are tied up by water beforehand and by protein afterward. There are possibly some such effects, but they would be small, and I wouldn't even want to predict their sign.

DR. GUTFREUND: I would like to ask Dr. Kauzmann whether he would agree with the following kinetic picture of the mechanism for the dependence of protein denaturation on pH. In the case of some proteins denaturation occurs in acid solutions. In this case, all that you are doing is breaking hydrogen bonds when you change the pH and thus affecting an equilibrium between bonding with hydroxonium ions and hydrogen bonds on the protein.

Whatever we find to be the final and detailed solution of the structure of the polypeptide chain in globular proteins, a helical configuration with internal hydrogen bonding is a good working hypothesis. In a molecule of such a structure hydrogen bonds are likely to be labile in aqueous solution because the energy difference for any one CN or CO group hydrogen bonding with solvent water or with the structurally correct group within the helix is small. However, for one step in irreversible denaturation to occur, several (three or four) neighboring hydrogen bonds have to be broken. Then one turn in the helix can unfold and a correct recombination is unlikely to occur. The rate of denaturation would therefore depend on the chances of these hydrogen bonding groups in the polypeptide chain combining with H_2O and $\overset{+}{H_3O}$ and will therefore be a function of the hydrogen ion concentration. The qualitative effect of temperature on the rate of denaturation could similarly be explained in terms of the rupture of hydrogen bonds.

This is analogous to denaturation with urea, where we have again a competition for hydrogen bonding with the solvent, urea being one of the solvents.

It is also well known that both urea and the hydrogen ion concentration have a large effect on dissociation of proteins into sub-units. This type of reaction is usually very rapid and reversible, while the irreversible denaturation can have a wide range of rates.

DR. KAUZMANN: Are you referring to the effect of pH on the rate of denaturation?

DR. GUTFREUND: Yes.

DR. KAUZMANN: The picture that I had was that the more highly charged the protein is, the larger the electrostatic repulsion is and the easier it is to make the protein unfold. It is not that any particular ionic form is less stable than another or that hydrogen bonds break somehow when the pH shifts; it is just that all highly charged forms would be less stable.

DR. GUTFREUND: Yes. Well, in that case it's just electrostatic.

But yours is a different mechanism and I think one could produce some calculations to determine which of the two would give a better explanation of the experimental results.

DR. KAUZMANN: It is purely electrostatic; and I merely wanted to show that this sort of picture quantitatively doesn't look too bad, because on that basis you can calculate the results. You can calculate that the ovalbumin molecules swell by about 8 per cent, which is about right for what you would expect of the activated complex.

DR. STURTEVANT: Does that go up very rapidly with n? Can you get up to $n = 5$?

DR. KAUZMANN: Yes. I can't do anything with pepsin (which you probably have in mind) because I haven't got the data on the W and the titration curves; but I am sure I could get a value as large as 5. A value of 5 for ovalbumin would mean that it was swollen by only about 20 per cent in the activated state.

DR. ANFINSEN: I wonder whether I could just draw a picture. Dr. Kauzmann did not mention any enzymatically catalyzed denaturations.

DR. KAUZMANN: Oh, yes I did—trypsin.

DR. ANFINSEN: We have been working on ribonuclease, which may be so small that you may not want to call it a protein. Anyway, there are

anomalies in regard to the denaturation of this protein. First of all, it has
the peculiarity of being most heat stabile at around pH 4, which is quite
far from pH 8, its isoelectric point. The experiments that I wanted to
briefly present—I promise it will be just about a minute and a half—are
interesting because Dr. Redfield and I have a little information on the
structure of the protein. Ribonuclease is a single-chain protein, but it contains
five crystallographic chains. I am not one to question the crystallographers—
I guess it means five—so that you might draw a figure (Fig. 1) containing

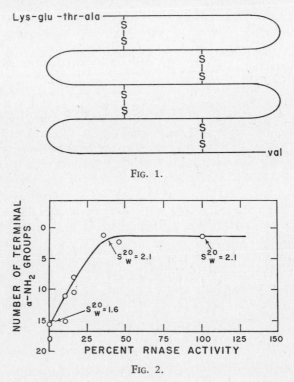

FIG. 1.

FIG. 2.

at one end the lysyl-glutamyl-threonyl-alanyl periodicity, and at the other a
valine residue. This can be drawn in such a way that the one chain goes
through five convolutions, with the parallel portions of the chain linked
together by S–S bridges. Ribonuclease contains eight cysteines, and these
are all present in disulphide linkage, thus accounting for the 4 S–S bridges
shown in the picture. We have here, then, a very small, highly coiled
molecule which is rigid and has a frictional ratio very near unity. Now, on
treatment with pepsin, one loses enzyme activity very rapidly, and if you

will allow me to call loss of enzyme activity denaturation one can make a plot in which either sedimentation constants or free N-terminal groups are plotted as ordinate and enzyme activity is plotted as abscissa, going from zero to 100 per cent. If you follow the digestion, the sedimentation constant remains the same down to rather low levels of enzyme activity—that is, to about 30 per cent of the initial value. Then there is a rapidly falling phase (Fig. 2). Apparently there are two processes, one rapid and one slow. The slow, secondary process becomes apparent when the population of " denatured " molecules becomes high enough. As this process proceeds no significant change in the number of free animo groups occurs until 60-80 per cent of the enzyme activity is destroyed. They then rapidly increase to about 15 per mole of ribonuclease in proportion to the falling enzyme activity.

DR. KAUZMANN: Is this one chain?

DR. ANFINSEN: It is one chain during the first phase of the process.

DR. KAUZMANN: Is there one end amino group?

DR. ANFINSEN: There is one N-terminal group.

DR. KAUZMANN: Until it starts to lose molecular weight.

DR. ANFINSEN: Yes. In other words, the initial denaturation process does not appear to involve any peptide bond splitting. The reason I mention this molecule at all is that it is a very small, compact little thing. There is certainly no change in the state of sulphur so far as I can tell; no SH is liberated during the early phase. It is an interesting dilemma also, in a sense, in relation to the discussion that you have made of the generalities of denaturation, because here is a rather atypical molecule which acts a little differently in regard to aggregation during denaturation. Even though you find no change in the chemically observable characteristics, there is a rapid aggregation as measured in the light-scattering apparatus up to several hundred thousand molecular weight.

DR. KAUZMANN: Yet there was no change in the molecular weight?

DR. ANFINSEN: No; the sedimentation constants were determined at a different pH (pH 7) from that at which the aggregation phenomena were observed (pH 1.8).

DR. DOUDOROFF: Have you tried this in the presence as well as in the absence of substrate?

DR. ANFINSEN: And doing what?

DR. DOUDOROFF: In studying the denaturation process.

DR. ANFINSEN: You mean in the presence of nucleic acid?

DR. DOUDOROFF: Yes. It seems to me that here is a wonderful opportunity to attack the problem from different angles, particularly with respect to the free enzyme compared to the substrate-enzyme coils.

Dr. Kirkwood: I had a brief remark to make in connection with the electrostatic theory. In order to further test the theory it might be interesting to go to aqueous solvents along with alcohol. One could then study two effects. The exterior dielectric constant is one of particular interest in connection with the Linderstrøm-Lang ideas. By lowering "that" one should increase the rate. One would also have to take into account the effect of the change in the medium. This would give you another degree of freedom. It might be interesting to investigate this point.

Dr. Kauzmann: One very important way to test this is to add salts, particularly in connection with the full theory of Linderstrøm-Lang, which contains a term involving electrolyte concentration.

Dr. Kirkwood: It increases the rate of aggregating enormously.

Dr. Anson: The Courtaulds people have studied S–S polymerization systems similar to those described by Kauzmann. Proteins were treated with alkali, with the liberation of SH groups. In the presence of oxygen, S–S bridges were formed and as a result there was a great increase in viscosity.

In general, it seems to me that by far the most important experimental work which could be done right now is the more complete study of the few good denaturation equilibrium systems mentioned by Kauzmann. One would want to know the effects of acids, alcohols, salts, etc., on the equilibrium between the native and denatured forms of the protein. And one would want to follow the changes in as many different properties as possible. I am sure that the detailed study of a few good equilibria would lead to more important results than have hitherto been obtained by incomplete observations of a great number of cases of denaturation, usually cases of irreversible, or incompletely reversible denaturation.

There have been many studies, to be found particularly in the older literature, of the effects of neutral salts on denaturation. The effect of neutral salt can sometimes be very marked. I observed that a saturated NaCl solution of edestin can be boiled without the edestin being denatured.

Dr. Kauzmann: I can add a little to that. It is known that sodium sulphate is a very potent inhibitor of denaturation. Mol per mol, sodium sulphate is a much more potent inhibitor of denaturation than is urea as a denaturing agent. Guanidine sulphate, of course, is completely inert. In the study of the urea denaturation of ovalbumin the effects of a number of salts have been investigated. Many salts (e. g. calcium chloride) strongly accelerated the denaturation.

Dr. Eyring: I would like to ask the group whether there has been any case of reversible denaturation after treatment with the kind of severity which Dr. Kauzmann has interpreted as complete unfolding, where it looks like subsequently the enzyme has returned to its native state and is perfectly normal. You have not observed return of enzymatic activity have you, Dr. Kauzmann?

DR. KAUZMANN: In our studies we did not determine enzymatic activity, but this has been done in the case of trypsin. However, I don't recall whether the viscosity of reversibly denatured trypsin has been measured. I think that the optical rotation method is an extremely useful one, particularly with the new sensitive instruments (the Rudolph polarimeter), and one should by this technique be able to make a study of unfolding even when only small amounts of material available.

DR. BOYER: I have a comment to make in relation to the possibility which Dr. Doudoroff raised of protein digestion in the presence of the substrate. We have done some experiments on trypsin digestion of aldolase, and the trypsin causes a loss of aldolase activity and a degradation at the same rate both in the presence and in the absence of the substrate. I would like to come back to the question of serum albumin denaturation. Would the increase of viscosity in the presence of urea be due to the formation of disulphide bonds? Would this give a possibility for each serum albumin molecule with one sulfhydryl group to form one linkage? This would seem to me to limit the amount of aggregation to the stage of that approximating a dimer.

DR. KAUZMANN: No, the sulfhydryl groups are not destroyed. Every time one reacts a new one is formed. This is a sort of chain reaction. If the solution is alkaline, however, then, of course, air oxidation does eventually destroy the sulfhydryls and stops the aggregation process.

DR. HERRIOTT: I wish to raise two questions on rather minor points in your paper. First, the relationship of number of amino groups and the state of reversibility has many exceptions. As you pointed out serum albumin is low in amino nitrogen compared to egg albumin and chymotrypsin, yet the latter is reversibly denaturable. Pepsin has only 3 amino groups and it is virtually irreversibly denatured. The next point concerns the relationship of isoelectric point and stability. The stability regions for chymotrypsinogen, chymotrypsin, and trypsin are far from their isoelectric points.

The final point is of more interest for you may have clarified a phenomenon which Dr. Kern observed during reduction of pepsin with thioglycol. If you denature pepsin, the intrinsic viscosity goes up from about 5 to 13. If now you reduce denatured pepsin, the intrinsic viscosity goes up from 13 to about 23. If however you reduce native pepsin, the intrinsic viscosity shoots up to the order of 100. You don't get this rise if you denature the material first. The thing we haven't determined is an increase in protein bound sulfur when the native protein is reduced. It may be that with the polymerization extra sulfurs have been added on from the reducing agent.

DR. KAUZMANN: Huggins and Jensen showed that very small amounts of sulfhydryl groups promote aggregation, whereas large amounts inhibit it.

DR. HERRIOTT: The point that interested me was the difference between the native and the denatured protein in response to the same concentration of agent.

DR. KAUZMANN: I was wondering whether aggregation took place. Were only small amounts of thioglycolate used?

DR. HERRIOTT: Approximately 5 per cent.

DR. KAUZMANN: It is a very interesting result.

DR. HEIDELBERGER: If you have another few minutes' patience, I would like to make a few points. While Dr. Kauzmann was talking I was wondering whether anything that we knew of the immunological behavior of native proteins on the one hand and of denatured proteins on the other hand was inconsistent with anything that he said. I couldn't pick any holes in his presentation. What most of us probably do not realize, however, is the importance of the immunochemical approach to problems such as these. If you will bear with me a moment, I would like to summarize for you very briefly what we do know immunologically about denatured proteins. If one plots micrograms of antibody nitrogen precipitated against micrograms of antigen nitrogen added with a native protein such as crystalline egg albumin, one gets an increase of the amount of antibody nitrogen precipitated with an increase of the antigen nitrogen concentration up to an optimum, and then there is a slight decrease in the amount precipitated with still more antigen. If we do the same thing with acid or alkali denatured egg albumin with the same antiserum against crystalline egg albumin, we get practically no precipitate at all along the entire range of amounts of antigen added. In other words, the denatured protein is immunologically an entirely different substance than the native protein. Suppose we have an antiserum against denatured egg albumin. That is still an antigen, although not as good an antigen as the native protein, and one gets antibodies in the rabbit. If one adds denatured egg albumin to this antiserum, one gets a curve similar to the one obtained with the native antigen-antibody reaction, except that the zone of inhibition with antigen excess is not so noticeable in this case. If we set up the antiserum against denatured egg albumin with crystalline egg albumin, then we get the same type of curve as in the reverse system—that is, practically no precipitate along the whole range of antigen concentration. Again, in the opposite direction, the native protein is an entirely different protein from the denatured protein. I think we can explain that along the conventional lines that have been dealt with today if we remember that in the native protein the specificity is probably determined by repetition of areas along the surface. Hooker and Boyd have calculated that these require somewhere between 1500 and 3000 of molecular weight. Such outcroppings on whatever functions as the surface of the molecule occur in multiple. Whatever the amino acids are that make up these chains from the adjoining amino acids in the molecule, these are what determine egg albumin specificity. If you uncoil the molecule by denaturation and make a more or less random coil out of it, these original areas will not exist in the uncoiled molecule, and you will have, therefore, a totally different molecule in which other groupings will determine the immunological specificity. Thus, as I said before, I could not find any immunological flaws in what Dr. Kauzmann said.

DR. KIRKWOOD: This is irreversible denaturation, isn't it?

DR. HEIDELBERGER: Yes.

DR. KIRKWOOD: Have you made similar tests on reversibly denatured antigens?

DR. HEIDELBERGER: No. We have not done that, but I think Dr. Neurath has made some studies on this point.

DR. NEURATH: Let me say first that our observations on the immunological properties of native, denatured and renatured proteins do not agree with those just cited by Dr. Heidelberger, indicating again the variations in response of different proteins to different denaturing agents. Thus, when Erickson and I compared the cross reactivity of native type I antipneumococcus horse globulin with that of the protein irreversibly denatured by guanidine hydrochloride, and with native and irreversibly denatured normal horse globulins, marked cross reaction between the native and denatured forms of each protein were found, indicating rather close immunological relations between native and denatured forms. When we extended these measurements to horse and bovine serum albumin, native, as well as '' regenerated '' after denaturation by 8 M guanidine hydrochloride, I believe, with both species were the native and '' regenerated '' forms immunologically equivalent, even though there were doubts on other grounds that refolding was complete. Of course, one might speculate that in vivo the antigen is in an unfolded form when it initiates antibody formation and that for this reason, native and denatured protein should be immunologically equivalent provided no chemical changes occur during denaturation. I think that one should await further experimental data before trying to resolve the discrepancy between Dr. Heidelberger's and our data.

DR. EYRING: It seems to me that reversible denaturation is nowhere near as drastic a process as we have just been talking about. It may be that you find hardly any change in optical rotation when you study reversible denaturation.

DR. KAUZMANN: Serum albumin denaturation can be brought about reversibly by strong urea. Here you get large viscosity changes, which certainly return to normal; but this protein doesn't, of course, have any enzyme activity, which is a much more specific criterion.

DR. NEURATH: I would agree with Dr. Eyring that in those cases which have been described as fully reversible denaturation, the structural changes are not very great.

DR. HUGHES: I would like to bring out that there are groups in proteins other than those which Dr. Kauzmann has discussed and that many of these may be important in the maintenance of the native structure. Thus in egg albumin the sulfhydryl groups are unreactive towards many reagents and become reactive following denaturation. This unreactivity of the sulfhydryl may be due to true chemical bonding as suggested by Linderstrøm-Lang some years ago. Also the phenolic hydroxyl groups of egg albumin are unreactive prior to denaturation, and this unreactivity has been laid to hydrogen bonding of these groups (Crammer and Neuberger). Therefore both the sulfyhydryl and the tyrosyl residues may form cross-struts in the egg albumin molecule which are important for the native structure. In serum albumin, on the other hand these groups seem to react quite as readily as in peptides and are therefore probably free. It seems to me that it would be interesting to study the rate of denaturation of oxidized and reduced egg albumin to see whether there are any marked differences.

DR. KAUZMANN: We have found that when iodine is added in excess of the amount required by the sulfhydryls, then the rate of denaturation by urea goes up very rapidly. But with less than this amount of iodine the denaturation rate isn't affected very much.

DR. HUGHES: One other linkage which may be important is the salt linkage. I think that this may make a large contribution in a molecule like serum albumin. Titration curves might seem to indicate that there is not much salt linkage. However, the carboxyl groups show an extremely weak binding for many cations. Thus the carboxyl group of serum albumin combines with zinc or calcium 10 to 100 times weaker than does a simple carboxylic acid. The simplest explanation for this would be that the cation is competing with cationic grouping of the protein.

Part II

KINETICS OF ENZYME–CATALYZED REACTIONS

KINETIC AND THERMODYNAMIC ASPECTS OF ENZYME–CATALYZED REACTIONS *

HENRY EYRING, RUFUS LUMRY, and JOHN D. SPIKES

University of Utah
Salt Lake City

INTRODUCTION

IN SOME SIMPLE bimolecular gas reactions a certain amount of success has been achieved by treating the colliding molecules as spheres which react whenever the potential energy stored in a collision exceeds a limiting activation energy. A better approximation has been to multiply such a rate expression by a steric factor which corrects for the likelihood that the collision will be properly oriented. As van't Hoff recognized long ago, the specific reaction rate in the forward direction divided by the specific rate in the backward direction must be equal to the equilibrium constant, a thermodynamic quantity. A little consideration will convince one that the ratio of two rate constants obtained from simple collision theory will have little chance of leading to suitable equilibrium constants in complicated cases.

ABSOLUTE RATE THEORY

The absolute rate theory (1) is the necessary refinement of collision theory in biomolecular cases, and in fact applies to reactions of all orders. The minimum number of distances between the atoms in reacting molecules required to fix the potential energy specifies a configuration of the complex. For a nonlinear complex of n atoms this number of distances is $3n - 6$; for a linear complex this number is $3n - 5$. To plot the energy as a function of configuration requires an additional coordinate. Thus a hyperspace of $3n - 5$ dimensions is required to plot this potential surface in configuration space for

* This work was supported by grants from the National Science Foundation and the U. S. Atomic Energy Commission.

non-linear complexes, and $3n - 4$ dimensions are needed when all atoms lie on a line.

If energy be thought of as plotted vertically like the altitude in an ordinary landscape, we have a ready-made language for discussing both equilibrium and reaction rates. Thus low basins or valleys on our hypersurface correspond to compounds. The passes over the mountain ranges separating valleys or basins are the activated complexes. The course followed by a particular activated complex from reactants to products will trace a path from the initial valleys up through one of the passes down into the final state.

In principle, at least, the potential energy surface can be constructed from quantum mechanics. The theory of small vibrations enables one to solve for the vibration frequencies, moments of inertia, and reduced masses for the various normal modes of vibration of reactants and of activated complexes. Statistical mechanics then provides the rate equation into which these quantities can be substituted to calculate the rate of the reaction. Although in theory we can calculate reaction rates from first principles, in fact, the calculations are usually too difficult. Instead we use reaction rate theory exactly as we use equilibrium theory in thermodynamics.

If we write the concentration, $C^{\ddagger}{}_i$, of activated complexes per cc. per length

$$\delta_i = \frac{h}{(2\pi m^{\ddagger}{}_i kT)^{\frac{1}{2}}} \tag{1}$$

at the barrier top along the i'th reaction coordinate, then absolute rate theory gives for the velocity of reaction

$$v = \frac{kT}{h} \sum_i \mathscr{H}_i C^{\ddagger}{}_i \tag{2}$$

Here h, $m^{\ddagger}{}_i$, T, k and $\mathscr{H}_i$ are as usual Planck's constant, the reduced mass along the reaction coordinate, the absolute temperature, Boltzmann's constant, and the transmission coefficient along the i'th reaction path, respectively. The length, δ_i, is readily calculable and is usually less than an Angstrom. If the reactants A, B, etc., unite to make $C^{\ddagger}{}_i$ plus D, etc., according to the following equation

$$A + B + \cdots \rightleftarrows C^{\ddagger}{}_i + D + \cdots \cdots \tag{3}$$

with the equilibrium constant $K^{\ddagger}_i$, then

$$\frac{[C^{\ddagger}_i][D_i] \cdot \cdot \cdot \cdot}{[A][B] \cdot \cdot \cdot \cdot} = K^{\ddagger}_i \tag{4}$$

and

$$(C^{\ddagger}_i) = \frac{K^{\ddagger}_i[A][B] \cdot \cdot \cdot}{[D_i] \cdot \cdot \cdot \cdot \cdot \cdot} \tag{5}$$

Substituting Eq. (5) in Eq. (2) gives the most general expression for an elementary rate process with the specific rate constant

$$k' = \frac{kT}{h} \sum_i \frac{\mathcal{H}_i K^{\ddagger}_i}{(D_i) \cdot \cdot \cdot \cdot} \tag{6}$$

The method of expressing $K^{\ddagger}_i$ in terms of partition function is routine and need not be repeated here. The factors such as $[D_i]$ drop out when there is no other product formed along with the activated complex $C^{\ddagger}_i$. When the process proceeds by way of the Michaelis-Menten equation (2), several specific rate constants like that in Eq. (6) enter into the over-all rate.

Oxidative Enzyme Behavior

Now $K^{\ddagger}_i$ and therefore k' in Eq. (6) may have a simple Arrhenius dependence on temperature and a simple dependence on pressure. Or it may have an extremely fancy one, as in the case where k' goes through a maximum as it does for luminescence and for many other biological processes (3). At this point one must take account of the fact that the reactants, A, B, etc., may exist in a variety of isomeric states as well as in combination with each other and in combination with inhibitors. We now consider the case where the enzyme A is present in limited amounts compared with substrate B. In luminescence, for example, the enzyme luciferase may be present in active form, A, in the inactive or denatured form, A_d, and if a competitive or "type I" inhibitor such as sulfanilamide, S, is present, compounds AS and A_dS also may be present. If a non-competitive or "type II" inhibitor such as alcohol, Y, is present, then an inhibitor-enzyme compound of the form A_dY_3 appears. Only the native enzyme A is active and available to catalyze the oxidation of the substrate, B, referred to as luciferin.

When the various inactive forms of the enzyme become an appreciable part of the total, one must sharply distinguish between total enzyme, A_o, and the active enzyme, A. In such cases the mathematical analysis of the data involves introducing a conservation equation

$$A_o = A + A_d + AS + A_d S + AY_3 \qquad (7)$$

where all of the compounds formed in appreciable amounts must be included. If there is in addition appreciable combination between A and the substrate as in the Michaelis-Menten case, such compounds too should be included in Eq. (7). Equilibrium theory then enables us to replace the concentration of each compound in Eq. (7) by the appropriate equilibrium constant times the products of the constituent compounds. The inhibition of this enzymic process is completely analogous to catalysis at surfaces, where there is likewise a fixed number of sites which may be partly poisoned by inhibitors adsorbed on the surface. The denatured form, A_d, is frequently overlooked. The luciferase system exemplifies the importance of this phenomenon and may well be typical of other enzymes. For this reason, the physical properties of the various states of the luciferase molecule seem of general interest.

Thus the reversibly denatured molecule, A_d, is about 75 cc. per mole more voluminous than the active molecule A. It likewise is 180 units richer in entropy, and 70 kcal. more energy-rich. These properties are unchanged when A_d is combined with three alcohol inhibitor molecules, except for the formation of three inhibitor-to-enzyme bonds of approximately 10 kcal. each. The activated luciferase-luciferin complex is some 50 cc. per mole more voluminous than the constituent molecules in the normal state. This suggests a loosening of structure in passing to the activated state. Although the properties have been enumerated for the luminescent system, there is much evidence that indicates this is not an unusual oxidative enzyme.

ENZYME STRUCTURE

We can speak of the primary bonds, including the peptide bonds, as the primary structure of the protein molecule. As Pauling and

Corey (4) have emphasized, the hydrogen bonds probably constrain the long peptide molecule to twist into a spiral which may be spoken of as the secondary structure of the molecule. At least it seems established that the peptide-chain folds on itself, making a stable structure possessing many hydrogen bonds between pairs of peptide linkages. Such pencil-like spirals must eventually terminate. Since the globular proteins are much thicker than the spiral, a number of the spiral pencils must pack side by side to form a low-energy tertiary structure. This tertiary structure is held together by hydrogen bonds, hydrophobic bonds, and S-S bonds, among others (5). Probably peptide bonds and prosthetic groups also join pencils together, especially at their ends. Any interstices left in the structure will be tightly packed with solvent and with inhibitors, with substrates, and with ionic substances in such a way as to minimize the free energy.

The compact solid-like tertiary structure will be especially sensitive to temperature and solvent composition, and under suitable conditions "melts" to form the inactive reversibly-denatured protein observed with purified trypsin (6), crystalline soy-bean trypsin inhibitor (7), pepsinogen (8), and many enzymes present in living systems, notably the luciferase of luminescent organisms, among many others (3). This reversible loosening of the tertiary structure parallels ordinary melting with its great absorption of heat, entropy increase, and expansion. The loosening of the structure decreases the stability of the protein and promotes aggregation, the breaking of primary bonds, and allied processes reversible with difficulty. Thus factors such as low temperature, hydrostatic pressure, the correct pH to prevent swelling, and the absence of the "type II," or non-competitive, inhibitors all act to prevent the reversible denaturation which, as stated above, is the prelude to the irreversible denaturation.

STRUCTURE AND STABILITY

It follows from well-known considerations that there will necessarily be a careful packing of molecules to avoid leaving any unnecessary cavities. If a molecule is lifted out of a solid or liquid phase, thus leaving a cavity, all bonds connecting the removed molecule to its neighbors are severed. On the other hand, if all the molecules in a liquid or solid are volatilized at once, all bonds again are broken. Since, however, each bond starts on one molecule and ends on another, it will be counted twice if all bonds for each molecule are enumerated. Thus the energy required to take a molecule into the gas phase leaving the hole behind is just twice the heat of vaporization, ΔH_v. The forming of the hole and the vaporization of the molecule can of course each be achieved separately, and each costs exactly the heat of vaporization. If such a hole is formed next to a large molecule having the wrong shape to permit sufficient additional freedom of motion, then the entropy gained, ΔS_v, times the absolute temperature will not compensate for the heat absorbed, ΔH_v, and the difference, $\Delta F_v = \Delta H_v - T\Delta S_v$, will be positive, and the process will represent an improbable deviation from the norm and will occur infrequently. If ΔF_v is expressed in small calories per mole of holes, the chance of such a hole existing is $e^{-\Delta F_v/RT}$, and at room temperature this has the value $10^{-\Delta F_v/1300}$. Thus to leave a hole the size of a water molecule costs a heat of vaporization of 10,000 calories. If this is uncompensated by an increase in entropy, so that $\Delta F_v = 10,000$ calories, the chance of getting such a hole compared with not having it in an otherwise equally good structure is only $10^{-10,000/1300}$, or one in 50 million. On the other hand, a molecular misfit leaving a hole one-eighth the size of a water molecule has about one chance in ten of occurring.

Whether a particular fluctuation from the norm will be observed depends on the method which is to be employed to observe it. Thus holes which involve increases in ΔF_v of only 2.6 kcal. will not contribute noticeably to the observed density, whereas activated complexes involving a positive increase of $\Delta F^{\ddagger}$ of even as much as 24 kcal. are regularly observed to have appeared from the formation of the products of reaction. This is because the activated complex only lasts 10^{-13} seconds, and it only has to appear once for this short time in order to produce the reaction products. Thus if the tiny fraction 10^{-16} of the molecules is in the activated state at any one time, the reaction still will be over in about an hour. Thus the observation of reaction products is an enormously sensitive way to observe that an extremely minute concentration of activated complexes is present.

To be stable, not only must a structure avoid cavity formation, it must also have compatible molecular surfaces opposite each other. A simple calculation illustrates this situation. For simplicity, imagine a molecule like ethyl alcohol with about 125 sq. Å. of hydrocarbon-like surface and 25 sq. Å of −OH bond surface dissolved in water. The interfacial surface energy of an oil-water interface is 50 ergs per sq. cm. Thus the free-energy decrease, which results when a mole of such molecules each gives up 125 sq. Å. of oil-water interface, is

$$\frac{125 \times 6.02 \times 10^{23} \times 50}{10^{16} \times 4.18 \times 10^{7}} = 9000 \text{ calories.}$$

If a mole of such molecules dissolved in water can dip into the oily part of a protein, this will lower the free energy of the system by 9000 calories and will behave exactly as a bond of this strength. It isn't difficult to see why three alcohol molecules can cause luciferase to shift from the native to the inactive or denatured state in order for them to become able to make these three hydrophobic bonds. This is apparently the basis of very much narcotic action. Thus enzymes or membrane proteins give up their native structure to make these hydrophobic bonds with dissolved oily molecules. The more insoluble the molecule because of its oily surface, the better the hydrophobic bond made with an enzyme. This is why the saturated solution of a long chain alcohol with its very few soluble molecules will have the same narcotizing effect as the saturated solution of the short chain alcohols containing many dissolved molecules.

CATALYSIS

The surface of a bright metal is covered with unsatisfied valences which behave much as free radicals in space. Thus reactions of the type $H_2 + I_2 \rightarrow 2HI$, involving two saturated diatomic molecules, require an activation energy of about 28 per cent of the two bonds broken, whereas a deuterium atom can steal a hydrogen atom from an H_2 molecule with an activation energy of only about eight kcal.

and most radicals enter into reactions with even lower activation energies. Any activated complex possesses fractional bonds. Thus certain bonds are in the process of breaking as others are forming. The important fractional bonds in the activated complex are about ten per cent expanded over their normal equilibrium distance. Further, any process which will extend a bond ten per cent will unsaturate it and make it into a reactive fractional bond.

It is of interest to examine some typical processes which decrease the strength of primary bonds and so make them reactive. The reaction $HCl + DBr \rightarrow DCl + HBr$ proceeds slowly in the gas phase but almost instantly in water solution. This is because the electrostatic bonds which water makes with charged ions pull the electron pair holding hydrogen ion to the anion completely over onto the negative ion. Thus water is a powerful catalyst which by using electrostatic bonding saps the strength out of primary bonds and sets the ions adrift. A sapping of the strength of the primary bonds of a substrate which makes strong electrostatic hydrogen bonds with an enzyme is thus to be expected.

Radicals or ions formed by the cleavage of the central bond in hexaphenylethane and its analogs are commonplace. Here the π electrons of the three phenyl groups make effective use of the empty orbital of the triphenyl methyl radical. This, with steric repulsion, weakens the bond to the point of dissociation. This is another method of making active fractional bonds of the type existing in activated complexes.

It is well known that the chloracetic acids are much stronger acids than acetic. This is because the chlorine atoms have drawn charge out of the O-H bond, again weakening it so that electrostatic bonding with the solvent more readily completes its task of completely sapping the strength of the O-H bond. Thus in this case internal substitution has sapped the strength of a primary bond and changed it over into a reactive partial valence state.

When diphenyl has three or four large groups in the ortho positions, the two phenyl groups twist out of the same plane so as to set their two planes at an angle. This is in spite of the fact that in so doing, the electron pair holding the two phenyls together gives up 5 kcal. of resonance binding with the ring and becomes more strongly localized in the C-C bond connecting the two phenyls. This shows how steric hindrance, by distortion, can modify the strength of a primary bond.

These examples illustrate the influences which can unsaturate the primary bonds in protein molecules. The strength can thus be sapped from primary bonds so as to make them into reactive fractional bonds (a) by electrostatic interaction, (b) by electron-hungry groups pulling, or electron groups pushing the electron pair out of a primary bond by induction or resonance effects, or (c) by any type of geometrical bond distortion. A substrate becomes reactive if an enzyme imposes on it any of these influences. If enzyme bonds themselves become fractional they tend to combine with neighboring atoms of the substrate and thus to sap the strength out of the substrate primary bonds and make them reactive, just as in ordinary contact catalysis.

The structural features which we have ascribed to proteins should produce enzymic properties. Thus any system acts as a catalyst which stabilizes the fractionally-bonded activated complex by bonding with it and so lessening the free energy of activation. In fact, most of the problems of chemical reactivity could well be discussed under such a title as "The Structure of Activated Complexes."

One of the most important and far-reaching general statements that can be made is that for enzymes no activated-complex structure will be important which requires a free energy much in excess of 20 kcal. to constitute it from the stable substances in the system. This means that one should not postulate as important in reactions any structure which differs very much from known stable structures in free energy. Thus chemists have been criticized for naively searching for intermediate compounds which would provide a clue as to the nature of the activated complex. Since activated complexes live only about 10^{-13} seconds, it is obviously hopeless to look for them. However, since 20 kcal. of activation free energy, or even double this amount, will buy only a little stretching and distorting of the reacting bonds, it follows that the activated complex will look very like some of the intermediate compounds that are already present, and that if one postulates a more exotic activated complex, one is almost certainly wrong. This idea we may call the " Principle of Similitude." It does not exclude major changes in tertiary structure in forming the activated complex, providing these changes involve a small free-energy change, and it requires only that the activated complex resemble closely some long-lived attainable state.

We suppose that what has been here called the tertiary structure is the site of the peculiar molecular arrangements which stabilize the activated complex formed of enzyme with substrate. This fit of substrate to enzyme, since it exists, necessarily leaves no bad cavities. We suppose this tertiary structure will have in it distorted primary bonds which have had part of their strength sapped away by their effort to contribute to the secondary bond structure. Also prosthetic groups which act as the site of enzyme function are sometimes bonded to the distorted proteins in ways which pump in or pump out charge and so enhance enzyme activity. With denaturation, reversible or irreversible, the close fitting of enzyme to substrate molecule as well as much of the strain which is responsible for the reactive fractional valences disappears with the tertiary structure, and with this disappearance goes enzyme activity. It is clear that the mirror image of the optically active substrate for an enzyme will generally not have its activated complex stabilized as well and so will react more slowly. One also has no trouble seeing how chelation or simple coordination of a metal into an activated complex might measurably stabilize it, just as ordinary stable compounds may be formed.

One out of several possible types of activated complexes deserves special mention. We can call it the " rack." In this complex the atoms of the substrate on both sides of the bond to be broken bind strongly with the enzyme, with the consequent sapping of the bond's strength by strain and by draining off the bonding electron pairs. Von Euler and Josephson (9) and Bergmann and coworkers (10) originally emphasized a complex of this sort in their " di " and " polyaffinity " theories. The matter has received more complete attention from Smith (11) in his theory for the mechanism of metal-activated peptidases. Enzymes catalyzing electron transfer frequently contain heme or other prosthetic groups providing a single point for substrate attachment. These cases will naturally involve a different type of activated complex. Nevertheless, the " rack " effect is probably important in bonds joining the prosthetic group to the protein, i. e., strain and electron induction in the prosthetic group induced by a poor connection between the latter and the protein can make the prosthetic group highly reactive as a source or sink for electrons of the substrate. The large positive volume of activation for luciferase originally provided an experimental indication that major changes in the structure of proteins occur during catalysis. Laidler (12) has emphasized this possibility in showing that unusually large volume and entropy changes occur in the slow steps of enzymic catalysis.

The attachment of antigen to antibody presumably also involves the tertiary structure of the antibody, the antigen, or some molecule very like it in structure, being temporarily built into the tertiary structure of the antibody at the time of its synthesis. This leaves a structure in the antibody having a strong predisposition to hook onto anything which resembles closely the original antigen. Haurowitz has given an interesting discussion of the problems involved (13).

Thus we may suspect that reversible denaturation and enzymic function are closely related. Perhaps the best evidence for this at present is the well-known fact that substrates stabilize enzymes against thermal denaturation. This condition is hardly possible unless the substrate by the very act and position of its binding can stabilize the native state of the protein.

Generally speaking, enzymes are more efficient than contact or homogeneous catalysis, in that smaller free energies of activation appear. At first glance it is strange to observe that weak secondary bonds, usually of less than 10 kcal. of heat and even smaller free energy, are involved. However, several such weak bonds optimally arranged can easily produce the required distortion of the activated complex, and the strong bonds of chemisorption usually observed in ordinary contact catalysis are merely an indication of the inefficiency of the latter type of catalysis.

Synthesis of Proteins

Proteins having molecular weights in the neighborhood of 17,000 are known. Thus Marrack (14) points out that ribonuclease, with a molecular weight of about 15,000 (Kunitz), and lysozyme with molecular weight of 15,000 to 18,000 (Abraham) are the smallest protein antigens to which antisera have been made. A central spiral surrounded by six parallel spirals each containing 24 amino acids of molecular weight 100 would form a roughly spherical barrel with a molecular weight of 16,800. Two general theories of how such a protein might be synthesized have been proposed. The " template " theory postulates a molecular pattern on which the enzymes fasten together the entire sequence of amino acids to conform with the pattern (14, 15). The " conveyor belt " theory (14) supposes the growing protein is passed on from one set of enzymes to another, with each enzyme adding the appropriate molecule. Bearing on these theories is what we have called the " Principle of Similitude " between the activated and some stable complex. The sole basis of this principle is that 24 kilocalories will permit very little divergence in structure from the nearest stable complex. Since one lacks evidence for or against uncoiled spirals stuck to templates, one possibility is to suppose that proteins fold into their tight spirals as fast as they are formed, and that the template which the enzyme carries only makes contact with a few amino acids preceding the particular molecule it is adding to the chain at any time.

Research on the fungus *Neurospora* (16) indicates that the factors directing the synthesis of a given protein are usually associated with a single gene. Thus the enzymes involved must form a single genetic nucleoprotein sequence. This conclusion leaves unanswered the question whether folding occurs stepwise, keeping up with the peptide bond formation, or whether it occurs simultaneously after the unfolded peptide is complete. It is well known that proteins must be unfolded to be digested by proteolytic enzymes. It can be assumed that misfits and incomplete peptide chains which may escape from the template are unable to achieve a stable tertiary structure and hence are rapidly destroyed.

SUMMARY

1. The absolute rate theory has been formulated to treat a group of parallel activated complexes.

2. The structures of globular proteins have been discussed in terms of the primary amino acid sequence, a secondary spiral structure, and a tertiary packing of spirals into compact low-energy structures.

3. Reversible denaturation and enzyme inactivation are associated with " melting " of the tertiary structure.

4. The weak partial bonds present in activated complexes are brought about (a) by secondary electrostatic bonds pulling and pushing the primary bond electron pair toward the anion, as in the ionization of an acid by a solvent such as water, (b) by addition to molecules of groups which labilize a bond by pushing or pulling charge out of the primary bond by induction or resonance, or (c) by mechanical strain connected with the tight packing in the tertiary structure.

5. The process of enzyme-bonding on both sides of a reacting bond in the substrate and thus inducing lability by mechanical strain, electron displacement, or both, has been called the " rack." The " rack " induced by tertiary structure may also weaken some enzyme bonds, and so increase their reactivity for substrates.

6. The importance in protein structure of avoiding holes without a compensating increase in entropy is discussed quantitatively.

7. A quantitative discussion of hydrophobic bonds is given. Their significance for tertiary structure and reversible denaturation with the accompanying narcotic effects on enzymes is pointed out.

8. Free energies of activation for important dilute enzyme systems involve standard free energies of activation as low as 12 kcal., and for concentrated enzymes the value seldom exceeds 24 kcal. Such small free energies insure that the activated complex can only be a moderate distortion of stable structures. Thus much importance is attached to the " Principle of Similitude," which states that any activated complex is at most a modest distortion of some stable enzyme structure.

REFERENCES

1. Glasstone, S., K. J. Laidler, and H. Eyring, *Theory of Rate Processes*, McGraw-Hill Book Co., New York (1941).
2. Michaelis, L., and M. L. Menten, *Biochem. Z.*, 49, 33 (1913).
   Haldane, J. B. S., *Enzymes*, Longmans, Green, and Co., New York (1930).
3. Johnson, F. H., H. Eyring, and M. J. Polissar, *Molecular Biology*, John Wiley & Sons, New York (in press).
4. Pauling, L., and R. B. Corey, *Proc. Nat. Acad. Sci. U. S.*, 37, 282 (1951).
5. Linderstrøm-Lang, K., *The Lane Medical Lectures, Proteins and Enzymes*, Stanford University Press, Stanford, Calif. (1952).
   Lumry, R., and H. Eyring. Paper presented at Symposium on Protein Denaturation, Spring Meeting, American Chemical Society, Los Angeles, California, *J. Phys. & Coll. Chem.* (1953) (in press).
6. Anson, M. L., and A. E. Mirsky, *J. Gen. Physiol.*, 17, 393, 17, 399 (1934).
7. Kunitz, M., *J. Gen. Physiol.*, 32, 241 (1948).
8. Herriott, R. M., *J. Gen. Physiol.*, 21, 501 (1938).
9. von Euler, H., and K. Josephson, *Z. physiol. Chem.*, 157, 122 (1926).
10. Bergmann, M., *Harvey Lectures*, 31, 37 (1935-36).
11. Smith, E. L., *Advances in Enzymol.*, 12, 191 (1951).
12. Laidler, K. J., *J. Am. Chem. Soc.*, 72, 2159 (1950).
    Laidler, K. J. Paper presented at A Symposium on Biochemical Kinetics at the Diamond Jubilee Meeting of the American Chemical Society, New York (1951).
    Laidler, K. J., *Arch. Biochem.*, 30, 226 (1951).
13. Haurowitz, F., *Biol. Rev.*, 27, 247 (1952).
14. Marrack, J. R., in *The Enzymes* (J. B. Sumner and K. Myrbäck, eds.), Vol. 1, Part 1, Chap. 8, Academic Press, New York (1950).
15. Haurowitz, F., *Chemistry and Biology of Proteins*, Chap. 17, Academic Press, New York (1950).
16. Beadle, G. W., *Currents in Biochemical Research* (D. E. Green, ed.), pp. 1-12, Interscience Publishers, New York (1946).

DISCUSSION

DR. BRINK: I think you will agree that there is a lot of leeway in applying this theory to biological systems. The role of the experimenter would seem to be to discover the natural constraints that will reduce the number of theoretical possibilities. I wonder if Dr. Kauzmann would care to make any comments.

DR. KAUZMANN: Rather than saying anything, I would like to go back to Princeton right now and do some of these experiments on urea and viscosity changes of reversibly denatured enzymes.

DR. EYRING: The thing I would guess is that you would get some increase in optical activity every time you unravel the protein a little bit, such as in reversible denaturation, but nothing like the violent sort of things you got in the experiments you described.

DR. SCHACKMAN: I would like to make a few comments on some work we have been doing which has a bearing on what Dr. Eyring has already said, and this is primarily based on the application of a new type of synthetic boundary ultracentrifuge cell. The goal here was really to see whether, when an enzyme attacked some protein or nucleic acid (as the case may be), the molecule was torn apart very rapidly—for example, whether the first step in the reaction is a very slow one and one saw intermediates in the process of the hydrolytic steps, or whether one saw only end products, meaning that the steps following the first one were very, very rapid. As models for this type of study we have chosen insulin and DNA. In some respects insulin is a very bad model—in other respects it is very interesting, in view of Sanger's work. We have used chymotrypsin for the digestion of insulin and DNAase to digest DNA. In the insulin case there doesn't seem to be any doubt but that, once the insulin molecule is attacked by chymotrypsin, it rapidly falls apart—that is, the steps after the first one are very rapid, with the result that one sees only insulin and very low molecular weight peptides of 800 to 1,000 molecular weight. One does not see the intermediate products of insulin going down to these end products. This is also of interest in terms of the specificity of chymotrypsin and the structure of insulin. Perhaps this has a bearing on the use of synthetic substrates to test enzyme specificity. With the DNA–DNAase system one finds the extreme opposite picture. There one never sees any low molecular weight products until all the DNA is digested. One sees a progressive decrease in molecular weight, more like the result one would expect if you consider DNA as a polymer and you were attacking bonds at random, with the result that the molecules are degraded, roughly speaking, to the same extent so that you are getting a relatively broad collection of molecules of different molecular weight. The results thus far show more about the applicability of the centrifuge technique in this regard than they do about the mechanism of enzyme action, but it seems to me that if this work is continued we will learn whether or not the first step is denaturation when a protein is attacked by an enzyme, and that, after the molecule is denatured according to the ideas of Linderstrøm-Lang, the molecule more or less explodes. This may not be the right idea, but at least one can see whether or not intermediates are formed, and therefore this should be a perfectly straightforward type of investigation using molecular weight as a criterion.

DR. KAPLAN: I was just wondering, Dr. Eyring, now that there is evidence on hydrolytic enzymes, where you have the splitting of an organic phosphate by a phosphatase where the phosphate actually moves from the substrate to the enzyme, and then the water hydrolyzes the compound at the surface of the enzyme, how would you reconcile the activation energy required by the enzyme for transferring the phosphate?

DR. EYRING: I am sure that you can do better on this than I could, since you have the details well in hand. I might say this, that the enzyme will serve the purpose of supplying a pocket for the substrate to fit into and thus lead to the formation of the activated complex. There is no limit, unfortunately, in this theory to the complication of the number of things that could enter into the formation of the activated complex. Everything can happen, and the molecules will try all possibilities—whichever one will give you the lowest energy of activation will predominate. What we ought to have at the present time is a theory of the structure of activated complexes. This is the book that someone should write. It will be entirely analogous to books written on the structure of ordinary molecules. If you could tell me in greater detail what the nature of the structure of the activated complex really is, then I think we could sit down together and figure out the most probable route, as well as the mechanism of the action. The activated complex is like ordinary structures except that it is a little more distorted. I don't know whether I have said anything to help you out in this matter, but unfortunately detailed information is lacking.

DR. HEIDELBERGER: There is one possible application of immunology in which Dr. Eyring's ideas might fit, and that is in the large heat effect which is obtained in cross reactions. In the homologous reactions between the antigens and antibodies in most instances the effect of temperature on the amount of precipitate formed is very slight, with a maximum usually of the order of 15 per cent between $0°$ and $37°$. However, in cross reactions—such as between reactions of type III polysaccharide and type VIII antibody, or between chicken egg albumin and anti-duck albumin—the amount of precipitate obtained at $37°$ is very much less than the amount obtained at $0°$, indicating that where the antigen-antibody don't fit particularly well in the beginning there may be very large activation effects. It may be profitable to explore some of these cases in greater detail.

DR. EYRING: The very localized special structures effective in enzyme activity are shown by the small size of inhibitors which stop reaction. Thus one sulfanilamide molecule absorbed on luciferase completely inhibits luminescence. Dr. Heidelberger pointed out yesterday that big patches are involved in antibody reactions. Worse fitting of structures may easily come with rise in temperature. If the fitting of antigen to antibody involves the coiling of tertiary structure the fit should disappear with reversible as well as irreversible denaturation. We do have quite a bit of evidence as to how big these areas of fit are by seeing how shape and size of inhibitor decrease reaction. An antibody may have several active patches which make it become a link in a chain by combining with one or more antigens. Certain enzymes link to a substrate on both sides of the bond to be broken in what we have called the rack mechanism. However, whether we are interested in equilibria or rates the key is always some critical structure.

DR. HEIDELBERGER: I don't think that that applies. I think that in immune reactions, too, you would have to have multiple reaction sites, in order to get visible effects. I don't know, however, whether you need them merely in order to get combination. For aggregation, however, I presume you have to have multiple combination.

DR. EYRING: I am afraid that I haven't made myself clear. Certainly from the study of the relative reaction rates of levo and dextro substrates it is clear that fitting is over a fairly wide area. Attack at a bond in a substrate involves a sizable surface of contact enzyme and substrate just as for antibody and antigen.

DR. BOYD: I just wanted to say I don't think that these patches in the immune reactions are always the same. In some they might be, but there is some evidence that at times these patches might be very small, because antibodies can recognize the difference between isomers of tartaric acid.

DR. GUTFREUND: I think we ought to draw a distinction between the reversible inactivation of enzymes and denaturation. This is not just a question of words; I believe there may be a fundamental difference. The reactions which Dr. Kauzmann was talking about yesterday are reactions involving the breaking of hydrogen bonds leading to an uncoiling of the helical backbone of the protein molecule. Once you have broken enough of these hydrogen bonds or have effected S–S linkages, then presumably parts of the molecule can uncoil. I don't know of any case where this has been carefully studied for reversible denaturation, that is, where any change in physical structure has been observed. I am asking for information on this point, but as far as I am aware there have not been any observed changes in the size or shape of the molecule or in the sedimentation constant or in any other measurable property—except, of course, enzymatic activity. This excludes the various phenomena of reversible dissociation into identical subunits.

DR. EYRING: I wonder if the thing that you are saying is that you would prefer to call what has been observed in the case of trypsin and soybean inhibitor reversible inactivation, rather than reversible denaturation.

DR. GUTFREUND: Yes.

DR. EYRING: I think that this is primarily a matter of taste

DR. KAUZMANN: I don't believe that it is just a case of quibbling about words. Both of these proteins, when reversibly denatured, become insoluble at the isoelectric point. This probably indicates a pretty big change in the state of the molecules.

DR. GUTFREUND: But the point I was making is that the size and shape of the molecule are not changing in cases where biologically active molecules are reversibly inactivated.

DR. ANSON: There have been no studies of the shape of the molecules of denatured protein in an equilibrium mixture of the native and denatured forms of a protein. But there is some evidence that considerable unfolding during denaturation is compatible with gross reversal of denaturation. One can prepare native, crystalline hemoglobin from surface coagulated hemoglobin. And presumably the surface denaturation involves considerable unfolding. Similarly, one can prepare native protein from protein which has been denatured by urea, with considerable changes in the individual molecules indicated by the change in the viscosity of the solution.

DR. GUTFREUND: But has there been a real change in the shapes of the molecules? My distinction is between radical structural changes in denaturation and some local change, affecting the active center in reversible inactivation.

DR. ANSON: The factors which determine whether denaturation is reversible or not, and whether the reversal of denaturation is complete or not, are not yet adequately understood. The degree of unfolding may be an important factor. But it is not yet possible to say that it is the critical or even the most important factor.

DR. NEURATH: I don't know whether I have fully understood this polemic but if the question is whether during reversible denaturation, that is, when the protein is still in the denatured form, any gross changes in size or shape occur, I believe that in all cases in which denaturation appears to be truly reversible, it has been brought about by heating. There is only one set of physical measurements of the heat denatured protein I know of, and that concerns the sedimentation rate and light scattering of chymotrypsinogen at 45° in the absence of salt. There, Eisenberg and Schwert failed to find any difference from the native protein, suggesting that there were no significant changes in size or shape. I think that Dr. Gutfreund is quite right on this point and that there is no experimental evidence to suggest that under conditions of truly reversible denaturation, and I don't mean " regeneration " of serum albumin from concentrated urea, the structural changes are very significant. Changes in hydration is really all one has to assume, as Eisenberg and Schwert have done for chymotrypsinogen.

THE ENZYME–SUBSTRATE COMPLEX AS AN INTERMEDIATE IN ENZYME–CATALYZED REACTIONS

HENRY B. BULL

Biochemistry Department, State University of Iowa, Iowa City

THERE IS MUCH we wish to know about enzymes and enzymatic reactions. In my opinion, however, the pressing need centers around two problems. First, we must have an appropriate measure of the rate of activation of the substrate by the enzyme, and, secondly, we are wanting an unambiguous measure of the affinity between the enzyme and its substrate.

Before we can establish a true measure of the rate of activation, we must settle on a standard reference state for the reactants of enzymatic reactions, otherwise, such rates as we determine by experiment will be largely meaningless and provide slight basis for interpretation.

The reference state which has been implicitly, if not always explicitly, employed by many enzymologists has been the condition of saturation of the enzyme by the substrate. The rate of decomposition of the substrate can then be expressed as the maximum velocity (V_m), a velocity which is calculated by some rearrangement of the original equations of Michaelis and Menten (7), (6). It is then considered that the maximum velocity (V_m) is

$$V_m = K'E_o \tag{1}$$

where K' is the rate constant for the decomposition of the enzyme-substrate complex and E_o is the concentration of the enzyme, E_o being much less than the concentration of the substrate.

It will be recalled that the Michaelis-Menten rate expression is a composite equation combining zero- and first-order kinetics, the integration (8) of which leads to

$$\ln \frac{S_o}{S} = \frac{V_m}{K_m} t - \frac{(S_o - S)}{K_m} \tag{2}$$

141

where S_o is the initial substrate concentration and S is its concentration after time t. K_m is the dissociation constant of the Michaelis-Menten enzyme-substrate complex. It is evident that at low initial substrate concentrations and for larger values of K_m, first-order reaction kinetics should be observed, in which case the rate constant would be equal to V_m/K_m. The standard reference state is then unit concentration of substrate.

Whereas the first-order constant is indeed a measure of the rate of enzymatic reaction, it is an unsuitable measure, since there is included in this rate constant both the affinity of the enzyme for the substrate, as well as the intrinsic rate of activation of the substrate by the enzyme.

Under certain very restrictive conditions, the maximum velocity (V_m), as estimated from an application of the Michaelis-Menten equation, is an acceptable and meaningful expression of the rate of activation of the substrate by an enzyme, but under most conditions serious ambiguity is involved. We wish to consider this problem in some detail.

It appears that the most meaningful standard reference state for an enzyme is the condition in which the enzyme is completely activated and is saturated with substrate, and the substrate has no inhibiting effect on the enzyme; the enzyme is activating the substrate at the maximum possible rate at a given temperature. Before we can specify such a standard state experimentally, we must deal with the general problem of enzyme kinetics and specifically with enzyme activators.

Much work has been done on the inhibition of enzymatic reactions, but there are comparatively few papers dealing with the theory of activation of enzymes. This is odd because the vast majority of enzymes must be activated before they are capable of serving as catalysts. Conspicuous as activators are hydrogen and hydroxyl ions.

Walker and Schmidt (9), Bull and Currie (3), Waley (8), and more recently Alberty (1) have attempted formulations of the role of hydrogen ions in enzymatic reactions. These papers have in common the consideration of the equilibria between hydrogen ions and the various components of the enzyme-substrate system, and the rate equations so derived are consistent with each other when recognition is taken of the specific equilibria considered.

Some reflection will convince one that the possibilities of formulation are very large and that a general formulation is probably impractical. Without claiming generality for our treatment, we wish to deal with some of the simpler and more plausible equilibria. We shall identify the enzyme and its concentrations by E, the substrate and its concentration by S, and the activator and its concentration by A. The concentrations of the complexes of these quantities we shall denote by combination of these symbols. We further consider the free energy of the enzymatically catalyzed reaction to be large and negative, so that we shall be untroubled by a reversal of the decomposition of the substrate.

The following equilibria appear to be of interest:

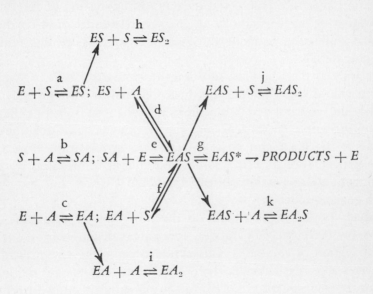

If the concentration of the substrate is much larger than that of the enzyme, the rate of formation of the reaction products can be expressed as a function of the concentration of the free enzyme and of the concentrations of the various enzyme complexes. This means that the equilibria involved in steps (b) and (e) can be omitted from consideration. Step (g) involves the formation of the activated complex EAS* from the active complex, EAS, in keeping with the transition state theory. We have introduced the idea of the activated complex because it is formally correct, but this conception does not provide us with any additional information which is useful for our immediate purposes and the magnitudes of the various constants leading up to this step would have identical values whether we used the transition state theory or not. Since its omission leads to simplification, step (g) will be omitted in what is to follow. No doubt Dr. Eyring will wish to view this matter in a different light.

The total enzyme (E_o) added to the system is equal to the various forms of the enzyme, free and combined.

$$E_o = E + ES + EA + EAS + ES_2 + EA_2 + EAS_2 + EA_2S \quad (3)$$

To obtain a useful velocity equation, we must express the concentration of the free enzyme and of the concentrations of the various enzyme complexes in terms of the concentration of the active complex, EAS. The dissociation constants to be considered are:

$$K_a = E \times S/ES \quad (4)$$

$$K_c = E \times A/EA \quad (5)$$

$$K_d = ES \times A/EAS \quad (6)$$

$$K_f = EA \times S/EAS \quad (7)$$

$$K_h = ES \times S/ES_2 \quad (8)$$

$$K_i = EA \times A/EA_2 \quad (9)$$

$$K_j = EAS \times S/EAS_2 \quad (10)$$

$$K_k = EAS \times A/EA_2S \quad (11)$$

Substituting equations (4), (5) (6), (7), (8), (9), (10), and (11) into equation (3), and rearranging, there results:

$$E_o = \left[\left(\frac{K_a K_d}{A} + K_f + \frac{K_f A}{K_i} \right) \frac{1}{S} \right.$$
$$\left. + \left(\frac{K_d}{K_h A} + \frac{1}{K_j} \right) S + \frac{K_d}{A} + \frac{A}{K_k} + 1 \right] EAS \quad (12)$$

The rate of decomposition of the active complex, EAS, to form the reaction products is:

$$V = K' \times EAS \qquad (13)$$

Combining equations (12) and (13) and rearranging, we have:

$$\frac{1}{V} = \left[\left(\frac{K_a K_d}{A} + K_f + \frac{K_f A}{K_i} \right) \frac{1}{S} \right.$$
$$\left. + \left(\frac{K_d}{K_h A} + \frac{1}{K_j} \right) S + \frac{K_d}{A} + \frac{A}{K_k} + 1 \right] \frac{1}{K' E_o} \qquad (14)$$

Steps (h), (i), (j), and (k) remove enzyme from participation in the activation of the substrate, and hence these steps are inhibitory. Steps (h) and (k) lead to inhibition by excess substrate.

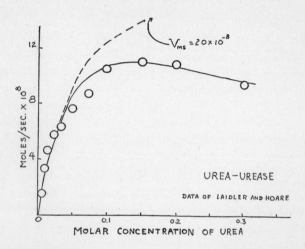

FIG. 1. Action of urease on urea at pH 6.6 and at 30° C. as a function of urea concentration (data of Laidler and Hoare). Solid curve is plot of equation (14). Broken curve is plot of equation (16).

Consider the data of Laidler and Hoare (5) on the decomposition of urea by urease which were obtained at 30° C. and at pH 6.6 as a function of the urea concentration. These rate data are shown replotted in Fig. 1. Indicated by the solid line is a plot of equation (14). This equation has the same form as that of Laidler and Hoare and, accordingly, the fit with the experimental points is no better or worse than that given by the Laidler-Hoare equation. We, however, place a more complex interpretation on the meaning of the constant terms. Equation (14) can be reduced to the following form:

$$V = \frac{S}{K_1 + K_2 S + K_3 S^2} \tag{15}$$

If urea had no inhibiting effect on the rate of activation at high urea concentrations, K_3 would be very small (K_h and K_j would be very large). Under these conditions equation (15) reduces to:

$$V = \frac{S}{K_1 + K_2 S} \tag{16}$$

The broken line in Fig. 1 shows a plot of equation 16. At high concentration of substrate the velocity of the reaction, if urea did not inhibit, would be $1/K_2$ and has the value of 20×10^{-8} moles per second, as indicated in Fig. 1. The enzyme, urease, would be in its hypothetical standard reference state in so far as the substrate was concerned, but not in respect to activators. It is clear that it would be impossible to realize such a standard state experimentally, but we feel that it is a meaningful and useful state, even though it has no experimental reality.

As noted above, for enzyme reactions which do not exhibit substrate inhibition, K_h and K_j may be regarded as very large, and under these conditions, equation (14) reduces to:

$$\frac{1}{V} = \left[\left(\frac{K_a K_d}{A} + K_f + \frac{K_f A}{K_i} \right) \frac{1}{S} + \frac{K_d}{A} + \frac{A}{K_k} + 1 \right] \frac{1}{K' E_o} \tag{17}$$

If the concentration of the substrate be sufficiently large to insure zero-order kinetics, the velocity of the enzymatic reaction which we shall, under these conditions, denote by V_{ms}, becomes:

$$\frac{1}{V_{ms}} = \left(\frac{K_d}{A} + \frac{A}{K_k} + 1 \right) \frac{1}{K' E_o} \tag{18}$$

Equation (18) provides for a maximum in V_{ms} as the concentration of the activator (A) is increased and would appear to describe the general situation where a maximum is observed in the velocity of an enzymatic reaction as a function of the activator concentration

Both trypsin and chymotrypsin, as well as many other enzymes, exhibit such a maximum. Unfortunately, there are few data in the literature dealing with the velocity of the enzymatic reactions as a function of the pH at sufficiently high substrate concentration to be certain that zero-order kinetics are obeyed. We have used the data of Walker and Schmidt (9) on the action of histidase on histidine as a function of pH, replotted in Fig. 2. These data are not entirely

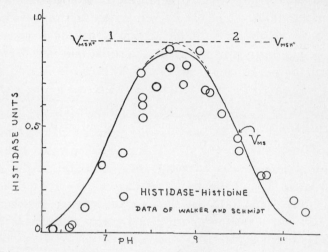

FIG. 2. Action of histidase on histidine, expressed as histidase units, as a function of pH (data of Walker and Schmidt). Solid line is a plot of equation (19). Broken line 1 is a plot of equation (20) and broken line 2 is a plot of equation (21).

suited to our purposes, since the histidase units in which these authors expressed the reaction velocities are in fact not initial rates, and further we have no real assurance that zero-order kinetics are obeyed throughout the pH range investigated. The authors simply state that they used " excess " substrate. The solid line in Fig. 2 shows a plot of equation (18). The agreement with the experimental points is not perfect, but in view of the experimental uncertainties mentioned above, it can be regarded as satisfactory. Equation (18) can be rearranged to give:

$$V_{ms} = \frac{K_k A \, K'E_o}{K_d K_k + K_k A + A^2} \tag{19}$$

If the hydrogen ions at higher concentration had no inhibitory effect on the reaction velocity, it would mean that K_k was very large, and under this condition, equation (19) reduces to:

$$V_{ms} = \frac{K_k A\, K'E_o}{K_d K_k + K_k A}$$ (20)

The broken line 1 in Fig. 2 shows a plot of equation (20). At high concentration of activator (hydrogen ions), V_{ms} becomes equal to 0.9 histidase units. We designate this velocity by $V_{ms}H^+$ and consider it refers to the standard reference state of the enzyme in respect to both the substrate and the activator (hydrogen ions).

Suppose we start with the enzyme (histidase) in an inactive state as a result of excess concentration of hydrogen ions and that we progressively decrease the hydrogen ion concentration, and at the same time prevent the active complex from dissociating hydrogen ions and becoming inactive. This amounts to setting K_d equal to zero. Equation (19) then reduces to:

$$V_{ms} = \frac{K_k K'E_o}{A + K_k}$$ (21)

Broken line 2 in Fig. 2 shows a plot of equation (21). At low concentration of activator (hydrogen ions), V_{ms} becomes equal to $K'E_o$. This then provides a method in addition to the use of equation (20) for the evaluation of $V_{ms}H^+$.

Some authors have used the so-called optimum pH as a reference state in respect to pH. It is clear that if K_k is large and K_d is small that V_{ms}, at the optimum pH, will approach $V_{ms}H^+$. But, on the other hand, if K_k is small and K_d is large, the activator will begin to act as an inhibitor long before the enzyme is fully active and V_{ms} at the optimum pH will be very much smaller than $V_{ms}H^+$. Of course, if groups referred to by K_d and K_k have the same intrinsic binding constant, K_k would have to be at least four times greater than K_d.

If the excess activator concentration does not lead to inhibition of the enzymatic reaction, it means that K_i and K_k are very large, and, accordingly, equation (18) reduces to:

$$\frac{1}{V_{ms}} = \left(\frac{K_d}{A} + 1\right)\frac{1}{K'E_o}$$ (22)

Equation (22) describes the results obtained by Bull and Currie

(3) in their study of the peptic hydrolysis of egg albumin as a function of pH. Fig. 3 shows a plot of their data and the solid line is a plot of equation (22). As the concentration of the activator (hydrogen ions) is increased, the velocity of the reaction reaches a limiting value which is equal to $K'E_0$ and which we have designated as $V_{ms}H^+$

It is appropriate to point out that a study of the variation of $V_{ms}H^+$ with temperature provides an unambiguous basis for the calculation

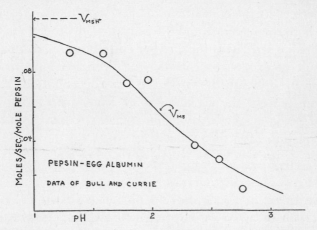

FIG. 3. Rate of attack of pepsin on egg albumin with excess substrate, as a function of pH (data of Bull and Currie). Solid line is a plot of equation (22).

of the energy of activation associated with the activation of the substrate by the enzyme and would not include the heats of dissociation of the enzyme-substrate complex or the heats of dissociation of any of the protogenic groups of the enzyme or of the substrate.

The maximum in the rate of hydrolysis as a function of pH exhibited by hydrolyzing enzymes is in our view a necessity if the enzyme is to act in this capacity. The active area of such an enzyme must have in it a proton-donating and a proton-accepting group to fulfill the Bronsted requirements for acid-base catalyst. In terms of our formulation, K_d refers to the dissociation of the proton-donating group. In keeping with the above discussion, the pH-maximum, which is obtained when zero-order kinetics are obeyed, has nothing to do with variation of the affinity between enzyme and substrate as a function of pH. Incidentally, we believe that the reason why a maximum in the rate of attack of pepsin on egg albumin as a function of pH was not observed resides in the impracticability of determining the rate at sufficiently low pH to titrate the proton-accepting group with hydrogen ions and hence to show inhibition.

In the light of the treatment given above, activators can be classified into rate activators and into affinity activators. Affinity activators, if maintained at constant concentration in the reaction mixture, cannot alter the maximum rate of reaction during zero-order kinetics in respect to the substrate concentration but do increase the rate of reaction up to the substrate concentration at which zero-order kinetics take over; such activators increase the affinity of the enzyme for the substrate. Rate activators, on the other hand, increase the rate of reaction at high and low substrate concentration; they must enter into combination with the enzyme-substrate complex in the last step leading to the decomposition of the substrate into the reaction products. Hydrogen ions can act as both affinity and as rate activators in the same enzymatic reaction.

This description of activators is analogous to that given enzyme inhibitors. In fact, we should prefer to call competitive inhibitors affinity inhibitors and non-competitive inhibitors we would designate as rate inhibitors; we regard this terminology as more descriptive. It is clear that rate activators and affinity activators can be distinguished from each other by a proper examination of the experimental data.

Having outlined some of the difficulties and ambiguities associated with the measurement of the rate of activation of the substrate by an enzyme, we turn attention to the affinity problem.

In the original theory of Michaelis and Menten, the dissociation constant of the enzyme-substrate complex was given as:

$$K_m = \frac{E \times S}{ES} \tag{23}$$

which describes the equilibrium in the reaction:

$$E + S \underset{K'_2}{\overset{K'_1}{\rightleftharpoons}} ES \overset{K'_3}{\longrightarrow} products + E$$

It was considered that K_m would be equal to K'_2/K'_1, as it should be for a simple dissociation constant. Subsequently, however, it has been pointed out on numerous occasions (2) that since the complex, *ES*, can decompose either into free enzyme and substrate or give rise to the reaction products and free enzyme, that K_m is equal to K'_2/K'_1 plus K'_3/K_1. It is only if K'_2/K'_1 is very much larger than K'_3/K'_1 that $1/K_m$ becomes a direct measure of the affinity of the enzyme for the substrate.

Whereas definite values for K_a, K_c, K_d, K_f, K_h, K_i, K_j, and K_k can be calculated from the appropriate experimental data, as outlined in the above discussion, the same kind of ambiguity is associated with these constants as that from which K_m suffers. If one makes the assumption that K'_3, the rate constant for the decomposition of the active complex, is small compared with the other significant rate constants leading to the formation of the active complex, it then becomes possible to calculate the various affinities from the equilibrium constants as obtained from the experimental kinetic data. This assumption, in many cases, is probably true, and is almost certainly true of equilibria which involve the transfer of protons. We cannot, however, avoid a feeling of uncertainty regarding the true meaning of such dissociation constants as can be calculated. To obtain a measure of the affinity between enzyme and substrate independently of kinetic data we must have some method which will permit us to determine the concentration of the enzyme-substrate complex.

If the enzyme-substrate complex has a characteristic absorption spectrum with a significant extinction coefficient, the concentration of the enzyme-substrate complex can be determined directly and, accordingly, the affinity of the enzyme for the substrate estimated. Probably none of the hydrolyzing enzymes will be found to form a complex with a substrate with this useful characteristic, and such measurements will probably have to be confined to contain favorable oxidation-reduction enzymes and their substrates.

Doherty and Vaslow (4), using equilibrium dialysis, have investigated the binding of N-acetyl 3, 5-dibromo-L-tyrosine by chymotrypsin. The enzyme-catalyzed reaction consisted of the exchange of the oxygen of the carboxyl group with water enriched with O^{18}. The binding of the substrate by the enzyme should be unaffected by the exchange of the oxygen isotopes and, accordingly, a good measure of the affinity between enzyme and substrate should have been obtained. It is evident, however, that the binding constant which the authors calculate is pH-dependent, and such affinities as they estimate must involve the ionization of the substrate, and possibly also of the enzyme. A recalculation of their data reveals that the percentage substrate bound by the enzyme is approximately proportional to the fraction of the substrate existing as the monovalent anion at the various pH values used. This very interesting approach should be greatly extended by additional experiments. It is possible that a complete solution of the influence of hydrogen ions on the affinity between chymotrypsin and this particular substrate could be achieved.

Another possible approach to the general problem of enzyme affinity is to shift the reaction mixture to a pH which is unfavorable for the enzyme-catalyzed reaction and to study the affinities between the enzyme and substrate in the absence of the decomposition of the substrate. The binding of the substrate by the enzyme could be measured by equilibrium dialysis or by other methods. This method, of course, does not give the affinity between enzyme and substrate in the pH region in which the enzyme is acting as an enzyme, but even so, such information as we can obtain by this method is not without interest.

Mrs. Yasnoff and I (10) have measured the concentration of the enzyme-substrate complex formed between pepsin and egg albumin at pH 4.0. At this acidity the hydrolysis of egg albumin by pepsin is very slow. We have found that when egg albumin and pepsin are mixed at about pH 4, a precipitate forms almost immediately and that maximum precipitation is achieved at a one to one mole ratio of the two proteins. The precipitate is soluble at higher ionic strengths, and the resulting solutions are completely clear to the eye at an ionic strength of 0.15.

Light-scattering measurements were made on solubilized equimolecular mixtures of pepsin and egg albumin as a function of the total protein concentration. When the function HC/τ, where C is the protein concentration, H is an apparatus constant, and τ is the turbidity, is plotted against the total protein concentration a curve with a negative slope is obtained. The initial slope of this line gives a measure of the degree of association between pepsin and egg albumin at pH 4.0. Calculated in this manner the association constant between egg albumin and pepsin is 1.46×10^7 ml. per mole. The value obtained by Bull and Currie (3) in their kinetic study of the rate of attack of pepsin on egg albumin and by the application of the treatment outlined in the above discussion was 0.14×10^{7} ml. per mole. It will be noted that the association constant calculated by light scatter is about 10 times greater than that obtained from kinetics.

This discrepancy could be due to several causes which can be outlined as follows:

(1) The kinetic constant for the decomposition of the enzyme-substrate complex in the direction of the reaction products might be significantly larger than the rate constant, leading to the dissociation of the complex into free enzyme and substrate.

(2) Only about a tenth of the associated forms between enzyme and substrate might be capable of being activated to give rise to reaction products.

(3) The affinity between the enzyme and substrate in the range of pH 1.8 to 3 might be about a tenth of what it is at pH 4.0, at which the light-scatter results were obtained.

REFERENCES

1. Alberty, R. A., *J. Am. Chem. Soc.*, 75, 1925, 1928 (1953).
2. Briggs, G. E., and J. B. S. Haldane, *Biochem. J.*, 19, 338 (1925).
3. Bull, H. B., and B. T. Currie, *J. Am. Chem. Soc.*, 71, 2758 (1949).
4. Doherty, D. G., and F. Vaslow, *J. Am. Chem. Soc.*, 74, 931 (1952).
5. Laidler, K. J., and J. P. Hoare, *J. Am. Chem. Soc.*, 71, 2699 (1949).
6. Lineweaver, H., and D. Burk, *J. Am. Chem. Soc.*, 56, 658 (1934).
7. Michaelis, L., and M. L. Menten, *Biochem. Z.*, 49, 333 (1913).
8. Waley, S. G., *Biochim. et Biophys. Acta*, 10, 27 (1953).
9. Walker, A. C., and C. L. A. Schmidt, *Arch. Biochem.*, 5, 445 (1944).
10. Yasnoff, D. S., and H. B. Bull, *J. Biol. Chem.*, 200, 619 (1953).

ELEMENTARY KINETIC THEORY OF ENZYMATIC ACTIVITY

FIRST ORDER THEORY *

Jonas S. Friedenwald and Gertrude D. Maengwyn-Davies
Wilmer Ophthalmological Institute of the Johns Hopkins University and Hospital

THE THEORY of enzyme kinetics, originally developed by Michaelis and Menten, has been amplified by numerous investigators (1). Lineweaver and Burk simplified the graphical analysis of data (2). Goldstein and Straus showed the applicability of the theory to the differentiation of competitive and non-competitive inhibitors (3, 4). Hunter and Downs suggested a graphical method of analysis to distinguish between these two types of inhibitors (5). Hellerman extended the theory to permit the recognition of inhibitors which act by competing with an activator (6).

The limitations of the theory have been discussed by many authors. The Michaelis theory was developed on the assumption that the rate of association and dissociation of the enzyme-substrate complex is very fast when compared with the irreversible reaction rate of catalytic decomposition into enzyme and products. When this assumption does not hold, the steady-state analysis of Michaelis must be replaced by kinetic theory (7, 8). For the purposes of the present discussion, elementary theory will be defined as that for which the assumptions of Michaelis and Menten hold true. These assumptions will be enumerated below. Advanced theory including the kinetic approach will not be considered.

The question may well be asked, why, with more advanced theory currently available, should the simple, elementary theory be re-examined. A review of the literature, however, makes it clear that the expansion of elementary theory to cover more and more complex

* This work was supported in part by a grant from the National Cancer Institute.

situations has been done largely in an ad hoc manner, directed toward a specific problem rather than by a systematic analysis of the theory itself; with the result that certain simplifications have been overlooked, that certain areas of feasible applications of the theory have remained unexplored and, particularly, that little guidance is given as to how to test the applicability of the theory to experimental data, and how to reach valid conclusions in the most economical manner. It was considerations of this latter type that have led us to the reexamination of the Michaelis-Menten theory. The present paper is designed primarily as a laboratory guide and manual rather than as an original contribution to the literature.

The Michaelis-Menten theory is based on the assumption that the enzyme forms reversibly dissociable complexes with substrate, activator, and inhibitor. Equilibrium of such complex formation is presumed to be reached instantaneously. First-order theory deals with those cases in which only one molecule each of substrate, activator, or inhibitor may combine with the enzyme for each active locus of enzymatic catalysis, and in which the thermodynamic activities of these substances in the reaction mixture can be represented by their concentrations.

Michaelis-Menten established the theory in its simplest form by the following argument: (a) The total concentration (E_t) of potentially active enzymatic loci for a given enzyme can be expressed as the sum of the concentrations of those loci that are coupled with substrate (ES) and those not so coupled (E).

$$(E_t) = (E) + (ES)$$

(b) They assumed that the velocity V of enzymatic catalysis is proportional to the concentration of the enzyme-substrate complex (ES) and reaches a maximum V_m when all available enzyme loci are so coupled. In general, the initial reaction rate in a solution, containing a known concentration of substrate and a fixed concentration of enzyme, is used as the estimate of V.

$$V \sim (ES) \qquad \frac{V}{V_m} = \frac{(ES)}{(E_t)}$$

(c) They assumed that the enzyme-substrate coupling is a reversible association, subject to first-order mass law equation:

$$\frac{(E) \cdot (S)}{(ES)} = K_S$$

(d) Since, over a wide range of experimental conditions, the total concentration of substrate present is vastly greater than that of enzyme loci or of enzyme-substrate complex, the thermodynamic activity of uncoupled substrate can be approximately represented by its total concentration (S).

(e) They disregarded the solvent phase, namely, water, and its change during the reaction process due to its infinitely large concentration when compared with either substrate or enzyme.

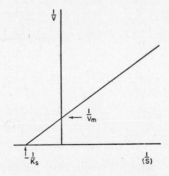

FIG. 1.   Plot of $1/V$ vs. $1/(S)$.

(f) Using these five assumptions, Michaelis-Menten obtained the equation

$$\frac{V_m}{V} = \frac{(E_t)}{(ES)} = 1 + \frac{K_S}{(S)} \tag{1}$$

Lineweaver and Burk pointed out that this equation is linear for $1/V$ vs. $1/(S)$ and suggested a graphical analysis of experiments in which the reaction velocities were determined at varying substrate concentrations by plotting $1/V$ vs. $1/(S)$. When the theory is applicable the data will fall on a straight line. The intercept of this line with the $1/(S)$ axis [1] occurs at the point having the numerical value $- 1/K_s$.

I. DISSOCIABLE INHIBITORS

In expanding the theory to include the presence of varying amounts of a dissociable inhibitor, equation (1) must be amplified to include the concentrations of enzyme-inhibitor (EI) and enzyme-inhibitor-substrate (EIS) complexes.

$$(E_t) = (E) + (ES) + (EI) + (EIS) \tag{2}$$

Applying mass action theory to the various possible dissociations one obtains:

$$\frac{(E) \cdot (S)}{(ES)} = K_s \qquad (E) = (ES) \frac{K_s}{(S)} \tag{3}$$

$$\frac{(E) \cdot (I)}{(EI)} = K_I \qquad (EI) = (E) \frac{(I)}{K_I} = (ES) \frac{(I) K_s}{(S) K_I}$$

$$\frac{(EI) \cdot (S)}{(EIS)} = aK_s \qquad (EIS) = (EI) \frac{(S)}{aK_s} = (ES) \frac{(I)}{aK_I}$$

$$\frac{(ES) \cdot (I)}{(EIS)} = \beta K_I \qquad (EIS) = (ES) \frac{(I)}{\beta K_I}$$

$$\therefore a = \beta$$

Considerations of possible inhibitor-substrate association are omitted for the present. It is evident that, when this theory is applicable, it will be fully satisfied by the evaluation of the four constants, K_s, K_I, a, and V_m. Previous analyses by others have focussed attention chiefly on the cases of competitive and non-competitive inhibition corresponding to the special values of $a = \infty$ and $a = 1$, respectively. The attempt to force the data into correspond-

---

[1] Lineweaver and Burk have determined K_s in a somewhat more complicated fashion. Having located the line that best fits the experimental data, they determine the numerical values of the slope of this line and of its intercept with the $1/V$ axis. The slope divided by the intercept equals K_s. The graphical procedure presented above is perhaps simpler and has the advantage that it demonstrates the extent of extrapolation from the experimental data involved in the estimate of K_s, and hence provides a visual index of the reliability of the estimate.

ence with one or the other of these special categories leads, in some instances, to incomplete accord between experimental data and theory. The actual evaluation of the factor a is by no means difficult.

If we substitute into the right-hand side of equation (2) the values indicated in (3), and apply the Michaelis-Menten concept of reaction velocity, we obtain:

$$\frac{V_m}{V} = \frac{(E_t)}{(ES)} = 1 + \frac{K_S}{(S)} + \frac{(I)K_S}{(S)K_I} + \frac{(I)}{aK_I} \tag{4}$$

$$= \left(1 + \frac{(I)}{aK_I}\right)\left[1 + \frac{aK_S}{(S)} \cdot \frac{(I)+K_I}{(I)+aK_I}\right] \tag{4a}$$

$$= \left(1 + \frac{K_S}{(S)}\right)\left[1 + \frac{(I)}{aK_I} \cdot \frac{(S)+aK_S}{(S)+K_S}\right] \tag{4b}$$

When $(I) = 0$ this equation reduces to that of Michaelis-Menten (1). When (I) is constant, it is still a linear equation in $1/V$ vs. $1/(S)$, though the intercept of this line on the $1/(S)$ axis gives, in general, an erroneous estimate of K_S. From (4b) it can be seen that for constant (S) the equation is linear for $1/V$ vs. (I). The first test of the applicability of the theory to a particular set of data consists in the demonstration of these linearities:

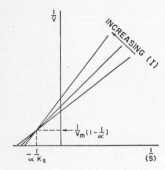

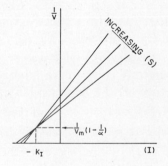

FIG. 2. $1/V$ vs. $1/(S)$ at various inhibitor concentrations.

FIG. 3. $1/V$ vs. (I) at various substrate concentrations.

If in an applicable case initial reaction rates are tested over a range of substrate concentrations at several different concentrations of inhibitor, then, as noted above, one should obtain a family of straight lines when plotting $1/V$ vs. $1/(S)$, one for each inhibitor concentration. It can easily be shown that this family of lines should, if the theory is applicable, meet in a point. Consider two arbitrary values of inhibitor concentration (I_1) and (I_2). Either of these, inserted into equation (4), yields a linear equation in $1/V$ vs. $1/(S)$. If we equate the right-hand sides of these equations with each other and solve for (S), we will obtain the value of (S) corresponding to the intersection.

$$1 + \frac{K_s}{(S)} + \frac{(I_1)K_s}{(S)K_I} + \frac{(I_1)}{aK_I} = 1 + \frac{K_s}{(S)} + \frac{(I_2)K_s}{(S)K_I} + \frac{(I_2)}{aK_I} \qquad (5)$$

$$\frac{(I_1)}{K_I}\left[\frac{K_s}{(S)} + \frac{1}{a}\right] = \frac{(I_2)}{K_I}\left[\frac{K_s}{(S)} + \frac{1}{a}\right]$$

Since (I_1) and (I_2) are arbitrarily chosen and K_I is not infinite, it follows that at the intersection:

$$\frac{K_s}{(S)} + \frac{1}{a} = 0$$

Hence at the intersection $1/(S) = -1/aK_s$; $1/V = 1/V_m$ $(1 - 1/a)$. The intersection is independent of (I), consequently the family of lines meet in a point.

Similarly on the $1/V$ vs. (I) plot, the family of lines corresponding to different fixed values of (S) will also meet in a point $(I) = -K_I$; $1/V = 1/V_m$ $(1 - 1/a)$. From these two intersections together with a Lineweaver-Burk plot in the absence of inhibitor, all four constants: K_s, K_I, a, and V_m can be evaluated. For the special cases $a = 1$ and $a = \infty$, i.e., for perfectly non-competitive and perfectly competitive inhibition, the intersections on both plots are shown in the following figures.

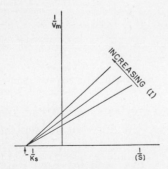

FIG. 4.   Non-competitive $a = 1$.

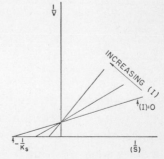

FIG. 5.   Competitive $a = \infty$.

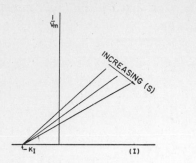

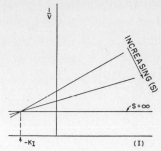

FIG. 6.   Non-competitive $\alpha = 1$.   FIG. 7.   Competitive $\alpha = \infty$.

It is possible to arrange experimental data described by equation (4) so as to yield a single curve instead of the families of straight lines already described. If we designate by V_o the reaction velocity at a particular substrate concentration in the absence of inhibitor, and by V_I the reaction velocity at the same substrate concentration in the presence of inhibitor, we can write:

$$\frac{V_m}{V_o} = 1 + \frac{K_S}{(S)} \tag{6}$$

$$\frac{V_m}{V_I} = \left(1 + \frac{K_S}{(S)} \right)\left[1 + \frac{(I)}{\alpha K_I} \cdot \frac{(S) + \alpha K_S}{(S) + K_S} \right] \tag{6a}$$

Dividing (6a) by (6)

$$\frac{V_o}{V_I} = 1 + \frac{(I)}{\alpha K_I} \cdot \frac{(S) + \alpha K_S}{(S) + K_S}$$

and rearranging

$$\frac{(I) \cdot V_I}{V_o - V_I} = \frac{\alpha K_I [(S) + K_S]}{(S) + \alpha K_S} \tag{6b}$$

The left side of equation (6b) includes only experimentally measurable quantities. Hunter and Downs have suggested that experimental data be plotted with $(I) \cdot V_I/V_o - V_I$ as ordinate versus (S) as abscissa, in order to distinguish competitive and non-competitive inhibitions. It will be seen that for the non-competitive case, $a = 1$, equation (6b) reduces to:

$$\frac{(I) \cdot V_I}{V_o - V_I} = K_I \tag{7}$$

While for the competitive case, $a = \infty$, and

$$\frac{(I) \cdot V_I}{V_o - V_I} = \frac{K_I[(S) + K_S]}{K_S} .$$

For each case the plot yields a straight line, with an upward slope as (S) increases, if the inhibition is competitive, but horizontal if the inhibition is non-competitive. An inspection of equation (6b) re-

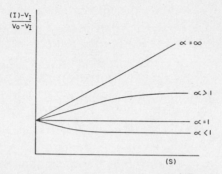

FIG. 8. Plot according to Hunter and Downs.

veals, however, that if a does not have one or the other of these extreme values, the Hunter and Downs plot yields a curve, not a straight line, this curve being a hyperbola with one horizontal asymptote. Examples of such curves are shown in Fig. 8. If the experimental data cover a sufficiently wide range with respect to substrate concentrations, the hyperbolas could easily be distinguished from the straight lines of the extreme cases; but if the experimental range in (S) is limited, either a sloping line or a horizontal line might give an apparently satisfactory fit, depending on where the experimental range of (S) was located. On the other hand, if the data cover a sufficiently wide range to permit determination of the horizontal asymptote of the hyperbola, its ordinate will be given by:

$$\left[\frac{(I) \cdot V_I}{V_o - V_I} \right]_{(S) \to \infty} = aK_I \tag{8}$$

Some of the experimental data plotted by the method of Hunter and Downs, and considered to indicate non-competitive inhibition, actually yield curves which slope gently upward to the right, conforming to values of a greater than 1 but less than ∞. Preoccupation with the special cases of competitive and non-competitive inhibition has obscured the fact that inhibitors exist whose mode of action is intermediate between these extremes.

The argument presented in this section makes it clear that the differentiation of competitive from non-competitive inhibitors depends on the influence of the inhibitor on the dissociation of the enzyme-substrate complex. The straightforward application of the Michaelis-Menten theory to cases involving dissociable inhibitors leads to the inclusion of a factor a into the equations. This factor is a direct measure of the influence of the inhibitor on the dissociation coefficient of the enzyme-substrate complex. When $a = 1$ the equations conform to those classically used to describe non-competitive inhibition. When $a = \infty$ the equations conform to those classically used to describe competitive inhibition. Most of the experimental data in the literature can be described with reasonable accuracy by one or the other of these special values of a. Exceptions, however, are not rare. There are many examples in the literature in which inhibitors have been classified as non-competitive when a had a value as large as 2, while other examples are to be found in which the inhibitor is classified as competitive when a is as small as 10. Some authors have been aware of these discrepancies (9). One encounters such statements as "a non-competitive inhibitor which shows slightly competitive action."

The concept of competitive and non-competitive inhibitors did not arise out of such thermodynamic arguments as those outlined above, but out of steric considerations. A competitive inhibitor has been conceived as one which sits on the throne normally reserved for the substrate. In many instances the chemical configuration of the competitive inhibitor sufficiently resembles that of the substrate to suggest its possible role as usurper to the throne. The utility of this steric intuition in the selection of test substances for possible inhibitory action has been very great, even though measurements of enzyme activity do not reveal the location of inhibitor on the enzyme in the enzyme-inhibitor complex. No devaluation of steric intuitions is implied if the precise estimation of the α factor is substituted for the rough dichotomy of inhibitors into competitors and non-competitors.

Up to the present we have considered only the possible values of α between 1 and ∞, that is, the action of inhibitors which leave undisturbed or which diminish the association of enzyme and substrate. There is no reason a priori why α should not have values less than 1, i. e., why some inhibitors should not increase the association of enzyme and substrate. Such agents might be called "coupling inhibitors." Inhibitors of this type have, indeed, been encountered. They reveal themselves by the fact that the family of lines in the $1/V$ vs. $1/(S)$ plot tend to meet in a point in the lower left-hand quadrant of the chart. Burk has been aware of the existence of cases of this type and has suggested the term "anti-competitive" for them (10).

If α were zero, either the association between substrate and enzyme in the presence of the inhibitor would be infinite (which is impossible), or the term (EI) in the Michaelis equation (2) must be zero. The inhibitor couples only with the enzyme-substrate complex but not with the free enzyme.

If (EI) is zero, K_I is infinite, therefore αK_I may be finite when $\alpha = 0$, and we can eliminate α from the equation by substituting $\alpha K_I = K'_I$. Instead of equation (2) we then have:

$$(E_t) = (E) + (ES) + (EIS) \tag{9}$$

Instead of (3)

$$\frac{(E) \cdot (S)}{(ES)} = K_s \qquad\qquad (E) = (ES) \frac{K_s}{(S)} \tag{10}$$

$$\frac{(E) \cdot (I)}{(EI)} = \infty$$

$$\frac{(EI) \cdot (S)}{(EIS)} = 0$$

$$\frac{(ES) \cdot (I)}{(EIS)} = K'_I \qquad\qquad (EIS) = (ES) \frac{(I)}{K'_I}$$

$$\frac{V_m}{V} = \frac{(E_t)}{(ES)} = 1 + \frac{K_s}{(S)} + \frac{(I)}{K'_I} \tag{11}$$

The Lineweaver-Burk plot for data conforming to this equation yields a family of parallel lines. The corresponding plot of $1/V$ vs. (I) for different fixed values of (S) also yields a family of parallel lines.

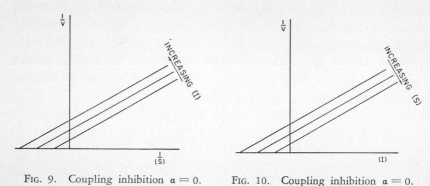

FIG. 9.   Coupling inhibition $\alpha = 0$.   FIG. 10.   Coupling inhibition $\alpha = 0$.

II. Coupling of Inhibitor with Substrate

A clear distinction must be made between the case of an inhibitor which increases the association of enzyme with substrate (the coupling inhibition referred to in the preceding paragraphs), and an inhibitor which couples with the substrate in the absence of enzyme. Under the latter circumstances an appreciable fraction of the total substrate may be bound by the inhibitor, and the total substrate concentration can no longer be used as an approximate measure of the thermodynamic activity of the unbound substrate in the solution. This contradicts one of the basic assumptions of the Michaelis theory. If, however, the dissociation coefficient of the substrate-inhibitor complex is known, then the concentration of free substrate can be calculated and the Michaelis-Menten theory can again be applied.

Serious difficulties are encountered in dealing with this situation if the dissociation coefficient of the substrate-inhibitor complex is not known from independent (non-enzymologic) measurements. Even worse troubles arise if substrate-inhibitor coupling occurs when not suspected. Under such circumstances the application of the method of analysis outlined in this paper will yield erroneous results. Two special cases will be considered in detail.

First case

The first case is that in which the inhibitor couples with the substrate but does not couple with the enzyme. The molecular species (E), (ES), (S), (I), and (IS) are presumed to exist in the solution, but (EI) and (EIS) are not formed. It is presumed in the following argument that the substrate-inhibitor complex follows bimolecular reaction kinetics.

In this case, if the dissociation coefficient of the substrate-inhibitor complex is known, the problem reduces itself to the Michaelis-Menten equation in its simplest form:

$$\frac{V_m}{V} = 1 + \frac{K_s}{(S_{\text{free}})}$$

with the proviso that the concentration of free, uncoupled substrate and not that of total substrate is used for the analysis. If the existence of the substrate-inhibitor complex is not suspected, and the data are plotted $1/V$ vs. $1/(S_t)$ or $1/V$ vs. (I_t), non-linear plots are to be expected. Unfortunately, however, the deviations from linearity are not very conspicuous, and are most marked in the regions close to the vertical axis in each of these plots, corresponding to very large substrate and very small inhibitor concentrations which might easily have been omitted from experiments. The figures drawn below are from theoretically calculated values, and show clearly that data conforming to such values would lend themselves to the erroneous interpretation that one was dealing with a competitive inhibitor. The analytical expressions for these curves are too complicated for easy use, and the figures have been calculated point by point for arbitrary values of (S) and (I).

For such a set of experiments we have:

$$(E_t) = (E) + (ES) \tag{12}$$

$$(S_t) = (S) + (SI) \tag{13}$$

$$(I_t) = (I) + (SI) \tag{14}$$

$$\frac{(E) \cdot (S)}{(ES)} = K_s \tag{15}$$

$$\frac{(S) \cdot (I)}{(SI)} = K_{SI} \tag{16}$$

$$(S) = (S_t) - \frac{(S_t) + (I_t) + K_{SI}}{2} + \frac{1}{2}\sqrt{[(S_t) + (I_t) + K_{SI}]^2 - 4(S_t)\cdot(I_t)}$$

$$(17)$$

$$\frac{V_m}{V} = 1 + \frac{K_S}{(S)}$$

The curves in Figs. 11 and 12 are calculated on the assumption that $K_S = K_{SI}$ and can be adjusted to $K_S \neq K_{SI}$ by appropriate changes in the ordinate scale and shifts in the location of the ordinate zero.

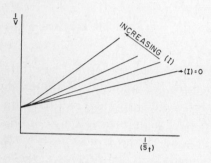

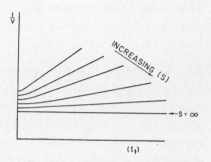

Fig. 11.   Coupling of inhibitor   Fig. 12.   Coupling of inhibitor
    with substrate.   with substrate.

It will be seen from an inspection of the figures that substantial deviations from linearity are visible only if the range of experimental concentrations of (S) and (I) is extended well above and well below K_{SI}. In order to perform this experiment within the optimum concentration range to exhibit the expected curvature, it is necessary, therefore, to have an estimate of K_{SI}, and we have assumed so far that this is not independently known. It is, however, possible, to estimate K_{SI} from such experimental data as are required to determine the apparent conformity of the system to competitive inhibition. Having such data, we make the tentative assumption that the true state is not competitive inhibition but coupling of the substrate with the inhibitor. Under such conditions the reaction velocity is solely dependent on the concentration of free uncoupled substrate in the mixture. We have determined the reaction velocity V for a given total substrate concentration (S_t) and total inhibitor concentration

(I_t). We can now find which substrate concentration (S) in the absence of the inhibitor gives this same reaction velocity. Assuming this to be identical with the concentration of free substrate in the mixture when inhibitor is present, we can apply equations (13) and (14), and thus calculate the data needed for the mass law equation (16). Such estimates for K_{SI} can be obtained when a large number of sets of data (S_t), (I_t), and V are available. Should the resulting evaluation of K_{SI} prove reasonably stable within the experimental errors, presumptive evidence is obtained for considering the inhibition as due to coupling of substrate with inhibitor. The value of K_{SI} found establishes the optimal range for the experimental tests outlined above.

Second case

The second case to be discussed is the somewhat more complicated one in which the inhibitor can couple with substrate not only in the absence of enzyme but also when the substrate is attached to the enzyme. In this case the molecular species (EIS), omitted from consideration in the first case, has to be included.

If the dissociation coefficient of the substrate-inhibitor complex is independently known, the free concentration of substrate and of inhibitor can be calculated and inserted into a Michaelis-Menten equation of the form:

$$\frac{V_m}{V} = 1 + \frac{K_S}{(S)} + \frac{(I)}{K'_I} \tag{18}$$

where K'_I is defined by the mass law equation as

$$\frac{(ES) \cdot (I)}{(EIS)} = K'_I \tag{19}$$

It will be noted that this equation is identical with that of (11) which describes " coupling inhibition."

If data conforming to the assumptions we have outlined are used in an ordinary Lineweaver-Burk plot — reciprocal of velocity vs. reciprocal of total (instead of free) substrate — non-linear results may be expected. The general pattern of the plot will vary depending on whether K'_I is greater or less than K_{SI}. If K'_I is much greater than K_{SI} the concentration of the complex (EIS) will be negligibly small, and the situation reduces to that described for Case 1 above. If K'_I is very much smaller than K_{SI}, the concentration of the complex (SI) will be negligibly small, and the situation reduces to that described under " coupling inhibition." We will limit our consideration here, therefore, to that defined by $K'_I = K_{SI}$.

In this case the $1/V$ vs. $1/(S_t)$ and $1/V$ vs. (I_t) plots will, in general, be similar to those of Case 1 illustrated above. If the experimental concentration range is not sufficiently wide, the results will erroneously suggest competitive inhibition. In contrast to Case 1, deviations from linearity will be less conspicuous in the $1/V$ vs. $1/(S_t)$ plot, more conspicuous in the $1/V$ vs. (I_t) plot. Moreover, there is in Case 2 no simple way of obtaining a preliminary estimate of the magnitude of K_{SI} from the enzymologic data. Independent non-enzymologic experiments for the determination of K_{SI} are, therefore, indispensable.

III. Dissociable Activators

The application of the Michaelis-Menten theory has been less extensively developed for dissociable activators than for dissociable inhibitors. (8). No doubt, this is due to the fact that many dissociable activators are effective at such low concentrations that thermodynamic activities of uncoupled activators cannot be adequately represented by the total concentrations of activator. Nevertheless, there are some activators for which these limitations do not vitiate the application of elementary first-order theory as a first approximation. It seems worthwhile, therefore, to develop the elementary theory with respect to dissociable activators in analogy to that for dissociable inhibitors. Advanced theory can then be applied by substituting an estimate of thermodynamic activities of free activator for total concentrations.

Expansion of the Michaelis-Menten equation to include the case of dissociable activator (A) can be expressed in equations analogous to those for dissociable inhibitors. The meaning of the symbols will be obvious by comparison with the previous sections.

$$(E_t) = (E) + (EA) + (ES) + (EAS) \qquad (20)$$

$$\frac{(E) \cdot (S)}{(ES)} = K_S \qquad (E) = (ES)\frac{K_S}{(S)} = (EAS)\frac{yK_SK_A}{(A) \cdot (S)} \qquad (21)$$

$$\frac{(E) \cdot (A)}{(EA)} = K_A \qquad (E) = (EA)\frac{K_A}{(A)} = (EAS)\frac{xK_SK_A}{(A) \cdot (S)} \quad \therefore y = x$$

$$\frac{(EA) \cdot (S)}{(EAS)} = xK_S \qquad (EA) = (EAS)\frac{xK_S}{(S)}$$

$$\frac{(ES) \cdot (A)}{(EAS)} = yK_A \qquad (ES) = (EAS)\frac{yK_A}{(A)}$$

$$\frac{V_m}{V} \equiv \frac{(E_t)}{(EAS)} = 1 + \frac{xK_SK_A}{(A) \cdot (S)} + \frac{xK_S}{(S)} + \frac{xK_A}{(A)} \qquad (22)$$

The Lineweaver-Burk plot is linear for $1/V$ vs. $1/(S)$ with (A) constant. On this plot the family of lines corresponding to various fixed values of (A) meet in a point having the abscissa $1/(S) = -1/K_S$, and the ordinate $1/V = 1/V_m (1-x)$. The plot for $1/V$ vs. $1/(A)$ with (S) constant is also linear, and the family of lines corresponding to various fixed values of (S) meet in a point having the coordinates $-1/K_A, 1/V_m (1-x)$. The values of $(x K_S)$ and V_m can be determined directly from the Lineweaver-Burk plot only if full saturation with activator can be achieved. However, one can use the $1/V$ vs. $1/(A)$ plot to determine the intercepts on the $1/V$ axis corresponding to various concentrations of (S). This extrapolation yields estimates of $1/V$ for various values of (S) and maximal values of (A). The Lineweaver-Burk plot of this set of data gives $x K_S$ and V_m and makes possible the calculation of x. The symmetrical relation of (A) and (S) in equation (22) suggests that this equation is applicable to enzyme catalysis of interaction between two substrates.

The factor x plays a role similar to that of the factor a in the inhibitor case. If x is small, the activator promotes association of enzyme with substrate. If $x \to 1$ the activator has little or no effect on enzyme-substrate association. By analogy with the inhibitors, it would seem appropriate to speak of activators for which x is small as "coupling activators," and those for which $x = 1$ as "non-coupling activators." Steric considerations may no doubt be employed fruitfully in the interpretation of such differences.

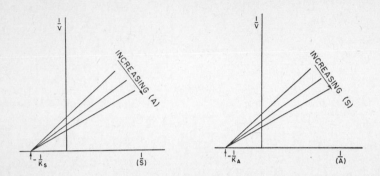

FIG. 13. Non-coupling activation $x = 1$.   FIG. 14. Non-coupling activation $x = 1$.

If x is greater than 1 but less than ∞ the activator would decrease the association of enzyme and substrate. No such "competitive activators" have so far been established, but there is no reason a priori against their possible existence.

If x is given the value zero, the equation becomes physically meaningless unless either K_S or K_A is infinite. Coupling activators conceivably are of two types — those in which the substrate will not couple with the enzyme unless the activator is already attached ($K_S = \infty$), and those in which the activator will not couple with the enzyme unless the substrate is already attached ($K_A = \infty$). The possibility that both K_S and K_A could be infinite will be considered below.

The first assumption ($x = 0$, $K_S = \infty$, $x K_S = K'_S$) leads to:

$$(E_t) = (E) + (EA) + (EAS) \tag{23}$$

$$\frac{V_m}{V} = 1 + \frac{K'_S}{(S)} + \frac{K'_S K_A}{(S) \cdot (A)} \tag{24}$$

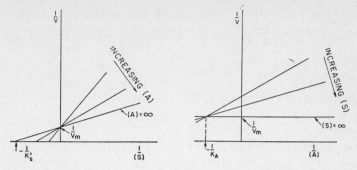

FIG. 15. Coupling activation of first type $x = 0$, $K_S = \infty$, $xK_S = K'_S$.

FIG. 16. Coupling activation of first type $x = 0$, $K_S = \infty$, $xK_S = K'_S$.

The second assumption $(x = 0, K_A = \infty, x K_A = K'_A)$ yields:

$$(E_t) = (E) + (ES) + (EAS) \tag{25}$$

$$\frac{V_m}{V} = 1 + \frac{K_S K'_A}{(S) \cdot (A)} + \frac{K'_A}{(A)} \tag{26}$$

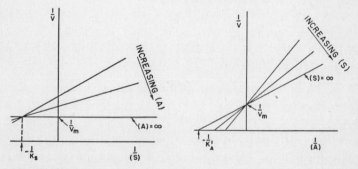

FIG. 17. Coupling activation of second type $x = 0$, $K_A = \infty$, $xK_A = K'_A$.

FIG. 18. Coupling activation of second type $x = 0$, $K_A = \infty$, $xK_A = K'_A$.

Coupling of activator with substrate

The problem of an activator which couples with the substrate can be pursued along lines similar to those used in the preceding section for inhibitors. In general, the determination of the dissociation constant of the substrate-activator complex by non-enzymologic techniques cannot be dispensed with. Four cases need to be distinguished, depending on the various routes which may be conceived, by which the active complex (EAS) forms.

First case

The simplest case is that in which the substrate and activator combine:

$$(S) + (A) \rightleftarrows (AS)$$

and the resulting complex (AS) is the true substrate.

$$(E) + (AS) \rightleftarrows (EAS) \qquad\qquad (27)$$

Enzyme molecular species (EA) and (ES) are assumed to be non-existent. The Michaelis-Menten equation takes on the simple form:

$$\frac{V_m}{V} = 1 + \frac{K}{(AS)}$$

The $1/V$ vs. $1/(S_t)$ plot will be approximately linear over a considerable concentration range and will simulate the plot given for equation (24) above. The $1/V$ vs. $1/(A_t)$ plot will also be approximately linear over a considerable concentration range and will simulate that given for equation (26) above.

Second case

The catalytically active complex may be formed not only by the route indicated in equation (27) but also by:

$$(E) + (A) \rightleftarrows (EA)$$
$$(EA) + (S) \rightleftarrows (EAS) \qquad\qquad (28)$$

The resulting Michaelis-Menten equation has the form of equation (24) above, but the concentrations of uncoupled (not total) (S) and (A) have to be used. In this case the mutually incompatible complexes (EA) and (SA) will be formed. At high concentrations of activator, inhibition by excess activator will be observed and the plot $1/V$ vs. $1/(A_t)$ will be grossly non-linear.

Third case

The catalytically active complex may be formed not only by the route indicated in equation (26) but also by:

$$(E) + (S) \rightleftarrows (ES)$$
$$(ES) + (A) \rightleftarrows (EAS) \qquad\qquad (29)$$

The resulting Michaelis-Menten equation has the form of equation (26) above, but the concentrations of uncoupled (not total) (S) and (A) have to be used. In this case the mutually incompatible complexes (ES) and (SA) will be formed. At high concentrations of substrate, inhibition by excess substrate will be observed and the plot $1/V$ vs. $1/(S_t)$ will be grossly non-linear.

Fourth case

The catalytically active complex may be formed by any of the three routes (27), (28), or (29). The Michaelis equation appropriate to this case has the form of (22) above, but again, the uncoupled (not total) (S) and (A) need to be used in its application. In this case inhibition both by excess substrate and excess activator will occur. Both the plots $1/V$ vs. $1/(S_t)$ and $1/V$ vs. $1/(A_t)$ will be grossly non-linear.

IV. DISSOCIABLE ACTIVATOR AND INHIBITOR

The case involving simultaneous presence of an activator and inhibitor is very commonly encountered experimentally and has, so far, been studied only by Hellerman, who was able to exhibit an example of an inhibitor competing with an activator (6). In most experiments using non-purified enzymes, unknown amounts of endogenous activators and inhibitors are likely to be present. It seems important to analyze the possible influence of these upon kinetic experiments performed with added substrate, activator, or inhibitor in order to discover the types of errors inherent in a naive approach to such a complex system.

The full equation (see Appendix) contains eight constants of which six, V_m, K_S, K_A, K_I, x, and a, have the same significance as that given them in the previous sections of this paper. The factor u concerns interaction between activator and inhibitor. $u \to \infty$ describes the situation of an inhibitor competing with an activator which was discovered by Hellerman. The factor q measures the influence of the interaction of any two of the three variables (S), (A), (I), on the affinity of the enzyme for the third variable. No example has so far been encountered requiring a value for q other than unity. Given an adequate array of experimental data, all eight constants can be evaluated either by the method of least squares or by an expansion of the graphical methods already described.

This tediously complex case has been discussed in order to show the general applicability of the Michaelis-Menten equation when it is expanded to include an increasing number of variables. Some of the general properties of such an expansion deserve comment.

No matter how many dissociable activators or inhibitors may be present, if only substrate concentrations are varied, a linear plot for $1/V$ vs. $1/(S)$ is to be expected as long as first-order theory is applicable. Similarly, if only activator concentrations, or only inhibitor concentrations are varied, linear plots are to be expected for $1/V$ vs. $1/(A)$ or for $1/V$ vs. (I). Deviations from linearity in any of these cases indicate that first-order theory is not applicable. The results of such plots yield estimates of apparent dissociation constants, but these apparent values cannot be accepted as true unless the association factors for all the significant components of the test solution are known to be equal to unity. This requirement may seem impossible to achieve but can actually be met quite easily in many situations.

Suppose, for instance, that a crude enzyme preparation which may contain unknown dissociable activators and inhibitors gives data conforming to the Michaelis-Menten equation when tested against varying concentrations of substrate. If varying dilutions of the enzyme preparation are tested against a fixed concentration of substrate, the presence of endogenous dissociable activators or inhibitors can be demonstrated. A plot of the initial reaction velocity versus the enzyme concentration will yield a straight line through the origin if neither dissociable activators nor inhibitors are present. If a dissociable inhibitor is present, the plot will yield a curve concave to the X-axis, since the concentration of the inhibitor increases with that of the enzyme. Similarly, if a dissociable activator is present, the curve will be concave to the Y-axis.

Experiments in which both the enzyme and the substrate concentrations are varied expose the underlying facts. If an inhibitor has been shown to be present, we wish to establish the character of this inhibition. To do so we need to plot $1/V$ vs. (I), but we do not know the concentration of (I). We can, however, plot $(E)/V$ vs. (E). The ordinate gives us $1/V$ per arbitrary unit of enzyme. The abscissa is proportional to the concentration of endogenous inhibitor in the reaction mixture. For each substrate concentration the data should fall on a straight line and the family of such lines may be dealt with as in Section I above. Similarly, if we plot $(E)/V$ vs. $1/(S)$ we should obtain a family of straight lines, one for each enzyme concentration. Using the methods of analysis in Section I, the nature of the inhibition, i. e., the value of the factor a can be obtained, and K_I can be estimated in arbitrary units of the unknown concentration of the inhibitor in the crude enzyme preparation.

This procedure has been followed by one of us (Maengwyn-

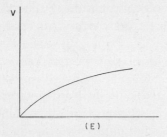

FIG. 19. Dissociable inhibitor present.   FIG. 20. Dissociable activator present.

Davies) in the study of phenol-sulfatase. An endogenous inhibitor was demonstrated which was shown to be non-competitive. The K_I for this inhibitor was estimated in terms of its unknown concentration in the crude extract. Subsequently, inorganic phosphate was found to be a non-competitive inhibitor. Estimation of inorganic phosphate in the crude extract showed that this could account for substantially all of the endogenous inhibitor, and the two separate estimates of K_I for phosphate were in good agreement. Moreover, K_S was found to have the same value at all enzyme concentrations tested, indicating that all endogenous dissociable factors were of the non-competitive — non-coupling varieties. The application of a similar method of analysis in the presence of an endogenous dissociable activator is obvious.

Even in experiments using highly purified enzymes, when all the components of the test solution are presumably known, the same type of questions arise, for the test solution contains not only enzyme and substrate, but also buffer, etc. In such a case, the concentration of all the components of the test solution except enzyme and substrate can be varied jointly in order to see whether an activator or inhibitor is included in the solution, and substrate concentrations can be varied at different levels of buffer concentrations to see if first-order theory is applicable and if any deviations from unity in the dissociation factors occur. When such deviations are found, the responsible substance has to be identified and its dissociation factor estimated. One can proceed in this way, step by step, until joint variation in all remaining components of the test solution is demonstrated to be without effect. At this point, evaluation of the relevant dissociation constants and dissociation factors yields valid results.

Summary

An attempt at the systematic analysis of first-order theory of enzyme kinetics is presented. Previous analyses of substrate-inhibitor interactions have been largely limited to examples described as competitive or non-competitive inhibition, though intermediate and even " anti-competitive " relations have been reported. It is shown that all these types of inhibition can be described by a single equation when an association factor, a, which may vary from zero to infinity, is included. The special cases, $a = \infty$, $a = 1$, $a = 0$, correspond to competitive, non-competitive, and " coupling " inhibitions, respectively.

A similar equation is developed to describe the interaction between substrate and activator. This includes, as special cases, " coupling " and " non-coupling " activation. Two forms of coupling activation can be distinguished, depending on whether substrate is coupled to enzyme by the activator, or activator is coupled to the enzyme by the substrate.

The well-known distinction between " apparent " and " true " Michaelis constants is expanded to include any number of dissociation constants, and a systematic method of procedure is outlined by which these " apparent " constants can be distinguished from " true " constants.

A method of graphical analysis applicable to these problems is presented.

Appendix

For the case involving both a dissociable activator and a dissociable inhibitor, the summation of enzyme molecular species becomes:

$$(E_t) = (E) + (ES) + (EA) + (EI) + (EAS)$$
$$+ (EAI) + (EIS) + (EAIS) \qquad (30)$$

$$\frac{(E) \cdot (S)}{(ES)} = K_S \qquad (E) = (ES)\frac{K_S}{(S)} = (EAS)\frac{K_S}{(S)}\frac{yK_A}{(A)}$$

$$\frac{(E) \cdot (A)}{(EA)} = K_A \qquad (E) = (EA)\frac{K_A}{(A)} = (EAS)\frac{K_A}{(A)}\frac{xK_S}{(S)} \therefore x = y$$

$$\frac{(E) \cdot (I)}{(EI)} = K_I \qquad (EI) = (E)\ \frac{(I)}{K_I} = (EAS)\frac{(I)}{K_I}\frac{xK_SK_A}{(A)\cdot(S)}$$

$$\frac{(EA) \cdot (S)}{(EAS)} = xK_S \qquad (EA) = (EAS)\frac{xK_S}{(S)}$$

$$\frac{(ES) \cdot (A)}{(EAS)} = yK_A \qquad (ES) = (EAS)\frac{yK_A}{(A)} = (EAS)\frac{xK_A}{(A)} \therefore x = y$$

$$\frac{(EI) \cdot (S)}{(EIS)} = aK_S \qquad (EIS) = (EI)\frac{(S)}{aK_S} = (EAS)\frac{xK_A(I)}{a(A)K_I}$$

$$\frac{(ES) \cdot (I)}{(EIS)} = \beta K_I \qquad (EIS) = (ES)\frac{(I)}{\beta K_I} = (EAS)\frac{x(I)}{\beta K_I}\frac{K_A}{(A)} \therefore a = \beta$$

$$\frac{(EA) \cdot (I)}{(EAI)} = uK_I \qquad (EAI) = (EA)\frac{(I)}{uK_I} = (EAS)\frac{(I)}{uK_I}\frac{xK_S}{(S)}$$

$$\frac{(EI) \cdot (A)}{(EAI)} = vK_A \qquad (EAI) = (EI)\frac{(A)}{vK_A} = (EAS)\frac{(A)}{vK_A}\frac{(I)xK_SK_A}{K_I(A)\cdot(S)}$$

$$= \frac{(I)xK_S}{vK_I(S)} \therefore u = v$$

$$\frac{(EAI)\cdot(S)}{(EAIS)} = paxK_S \quad (EAIS) = (EAI)\frac{(S)}{axpK_S} = (EAS)\frac{(S)}{axpK_S}\frac{(I)xK_S}{uK_I(S)}$$

$$= (EAS)\frac{(I)}{pauK_I}$$

$$\frac{(EAS)\cdot(I)}{(EAIS)} = q\beta uK_I \quad (EAIS) = (EAS)\frac{(I)}{\beta quK_I} = (EAS)\frac{(I)}{aquK_I}$$

$$\frac{(EIS)\cdot(A)}{(EAIS)} = ruxK_A \quad (EAIS) = (EIS)\frac{(A)}{xurK_A} = (EAS)\frac{(A)}{xurK_A}\frac{xK_A(I)}{a(A)K_I}$$

$$= (EAS)\frac{(I)}{ura K_I} \quad\therefore p = q = r$$

The Michaelis equation can be generalized:

$$\frac{V_m}{V} = 1 + \frac{xK_SK_A}{(A)\cdot(S)} + \frac{xK_A}{(A)} + \frac{xK_S}{(S)} + \frac{xK_SK_A(I)}{K_I(A)\cdot(S)} + \frac{xK_S(I)}{uK_I(S)}$$

$$+ \frac{xK_A(I)}{aK_I(A)} + \frac{(I)}{aquK_I} \quad (31)$$

This equation can be rearranged to yield linear functions of $1/V$ vs. either $1/(S)$, $1/(A)$, or (I), when two of the three variables are held constant at one time.

$$\frac{V_m}{V} = 1 + \frac{xK_A}{(A)} + \frac{xK_A(I)}{aK_I(A)} + \frac{(I)}{aquK_I} + \frac{xK_S}{(S)}\left[1 + \frac{K_A}{(A)} + \frac{K_A(I)}{K_I(A)} + \frac{(I)}{uK_I}\right]$$

$$= 1 + \frac{xK_S}{(S)} + \frac{xK_S(I)}{uK_I(S)} + \frac{(I)}{aquK_I} + \frac{xK_A}{(A)}\left[1 + \frac{K_S}{(S)} + \frac{K_S(I)}{K_I(S)} + \frac{(I)}{aK_I}\right]$$

$$= 1 + \frac{xK_S}{(S)} + \frac{xK_A}{(A)} + \frac{xK_AK_S}{(A)\cdot(S)} + \frac{(I)}{K_I}\left[\frac{1}{aqu} + \frac{xK_S}{u(S)} + \frac{xK_A}{a(A)} + \frac{xK_SK_A}{(A)\cdot(S)}\right]$$

From these equations the apparent dissociation constants are immediately obtainable. For instance, writing k_S for the apparent Michaelis constant:

$$k_S = xK_S \frac{1 + \dfrac{K_A}{(A)} + \dfrac{K_A(I)}{K_I(A)} + \dfrac{(I)}{uK_I}}{1 + \dfrac{xK_A}{(A)} + \dfrac{xK_A(I)}{aK_I(A)} + \dfrac{(I)}{aquK_I}}$$

Only if the dissociation factors x, a, q, and u are equal to unity will the apparent k_S equal the true dissociation constant K_S. Similar results can be obtained for K_A and K_I.

One may use equation (31) also to inquire whether a double array of experiments in which two of the three variables (S), (A), (I) are varied, but the third is held constant, will give a correct estimate of the appropriate dissociation factor. The answer is that the data will conform to the pattern illustrated in Sections I and II of this paper, but that the apparent dissociation factor will not have the true value unless all the other dissociation factors are each equal to unity.

REFERENCES

1. Michaelis, L., and M. L. Menten. 1913. Die Kinetik der Invertinwirkung. *Biochem. Z.*, **49**, 333.
2. Lineweaver, H., and D. Burk. 1934. The Determination of Enzyme Dissociation Constants. *J. Amer. Chem. Soc.*, **56**, 658.
3. Straus, O. H., and A. Goldstein. 1943. Zone Behavior of Enzymes. *J. Gen. Physiol.*, **26**, 559.
4. Goldstein, A. 1944. The Mechanism of Enzyme-Inhibitor-Substrate Reactions. *J. Gen Physiol.*, **27**, 529.
5. Hunter, A., and C. E. Downs. 1945. The Inhibition of Arginase by Amino Acids. *J. Biol. Chem.*, **157**, 427.
6. Hellerman, L., A. Lindsay, and M. R. Bovarnick. 1946. Flavoenzyme Catalysis. Inhibition of D-Amino Acid Oxidase by Competition with Flavin-Adenine-Di-nucleotide of Atabrine (Quinacrine), Quinine and Certain Other Compounds. *J. Biol. Chem.*, **163**, 553.
7. Hofstee, B. H. J. 1952. On the Evaluation of the Constants Vm and Km in Enzyme Reactions. *Science*, **116**, 329.
8. Segal, H. L., J. F. Kachmar, and P. D. Boyer. 1952. Kinetic Analysis of Enzyme Reactions. *Enzymology*, **15**, 187.
9. Massart, L. 1950. Enzyme Inhibitions, in *The Enzymes*, Vol. 1, Part 1, p. 307 (J. B. Sumner and K. Myrbäck, eds.). Academic Press, New York.
10. Burk, D., quoted by E. R. Ebersole, C. Guttentag, and P. W. Wilson. 1944. Nature of Carbon Monoxide Inhibition of Biological Nitrogen Fixation. *Arch. Biochem.*, **3**, 399.

ELEMENTARY KINETIC THEORY OF ENZYMATIC ACTIVITY

SECOND ORDER THEORY *

JONAS S. FRIEDENWALD and GERTRUDE D. MAENGWYN-DAVIES

Wilmer Ophthalmological Institute of the Johns Hopkins University and Hospital

IN THE PRECEDING paper an attempt was made to make a systematic analysis of the effect of varying concentrations of substrate, inhibitor, and activator on enzymatic activity, under the assumption that each of these formed dissociable complexes with the enzyme. In what we have called first-order theory, consideration was limited to those cases in which no more than one molecule each of substrate, inhibitor, and activator was coupled per active locus of the enzyme. In the present discussion, this restriction will be relaxed, and consideration given to the possibility that two molecules of a given sort may be coupled per active locus of enzyme. The arguments of the preceding paper will be assumed.

I. INHIBITION BY EXCESS SUBSTRATE

For many systems the Lineweaver-Burk plot shows deviations from linearity for high substrate concentrations (1). The rate of the reaction declines with increasing substrate concentration, i. e., excess substrate acts as an inhibitor. Consideration of the possible modes of such inhibition leads to two general cases.

A. The inhibitory molecule of substrate may attach itself to the enzyme like any other inhibitor. Even the possibility of truly competitive inhibition is not excluded, since the substrate molecule might affix itself to the active locus of the enzyme in such steric orientation

* This work was supported in part by a grant from the National Cancer Institute.

as to prevent its own activation while, at the same time, blocking access to the enzyme locus by a correctly oriented substrate molecule.

B. The second possibility is that the active area of the enzyme surface is constituted of several different attracting groups to which normally only one molecule of the substrate becomes affixed. At high concentrations of substrate, separate molecules of substrate may become attached to these several attracting groups in such fashion that none of these molecules becomes activated. Only the second of these two possibilities has heretofore been considered.

The mathematical formulation of the first possibility follows directly from equation (4) of the preceding paper:

$$\frac{V_m}{V} = 1 + \frac{K_s}{(S)} + \frac{K_s}{K_I} + \frac{(S)}{aK_I} \tag{1}$$

Furthermore, one can distinguish competitive, non-competitive, and coupling forms of inhibition depending on the values:

$$a = \infty, \quad a = 1, \quad a = 0$$

$$\frac{V_m}{V} = 1 + \frac{K_s}{(S)} + \frac{K_s}{K_I} \qquad \text{(competitive)} \quad a = \infty \tag{2}$$

$$\frac{V_m}{V} = 1 + \frac{K_s}{(S)} + \frac{K_s}{K_I} + \frac{(S)}{K_I} \qquad \text{(non-competitive)} \quad a = 1 \tag{3}$$

$$\frac{V_m}{V} = 1 + \frac{K_s}{(S)} + \frac{(S)}{K'_I} \qquad \text{(coupling)} \quad \begin{matrix} a = 0 \\ K'_I = aK_I \end{matrix} \tag{4}$$

The second hypothesis of the possible mode of inhibition by excess substrate leads to an equation identical with (4), provided we consider at most two molecules of substrate on the active locus. All four of these equations can be represented by:

$$\frac{CV_m}{V} = 1 + \frac{K_1}{(S)} + \frac{(S)}{K_2} \tag{5}$$

in which the significance assigned to C, K_1, K_2 by various formulations is given in Table 1:

TABLE 1

SIGNIFICANCE ACCORDING TO FORMULA

	(1)	(2)	(3)	(4)
C	$\dfrac{K_I}{K_I + K_s}$	$\dfrac{K_I}{K_I + K_s}$	$\dfrac{K_I}{K_I + K_s}$	1
K_1	$\dfrac{K_s K_I}{K_I + K_s}$	$\dfrac{K_s K_I}{K_I + K_s}$	$\dfrac{K_s K_I}{K_I + K_s}$	K_s
K_2	$\alpha(K_I + K_s)$	∞	$K_I + K_s$	K_T

It will be seen that only formula (2) is experimentally distinguishable from the remaining three other formulations, but that it is not distinguishable experimentally from the simplest form of the Michaelis-Menten equation (2). We can dispose of equation (2) by calling attention to the fact that it represents yet another example of the considerations that must be kept in mind in giving physico-chemical significance to the constants of the Michaelis-Menten equation. If $K_s \ll K_I$, then equation (2) becomes identical with the Michaelis-Menten equation.

Since equations (1), (3), and (4) cannot be distinguished from one another, we shall write v_m (apparent maximum reaction velocity) for CV_m in equation (5).

$$\frac{v_m}{V} = 1 + \frac{K_1}{(S)} + \frac{(S)}{K_2} \tag{6}$$

First let us find the optimal substrate concentration (S_o) at which the highest experimental reaction velocity is obtained (V_o). Differentiating (6) with respect to (S) and equating to zero, we obtain:

$$(S_o)^2 = K_1 K_2 \tag{7}$$

If we now introduce a new constant k defined by $K_1 = k(S_o)$, $K_2 = (S_o)/k$, $k^2 = K_1/K_2$ equation (6) may be rewritten:

$$\frac{v_m}{V} = 1 + k \left[\frac{(S_o)}{(S)} + \frac{(S)}{(S_o)} \right] \tag{8}$$

At optimal substrate concentration $(S) = (S_o)$, $V = V_o$, $v_m/V_o = 1 + 2k$.

The coefficients of either equation (6) or (8) can be obtained from appropriate experimental data by the least squares method, but a graphical solution is also possible and has some merit. Inspection of equation (8) makes clear that by plotting V vs. log (S), one should obtain a curve symmetrical about its maximum at log (S_o).

This conclusion may be demonstrated as follows:

For any given value of (S), say (S_1), we have:

$$\frac{v_m}{V_1} = 1 + k \left[\frac{(S_o)}{(S_1)} + \frac{(S_1)}{(S_o)} \right]$$

Let $(S_o)/(S_1) = t$. Then

$$\frac{v_m}{V_1} = 1 + k \left(t + \frac{1}{t} \right)$$

Now choose (S_2) such that $(S_2)/(S_o) = t$. Then

$$\frac{v_m}{V_2} = 1 + k \left(\frac{1}{t} + t \right)$$

Consequently $V_2 = V_1$; the reaction velocities at substrate concentrations (S_1) and (S_2) will be equal. Moreover we have $(S_o)/(S_1)$ $= (S_2)/(S_o)$ or log (S_o) — log $(S_1) = -[\log(S_o) - \log(S_2)]$. Consequently on a logarithmic scale the points $\log(S_1)$ and $\log(S_2)$ lie on opposite sides of the point $\log(S_o)$ and equidistant from $\log(S_o)$. These equidistant points correspond to equal values of V. Consequently the plot V vs. $\log(S)$ should be symmetrical about its maximum at $\log(S_o)$.

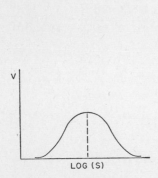

FIG. 1. V vs. log (S).

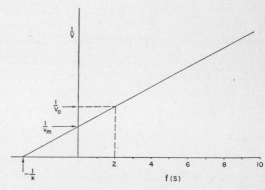

FIG. 2. $1/V$ vs. $f(S)$ where $f(S) = [(S_o)/(S) + (S)/(S_o)]$.

From such a plot (S_o) can readily be estimated. Moreover, equation (8) is linear for $1/V$ vs. $f(S)$, where $f(S) = (S_o)/(S) + (S)/(S_o)$. It will be noted that $V_o < v_m \leq V_m$.

Turnover rates based on V_o or even on v_m will, in general, underestimate the true reaction velocity of the enzyme-substrate complex. It will also be noted that k is inversely related to the width of the concentration zone in which the enzyme operates at nearly optimum rate. When k is small, this zone is wide. As k increases, the zone shrinks, the plot V vs. $\log(S)$ becomes more sharply peaked, but there is a limit to the sharpness of the peak.

If we define the spread as that concentration range over which V is at least $\frac{1}{2} V_o$, then we find that as $k \to \infty$ the spread approaches the limits defined by $f(S) = 4$. Since $f(S) = (S_o)/(S) + (S)/(S_o)$ $= 4$, the limiting concentrations of substrate are $(S_o) (2 \pm \sqrt{3})$ $= (S_o) (3.732 \text{ or } 0.268)$. Dividing the first of these numbers by the second, we find that the minimum spread as defined above corresponds to a 14-fold range of concentration or to 1.15 log units. With the aid of this analysis it is possible by inspection of the V vs. $\log(S)$ curves to tell whether the spread is large or small, i. e., whether k is small or large. If k is large then $K_1 > K_2$, i.e., the apparent dissociation constant is greater for the substrate in the activable position than in the inhibitory position. Teleological considerations might suggest that this is not a very efficient arrangement, and most of the experimental data so far published correspond to $k < 1$. The relations between the logarithm of the spread $(V \geq \frac{1}{2}V_o)$ and $\log k$ is given in Fig. 3.

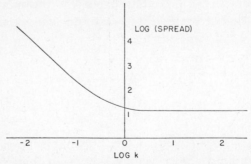

FIG. 3. Log (Spread) vs. Log k. The " spread " is defined as the concentration range within which the reaction velocity is equal to or greater than one-half the reaction velocity at optimum substrate concentration.

In the preceding paper we have discussed the possibility of inhibition by excess substrate due to coupling of substrate and activator. This type of interaction is to be distinguished from that presented here. When coupling occurs between activator and substrate, the V vs. $\log(S)$ plot will, in general, not yield a symmetrical curve and the $1/V$ vs. $f(S)$ plot will not, in general, yield a straight line.

II. Inhibition by Excess Concentration of Activators

The literature is replete with examples of substances which are activators for certain enzyme systems but which do not follow the first order requirement of yielding linear plots for $1/V$ vs. $1/(A)$. In fact, at high activator concentrations, enzyme activity often diminishes with increasing concentration of the activator. Therefore, these substances must function both as activators and as inhibitors. In the following discussion we shall see that second-order theory analogous to that presented in the previous section is applicable in many instances. The hypothesis we wish to test is whether such a substance can attach itself separately to two loci on the enzyme, attachment at one locus activating the enzyme-substrate complex, attachment at the other locus inhibiting the enzyme system. Since we consider the substance both as an activator and as an inhibitor, we will designate its concentration by the noncommittal letter M, but shall continue to use K_A and K_I to designate the dissociation constants for the coupling of the substance M with the enzyme at the activating and inhibiting loci, respectively.

In the appendix to the preceding paper, the formula is given describing the relation of reaction velocity to the simultaneous presence of activator, inhibitor, and substrate:

$$\frac{V_m}{V} = 1 + \frac{xK_sK_A}{(A)(S)} + \frac{xK_A}{(A)} + \frac{xK_sK_A(I)}{K_I(A)(S)}$$
$$+ \frac{xK_s(I)}{uK_I(S)} + \frac{xK_A(I)}{aK_I(A)} + \frac{(I)}{aquK_I} \tag{9}$$

This formula can be adapted to our present purposes by the following considerations. Since we are supposing that the same substance acts as activator and inhibitor, the concentrations (A) and (I) will both be represented by (M). The dissociation factor u, representing interaction between activator and inhibitor, is meaningless in the present situation and is to be replaced by unity. The same holds for the factor q. We thus obtain:

$$\frac{V_m}{V} = 1 + \frac{xK_A}{aK_I} + \frac{xK_A}{(M)} + \frac{(M)}{aK_I}$$

$$+ \frac{xK_S}{(S)}\left[1 + \frac{K_A}{K_I} + \frac{K_A}{(M)} + \frac{(M)}{K_I}\right] \qquad (10)$$

which shows that for (M) constant the relation $1/V$ vs. $1/(S)$ is still linear.

The equation can be rearranged to consider (S) constant and (M) variable:

$$\frac{V_m}{V} = 1 + \frac{xK_A}{aK_I} + \frac{xK_S}{(S)} + \frac{xK_S K_A}{(S)K_I}$$

$$+ \frac{1}{(M)}\left[xK_A + \frac{xK_S K_A}{(S)}\right] + (M)\left[\frac{1}{aK_I} + \frac{xK_S}{(S)K_I}\right] \qquad (11)$$

which may be reduced to

$$\frac{V_m}{V} = 1 + \frac{K_1}{(M)} + \frac{(M)}{K_2} = 1 + k\left[\frac{(M_o)}{(M)} + \frac{(M)}{(M_o)}\right] \qquad (12)$$

in which the symbols have meanings corresponding to those in equations (6) and (8) above. The test of applicability of these equations is whether the plot $1/V$ vs. $f(M)$ yields a straight line when $f(M) = (M_o)/(M) + (M)/(M_o)$, the concentration of (M) which yields maximal activation being designated as (M_o). There are many instances conforming to the proposed theory.

Equation (9) contains the following constants: V_m, K_S, K_A, K_I, x, a, all of which could be evaluated by least squares from an adequate array of experimental data covering variations in concentration of both substrate (S) and activator (M). In most instances, however, the exact dissociation constants are of no special interest. What one would like to know is whether the activation is coupling or non-coupling in type, whether the inhibition is competitive or non-competitive. This information can be obtained by considering the influence of variations in substrate concentration on the co-efficients (M_o), k, and v_m obtained from graphical analysis as indicated above, and of the influence of variations in activator concentration on the apparent Michaelis-Menten constant k_s. Analysis of these four coefficients discloses that the apparent Michaelis-Menten constant k_s is the most revealing one, and the following discussion will be limited to consideration of the variations in k_s with variations in (M).

Equation (10) may be rewritten in the form:

$$\frac{V_m}{V} \frac{1}{1 + \dfrac{xK_A}{aK_I} + \dfrac{xK_A}{(M)} + \dfrac{(M)}{aK_I}} = \frac{v_m}{V}$$

$$= 1 + \frac{xK_S}{(S)} \frac{1 + \dfrac{K_A}{K_I} + \dfrac{K_A}{(M)} + \dfrac{(M)}{K_I}}{1 + \dfrac{xK_A}{aK_I} + \dfrac{xK_A}{(M)} + \dfrac{(M)}{aK_I}} \tag{13}$$

Consequently the apparent Michaelis-Menten constant

$$k_S = xK_S \frac{1 + \dfrac{K_A}{K_I} + \dfrac{K_A}{(M)} + \dfrac{(M)}{K_I}}{1 + \dfrac{xK_A}{aK_I} + \dfrac{xK_A}{(M)} + \dfrac{(M)}{aK_I}} \tag{14}$$

We may now explore the effects on equation (14) of the assumptions that the inhibition is competitive $(a = \infty)$ or non-competitive $(a = 1)$, and that the activation is coupling $(x = 0)$ or non-coupling $(x = 1)$. In the case of coupling activation, as shown in the preceding paper, the equation becomes meaningless $(k_S = 0)$ unless one makes the additional assumption that either xK_S or xK_A is finite. This may be expressed by defining $K_S = \infty$, $xK_S = K'_S$ (coupling activation of the first type); or $K_A = \infty$, $xK_A = K'_A$ (coupling activation of the second type).

Table 2 shows the influence of variations in the concentration of the activator-inhibitor M on the apparent Michaelis-Menten constant k_S under different assumptions as to its mode of activation and inhibition.

The graphical test for the applicability of this analysis is as follows: assuming that data are available for the velocity of enzymatic catalysis over a series of concentrations of the activator-inhibitor

TABLE 2

Character of Influence	Assumed Values	k_S
Non-competitive inhibition Non-coupling activation	$a = 1$ $x = 1$	K_S
Competitive inhibition Non-coupling activation	$a = \infty$ $x = 1$	$K_S\left[1 + \dfrac{(M)}{K_I}\right]$
Non-competitive inhibition Coupling activation first type	$a = 1$ $x = 0$ $K_S = \infty$ $xK_S = K'_S$	$K'_S\left[1 + \dfrac{K_A}{(M)}\right]$
Non-competitive inhibition Coupling activation second type	$a = 1$ $x = 0$ $K_A = \infty$ $xK_A = K'_A$	$K_S\dfrac{K'_A}{K'_A + (M)}$
Competitive inhibition Coupling activation first type	$a = \infty$ $x = 0$ $K_S = \infty$ $xK_S = K'_S$	$K'_S\left[1 + \dfrac{K_A}{K_I} + \dfrac{K_A}{(M)} + \dfrac{(M)}{K_I}\right]$
Competitive inhibition Coupling activation second type	$a = \infty$ $x = 0$ $K_A = \infty$ $xK_A = K'_A$	$K_S\dfrac{K'_A[K_I + (M)]}{K_I[K'_A + (M)]}$

(M), at each of several substrate concentrations, then for each fixed substrate concentration the plot $1/V$ vs. $f(M)$ should yield a straight line. For each fixed concentration of (M) the plot $1/V$ vs. $1/(S)$ should yield a straight line. From the latter plot the apparent Michaelis-Menten constant k_S can be obtained. The mode of dependence of k_S on (M) can then be tested to see which of the six possibilities listed in Table 2 are applicable.

We have omitted consideration of the possible cases in which the dissociation factors a and x have values other than 1 and ∞, or 1 and 0 respectively, but the solution in such instances follows directly from the argument outlined above together with that presented in the preceding paper.

It should be pointed out that an activator which couples with substrate as well as with enzyme will yield the mutually incompatible complexes (EA) and (SA) from which the catalytically active complex (EAS) cannot be formed. When this occurs there will be inhibition by excess activator, but the relations will not follow the simple equations outlined above. The V vs. $\log(M)$ plots in such cases will, in general, be asymmetrical, and the $1/V$ vs. $f(M)$ plot will, in general, be non-linear.

This form of inhibition by excess activator and the related cases of inhibition by excess substrate have been discussed in the preceding paper.

III. Other Types of Second Order Reactions

The systematic analysis of second-order theory should include reference to the possibility that the same substance may act both as substrate and as activator. If the activation is non-coupling, an equation of the following form is applicable:

$$\frac{V_m}{V} = 1 + \frac{K_1}{(S)} + \frac{K_2}{(S)^2} \tag{15}$$

The Lineweaver-Burk plot in such a case would yield a curve concave upwards but not possessing a minimum as in the case of " inhibition by excess substrate." Some data in the literature suggest this form, but none are sufficiently extensive for detailed analysis.

If the activation is coupling, the appropriate equation is:

$$\frac{V_m}{V} = 1 + \frac{K}{(S)^2} \tag{16}$$

We have found no data conforming to this type. It should be pointed out that this equation is also appropriate for the case of a dimeric substrate.

Mention should also be made of the possible cases where two molecules of the same substance are required to inhibit or to activate.

SUMMARY

An attempt at the systematic analysis of second-order enzyme kinetics is presented. For the purpose of this discussion, second-order theory is defined as that describing the possibility that two molecules of the same substance may be coupled per active locus of the enzyme. The theory is applied to the familiar cases of " inhibition by excess substrate " and " inhibition by excess activator."

It is shown that inhibition by excess substrate does not necessarily imply that the active locus possesses two attracting groups, as has heretofore been supposed.

In the case of " inhibition by excess activator," i. e., the case of a substance which can act both as an activator and as an inhibitor, coupling and non-coupling activation, competitive and non-competitive inhibition can all be distinguished.

A graphical method for analysis of various second-order cases is given. With this method the applicability of second-order theory may be tested, and the various constants of the equations determined.

REFERENCES

1. Lineweaver, H., and D. Burk. 1934. The Determination of Enzyme Dissociation Constants. *J. Am. Chem. Soc.*, 56, 658.
2. Michaelis, L., and M. L. Menten. 1913. Die Kinetik der Invertinwirkung. *Biochem. Z.*, 49, 333.

ELEMENTARY KINETIC THEORY OF ENZYMATIC ACTIVITY

INFLUENCE OF pH *

JONAS S. FRIEDENWALD and GERTRUDE D. MAENGWYN-DAVIES

Wilmer Ophthalmological Institute of the Johns Hopkins University and Hospital

IN THE TWO preceding papers the elementary theory of enzyme kinetics has been presented at the successive levels of first- and second-order theory. The present paper represents an extension of the preceding argument. The conclusions reached in the previous papers will be assumed. We are indebted to Dr. W. M. Clark for having raised the question as to how the Michaelis-Menten theory (1), as developed in the preceding papers, would be influenced by consideration of the multiplicity of ionic species of enzyme, and even of substrates, activators, and inhibitors, which may be simultaneously present in the test solutions.

Consideration of this problem revealed that there are really three questions involved.

(A) Is there any reason for believing that hydrogen-ion associations play a role qualitatively different from that of other activators and inhibitors of enzymatic activity? If the answer to this question is negative, then it would be worthwhile to attempt to expand the Michaelis-Menten theory to include this complex case.

(B) The second question is the practical one, whether the Michaelis-Menten theory can be expanded to higher orders than the second, without becoming mathematically unmanageable. It will be shown below that many of the problems of hydrogen-ion effects can be reduced as a first approximation to second-order theory, or to more complicated formulations that can be factored into several items, each of which is not higher than second order.

* This work was supported in part by a grant from the National Cancer Institute.

191

(C) The third question is whether such an approximate theory provides a useful description of any considerable group of experimental facts.

I. Preliminary Considerations

Before entering into the questions outlined above, it will be instructive to inquire whether the Michaelis-Menten theory can be expanded to include the possible multiplicity of catalytically active enzyme ionic species. There are many enzyme systems which yield data conforming to the simplest expression of the Michaelis-Menten theory. Does this fact in itself impose any limitations on the possible multiplicity of catalytically active enzyme ionic species?

Let us suppose that at a given pH in the presence of substrate the total enzyme concentration may be represented by the summation:

$$(E_t) = \sum_i (E_i) + \sum_i (E_i S) \tag{1}$$

We assume that each ionic species E_i may be converted into any other E_i by a finite number of hydrogen-ion associations or dissociations, subject to mass law equations such as:

$$\frac{(E_1)\,(H^+)}{(E_2)} = K_{1,2} \tag{2}$$

It follows that, at fixed hydrogen-ion concentration, the concentrations of each ionic species E_i will be a fixed fraction of the total ionic species $\sum_j (E_j)$. For each E_i:

$$\frac{(E_i)}{\sum_j (E_j)} = c_i \quad \text{and} \quad \sum_i c_i = 1 \tag{3}$$

This relation will hold independent of the concentration of substrate (S).

The same argument may be applied to the ionic species $E_i S$. For each $E_i S$:

$$\frac{(E_i S)}{\sum_j (E_j S)} = C_i \qquad \sum_i C_i = 1 \tag{4}$$

Equation (4) is likewise independent of the concentration of substrate and may be applied in particular to the situation in which the enzyme is fully saturated with substrate.

$$\frac{(E_i S_{max})}{\sum_j (E_j S)_{max}} = C_i \qquad (5)$$

Let us now apply the Michaelis-Menten assumption by defining V_i, the catalytic reaction velocity for the ionic species $E_i S$ according to the equations:

$$V_i = x_i (E_i S) \qquad V_{i\,max} = x_i (E_i S)_{max} \qquad (6)$$

where x_i is the reaction velocity per unit concentration of $E_i S$. It follows that:

$$\frac{V_{i\,max}}{V_i} = \frac{x_i (E_i S)_{max}}{x_i (E_i S)} = \frac{C_i \sum_j (E_j S)_{max}}{C_i \sum_j (E_j S)} = \frac{\sum_j (E_j S)_{max}}{\sum_j (E_j S)} \qquad (7)$$

It is plain that the ratio $V_{i\,max}/V_i$ is the same for every i. Moreover, defining:

$$V_m = \sum_i V_{i\,max}$$

$$V = \sum_i V_i$$

we obtain:

$$\frac{V_m}{V} = \frac{\sum_i (E_i S)_{max}}{\sum_i (E_i S)} \qquad (8)$$

Moreover $\sum_i (E_i S)_{max}$ represents full saturation of the enzyme with substrate.

$$\sum_i (E_i S)_{max} = (E_t) = \sum_i (E_i) + \sum_i (E_i S).$$

Consequently

$$\frac{V_m}{V} = \frac{\sum_i (E_i) + \sum_i (E_i S)}{\sum_i (E_i S)} = 1 + \frac{\sum_i (E_i)}{\sum_i (E_i S)} \qquad (9)$$

We may now make use of the mass law equations:

$$\frac{(E_i)(S)}{(E_i S)} = K_{Si}$$

Then:

$$\frac{V_m}{V} = 1 + \frac{1}{(S)} \frac{\sum_i K_{Si}(E_iS)}{\sum_i (E_iS)}$$

Dividing the numerator of the fraction on the right, term by term by the denominator, with the aid of equation (4) we obtain:

$$\frac{V_m}{V} = 1 + \frac{1}{(S)} \sum_i K_{Si}C_i \tag{10}$$

If we compare this equation with the classical formulation of the Michaelis-Menten theory:

$$\frac{V_m}{V} = 1 + \frac{K_S}{(S)}$$

we see that experimental conformity to the classical equation does not in itself place any restrictions on the homogeneity or inhomogeneity of the catalytically active enzyme ionic species. If these species are many and varied, then the Michaelis constant K_S merely represents the weighted mean of the multiplicity of enzyme-substrate dissociation constants. Similarly, the reaction velocity at saturating concentrations of substrate V_m can be considered the sum of the reaction velocities of the various catalytically active ionic species, each characterized by a different turnover rate.

The possible multiplicity of enzyme-substrate dissociation constants and turnover rates, while permissible in a system conforming to the Michaelis-Menten equation, is, however, not required by any a priori considerations. If this multiplicity were the true state of affairs, then, since the population of enzyme ionic species necessarily shifts with changing pH, the Michaelis constant K_S would change with change in pH. Not many investigations have been directed specifically to elucidate this point, but there are very many enzyme systems for which it has been shown that the pH optimum and the shape of the pH vs. activity curve does not change markedly with change in substrate concentration. When this is the case, the variability of the K_{Si} must be negligibly small. There is, therefore, no compelling reason to assume that the K_{si} are generally unequal to one another.

In the argument which follows, we will assume that the K_{si} are in general all equal to one another, except for the special cases in which hydrogen-ion associations act as coupling activators or competitive inhibitors. Only three types of hydrogen-ion associations with the enzyme will be considered: (a) those in which the association acts as a coupling activator or a competitive inhibitor, (b) those in which the association acts as a non-coupling activator or a non-competitive inhibitor, (c) those in which the hydrogen-ion association is without effect on the catalytic system. Partial activations or inhibitions, i. e., variations in the turnover rates of the catalytically active enzyme-substrate complexes, will not be considered. We do not assert that these simplifying assumptions are generally true. We wish merely to explore the consequences of these assumptions to see whether a substantial number of experimental data can be fitted into this scheme.

II. SIMPLIFYING SELECTIONS

Hydrogen-ion dissociation can affect not only the enzyme but also the substrate. We can avoid this additional complication, at least in the initial stages of the present argument, by focussing our attention first only on those enzyme systems in which the substrate exists in only one ionic or molecular form in the pH range of enzymatic activity. There are many enzyme systems in this simpler group, those in which the substrate is un-ionized, such as saccharase and glucosidases, or those in which the substrate is a strong base or a strong acid, such as choline esterase, phenol sulfatase, etc.

A further complication arises from the fact that some of the hydrogen-ion associations may behave as coupling activators or competitive inhibitors. The dissociation constants characterizing hydrogen-ion associations at these particular loci on the enzyme will be different for the enzyme molecule itself and for the enzyme-substrate complex. We can avoid this complication by considering in the first instance only those situations in which the enzyme is fully saturated with substrate. Experimentally, this means that at each pH studied, reaction velocities must be tested at different substrate concentrations. The data for any given pH can then be subjected to a Lineweaver-Burk plot and the reaction velocity at substrate saturation estimated (2). We shall now consider the variation of this maximal reaction rate, that is to be expected with pH, if the Michaelis-Menten theory with the simplifying assumptions outlined above is applicable to hydrogen-ion dissociations.

We will, in the first instance, assume that there is only a single catalytically active enzyme ionic species. Later this restriction will be relaxed to include the possibility that the catalytically active enzyme ionic species compose a group, the members of which differ from each other only in respect to hydrogen-ion associations that are neither activating nor inhibiting, that are in fact catalytically indifferent.

III. MICHAELIS-MENTEN THEORY OF pH OPTIMUM

In applying the Michaelis-Menten theory to the conditions outlined in the preceding section, we assume that the total concentration of enzyme can be expressed as the sum of terms:

$$(E_t) = \cdots + (E''_1) + (E'_1) + (E_1) + (E^*)$$
$$+ (E_2) + (E'_2) + (E''_2) + \cdots \quad (11)$$

where E^* represents the catalytically active ionic species; E_1, E'_1, E''_1, etc. represent ionic species which lack 1, 2, 3, etc., hydrogen-ion associations that are necessary for enzymatic activity; E_2, E'_2, E''_2, etc., represent ionic species coupled with 1, 2, 3, etc., inhibiting hydrogen-ion associations. With these assumptions the mass law equations can be written:

$$\frac{(E_1)(H^+)}{(E^*)} = K_1 \qquad (E_1) = (E^*)\frac{K_1}{(H^+)} \qquad (12)$$

$$\frac{(E'_1)(H^+)}{(E_1)} = K'_1 \qquad (E'_1) = (E^*)\frac{K_1 K'_1}{(H^+)^2}$$

$$\frac{(E''_1)(H^+)}{(E'_1)} = K''_1 \qquad (E''_1) = (E^*)\frac{K_1 K'_1 K''_1}{(H^+)^3}$$

$$\text{etc.} \qquad\qquad\qquad \text{etc.}$$

$$\frac{(E^*)\,(H^+)}{(E_2)} = K_2 \qquad\qquad (E_2) = (E^*)\,\frac{(H^+)}{K_2}$$

$$\frac{(E_2)\,(H^+)}{(E'_2)} = K'_2 \qquad\qquad (E'_2) = (E^*)\,\frac{(H^+)^2}{K_2 K'_2}$$

$$\frac{(E'_2)\,(H^+)}{(E''_2)} = K''_2 \qquad\qquad (E''_2) = (E^*)\,\frac{(H^+)^3}{K_2 K'_2 K''_2}$$

etc.   etc.

In general, $K_1 > K'_1 > K''_1 >$ etc.; $K_2 < K'_2 < K''_2 <$ etc. The Michaelis-Menten equation, under the assumption that all these ionic species are fully saturated with substrate becomes:

$$\frac{V_m}{V} = \cdots + \frac{K_1 K'_1 K''_1}{(H^+)^3} + \frac{K_1 K'_1}{(H^+)^2} + \frac{K_1}{(H^+)} + 1 + \frac{(H^+)}{K_2}$$

$$+ \frac{(H^+)^2}{K_2 K'_2} + \frac{(H^+)^3}{K_2 K'_2 K''_2} + \cdots \qquad (13)$$

Considering the series involving K_1, it is evident that each successive member is formed by multiplying the term to its right by a factor $K_1^{(n)}/(H^+)$, where n represents the number of primes. Now if we consider only values of $(H^+) > K_1$, the terms involving K_1 form a rapidly converging series, and all those to the left of $K_1/(H^+)$ may be omitted in a first approximation. Similarly, if we consider only values of $(H^+) < K_2$, the terms to the right of $(H^+)/K_2$ may be disregarded.

Consequently for $K_1 < (H^+) < K_2$, the hydrogen-ion effect may be approximately described by the second-order equation:

$$\frac{V_m}{V} = 1 + \frac{K_1}{(H^+)} + \frac{(H^+)}{K_2} = 1 + k\left[\frac{(H^+_o)}{(H^+)} + \frac{(H^+)}{(H^+_o)}\right] \qquad (14)$$

where (H^+_o) is the hydrogen-ion concentration at the pH optimum, and $k = \sqrt{K_1/K_2}$.

The extent of the pH range within which it is valid to make this approximation is the greater the smaller the value of k, and for values of k that are not too large it covers approximately the range $V > \frac{1}{2} V_o$, when V_o is the reaction velocity at the pH optimum. The range of valid approximation may, in fact, be much larger depending on how widely spaced in order of magnitude are the successive K'.

Following the argument in the preceding paper, one would expect the plot $1/V$ vs. $f(H^+)$ where

$$f(H^+) = \left[\frac{(H^+_o)}{(H^+)} + \frac{(H^+)}{(H^+_o)}\right], \text{ to be linear.}$$

Where higher powers of (H^+) become significant, the plot should yield curves concave toward the y-axis.

In the argument outlined above, several considerations have been omitted.

(A) In all probability many of the hydrogen-ion associations of which the enzyme-protein is capable are without influence on its catalytic activity. Each of the enzyme species listed in equation (11) can therefore be regarded as representing an aggregate of ionic species which differ from each other in hydrogen-ion dissociations that are neither activating nor inhibiting with respect to the enzymatic catalysis.

(B) No consideration has been given to the possibility that ionic species may exist which have insufficient hydrogen-ion associations for activation, but nevertheless have one or more hydrogen-ion associations in inhibiting positions. Such ionic species will not generate new terms in the power series of the Michaelis-Menten equation (13) but merely represent addenda to some neighboring term. Such addenda, depending on their location in the power series, may either increase or decrease the reliability of the approximation formula (14).

(C) The possibility should also be mentioned that several different loci of hydrogen-ion association may be equivalent in activating the enzyme. The terms $E_1^{(n)}$ of equation (11) may each represent the sum of a set of equivalent ionic species. In the Michaelis-Menten equation this means that the corresponding $K_1^{(n)}$ represents the weighted average of the group of dissociation constants describing these equivalent dissociations.

There are not many sets of data in the literature in which the pH optimum has been studied over a wide range of substrate concentration, sufficient to enable one to extrapolate to the hypothetical state of full saturation with substrate as considered in this section. Before comparing the theory with experimental data, it is necessary, therefore, to include the effect of varying substrate concentrations.

IV. INFLUENCE OF SUBSTRATE CONCENTRATION

In the present section we will still hold to the limitation that the substrate is present in only one ion or molecular species, but will remove the limitation of considering only systems fully saturated with substrate. If all the significant hydrogen-ion associations are either non-coupling activators or non-competitive inhibitors, then each item in equation (11) must now be represented by two, one coupled, and the second not coupled with substrate. Moreover, since we have assumed that each of the significant dissociations is non-competitive or non-coupling, the same dissociation coefficient K_S will describe each of these substrate couplings. The pair of terms in the Michaelis-Menten equation, representing this coupled and uncoupled pair of enzyme species will be related to one another as $1 : K_S/(S)$. Applying this reasoning to the approximation from equation (14) we obtain:

$$\frac{V_m}{V} = \left\{ 1 + k \left[\frac{(H^+_o)}{(H^+)} + \frac{(H^+)}{(H^+_o)} \right] \right\} \left\{ 1 + \frac{K_S}{(S)} \right\} \tag{15}$$

It follows that for the case of non-coupling, non-competitive hydrogen-ion effects, the activity vs. pH curve merely changes in altitude with change in substrate concentration. Its spread and the location of its maximum are unaffected. Moreover, the Michaelis-Menten constant is independent of pH. The plot $1/V$ vs. $f(H^+)$ should yield a family of straight lines, one for each substrate concentration, which intersect in a point on the horizontal axis.

If we consider now the case that in addition to an indefinite number of non-coupling, non-competitive hydrogen-ion associations, there is also one locus where affixing a hydrogen ion results in competitive inhibition, then an argument similar to that of the previous paragraph leads to the approximation equation:

$$\frac{V_m}{V} = \left\{ 1 + k \left[\frac{(H^+_o)}{(H^+)} + \frac{(H^+)}{(H^+_o)} \right] \right\} \left\{ 1 + \frac{K_S}{(S)} \left[1 + \frac{(H^+)}{K_I} \right] \right\} \tag{16}$$

Here K_I is the dissociation constant of the competitive hydrogen-ion association. (H^+_o) is the hydrogen-ion optimum at full saturation with substrate, and is not identical with the optimum at other substrate concentrations.

If we consider this equation for a fixed value of (S), it is a cubic function of (H^+) and difficult to handle. The plot V vs. pH will be asymmetrical, steeper on the low pH side. This case can be solved by first studying the influence of pH on the apparent Michaelis-Menten constant. By plotting the apparent Michaelis-Menten constant versus (H^+), one should obtain a straight line from which K_S and K_I can be estimated. Extrapolation to maximal substrate concentration should yield a curve suitable for the second-order approximation formula.

It should be pointed out that with $K_I \gg (H^+)$ this formula collapses into that for the non-competitive, non-coupling case. The range of concentration over which (H^+) can be effectively varied is limited not only by the decline in activity far from the pH optimum, but also by the more limited range in which the approximation formula is applicable. Failure to find experimental evidence that the apparent Michaelis-Menten constant is a linear function of hydrogen-ion concentration does not mean, for instance, that there is no anionic group in the active locus of the enzyme, essential for coupling with substrate. Such experimental results would only mean that if an anionic group in the enzyme is essential for substrate coupling, that anionic group is a sufficiently strong acid not to have its dissociation significantly suppressed in the pH range accessible to study.

With further comment, but subject to the same limitations, we can write the equations for the case of coupling activation by hydrogen-ions:

$$\frac{V_m}{V} = \left\{ 1 + k \left[\frac{(H^+_o)}{(H^+)} + \frac{(H^+)}{(H^+_o)} \right] \right\} \left\{ 1 + \frac{K_S}{(S)} \left[1 + \frac{K_A}{(H^+)} \right] \right\} \quad (17)$$

and for the case of combined coupling activation and competitive inhibition:

$$\frac{V_m}{V} = \left\{ 1 + k \left[\frac{(H^+_o)}{(H^+)} + \frac{(H^+)}{(H^+_o)} \right] \right\} \left\{ 1 + \frac{K_S}{(S)} \right.$$

$$\times \left[1 + \frac{K_A}{(H^+)} \right] \left[1 + \frac{(H^+)}{K_I} \right] \right\} \quad (18)$$

In most experimental situations we shall expect $K_A \ll (H^+)$, and $K_I \gg (H^+)$, so that the results should be indistinguishable from the

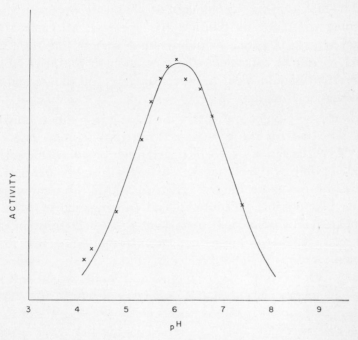

FIG. 1.   Activity vs. pH for aryl-sulfatase (7).
The curve fits equation (14) with $k = 0.11$, $(H^+_o) = 8 \times 10^{-7}$.

non-competitive, non-coupling case (eq. 8). The experimental facts show that the pH optimum curves, in almost all cases in which only one species of substrate-ion is present, are nearly symmetrical, fairly well fitted by the approximation formula (eq. 14), and fail to show a significant drift in the pH optimum with change in substrate concentration.   An exception to this rule is saccharase, which shows a small shift in its pH optimum with change in substrate concentration. (3).

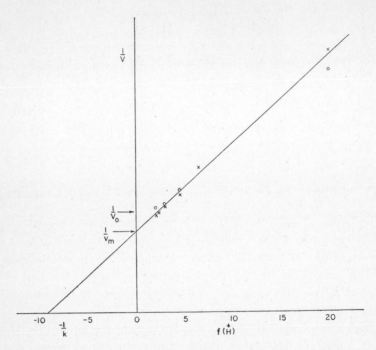

FIG. 2. Same data as shown in Fig. 1, plotted $1/V$ vs. $f(H^+)$ where $f(H^+) = \dfrac{(H^+_o)}{(H^+)} + \dfrac{(H^+)}{(H^+_o)}$ with $(H^+_o) = 8 \times 10^{-7}$.

V. Multiple Ionic Species of Substrate

Many substrates are characterized by hydrogen-ion dissociations such that, in the experimentally significant pH range, several ionic species of substrate may be present. The possible effects of this can be pursued in a chain of increasing complexity. The present analysis makes no pretense at being exhaustive, but a few examples for which there are data in the literature will be discussed.

The simplest situation is that in which the substrate is present in two ionic forms, say $\bar{S}$ and SH, only one of which is coupled by the enzyme. If $\bar{S}$ is the true substrate, then the approximation formula should hold:

$$\frac{V_m}{V} = \left\{ 1 + k \left[\frac{(H^+_o)}{(H^+)} + \frac{(H^+)}{(H^+_o)} \right] \right\} \left\{ 1 + \frac{K_S}{(\bar{S})} \right\} \qquad (19)$$

In addition we can write for total substrate:

$$(S_t) = (\bar{S}) + (SH)$$

$$\frac{(\bar{S})(H^+)}{(SH)} = K$$

$$(\bar{S}) = (S_t) \frac{K}{K + (H^+)}$$

If we substitute this value for $(\bar{S})$ in equation (19) we obtain:

$$\frac{V_m}{V} = \left\{ 1 + k \left[\frac{(H^+_o)}{(H^+)} + \frac{(H^+)}{(H^+_o)} \right] \right\} \left\{ 1 + \frac{K_S}{S_t} \left[1 + \frac{(H^+)}{K} \right] \right\} \qquad (20)$$

This equation is formally identical with (16), but the quantity $(H^+)/K$ cannot be assumed to be negligibly small.

If SH is the true substrate, the corresponding argument leads to an equation formally identical with (17).

There have been two examples reported in the literature illustrative of the argument just outlined. Both of these examples concern substrates which are present in three ionic or molecular species within the pH range of the enzymatic activity. The first example is that published by Mohamed (4) in his study of arginase, the second is that by Hogness and Niemann (5) of the hydrolysis of acetyl-L-tyrosinhydroxamide by α-chymotrypsin. Since in both these reports there appear to be minor algebraic errors, we shall develop the formulas for both cases together. If, in consequence of hydrogen-ion dissociations, there are three ionic or molecular species of substrate, then:

$$(S_t) = (\bar{S}) + (SH) + (SH^+_2)$$

$$\frac{(\bar{S})(H^+)}{(SH)} = K$$

$$\frac{(SH)(H^+)}{(SH^+_2)} = K'$$

Combining these equations

$$(S_t) = (\bar{S}) \left[1 + \frac{(H^+)}{K} + \frac{(H^+)^2}{KK'}\right]$$

$$= (SH) \left[1 + \frac{K}{(H^+)} + \frac{(H^+)}{K'}\right]$$

$$= (SH^+_2) \left[1 + \frac{K'}{(H^+)} + \frac{KK'}{(H^+)^2}\right]$$

In the case of arginase studied by Mohamed, it was assumed that the true substrate was that which we have designated SH. The appropriate Michaelis-Menten equation is:

$$\frac{V_m}{V} = \left\{1 + k\left[\frac{(H^+_o)}{(H^+)} + \frac{(H^+)}{(H^+_o)}\right]\right\} \left\{1 + \frac{K_S}{(S_t)}\right.$$
$$\left. \times \left[1 + \frac{K}{(H^+)} + \frac{(H^+)}{K'}\right]\right\}$$

from which one can obtain the apparent Michaelis-Menten constant:

$$k_S = K_S \left[1 + \frac{K}{(H^+)} + \frac{(H^+)}{K'}\right]$$

Mohamed, by a different argument which we believe to be erroneous, obtained the following formula:

$$k_S = K_S \left[1 + \frac{K}{(H^+)} + \frac{(H^+)}{K'} + \frac{K}{K'}\right]$$

He found that his experimental data for the apparent Michaelis-Menten constant were well fitted by his formula, when the estimates of the substrate–hydrogen-ion dissociation constants K, K' obtained by direct acid-base titration were inserted into the formula. The difference between Mohamed's formula and that which we regard as correct is the addition by Mohamed of the term K/K' in the definition of the apparent Michaelis-Menten constant. Since, in the case of arginine, the actual numerical value of this added term is less than 0.01, the two formulations would not be experimentally distinguishable.

In the case studied by Hogness and Niemann, it was assumed that the true substrate is the species we have designated by $(\bar{S})$.

Hogness and Niemann did not attempt to measure the apparent Michaelis-Menten constant at different pH, but instead compared the activity vs. pH curve for acetyl-L-tyrosinhydroxamide with that found for the closely related substrate acetyl-L-*tyrosinamide*. Since the amide exists in only one molecular form over the pH range studied, they assumed that the activity vs. pH curve for this substrate represented, within a constant factor, the influence of pH on the hydrolysis of the susceptible ionic species of the hydroxamide. In terms of the argument we have outlined, the assumptions of Hogness and Niemann can be expressed in the following equations in which the subscripted H and A refer to the hydroxamide and amide respectively.

$$\frac{V_{mH}}{V_H} = \left\{ 1 + k\left[\frac{(H^+{}_o)}{(H^+)} + \frac{(H^+)}{(H^+{}_o)}\right]\right\}\left\{1 + \frac{K_{SH}}{S_{tH}}\right.$$

$$\times \left[1 + \frac{(H^+)}{K} + \frac{(H^+)^2}{KK'}\right]\left.\right\}$$

$$\frac{V_{mA}}{V_A} = \left\{ 1 + k\left[\frac{(H^+{}_o)}{(H^+)} + \frac{(H^+)}{(H^+{}_o)}\right]\right\}\left\{1 + \frac{K_{SA}}{(S_A)}\right\}$$

Dividing the first of these equations by the second and eliminating constants, we find that comparing the reaction velocities for the two substrates at the same pH:

$$\frac{V_A}{V_H} \frac{(S_{tH}) + K_{SH}\left[1 + \frac{(H^+)}{K} + \frac{(H^+)^2}{KK'}\right]}{(S_A) + K_{SA}} = \frac{(S_{tH}) + K_{SH}R}{(S_A) + K_{SA}}$$

Now, since R is greater than one, and since the substrate concentrations used were constant over the pH range, it follows that, if $(S_{tH}) \ll K_{SH}$ this formulation reduces to:

$$\frac{V_A}{V_H} \sim R$$

The latter is equivalent to the formulation reached by Hogness and Niemann, and which they found in agreement with their experimental data. Unfortunately the actual substrate concentration (S_{tH}) used in these experiments is not reported.

A somewhat more complex case is that in which the rejected ionic species of substrate acts as a competitive inhibitor. If $\bar{S}$ is the true substrate, SH the competitive inhibitor, the Michaelis-Menten equation takes the form:

$$\frac{V_m}{V} = \left\{ 1 + k\left[\frac{(H^+_o)}{(H^+)} + \frac{(H^+)}{(H^+_o)} \right] \right\} \left\{ 1 + \frac{K_S(H^+)}{K'_I K} \right.$$
$$\left. + \frac{K_S}{(S_t)}\left[1 + \frac{(H^+)}{K} \right] \right\} \quad (21)$$

where the new symbol K'_I is the dissociation constant for the conversion of enzyme-coupled-$\bar{S}$ to enzyme-coupled SH. Equation (21) yields an asymmetrical curve of the third order when saturation with substrate is considered, and (H^+_o) does not correspond to the pH optimum.

If the rejected ionic species of substrate acts as a non-competitive inhibitor, the result is more complex still. At any given pH such a situation leads to an example of " inhibition by excess substrate," similar to that discussed in the preceding paper, in which the same ionic species was supposed to act both as substrate and as inhibitor. One can distinguish these two types of inhibition by excess substrate quite readily. When there is only one ionic species acting as both substrate and inhibitor, the substrate optimum does not shift with pH and the pH optimum need not shift with variations in substrate concentration, as may be illustrated by acetylcholine esterase. When one ionic species is the substrate and the other the non-competitive inhibitor, there is both a change in the substrate optimum with shift of pH and a change in pH optimum with variation in substrate concentration. If $\bar{S}$ is the substrate, SH the non-competitive inhibitor, then the Michaelis-Menten equation has the form:

$$\frac{V_m}{V} = \left\{ 1 + k\left[\frac{(H^+_o)}{(H^+)} + \frac{(H^+)}{(H^+_o)} \right] \right\} \left\{ 1 + \frac{(H^+)K_S}{KK_I} \right.$$
$$\left. + \frac{K_S[(H^+) + K]}{K(S_t)} + \frac{(H^+)(S_t)}{K_I[(H^+) + K]} \right\} \quad (22)$$

The symbol K_I in this case denotes the dissociation coefficient of the complex formed with the inhibiting ionic species of substrate. (H^+_o)

does not correspond to the pH optimum. An example which can be fitted approximately by this equation is to be found in the work of Ross, Ely, and Archer on alkaline phosphatase (6).

DISCUSSION

At the beginning of this paper the question was posed whether the influence of hydrogen-ion associations might be qualitatively different from that of previously studied activators and inhibitors. It was conceivable that different ionic species of enzyme might differ in their rate of catalysis. One could possibly explain the decline of enzyme activity, as the pH is shifted from its optimum position, as being due to a shift in the population of enzyme ionic species from a predominance of the most rapidly catalytic types toward a predominance of more slowly reacting types. The present study shows that there is no need for this assumption—at least over a considerable range of currently available experimental data. Enzymatic catalysis appears to be an all-or-nothing affair, the catalytic velocity for a particular substrate being apparently identical for all potentially active ionic enzyme species. The present study does not establish whether this rule is a universal one, but it would appear to have quite wide validity.

The predominant effect of hydrogen-ion association on enzymatic activity appears to be that of non-coupling activation, non-competitive inhibition. This finding does not imply that the active locus of the enzyme is devoid of charged groups. What is implied is merely that the potentially charged groups at the active locus represent such strong or such weak acids or bases that their state of dissociation does not vary significantly within the pH range of enzymatic activity. From a teleologic point of view, any other arrangement would be quite inept, but the universal applicability of this rule cannot be asserted from the present study.

The fact that second-order theory provides a good approximation to experimental findings for many enzyme systems is quite remarkable. It would appear that in many instances, over a range of several pH units (between pK_1 and pK_2), there may be no hydrogen-ion dissociations which are critical for enzyme activity. This suggests that only a quite small portion of the enzyme molecule participates actively in the resonance states associated with activation of the substrate. The good agreement between experimental findings and second-order theory is all the more surprising since in the extreme ranges of pH irreversible inactivation of the enzyme may be expected, and not many experimenters have troubled to demonstrate that the decline in activity far from the pH optimum is fully reversible.

When second-order theory is applicable to the pH effect, the maximum velocity of enzymatic catalysis, obtainable by saturation of the enzyme with substrate at the optimal pH, is not identical with the activity that would be obtained if all enzyme molecules in the solution were active. If V_m is that hypothetical maximum, and V_o the maximum extrapolated from experiments at the pH optimum, the relation between these two quantities is:

$$\frac{V_m}{V_o} = 1 + 2k$$

Since k is usually found to lie between 0.1 and 0.01, the error in assuming $V_o = V_m$ is negligibly small. This conclusion, however, by no means applies to those cases in which kinetic theory of higher order than the second is required to describe the experimental data. Estimated turnover rates in these more complicated situations need to be accepted with considerable reserve.

REFERENCES

1. Michaelis, L., and M. L. Menten. 1913. Die Kinetic der Invertinwirkung. *Biochem. Z.*, 49, 333.
2. Lineweaver, H., and D. Burk. 1934. The Determination of Enzyme Dissociation Constants. *J. Am. Chem. Soc.*, 56, 658.
3. Myrbäck, K. 1951. Enzyme-Substrate Compounds and Activity-pH-Curves of the Amylases. *Arkiv Kemi*, 3, 437.
4. Mohamed, M. S., and D. M. Greenberg. 1945. Liver Arginase. I. Preparation of Extracts of High Potency, Chemical Properties, Activation-Inhibition, and pH Activity. *Arch. Biochem.*, 8, 349.
5. Hogness, D. S., and C. Niemann. 1953. The Kinetics of the α-Chymotrypsin catalized hydrolysis of Acetyl-L-tyrosinhyroxamide in aqueous solutions at 25° and pH 7.6. *J. Am. Chem. Soc.*, 75, 884.
6. Ross, M. H., J. O. Ely, and J. G. Archer. 1951. Alkaline Phosphatase Activity and pH Optima. *J. Biol. Chem.*, 192, 561.
7. Maengwyn-Davies, G. D. Mammalian aryl-sulfatase. To be published.

DISCUSSION

DR. HERRIOTT: I would like to ask Dr. Bull whether the light-scattering properties change with time.

DR. BULL: Yes indeed. There is a small digestion of egg albumin by pepsin even at pH 4, and these values were extrapolated to zero time.

DR. WILSON: There is another method of obtaining information about enzyme substrate interaction and that is by means of competitive inhibitors.

DR. McELROY: I would like to ask both Dr. Bull and Dr. Eyring if they would like to comment with respect to Dr. Bull's classification of competitive and non-competitive inhibitors. If you take your theory and classify various inhibitors of enzyme reactions it so happens that these molecules that you are talking about which move into these fatty areas turn out to be non-competitive inhibitors, whereas those molecules which presumably do not enter the fatty phase and inhibit apparently at the surface of the molecule turn out to be competitive inhibitors. There does appear to be some thermodynamic relationship between these two types of classifications. This also relates, by the way, to the partition coefficient, a point which we have talked about several times.

DR. EYRING: Dr. Johnson and I have pictured the situation just as you have described it. Type II or non-competitive inhibitors inactivate by penetrating into the fatty enzyme groups whereas type I inhibitors such as sulfanilamide apparently compete with some compound like para aminobenzoic acid at the surface of the enzyme. They were called type I and type II inhibitors by Johnson and me and by Dr. McElroy but can equally well be called competitive and non-competitive inhibitors.

DR. McELROY: I think that there is a very important distinction, though, when you are talking about inhibitors in the intact organism compared to the action of these substances on an isolated enzyme. It may be that these energy barriers that you are talking about are really energy barriers involving the complexes of enzymes with lipids, rather than the lipid phase in the protein structure itself, and I think that this is supported from the observations that such compounds as alcohol and urethane work in vivo at much lower concentrations than are required to inhibit enzymes once they are isolated from the cell. This may be particularly important when we think about the action of various inhibitors of such processes as oxidative phosphorylation. The structural problem may be very important here, particularly with respect to spatial arrangement of various enzymes in particles. This may also explain why the action of a variety of these inhibitors are both pressure and temperature sensitive when studied in the intact cell.

DR. WILSON: I would like to mention that Drs. Bergman, Nachmansohn and myself have derived equations in our work with cholinesterase similar to those described by Dr. Friedenwald. We have found experimentally, as anticipated by these equations, that the ratio of the velocity at optimum pH to the velocity at other pH varies directly as the hydrogen ion concentration in more acid media and directly as the hydroxyl ion concentration in more alkaline media.

Dr. E. Smith: Those of us who have worked with specificity particularly have been impressed by the fact that there is probably multiple interaction of sites on the substrate with the enzyme surface, and if we have 3-point, 4-point, or n-point attachment it is quite clear that these things cannot occur simultaneously. In other words, we should postulate that there are a large number of complex reactions and that these things go stepwise, forming ES_1, ES_2, etc., to ES_n. After these complexes are formed there follow the necessary activation processes and dissociation processes or whatever is required for the reaction. What the Michaelis-Menten scheme simply says is that we are dealing with an over-all process in which two steps are rate-limiting. If one thinks in terms of a stepwise mechanism then the rate-limiting steps can be at almost any of the steps in the series. I think we have to be careful to recognize that what we are calling the activation step or product association step may not always be so in particular situations. The step from ES_1 to ES_2 may be rate-limiting, or the step ES_2 to ES_3 may be rate-limiting. In either case the Michaelis-Menten concept will hold quantitatively, since all the rest is so fast that we don't measure it. This type of approach in thinking has come from some experiments on carboxypeptidase which Dr. Lumry and I and a number of colleagues have been doing for some years. What has come out of these experiments is that there are various ways of changing the rate-limiting step. One of the simplest ways to show this is that from pH 7.3 up to about 8.3 there is no effect on either K_m or K_3 as we measure it—that is, K_m and K_3 essentially remain constant over this pH range. At pH 7.3 measurements carried out in heavy water give exactly the same values for K_m and K_3. When we go up to pH 8.3 heavy water acts as an inhibitor—that is, it lowers the value of K_3 by about 25 per cent and the dimensions of K_m by exactly the same amount. The only simple interpretation is that we are changing the nature of the rate-limiting step from one which is not influenced by the kind of water we happen to have to a rate-limiting step which is influenced by the kind of water or its ions. If one thinks of an over-all mechanism of this sort, the job becomes one of determining the nature of the rate-limiting steps in the particular instances, and of finding ways and means to alter these steps so that we can get information as to their nature and number.

Dr. Sturtevant: I would like to comment briefly on the inhibition of enzymes by reaction products. Numerous investigations of enzyme-catalyzed reactions have demonstrated that the mechanism proposed in 1913 by Michaelis and Menten (Michaelis, L., and Menten, M. L., *Biochem. Z.*,49, 333 [1913]) leads to kinetic equations which are formally adequate to describe the course of such reactions in many cases. The Michaelis-Menten concept of intermediate enzyme-substrate complexes has been extended (Lineweaver, H., and Burk, D., *J. Am. Chem. Soc.*, 56, 658 [1934]) to include complexes involving inhibitors of various types.

It is probable that enzymes behave as true catalysts, at least when present in the usual small concentrations, in that they do not affect the equilibrium concentrations established in reversible reactions. The large majority of enzyme reactions which have been studied are presumably reversible, although in many instances the equilibrium is so far on one side that the reverse reaction cannot be detected analytically. It is necessary to conclude that the products of a reversible enzyme-catalyzed reaction form as good a substrate for the enzyme as do the reactants; and it seems reasonable to assume that the reverse reaction involves the same enzyme sites as does the forward reaction. If this is true, the products must in all such systems act as competitive inhibitors so far as the forward reactions are concerned.

Competitive inhibition by reaction products has been discussed by Harmon and Niemann (Harmon, K. M., and Niemann, C., *J. Biol. Chem.*, 178, 743, [1949]), who formulated the inhibition as follows:

$$E + S \rightleftarrows ES \rightleftarrows E + P \tag{1}$$

$$E + P \rightleftarrows EP \text{ (Inactive)} \tag{2}$$

Here E, S and P represent enzyme, substrate and product, and ES and EP represent complexes of which only ES is directly involved in the conversion of S to P. As pointed out above, it seems inconceivable that the product can form a complex with the enzyme, utilizing the catalytically active sites, without any possibility of this complex decomposing to regenerate the original substrate. It would thus appear that the above scheme must be modified in a way to allow for the occurrence of the reverse reaction.

By analogy with current views of heterogeneous catalysis, it may be assumed that the substrate is converted to something fairly closely resembling the product during the interval between its adsorption and the desorption of the product. It is probable that the two extreme configurations of the complex, which may be represented by ES and EP, are separated by a high energy barrier the top of which corresponds to the configuration of the transition state common to the forward and reverse reactions. However, even though the interconversion of ES and EP may be the rate determining steps for the forward and reverse reactions, it is permissable to consider ES and EP as indistinguishable for purposes of investigating the overall kinetics.

We will thus take C to represent the total enzyme complex, so that the modified reaction scheme is

$$E + S_1 + S_2 \underset{k_2}{\overset{k_1}{\rightleftharpoons}} C \underset{k_4}{\overset{k_3}{\rightleftharpoons}} E + P_1 + P_2 \tag{3}$$

Here we have included explicit statement of the fact that in general an enzymatic reaction involves more than one substrate molecule and yields more than one product molecule.

Application of the usual steady-state approximation,

$$\frac{d(C)}{dt} = k_1(E)(S_1)(S_2) + k_4(E)(P_1)(P_2) - (K_2 + k_3)(C) = 0 \tag{4}$$

where the capital letters in parentheses represent the concentrations of the corresponding species, leads to the rate equation

$$v = -\frac{d(S_1)}{dt} = \frac{d(P_1)}{dt} = v_{max} \frac{(S_1)(S_2) - (P_1)(P_2)/K}{(S_1)(S_2) + K_m(1 + (P_1)(P_2)/Kp)} \tag{5}$$

Here $v_{max} = k_3(E)_0$ is the maximum rate observed at high substrate concentrations, $(E)_0$ being the total enzyme concentration. $K = k_1 k_3/k_2 k_4$ is the over-all equilibrium constant, $k_m = (k_2 + k_3)/k_1$ is the Michaelis-Menten constant, and $K_p = (k_2 + k_3)/k_4$.

It is evident that the *initial* forward rate, in the absence of products, is given by

$$v_0 = \frac{v_{max}}{1 + K_m/(S_1)_0(S_2)_0} \tag{6}$$

A similar equation holds for the initial rate of the reverse reaction in the absence of reactants. It will be possible to evaluate Kp from initial rate measurements only in those cases where the reaction is sufficiently reversible so that the reverse reaction can be accurately measured. However, a great many reactions of interest proceed so far in the forward direction that direct observation of the reverse reaction is not feasible. Most peptide hydrolyses, and the hydrolysis of inorganic pyrophosphate and other substances containing high-energy phosphate bonds, fall in this category. It is important to see whether detectable product inhibition can be expected in such cases.

A non-measurable reverse reaction implies that

$$(S_1)(S_2) \gg (P_1)(P_2)/K \tag{7}$$

at all stages of the forward reaction. Thus the rate of the forward reaction becomes

$$v = \frac{v_{max}(S_1)(S_2)}{(S_1)(S_2) + K_m(1 + (P_1)(P_2)/Kp)} \tag{8}$$

In order for there to be no detectable inhibition it would be necessary that

$$k_2 + k_3 \gg k_4 (P_2)(P_1)$$

which does not necessarily follow from the inequality (7). It would thus appear that cases might arise in which a concentration of products high enough to produce definite inhibition would not be high enough to produce observable reversal of the reaction.

Equation (8) can be rearranged to give

$$\frac{1}{v} = \frac{1}{v_{max}} + \frac{1}{v_{max}} \frac{Km}{(S_1)(S_2)} (1 + (P_1)(P_2)/Kp) \tag{9}$$

Lineweaver-Burk (2) plots, based on this equation, of initial rate measurements at various reactant and product concentrations could be employed to evaluate K_m and K_p. It should be noted that if inequality (7) is satisfied, and if $(P_1)_0 (P_2)_0 \gg (S_1)_0 (S_2)_0$, the kinetics will be of the same form as in the absence of product, since the factor $1 + (P_1)(P_2)/Kp$ will be essentially constant.

Very recently, Alberty (Alberty, R. A., *J. Am. Chem. Soc.*, **75**, 1928 [1953]) has applied the steady state approximation to a variety of enzyme-substrate mechanisms, all of which include the possibility of reversal of the over-all reaction. However, he was only concerned with the initial rates of the forward and reverse reactions in the absence, respectively, of products and reactants. One of the more elaborate mechanisms considered by Alberty, such as

$$S_1 + E \underset{k_2}{\overset{k_1}{\rightleftharpoons}} S_1 E$$

$$S_1 E + S_2 \underset{k_4}{\overset{k_3}{\rightleftharpoons}} P_1 E + P_2$$

$$P_1 E \underset{k_6}{\overset{k_5}{\rightleftharpoons}} P_1 + E$$

might well be a closer approach to the truth in any given case than the simpler one assumed here. A more complicated mechanism will lead to a more complicated rate equation, which will, however, include the same general type of dependence of rate on product concentrations as expressed in equation (5).

There appear to be no data available in the literature which can be employed to test the above equations. Schwert and Eisenberg (Schwert, G. S., and Eisenberg, M. A., *J. Biol. Chem.*, **179**, 665 [1949]) studied the inhibitory effect of benzoylarginine on the tryptic hydrolysis of benzoylargininamide. However, they did not add ammonium ion at the same time, and it is only the mixture of the two which can be expected to show inhibitory action attributable to the reaction products. Harmon and Niemann (3) had previously concluded that this system was subject to product inhibition, but their data are insufficiently extensive to serve as a test of equation (8).

DR. WILSON: The usual way that we write an enzyme reaction is that the enzyme and the substrate combine to form an enzyme-substrate complex, which in turn is converted to an activated complex, which in turn decomposes to form product and free enzyme. If you leave out the enzyme-substrate complex as an intermediate and go directly to the activated state, then one should not obtain the saturation type of curve as demanded by the experimental findings. This would suggest that the formation of ES is mandatory. But it is not necessary that ES be a step in the catalytic pathway—the enzyme saturation will be explained even if ES is inactive. I would like to raise the question whether the actual catalytic mechanism may not bypass the ES complex and go directly to the activated complex. The ES complex by binding enzyme is actually inhibitory, if it does not serve a catalytic function.

DR. EYRING: It seems to me that the only question is that of the limited amount of enzyme. After you have used up all the enzyme there is, then the rate cannot increase, and thus one gets an apparent inhibition. It is this business of conservation that is important. Sometimes you have to introduce conservation equations for both substrate and enzyme. If you leave out the equation for the conservation of the enzyme, the calculated rate rises continuously with substrate concentration. The reversible or irreversibly denatured enzyme must be included as a species if temperature and pressure maxima are to be understood.

DR. WILSON: The question I am raising, however, is whether the formation of the enzyme-substrate complex is, as we usually write it, necessary for the catalysis, or whether the activated complex can be formed directly from the enzyme and substrate.

DR. EYRING: Experiment establishes the existance of many enzymatic species. Thus enzymes compound with substrate, inhibitors, oxygen and exist in active and inactive forms. It is a marvel how much the Michaelis-Menten concept comes into this field (properly so, since it came early), but it seems to me that it simply introduces a conservation equation. Langmuir, of course, discussed this long ago and made the point that when you have all the surfaces covered—and this holds for enzymes, too—you can't get anything more happening with increase of substrate concentration.

DR. WILSON: I am asking, however, about the conceptual aspects. One conceives of the formation of an enzyme-substrate complex as being necessary for the process, and a lot of attention is paid to the enzyme-substrate complex; but it may have no direct bearing on the catalysis.

DR. EYRING: You are asking a question as to how you get the activated state; and I am afraid that we can't give you an answer to this problem except by experiments in each case.

DR. WILSON: This is the point. We don't know that we have to go through an enzyme-substrate complex to get to the activated state, and the enzyme-substrate complex may therefore actually be a side inhibitory reaction.

DR. EYRING: I think it is a good time to get away from the Michaelis-Menten formulations. As we get more and more detailed information concerning the mechanism, one can get at these complications in a variety of ways. It is equally useful to use the Langmuir language. If you have a lot of inhibitors, they form compounds and these require that a conservation equation be used for the enzyme. We make trouble for ourselves in going back to the Michaelis-Menten concept except as our kinetics require a stable substrate enzyme complex.

DR. BRINK: I think part of the difficulty in a situation of this sort is that the investigation of over-all kinetics will only suggest an equivalent reaction system. The establishment of the actual reaction system requires some experimental identification of the postulated intermediates—that is, the chemical "way stations" where groups of atoms sit around long enough to be identified as molecular entities. I think a good example of this problem is the type of work that Dr. Chance has been doing on catalase. He has proceeded experimentally from over-all kinetics to a more detailed picture of the intermediate steps, which seem to be getting more numerous as the study continues.

DR. EYRING: I would like to add just one more thought. In monomolecular reactions we also use a parallel language—that is, we have an activating process and a deactivating process, with the activated compound decomposing. Thus the Langmuir scheme, the Michaelis-Menten scheme, and the monomolecular scheme formally parallel each other in introducing intermediate compounds which are sometimes required by experiment.

DR. KLOTZ: I would like to bring out an example which may make Dr. Wilson and some of the others feel a little better about this. In the case of the ionization of ammonia or ammonium hydroxide, whichever you have in water, you can represent that scheme as ammonia plus water to give ammonium ions plus OH ions. Or you can say that ammonia plus water gives NH_4OH, which goes to ammonium ions and OH ions, or if you like you can say that ammonia plus 52 waters gives $NH_4OH + 51 H_2O$. And this then decomposes to ammonium ions and OH ions. Now none of those is distinguishable thermodynamically. Now, if you have another method, such as Chance's methods, where you can identify some of these intermediates, then you can distinguish between these three possibilities.

I would like to ask Dr. Bull a question or make a suggestion. In connection with the discussion of the discrepancy between your two constants— would your third explanation deserve a little more investigation? One wonders about the change in pH. In going from pH 4 to 1.5 wouldn't you be changing the charge on the molecular species involved, egg albumin becoming somewhat more positive and pepsin a little less negative? I don't know quite how this would work out; but if you have titration curves you could get the net electrostatic effect, and this may be enough to account for the deviations. It seems to me that these calculations would be worth making.

DR. BULL: Yes, we had titration curves of egg albumin and pepsin; and it is true that at pH 4, where this complex precipitates, it turns out that the electrostatic charge of the egg albumin is relatively negative to pepsin. I think that this interaction of egg albumin is certainly electrostatic in nature, since it is extremely sensitive to ionic strength, and it may be that the corrections for this would eliminate some of the discrepancies.

DR. KIRKWOOD: I just wanted to make some remarks relating to matters of principle, but I think Dr. Klotz has taken care of them. This has to do with the various forms of the Michaelis-Menten complexes and also the question about paths. First, about the paths: if one makes the assumption that one has equilibrium derived from the statistical mechanical point of view, that implies microscopic reversibility. All possible processes are going forward and backward at the same rates, and so the question really isn't an easy one whether you go directly to the activated state or through the enzyme-substrate complex. One can make no statements about the individual rates of these various hypothetical steps. In connection with the various forms of ES which Dr. Smith raised, the point is that they are not sufficiently thermodynamically defined, so it has no bearing on the validity of the Michaelis-Menten theory. It is true that if you could devise microscopic measurements for identifying one of these several ES intermediates which are supposed to be in equilibrium with one another you would essentially give yourself another degree of freedom. We could then talk about the individual steps, rather than the over-all sum which the Michaelis-Menten theory implies. As an example, there are certain compounds in which rotational isomers can be identified by infrared. Although they are in equilibrium—here I am thinking about some compound as 1, 2-dichloropropane—they are still separated by these rotational energy barriers. Because they are in equilibrium, the individual molecules are not thermodynamically defined. Sill, by special methods, such as the use of infrared, one can identify and talk about a single isomer.

Dr. HAMMETT: Dr. Wilson's question refers to a matter which has caused much confusion in discussions of reaction mechanism. A system in which the mobile and reversible reaction $E + S \rightleftharpoons ES$ is followed by a rate-determining reaction of ES shows exactly the same dependence of rate on time and composition of the system as one in which the same mobile and reversible first step is followed by a different and irreversible rate-determining of E with S to form the reaction products. Consequently no study of the over-all kinetics of the reaction can distinguish between these mechanisms.

If the rate of the process $E + S \rightleftharpoons ES$ is of the same order of magnitude as that of the second stage of the reaction one encounters a very complicated dependence of rate on time and composition so that one needs a differential analyzer or other high speed computer if one is to evaluate experimental data.

Dr. E. SMITH: What I would like to point out is that you don't have to be discouraged that you may have different rate-limiting steps, since many reactions are now lending themselves to direct experimentation in measuring the individual steps involved. There are several ways of altering these various steps—pH as well as ionic strength are two ways.

Dr. CHANCE: I just want to make a short remark. What I am going to say has already been said in part by Dr. Brink and Dr. Klotz.

Whenever possible, the enzyme substrate complex should be studied directly so that its steady-state concentration and, even better, the rates of its formation and decomposition are measured. It is indeed surprising how many systems can now be studied by direct measurements of the reaction intermediates with the aid of sensitive and rapid spectroscopic techniques: four type of peroxidases (horse-radish, milk, leucocyte, and yeast), four types of catalase (blood, liver, bacterial, and plant), seven or more types of cytochromes (a_3, a, c, b, a_1 a_2, b_3), various flavoproteins, and some DPN linked dehydrogenases (horse liver, alcohol dehydrogenase, heart muscle, lactic dehydrogenase, muscle and yeast glyceraldehyde-3-phosphate dehydrogenases). It seems probable that many new types of systems will soon be added and an important example is the spectroscopically defined acyl enzyme compound in the triosephosphate dehydrogenase system which may be used to study the mechanism of transfer reactions (see Harting, J., and Chance, B., *Fed. Proc.*, in press). And new physical methods may soon be usable for direct kinetic studies, for example, the Rankine type of paramagnetic susceptibility apparatus and the electronic resonance absorption apparatus.

Lastly, I would like to make a remark on the question of nomenclature of the intermediate compounds that intervene between the formation of the enzyme substrate compound and the release of the free enzyme with the formation of the final reaction products:

$$E + S \rightarrow ES_I \rightarrow ES_{II} \rightarrow ES_{III} \rightarrow E + P$$

We would term these intermediates enzyme substrate compounds, even though the substrate may have been altered somewhat during the process of transition from ES_I to ES_{III}. (The intermediates may also be given a chemical name, if and when their structure is known.) Under a particular set of experimental conditions, one of the intermediates, for example, ES_{II} will be rate determining and the reaction sequence may be represented:

$$E + S \rightarrow ES_{II} \rightarrow E + P$$

This is the classical formulation of Michaelis and Menten. In appreciation of the achievements of the early workers on enzyme kinetics (Henri, Brown, and Michaelis and Menten), we desire to retain the name of Michaelis enzyme substrate compound for that intermediate which is rate limiting for particular conditions in a complex enzymatic sequence and which is responsible for the usual activity-substrate concentration relationship. Under different experimental conditions, another enzyme substrate compound may become the Michaelis compound. This nomenclature appears to be flexible and to be a suitable description of a number of enzyme systems.

Part III

THE FUNCTION OF METALS IN ENZYME CATALYSIS

CHELATION AND CATALYSIS

MELVIN CALVIN

Department of Chemistry,
University of California, Berkeley

ANY EXAMINATION of the nature of the substances which function as catalysts in biological transformations cannot fail to impress you with the fact that metals are obviously involved, and only a slightly closer examination brings out the rather pronounced fact that in those cases in which the nature of the combination of the metal has been determined, it is a chelate compound of some sort. It was this fact which, some fifteen years ago, first impressed me and resulted in the initiation of a series of studies, some of the results of which I would now like to describe.

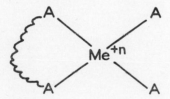

FIG. 1. Complex ions and Chelate compounds.

First of all, it is necessary to define what we mean by the term "chelate." In Fig. 1 we show diagrammatically that structural element for which the term chelate is used. In general, metal ions may be said to form complex compounds with a wide variety of ligands. The term ligand may be described as an atom or a group of atoms which generally donate electrons to a separate metal atom, to form a more or less homopolar bond, as distinguished from purely coulombic interaction between ions, dipoles, or combinations of these. If two or more of these ligands are themselves tied together in some way, as yet unspecified, the compound is said to be a chelate compound. The word comes from Greek and means claw, and it is quite clear how the word was derived. Thus, chelate compounds, especially the ones that I am going to speak about now, may be said to be a special class of the more general type of compounds which we call " complex " compounds. Some specific examples of chelate compounds are shown in Fig. 2, in which the ordinary complexes are

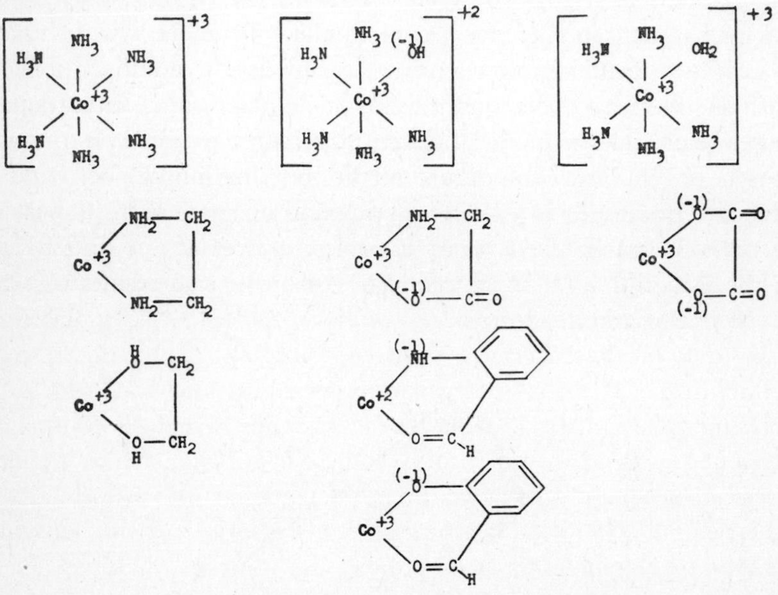

FIG. 2. Various types of complex ions and chelate compounds.

given in the top row and a wide variety of chelate complexes related to them, by one or another means of classification, are shown below. Thus, in the first column, we have hexamminocobaltic ion, in which the ligands are all separated — an ordinary complex compound. If, however, two or more of those amino groups are bound togther, as in ethylenediamine, we then speak of the compound as being a chelate compound. In this case, the ligands are all uncharged atoms — uncharged nitrogen atoms in the amino compounds and uncharged oxygen atoms in the hydroxylated compounds. In the next case of a complex ion (hydroxypentammine cobaltic ion), we have an example of a mixture of ligands, some of which are charged (in this case, only one). Correspondingly, one can make chelate compounds in which the mixture of the ligands is changed in the same way; below we have a neutral nitrogen and a charged oxygen; a neutral oxygen and a charged nitrogen; one neutral oxygen and one charged; finally, both are charged (in the oxalate compound) and uncharged (in the glycol compound). There is a wide variety of such arrangements which can be made, and a number of classifications of chelate compounds have been devised which depend upon one or another mode of description. One major type of classification of chelate compounds would be the number of ligands which are tied together in a single or multiple claw. This is perhaps the most useful single type of classification. Thus, a single, non-chelating ligand such as ammonia is said to be monodentate, while the ethylenediamine compound would be spoken of as a bidentate compound, in that there are two coordinating groups in a single chelate ring. If three coordinating atoms are part of the same chelating group, then it would be a tridentate chelate compound. A bidentate ligand would form a single chelate ring, while a tridentate reagent would form two rings. I can't go into the details of this type of mechanical classification. A very nice treatise, in which this type of classification is described, was written by Harvey Diehl (1) at Iowa some fifteen years ago.

To pursue this interest and work in chelate compounds and the part they might play in biocatalysis, we had to decide what type of measurements — physical or chemical — might be the most useful for the purpose of giving information about the nature of chelate compounds, and lead ultimately, of course, to some clues as to why they are important in biocatalysis. One very simple type of measurement which could be made and which is easily defined was the stability of the chelate compound. The way the stability of the chelate compound was measured depended upon the particular system. Fig. 3 shows how such association constants are defined algebraically — the metals plus the chelate group form a metal-chelate associate. I have here written the chelating group as a charged one; it doesn't necessarily have to be; n could be zero, positive, or negative. Most of them are either neutral or negative, at least this is true of most of the ones I am going to talk about here.

$$Me^{+n} + Ke^{-m} \rightleftarrows [MeKe]^{+n-m} \qquad k_1 = \frac{[MeKe^{+n-m}]}{[Me^{+n}][Ke^{-m}]}$$

$$MeKe^{+m-m} + Ke^{-m} \rightleftarrows [MeKe_2]^{+n-2m} \qquad k_2 = \frac{[MeKe_2^{+n-2m}]}{[MeKe^{+n-m}][Ke^{-m}]}$$

For the case n = 2, m = 1 $\qquad\qquad\qquad k_3$

Fig. 3. Stability defined in terms of association constants.

The various types of constants are defined quite clearly here in terms of equilibrium and dissociation constants, and most of the data now being collected are expressed in terms of the successive stepwise stability constants, k_1, k_2, etc., and of K, which represents the product of the stepwise stability constants.

TABLE 1

FACTORS INFLUENCING THE STABILITY OF COMPLEX COMPOUNDS

Metal	*Complexing Group*
charge	polarizability
radius	size (steric repulsion)
available orbitals	basicity
	steric effects
	entropy effects
	resonance effects

Having such measurements at hand, the next stage in the study was an attempt to deduce what the factors are which influence the stability constants for a variety of chelate compounds. The classification of effects shown in Table 1 resulted after a considerable amount of work and after it was clear that a number of factors play a part in determining the value of such an " association " constant. Some of these were also playing a part in the binding of ordinary complex compounds; that is, they are not necessarily limited to chelate compounds. The dotted line is the line which divides the two areas — those factors which are related to the stability of

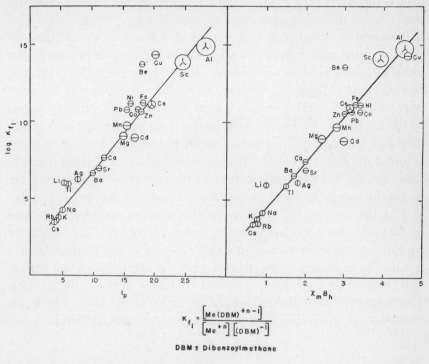

$$K_{f_1} = \frac{\left[Me(DBM)^{+n-1} \right]}{\left[Me^{+n} \right] \left[(DBM)^{-1} \right]}$$

DBM = Dibenzoylmethane

FIG. 4.

complex compounds in general, not limited necessarily to chelate compounds — are to be found above that dotted line; those which are characteristic and limited to chelate compounds themselves are below the line. Such things as steric effects due to limitations imposed by the rings, entropy effects, and resonance effects are not to be found in simple complex compounds, at least in the form in which we will talk about them here. It is my purpose to try to limit our examination to the variation of stability constants of chelate compounds with factors that are characteristic of the chelating group itself. However, in order to make possible some discussion of the effect of variation of metal ion on properties related to chelation and catalysis it will be useful to point out at least one rather simple empirical relationship between a fundamental property of the electron configuration of the metal atoms and the stability of the complex compounds they form. This relationship provides a first approximation toward a more fundamental theory.

It should be noted that in the types of complexes we are describing, the coordinating atom always donates a pair of electrons to the metal ion with which it complexes. In so far as these electrons may be conceived as returning to vacant orbitals in the metal ion, one might expect that the energy of such a bond would be determined by the depth (on the energy scale) of the vacant orbitals into which they fall. This depth, in turn, might be measured by the energy required to remove electrons from those and closely related orbitals. Thus, we are led to expect some sort of monotonic relationship between the energy required to remove the last electron in the production of the ion and the stability of the complex compound formed by that ion. Such a relationship is shown in Fig. 4. The ionization potential required to remove the last electron in the formation of a specific ion is plotted as the abcissa with the logarithm of the formation constant of a chelate compound with that ion as ordinate (2). The formation constant is defined by equation (1), in which the coordinating group is the anionic dibenzoylmethane (DBM).

$$K_f = \frac{[Me(DBM)^{+n-1}]}{[Me^{+n}][DBM^{-1}]} \tag{1}$$

Other derived or secondarily determined properties of the metals have also been used to demonstrate such relationships, and a comparable graph involving χ_m, which is the electronegativity, and B_h, which is the hybrid bond orbital strength, is shown alongside the ionization potential plot. Further description of the latter two is to be found in connection with experimental work in which the data were obtained.[2] It is to be expected that such a plot of the ionization potential complexing constant would contain fewer deviations if it were made with a simple complexing constant such as amine formation or even complexing constants with ethylenediamine rather than the β-diketone for which it was first produced. One could then proceed to examine the larger deviations from the plot in terms of special chelation effects. Even in the present plot, Fig. 4, it is interesting to observe that the stability constant of cupric ion for this β-diketone seems to be too great for its simple ionization potential. We will come back to this characteristic of cupric ion again later.

We can return now to a consideration of those factors more closely dependent upon the existence of chelation itself — those listed below the dotted line in Table 1. These three factors can be grouped into two types. The steric and entropy effects are the effects in which chelation changes the translational, rotational, and vibrational energy distribution of the chelate group. The resonance effects, on the other hand, are effects which have to do with the change in the electronic energy of this chelating group, not to the exclusion of translational, vibrational effects, but in addition to those. Let us have a look at each of these, in the order shown, and pick out more or less clearly defined examples of each case.

The first of these, the steric effect, is quite easily defined. A type of compound upon which Schwarzenbach (3) made a series of measurements, and which is shown in Fig 5, will exemplify such steric effects. He measured the binding constant of a series of metals with a series of polymethylenediaminetetraacetic acid derivatives as a function of the size of this ring. He found that there was a definite sequence of stability constants depending on the size of the ring, as shown in Table 2. Here, the size of the ring is given by n, the

number of methylene groups between the two nitrogen atoms.   In
the alkaline earth sequence there is a maximum for calcium.   You
will also notice that as the number of carbon atoms lying between

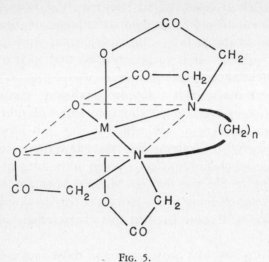

Fig. 5.

TABLE 2

STABILITY CONSTANTS OF ALKALINE EARTH COMPLEXES WITH
HOMOLOGS OF ETHYLENEDIAMINETETRAACETIC ACID

| | | | | | | Log K | | |
n	pK_1	pK_2	pK_3	pK_4	Mg^{+2}	Ca^{+2}	Sr^{+2}	Ba
2	2.0	2.7	6.16	10.26	8.7	10.5	8.6	7.
3	2.0	2.7	7.91	10.27	6.0	7.1	5.2	4.
4	1.9	2.7	9.07	10.45		5.0		
5	2.2	2.7	9.50	10.58		4.6		

the two nitrogens increases, the binding of calcium decreases. However, the binding of hydrogen does not change very much; in fact,
the binding of hydrogen actually increases a bit, if anything.   The
quantities labeled K_i are the acidity constants for the corresponding hydrogen ion dissociation.   Why do we put the binding of
hydrogen ion down for comparison?   The chelating agent is, in

effect, donating a pair of electrons to the central metal ions and this is chemically the function of a base. The metal is performing the acid function in place of hydrogen ion, so one would expect that there should be some parallelism between the binding of the metal and the binding of hydrogen ion. Whatever factor is involved in the binding of the hydrogen ion in the acid-base reaction should be, in some part at least, involved in the binding of the metal ion. In order to compensate for that factor, which really has nothing to do with the chelate phenomenon itself, we should compare chelate groups of like acidity with each other. We cannot always, or even frequently, make chelating groups of like acidity for comparison, but we can extrapolate the chelation constants to the corresponding acidities. Later on we will see how this can be done quite readily.

It is quite clear that the ring size has a pronounced influence on the binding of calcium which it does not have on the binding of hydrogen. This is the result of an interaction between the steric requirement of the chelating groups, which is determined by, among other things, the number of atoms, their distances apart, and the angular requirement of the bonds.

There is another very nice example of steric effects on stability constants to be found in a comparison of the binding of ethylenediamine and ammonia by silver ion (4). Silver ion binds ammonia (two of them) to form a complex ion with a fairly good stability constant. Log K is of the order of 7. If, however, one compares that with the binding of the two amino groups in ethylenediamine, one finds that the log K of this chelate ion is only around 4.7. Now here is a case in which the complex ion is a linear ion, $H_3N : Ag : NH_3$, while the ethylenediamine ligand cannot readily form a linear complex with a single silver ion. In effect, then, the K value for ethylenediamine is really the stability constant of a single bound nitrogen or that of a chelate with a highly-strained metal bond, while that for the simple amine involves the binding of two nitrogen atoms in the most favored positions. This is an extreme case, wherein the steric requirement of the metal and the steric possibilities of the chelating agent make their chelating combination very difficult or even impossible.　There are many other examples of steric effects on stability constants (5).

The next type of effect to be considered is the one which we have chosen to call the entropy effect.　The reason for calling it the entropy effect is that in those cases in which we have been able to determine the heat and entropy of the reaction by measuring temperature

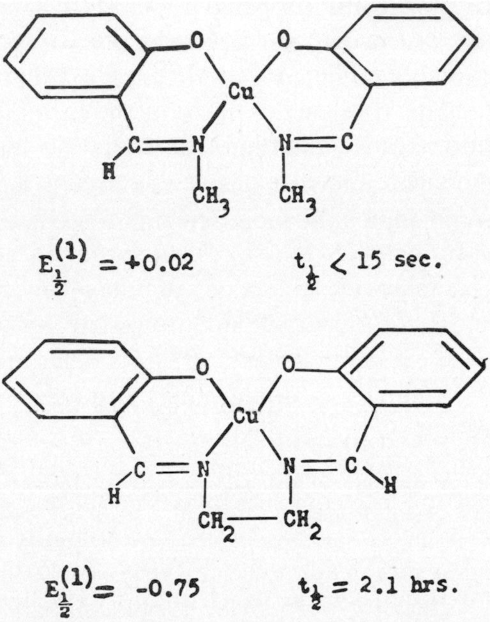

$$E_{\frac{1}{2}}^{(1)} = +0.02 \qquad t_{\frac{1}{2}} < 15 \text{ sec.}$$

$$E_{\frac{1}{2}}^{(1)} = -0.75 \qquad t_{\frac{1}{2}} = 2.1 \text{ hrs.}$$

FIG. 6.

coefficients of the equilibrium constant, K, we find that the influence we have called the "entropy" effect in log K is found almost exclusively in the ΔS part of the free energy change and not in the ΔH part.　There are various ways to formulate the effect, and I will choose only one; others are described in the literature.　Fig. 6 shows an example of such a case, in which the stability of the compound is enormously enhanced by simply binding two sets of ligands together; the mere unification of the ligands to make a single molecule from two of them increases the stability enormously. These data are not stability constants themselves. They are quantities more or less directly dependent upon stability constants. $E_{1/2}^{(1)}$ happens to be a polarographic half-wave reduction potential, and $t_{1/2}$ is a half-time for exchange of cupric ion with the chelate-bound copper; and in both cases an enormous increase in stability is apparent when two C–H bonds are replaced by one C–C bond. With the two pairs of bidentate donor atoms, the copper is reduced at a potential almost equal to that at which one can get reduction of aqueous copper; with the cupric ion bound by one tetradentate ligand, we have ¾ volt more stability. The contrast in the rate of exchange of chelated copper with cupric ion is equally great. There are many such cases, but no matter how you interpret them you can be confident that they will reflect in some degree the increased stability constants when they can be measured.

TABLE 3

THE ENTROPY EFFECT

$$Ni^{++}(H_2O)_x + 6\,NH_3(aq) \rightleftarrows Ni(NH_3)_6^{++} + xH_2O \quad \Delta H \simeq -19; \; \Delta S \simeq -22$$

$$Ni^{++}(H_2O)_x + 3\,en(aq) \rightleftarrows Ni(en)_3^{++} + xH_2O \quad \Delta H \simeq -25; \; \Delta S \simeq +2$$

$$Ni(NH_3)_6^{++} + 3\,en(aq) \rightleftarrows Ni(en)_3^{++} + 6\,NH_{3aq} \quad \Delta H \simeq -6; \; \Delta S \simeq +24$$

en = ethylenediamine

Table 3 shows some cases in which stability constants were measured for such systems as these. Here, we have the equilibrium constant of the binding of six ammonias to nickel, for which the temperature coefficient has been determined, and we can separate out the heat and entropy terms. We have also the binding constant of three ethylenediamines by nickel, and again the heat and the entropy terms have been separated. By combining these two, one can get the reaction involving the replacement of six ammonias by three ethylenediamines, to give the nickel ethylenediamine and six ammonias. The ΔH term is a small one; the "force" that drives this reaction to the right is the large increase in entropy. There are many other such cases; however, not enough as yet have been determined with temperature coefficients so that we can say with a high degree of certainty that the mere tying together of the ligands increases the stability, not by an increase in the binding heat but by means of a change in the way the entropy is distributed on the two sides of the reaction.   Fig. 7 shows three more such cases which can be interpreted in this way (4).   Unfortunately, for this system, one doesn't have temperature coefficients; one has only the log K values at one temperature.   In $Zn(NH_3)_4^{+2}$ there are four separate nitrogens on zinc (a log K of 9.5); when you tie them together in

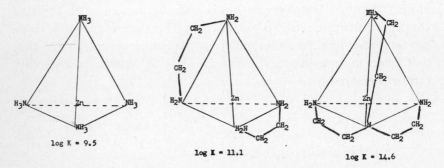

FIG. 7. Effects of Chelation on Stability Constants.

pairs the log K goes up to 11; and when you tie them all together in a single ligand the log K goes up to almost 15.   Here, we have all four nitrogens as part of a single chelating molecule.   This would be spoken of as a tetradentate molecule, and the equilibrium constant is very much in favor of the binding.   I suspect that when these log K's are determined as a function of temperature so that we can separate the heat and entropy terms, most of this extra stability will appear in an entropy term.   The simplest interpretation is that on the left-hand side of the reaction one has zinc binding four or five water molecules plus the tris-β-aminoethylamine, while on the right-hand side one has the zinc complex, plus four or five free water molecules, and thus a net increase in total number of molecules, or the total number of translational degrees of freedom.   One could describe it also in terms of the relative probabilities of forward and reverse reactions, and thus translate the thermodynamics into the language of kinetics. So much, then, for the so-called entropy effect.

The third and last factor listed as especially concerned in determining chelate stability is the resonance effect. In all of the previous cases of binding together of the ligands to make the chelate compounds, the two bound donor atoms have no electronic interaction with each other outside the chelated element. In Fig. 8 we see

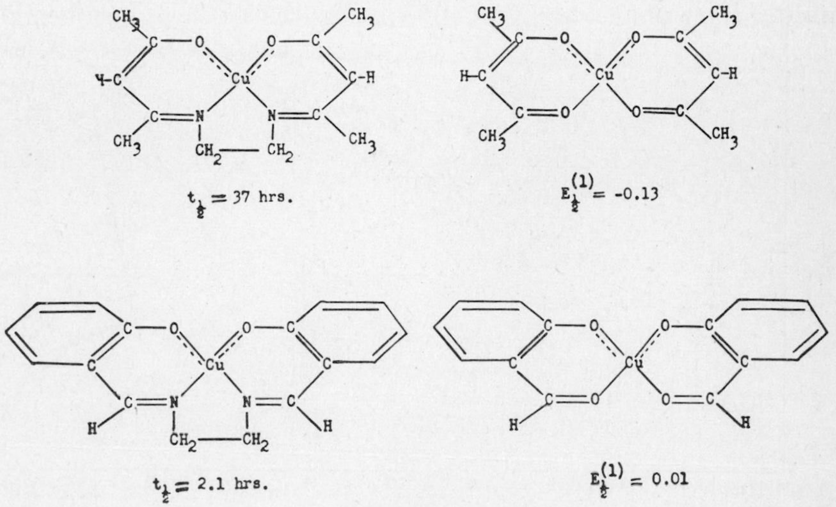

$t_{\frac{1}{2}} = 37$ hrs. $E_{\frac{1}{2}}^{(1)} = -0.13$

$t_{\frac{1}{2}} = 2.1$ hrs. $E_{\frac{1}{2}}^{(1)} = 0.01$

Fig. 8.

examples of chelate compounds in which this is not so, in which there is, at least possibly, a direct electronic interaction between the two donor atoms. In each acetylacetonate (and salicylaldehyde) chelate ring, there is a direct electronic interaction possible between two oxygen atoms (or between one oxygen and one nitrogen atom), through the conjugate system. These are quite different sorts of chelating systems from the others, such as ethylenediamine, in which there is no possibility of electronic interaction between the ligands. It is the peculiar characteristics of such chelate compounds that arise from the possibility of forming closed cyclic resonance systems through the orbitals of the bound metal atom that next claim our attention.

How can we find the nature of the effect of such a possibility on the stability constant? We could compare each of the upper compounds in Fig. 8 with the corresponding lower one. For the pair on the right, the comparison is made via polarographic half-wave potential which, for salicylaldehyde, is very nearly that of unchelated

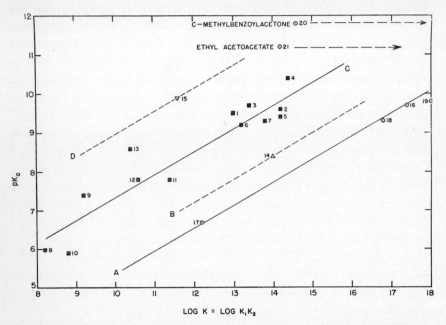

FIG. 9. 1 Salicylaldehyde, 2 3-n-propyl-salicylaldehyde, 3 5-methyl-salicylaldehyde, 4 4, 6-dimethyl-salicylaldehyde, 5 3-ethoxy-salicylaldehyde, 6 3-methoxy-salicylaldehyde, 7 4-methoxy-salicylaldehyde, 8 3-nitro-salicylaldehyde, 9 4-nitro-salicylaldehyde, 10 5-nitro-salicylaldehyde, 11 3-fluoro-salicylaldehyde, 12 3-chloro-salicylaldehyde, 13 5-chloro-salicylaldehyde, 14 2-hydroxy-1-naphthaldehyde, 15 2-hydroxy-3-naphthaldehyde, 16 acetylacetone, 17 trifluoroacetylacetone, 18 furoylacetone, 19 benzoylacetone, 20 C-methylbenzoylacetone, 21 ethyl acetoacetate.

free copper ion, while the acetylacetonate is slightly more stable than the copper ion. In the pair on the left, we have the same difference; the comparison here is via half-time for exchange between aqueous copper ion and bound copper ion. In both cases, the acetylacetone molecule (or the derivative of acetylacetone) is the more stable one, when compared with the corresponding derivative of salicylaldehyde. Now, one can make a more detailed examination of the same structures in terms of binding constants, and Fig. 9

shows the results of such measurements which were made quite a number of years ago. There are better ones available now, but these show the essence of the effect. This is a plot of the binding constant for copper against the acidity constant of the same chelating group. The upper solid line corresponds to a series of substituted salicylaldehydes, while the lower solid line corresponds to a series of β-diketones related to acetylacetone. It is thus clear that there is a component in the binding of copper ion which is exactly parallel in the binding of a proton. There is also a component which is very different for the two cations. Thus, when we compare the binding of copper ion by a salicylaldehyde with the binding by an acetylacetone residue of the same acidity, we find that the acetylacetone binds copper some two powers of ten more strongly than does the salicylaldehyde. Here we have the essence of this so-called " resonance " effect. You see in the direct measurement of the stability constant how the acetylacetone binds the copper much more strongly than does the salicylaldehyde. There are two other dotted lines in Fig. 9, but one can hardly speak of them as being defined by experimental results, since each line has a single point on it. The reason they are drawn that way is my faith that when such a series of compounds is made they will fall on these lines; perhaps one day one of you will have an opportunity to do this. The question now arises as to why these compounds fall in the series they do. Comparing at constant acidity, you find that the 2-hydroxy-3-naphthaldehyde binds copper the poorest, the salicylaldehyde is next, the 2-hydroxy-1-naphthaldehyde next, and the β-diketones (acetylacetone) most strongly.

Fig. 10 shows the elements of structure which are involved in these four compounds in inverse order. The essence of structure which runs in that order is the double-bond character of the carbon-carbon bond adjacent to the anionic oxygen. In acetylacetone, there is nothing to interfere with the double bond. In 2-hydroxy-1-naphthaldehyde, the double bond is double two-thirds of the time — the other one-third of the time it is a single bond, because it is involved in this naphthalene resonance. This is the simplest and most naive description, and it is the most readily visualized. In salicylaldehyde, the bond is part of a benzene ring and thus is double only one-half of the time, and in 2-hydroxy-3-naphthaldehyde the bond in the naphthalene is present only one-third of the time.   These numbers, then, would correspond to what we might call a bond-order designa-

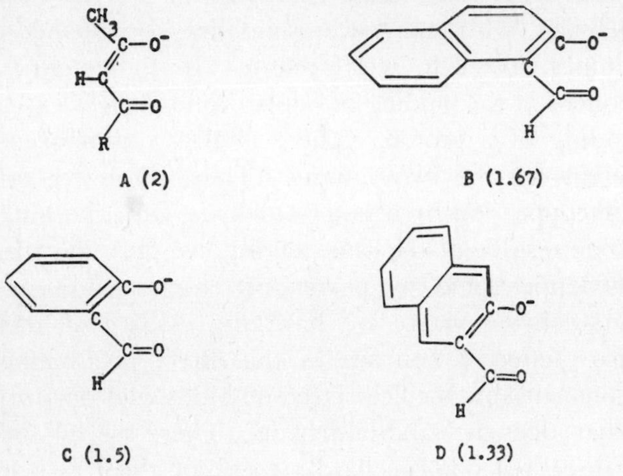

FIG. 10.   The Resonance Effect.

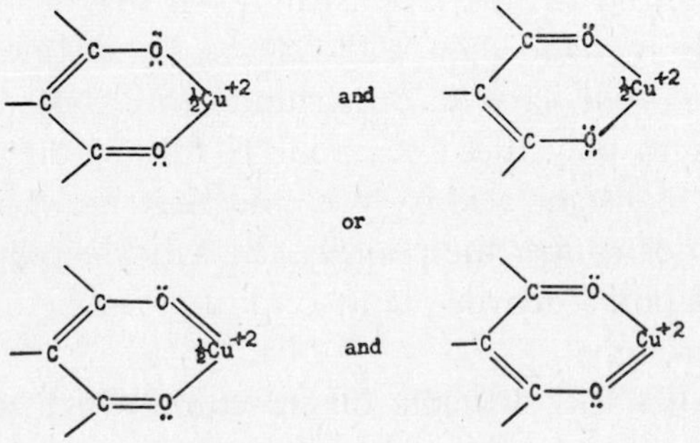

FIG. 11.

tion, and this is exactly the stability constant order found for the binding of copper. This suggests the fundamental structural origin of the effect of electronic interaction between two ligands.

It would appear, then, that the resonance forms which play an important part in the binding of copper could be represented as in Fig. 11. The two resonance forms characteristic of acetylacetonate ion would be those two represented as the upper pair, in which a single electron pair on each of the two oxygens is involved in the bonding of copper ion. The only difference between the two forms is the shift of an electron pair between the two oxygen atoms through the conjugated carbon chain. Actually, that is only one way of representing it, and doesn't give any real reason for understanding why copper should be bound more strongly to a compound in which this is possible than to one in which it is not possible (or possible to a smaller extent). Therefore, I think it would be better to represent the binding as shown in the lower set of formulas in which a pair of electrons has actually gone over and formed, formally at least, a double bond with the copper, so that one has what looks like a benzenoid type of system involving the copper atom. These, then, are the two benzenoid, or Kekulé-type, forms if one uses the valence bond mode of expression. When this was first done, some ten years ago, it required a good deal of fortitude to write this double bond. Nowadays, it isn't such a shock to do it, because one can avoid the actual writing of a double bond to the copper by using the molecular orbital mode of representation in which the one d-orbital together with one s, and two of the p-orbitals of the copper are used to make the four single bonds, and the remaining p-orbital of the copper is the one that is used to form a π-bond system with the p-orbitals of the oxygen and carbon atoms of the conjugate ring. Thus, one gets a straightforward representation of the π molecular orbital system which requires resonance between Kekulé-type forms in the valence bond representation (Fig. 12).

We have described at some length the various ways in which the metals will interact with the chelating groups and the particular factors which influence that interaction. The next phase of our discussion is to try to apply these principles to the catalytic functions which chelate compounds have. The chelate compounds most familiar to us in biology are the ones responsible for the red of hemoglobin(hemin) and the green of plants (chlorophyll), but there are many others which are not so well known and which are somewhat simpler in structure. Actually, rather than try to devise a detailed description of the mode of catalysis of such substances as hemoglobin (or hemin), or catalase and chlorophyll, I think it might be better to examine a few suggestions of chelate action — catalytic action — pretty much along the lines we have just described for stability constants. I suspect that one will be able to divide the catalytic functions of chelates into two general types, as were used to describe the stability constants, namely, those interactions which involve the

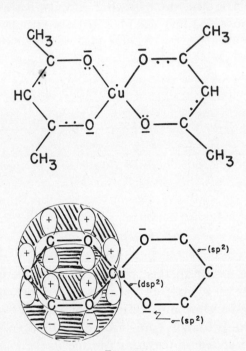

Fig. 12.

changes in translational, rotational, and vibrational energy systems of the chelating group, and those involving electronic changes.

The ones that involve changes in translational, rotational, and vibrational degrees of freedom will be those which are primarily entropy effects, and we sometimes speak of them as steric effects in reaction rates. A particular biochemical example of that comes out when one examines the fact that in practically every phosphatase that has been described to any extent at all, where the enzyme has been isolated, or at least partially purified, and the nature of the metal requirements are known, it has been found that either magnesium or manganese is usually required. I would like to suggest that the nature of the magnesium or manganese function is a chelating function — a chelating action — which has to do with the bringing together of the coenzymes and the enzyme, through a double chelate ring. The structure of such a complex is shown in Fig. 13. The enzymes involved here are phosphatases (or phosphate-transfer

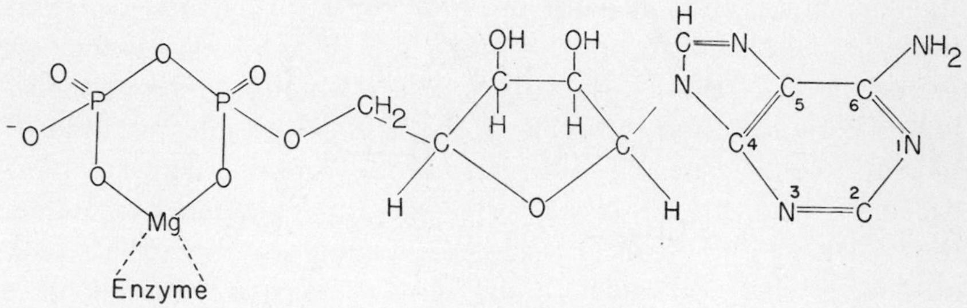

FIG. 13. Binding to Enzyme through chelation by metal ion, usually Mg.

ADP (ATP, UDP, CoA)

systems of one sort or another) and they participate in the action of one or another of a group of coenzymes, everyone of which has a pyrophosphate structure in it. The reason that this can occur is the presence of the pyrophosphate linkage in the coenzyme and some similar or corresponding chelating linkage in the enzyme itself. If the coenzymes were simple phosphates, or if they were single binding ligands on the enzyme, they would not have the binding constants required to bring the coenzyme and the enzyme together. This would show up, for example, not in the heat of activation of an enzymic reaction, but rather in its so-called "temperature-independent" factors.

The next case is one from straight organic chemistry, in which possibly both the entropy and the electronic, or resonance, effects might play a part. This is the reaction of an alkylation of a β-keto ester, using the sodium salt on the one hand, and the copper salt of the β-keto ester on the other. It might be worth-while to set down that reaction as you normally see it:

$$\underset{\substack{\|\\ O}}{\overset{\substack{R-C-O^- \\ \|}}{R'O-C-CH}} + R''X \rightarrow \underset{\substack{\|\\ O}}{\overset{\substack{R-C-O-R'' \\ \|}}{R'O-C-CH}} \quad \text{and/or} \quad \underset{R'O-C=O}{\overset{R-C=O}{\underset{}{C}}}\overset{R''}{\underset{H}{}}$$

Sometimes one gets the O-alkylated product of the ketonic oxygen, and sometimes the C-alkylated product. Recently a comparison was made of the alkylation of the sodium salt and the copper salt, not of acetoacetic ester itself, but of its diethyl amide. A very interesting difference became apparent. Fig. 14 shows an interpretation of the effect (6). When one alkylates the sodium salt, one gets almost exclusively the normal alkylation reaction, or sometimes perhaps on the enolic oxygen. On the other hand, when one alkylates the copper salt, one gets a ketene acetal derivative. In other words, one alkylates the amide carbonyl instead of the ketonic carbonyl. This is presumed to be due to the establishment of an equilibrium between two different chelate compounds, one in which the two ligands are both oxygen atoms and one in which the carboxamide group is turned around, and the copper binds the nitrogen better than does the sodium. The copper, in other words, forms a relatively stable chelate compound with the oxygen and nitrogen, and the sodium does not. The sodium gives the ordinary alkylation; the copper exposes the amide carbonyl in an anionic form, so that it alkylates to a ketene acetal. This is almost a qualitative difference.

Let us go back again to cases closer to biochemistry and in which the situation is more nearly an electronic one; for example, the catalysis of decarboxylation of ketosuccinic acid derivatives. Fig. 15 shows how these catalyses have been formulated (7). Here, we have copper catalysis of the decarboxylation of a number of keto acids through the formation of a chelate ring between the carbonyl and the α-carboxyl group. The demand for electrons by Cu^{+2} results in an electron shift from the β-carboxyl toward the carbonyl, liberating the carbon dioxide and forming an unstable intermediate. This then loses copper, forming the unstable enol of the simple α-keto acid. This is the way in which the catalysis of the decarboxylation of oxalacetic and oxalsuccinic acid has been formulated, because one can't get that catalysis, whether one has hydrogen on the reduced carbon atom or not.

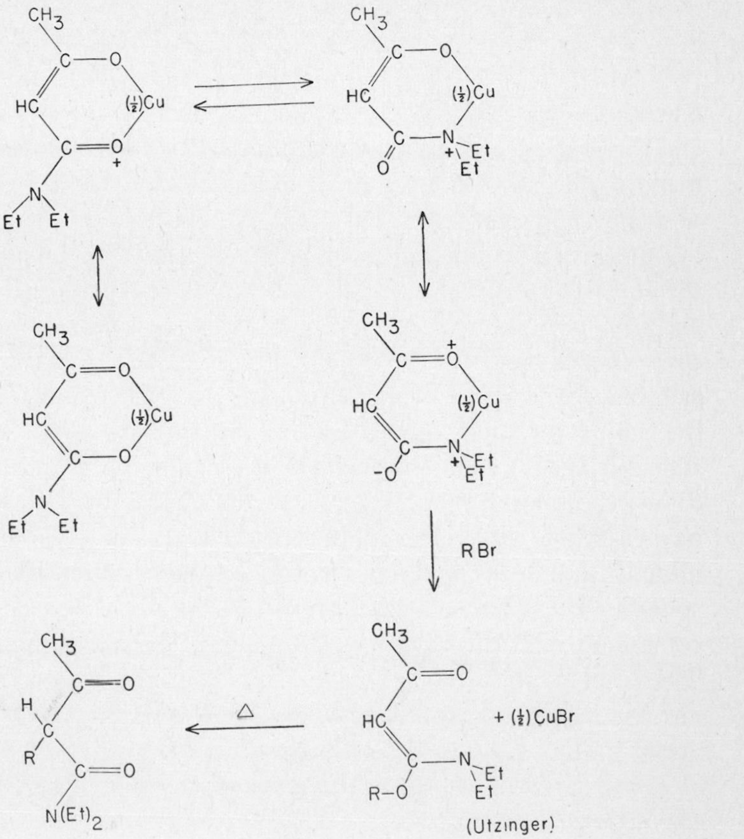

FIG. 14.

The next such case is somewhat less explicit but perhaps more spectacular. It is an example encompassing a whole variety of reactions which take place essentially only in the chelate compound and which are very difficult to perform in the absence of a chelate compound. Fig. 16 shows such a model substance. It consists of the

Cu (or Ni) chelate of salicylaldehyde, which can form a Schiff base with an amino acid ester. This is the ester of an α-amino acid.

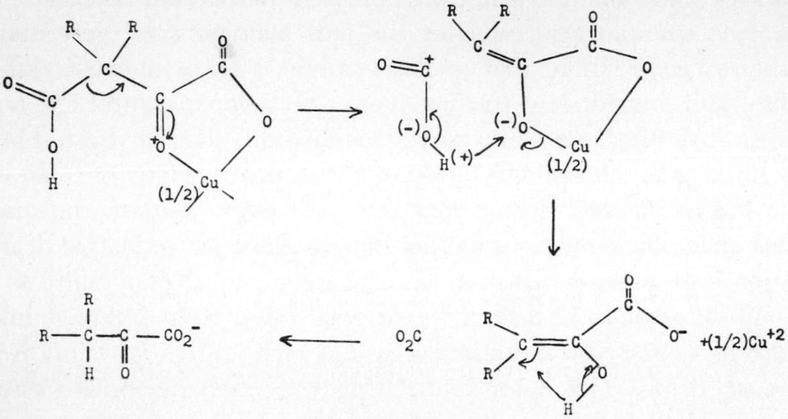

FIG. 15. Metal catalyzed decarboxylation of keto-succinic acid derivatives.
(Oxaloacetic)
(Oxalosuccinic)

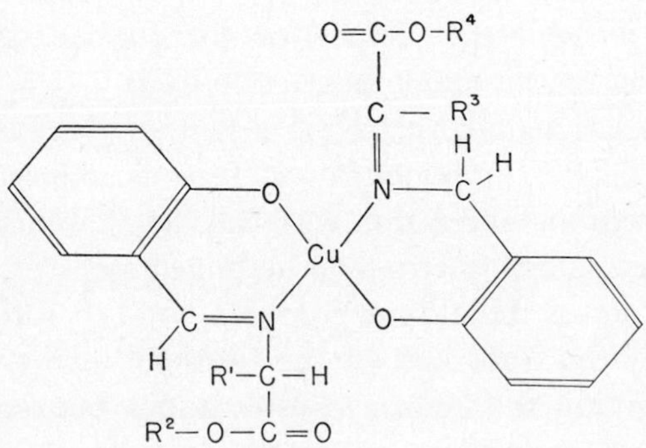

FIG. 16.

A. Racemization.

B. Oxidative deamination.

C. Ester exchange.

When one forms such a Schiff base between salicylaldehyde and some α-amino acid ester, one can make a copper chelate of it, which is represented by the left half of the formula. However, as soon as one makes the copper chelate, a number of reactions take place very readily on the α-amino acid ester portion which do not take place on the free α-amino acid ester, or the free α-amino acid, very easily. First, is racemization; that is, the α-carbon is an asymmetric carbon atom, and immediately you put it into the copper complex it racemizes. Another one is oxidative deamination; that is, if one blows air through an alcoholic solution of this copper chelate, one can isolate the oxidatively deaminated keto acid ester. Or, if one maintains anaerobic conditions so that one does not get oxidative deamination, but instead dissolves the chelate in an alcohol with an R group different from that of the original ester, ester exchange takes place as fast as you can dissolve it and recrystallize it. This is an unusual thing. One doesn't usually get ester exchange on any esters, except α-keto esters, very rapidly. Certainly amino acid esters do not undergo ester exchange by simply dissolving them in an alcohol and recrystallizing them. Thus, there take place on the chelate at least these three reactions which do not take place at all, or very reluctantly, on the non-chelated molecules — the salicylaldehyde Schiff's base without the copper, or the copper salt without the salicylaldehyde, or the amino acid ester itself. It is presumed that all of these reactions take place via a tautomerization which is possible in the chelate compound, or at least is induced by chelation, due to the electronic interaction with the chelated metal. The α-carbon atom loses its asymmetry by a hydrogen transfer, a sort of keto-enol transfer across the aldimine double bond to form the molecule represented by the right half of the formula. This, then, could be hydrolyzed, giving the keto acid ester and a benzilamine which is very easily auto-oxidized by air, in the form of its copper complex. Thus, the net result would be either isomerization, or oxidative deamination. Why the ester exchange take place so rapidly is not so readily apparent from the formulas as written, but it has been interpreted (5, p. 400), in terms of the withdrawal of electrons from the ester grouping through the conjugate ketimine toward the copper, giving it a more reactive oxygen function.

One can carry this analogy one step further to the well-known structure of pyridoxal, which is very close to salicylaldehyde and which does this very thing in nature. Pyridoxal, as we know, is involved in transamination reactions, and it has been suggested that it functions as a chelate (8). As a matter of fact, recently the copper chelate compounds of pyridoxal and α-amino acids have been made, and their structure is shown in Fig. 17. Here the relationship between pyridoxal and salicylaldehyde is very clear, and the transamination reaction (oxidative deamination on the one hand and reduction on the other) all can take place via such transfers as I have just described for the salicylaldehyde complex. Baddiley (9)

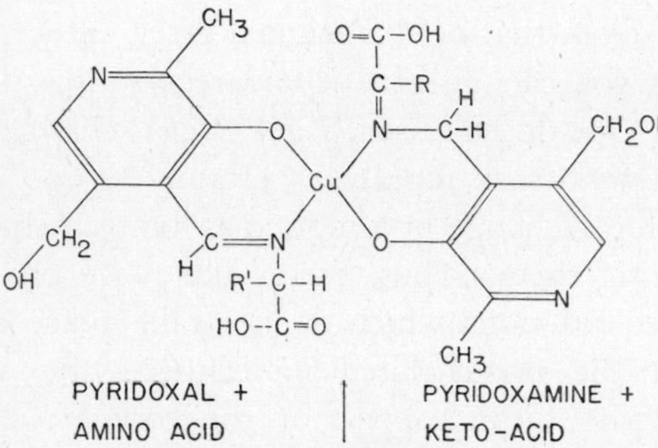

PYRIDOXAL +   PYRIDOXAMINE +
AMINO ACID   KETO-ACID

Transamination; oxidative deamination and reductive amination.

$Cu^{+2} > Al^{+3} = Fe^{+2} = Fe^{+3} > Ni^{+2} = Co^{+2}$
(relative activities in non-enzymatic reaction)

Fig. 17.

at the Lister Institute, who made these complexes, showed that the reaction did take place quite readily without enzymes in ordinary aqueous systems. The transformation from pyridoxal and amino acid to pyridoxamine and keto acid, and the order of activity of the elements in the non-enzymatic reaction is shown here, and you will notice that the copper outshines them all. This is undoubtedly due to the unique position of cupric ion with respect to the energy level of its unoccupied dsp-orbitals. One could go on collecting other such cases of catalytic activity of metal chelates over a wide range, and the cases become less and less definitive and more and more open to speculation (5, Chapter 8). This, I think, is one of the areas in which we can stand a great deal of investigation. I have no doubt that such studies will contribute toward an understanding of the nature of catalytic function in general, and particularly in such extreme cases as those of catalase, hemoglobin, and chlorophyll.

REFERENCES

1. Diehl, H., *Chem. Rev.*, 21, 39 (1937).
2. Van Uitert, Fernelius, and Douglas, Studies in Coordination Compounds. VII. Chelate Compound Dissolved State. *J. Am. Chem. Soc.*, in press.
3. Schwarzenbach and Ackerman, *Helv. Chim. Acta*, 31, 1029 (1948).
4. Schwarzenbach, *Helv. Chim. Acta*, 35, 2344 (1952); 36, 23 (1953).
5. Martell and Calvin, *The Chemistry of the Metal Chelate Compounds*, Prentice-Hall, New York (1952).
6. Utzinger, *Helv. Chim. Acta*, 35, 1359 (1952); *Angew. Chem.*, 64, 622 (1952).
7. Steinberger and Westheimer, *J. Am. Chem. Soc.*, 73, 429 (1951).
8. Snell, *J. Am. Chem. Soc.*, 67, 194 (1945).
9. Baddiley, *Nature*, 170, 711 (1952).

DISCUSSION

DR. CALVIN: There have been certain points in which interest has been evinced lately, and I thought it might be worthwhile to call your attention to them. They are not formally in the manuscript. These are the preparation of the synthetic oxygen carriers which Dr. Hellerman mentioned and which are, again, salicylaldehyde compounds containing cobalt. A whole variety of these were made having different oxygen equilibrium responses which could be controlled at will. One of these molecules can be crystallized in nice long needles, and if I didn't have to travel so far and carry a heavy bag I would have brought along two more slides of the needles showing them breathing—literally that. When they absorb oxygen the crystal gets longer and thinner, and when the oxygen goes off it gets shorter and fatter. The reason for that is the arrangement of these flat planar molecules in the crystal. When oxygen atoms move in between the planar molecules they cause a twisting which results in this effect. The x-ray work on this material has been completely worked out by Hughes at Cal. Tech. and gives a very clear picture of what is going on (Martell and Calvin, " The Chemistry of Metal Chelate Compounds " — Prentice-Hall, 1952). Another example is that of a hydrogen carrier, also a synthetic chelate compound, which is capable of activating and moving molecular hydrogen and could conceivably be used as a model for hydrogenase. These are a series of cuprous compounds which are held together in a dimeric form by various oxygen-containing compounds such as acetate or salicylaldehyde (Martell and Calvin, "The Chemistry of Metal Chelate Compounds" — Prentice-Hall, 1952). As the hydrogen comes into this molecule, the bond between the two hydrogen atoms is weakened as a bond or quasi-bond is formed between the two copper atoms which are held together in dimeric form. This hydrogen now is capable of reducing and exchanging and doing other reactions which we normally think of as not possible for ordinary molecular hydrogen but requiring catalytically activated molecular hydrogen.

DR. MILDRED COHN: I would like to present a brief discussion of the application of a new method to the study of metal complexes—namely, the paramagnetic resonance absorption method. It should be stated at the outset that the method has the obvious limitation, in common with other magnetic methods, that it is confined to those ions and molecules which are paramagnetic. On the other hand, the method has the advantage that it can measure directly and rapidly the concentration of the free metal ion in solution without disturbing any preexisting equilibrium state. Furthermore, the method can, in certain cases, yield information about the electronic structure of the complex which cannot be obtained in any other way.

Manganous ion is the ideal paramagnetic ion to study for reasons which will be outlined shortly. This is indeed fortunate since it is also an ion of great biochemical interest. Many enzymatic reactions involve manganous ion; in particular, it mediates most of the phosphate reactions in which I have been interested.

The fundamental basis of the paramagnetic resonance absorption method involves the following considerations: If we place a material with one or more unpaired electrons per molecule in a magnetic field, the resultant electron spin will become oriented in a specific direction. This would, of course, happen with compounds of the transition elements and free radicals. If a beam of micro-waves is now directed through the sample, absorption will occur for a given magnetic field at a frequency corresponding to the energy required for a transition from one possible resultant spin orientation to another. In practice, the frequency is kept constant and the magnetic field is varied, so that absorption occurs at a particular value of the magnetic field. The location of the absorption peak will be independent of the number of unpaired electrons but the area under the absorption curve is a function of the number of unpaired electrons or the total magnetic susceptibility. Thus, one can get the same value of magnetic susceptibility which is usually obtained by conventional static magnetic susceptibility measurements. However, in the case of manganous ion, in dilute crystals or in solution, one obtains in addition, by the paramagnetic resonance absorption method, a hyperfine structure in the absorption consisting of six individual peaks. The spectrum of the manganous ion in a ZnS phosphor obtained by Hershberger and Leifer (Hershberger, W. D. and Leifer, H. M., *Phys. Rev.* **88**, 714 [1952]) is shown in Fig. 1. It is the existence of this hyperfine structure with its sensitive dependence on the chemical environment of the manganous ion and on bond type involved in the molecule which makes paramagnetic resonance absorption a unique tool for studying manganese complexes.

The apparatus used in these studies was designed and constructed by Dr. Townsend of the physics department of Washington University for a study of free radicals. The instrument records the derivative of the absorption with respect to magnetic field rather than the absorption curve itself. The advantage of this method is the very high sensitivity for sharp narrow peaks. In fact, the sensitivity is inversely proportional to the square of the width of the absorption curve. Fig. 2 shows a typical record of the spectrum of manganous chloride in aqueous solution. Such spectra can be obtained at concentrations ranging from .001 M to 0.5 M with approximately 0.1 ml. solution. This particular record was scanned in five minutes. The separation of the peaks represents about 60 gauss or .005 wave number.

It was found that it was not necessary to integrate the curves; that the height from the maximum to the minimum was a linear function of manganous ion concentration in the range investigated, .001 M to .01 M. A series of phosphate esters was investigated and it was found that the height of the curves corresponded to the free manganous ion concentration; when the manganese was completely complexed, the hyperfine structure disappeared completely. For example, with a series of increasing concentrations of glucose-6-phosphate, one obtains progressively smaller peaks. From this data a dissociation constant for a complex of one manganese ion to one divalent glucose-6-phosphate ion can be calculated of 3×10^{-3} M/1. A similar constant was obtained for glucose-1-phosphate. This dissociation constant of the Mn complex of fructose 1, 6 diphosphate is much smaller than for the monophosphates. This finding is consistent with the fact that the equilibrium constant of the aldolase reaction, fructose 1, 6 diphosphate in equilibrium with 2 triose monophosphates, is shifted in the direction of the diphosphate with increasing metal ion concentration. The reaction itself does not require a metal ion.

The dissociation constants for manganese adenosine diphosphate and adenosine triphosphate are unfortunately too small to measure. When .001 M ATP is added to .001 M $MnCl_2$ at pH 7.5, the hyperfine structure corresponding to free manganous ion, completely disappears. This sets an upper limit on the dissociation constant. Until a more sensitive apparatus is available which can detect concentrations of manganese below 10^{-4} M, one can only say that the Mn ATP complex has a dissociation constant less than 10^{-5} M/1. When one investigates the complexing in the range where the manganese concentration exceeds the ATP concentration, one finds a mixture of complexes with more than one Mn atom per ATP.

The dissociation constants of the manganese complexes of glycyl glycine and histidine have been determined and compared to values found in the literature which had been determined by titration. The value for glycyl-glycine, approximately 1×10^{-2} M/1, agreed very well (Monk, C. B., *Trans. Far. Soc.* 47, 297 [1951]), but the value for histidine was approximately 100 times larger than Kroll's value (Kroll, H., *J. Amer. Chem. Soc.* 74, 2034 [1952]) for the imidazole group complexing. However the assumptions involved in the titration method are probably not correct for a compound with three ionizing groups such as histidine; the shift observed in pH may be due to the effect on the acid strength of the amino group in the Mn complex formed between the carboxyl group and the imidazole group rather than to complex formation itself.

The paramagnetic resonance absorption method can also be used to follow the rate of a reaction. One of these absorption peaks can be scanned in about 1 minute, so that one can follow changes in complexing at one minute intervals. This was actually done for the decarboxylation of oxalacetic acid. Since the pyruvic acid formed complexes less strongly than the oxalacetate, one observes increasing peaks with time. It is hoped that it will eventually be possible to study the formation of the elusive metal enzyme substrate complexes.

It will be noted that all the complexes which I have mentioned cause a disappearance of the hyperfine structure. However, it should be emphasized that this is not true of all types of complexes. Bleaney (Bleaney, B. and Ingram, D. J. E., *Proc. Roy. Soc.* [London] A205, 336 [1951]) has examined manganese ammonium sulfate and manganese fluorosilicate $6H_2O$ in dilute crystals and here the hyperfine structure persists. It is obvious that it also persists in aqueous solution of manganous salts where the manganous ion is coordinating water molecules. In fact, the existence of the hyperfine structure is an excellent criterion for an ionic type of bond for the reasons discussed below.

If we now examine the electronic configuration of the manganous ion and the source of the hyperfine structure, we can understand why any type of covalent bonding will destroy the hyperfine structure and that ionic binding will not.

The manganous ion has two 3s electrons, six 3p electrons and 5 unpaired electrons. The source of hyperfine splitting is the interaction of the resultant electron spin with the nuclear spin. When first observed in crystals, the hyperfine structure of the manganous ion was quite unanticipated. For, if the structure of the manganous ion were truly $(3s)^2(3p)^6(3d)^5$, there should be no appreciable hyperfine structure since the five 3d electrons have negligible interaction with the nucleus while the interaction of the two 3s electrons of opposite spin should cancel. The explanation of the existence of the hyperfine structure as given by Abragam and Pryce (Abragam, A. and Pryce, M. H. L., *Proc. Roy. Soc.* [London] **A205**, 135 [1951]) is that the electronic state is actually more correctly expressed as a superposition of two distinct electronic configurations: the configuration usually given, namely $(3s)^2(3p)^6(3d)^5$ plus a small amount of $(3s)^1(3p)^6(3d)^5(4s)^1$. In other words, one of the 3s electrons is actually in the 4s state part of the time. Under these circumstances the interactions of the s electrons with the nucleus (nuclear spin of Mn, 5/2) do not entirely cancel and the splitting of any resultant electron spin orientation level into 6 hyperfine levels results. The importance of this phenomenon lies in the fact that the amount of admixture of the 4s state must depend sensitively on the chemical environment of the Mn ion and should lead to a complete loss of hyperfine structure in a complex if the 4s Mn orbital is occupied by electrons from other atoms in the complex.

Changes in the static magnetic susceptibility values upon complexing, reflect changes solely in the number of unpaired 3d electrons. Such a change occurs in manganous compounds only if an octahedral complex is formed, where two 3d orbitals, the 4s, and three 4p orbitals are occupied by electrons from the complexing groups. In this case, four of the 3d electrons pair up, leaving 1 unpaired electron. On the other hand, a tetrahedral complex involving only the 4s and three 4p orbitals would not change the number of unpaired 3d electrons and therefore not change the measured static magnetic susceptibility. But any covalent type of bond must involve the 4s orbital and therefore suppress the hyperfine structure. Hence we have a criterion of bond type, ionic or covalent, far more discriminating than the usual magnetic criterion. Of all the manganous complexes studied by static methods, only the cyanide complex has a static magnetic susceptibility different from the free ion. Those which we have measured such as complexes with phosphate, carboxylic acids, and amino acids have the same static susceptibility as free manganous ion. We have now established the covalent nature of the bonds in these cases by the disappearance of the hyperfine structure. Thus, the paramagnetic resonance absorption method is not only useful for the measurement of the dissociation constants of metal complexes but also for determining whether the bond is ionic or covalent.

We have not yet been able to detect the paramagnetic resonance spectrum of *any* complex. Even in the cases discussed where the hyperfine structure disappears due to complex formation, there should appear a single peak characteristic of the unfilled 3d shell of the manganese in the complex. The failure to detect such a peak is probably due to its broadness. As I pointed out earlier, the sensitivity of the apparatus is inversely proportional to the breadth of the absorption peaks and if the complexes have very broad peaks, we cannot detect them. However, the limit of sensitivity of detectors of this type has not yet been approached and Dr. Townsend is now building a

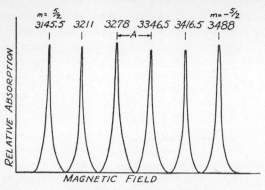

Absorption of cub. ZnS:Mn (0.001).

FIG. 1. Absorption of cub. ZnS:Mn(0.001). (Hershberger, W. D., and Leifer, H. N., *Phys. Rev.*, 88, 714 (1952).)

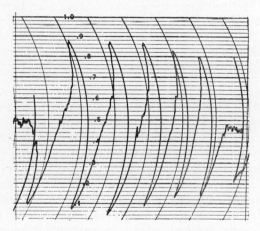

FIG. 2. MnCl₂ (.005 M) in aqueous solution.

new instrument which we hope will be far more sensitive and able to yield further information.

DR. RACKER: I would like to ask Dr. Calvin why he included the pyridine nucleotides in his list of magnesium chelating compounds. As far as I am aware, the only DPN or TPN linked enzymes which require magnesium cata-lyze oxidative decarboxylation. I think that the reason why in the reactions you are referring to (triose phosphate dehydrogenase) the magnesium con-centration was kept constant was because it was zero.

DR. CALVIN: The one I am referring to came from Corey's laboratory that appeared in *Biochemica et Biophysica Acta* about a year ago.

DR. RACKER: There is no magnesium requirement for triose phosphate dehydrogenase.

DR. CALVIN: Then it was another one. The particular enzyme involved is not the point here. I don't remember which one it was, but there are very good measurements of the equilibrium constant but always with a con-stant magnesium ion concentration.

DR. MEHLER: I would like to suggest that Dr. Calvin also remove Coen-zyme A from his list of magnesium-chelating compounds. As far as I know, the only enzyme reactions involving CoA and magnesium also require ATP.

DR. STURTEVANT: I would like to ask Dr. Calvin about the case of the zinc ammonia complexes in which the K values for chelation increase as you replace ammonias by diamines and as you increase the length of the alkyl chains. Could you explain why there would be an entropy increase there?

DR. CALVIN: In the case of the reaction of zince with four ammonias the value for log K was 10. In the case of the reaction of zinc with two ethy-lene diamines the value for log K was 14. This means that the latter reaction involves greater increase in entropy.

DR. STURTEVANT: I wondered if you wanted to suggest a mechanism for explaining this.

DR. CALVIN: Well, one naive way of doing it is to say that a certain amount of water is liberated in both cases and that you are getting the entropy of those water molecules. In the first case you are losing the entropy of four ammonias—that is, four translational degrees of freedom—and in the second case you are losing only two. That is a naive way of doing it, but it fits.

DR. SCHMIDT: This morning the question was discussed that if an enzyme-substrate complex were formed in such a way that the substrate had several groups binding to the enzyme, and the affinity constant would have to con-sist of several subconstants, each representing a group. On these chelate reactions I would like to ask Dr. Calvin whether, like Werner complex reac-tions, they apparently proceed without any intermediates. On the one side one has the metal, apparently, and on the other side one has the complete complex compound. If chelate formation could be considered as a mechan-ism, probably for many enzyme reactions in which the enzyme combines with several active groups of the substrate then the assumption of different rates of reaction for each group would be unnecessary.

DR. CALVIN: As I understand the question—maybe I am oversimplifying it—I believe that what you are asking is whether, for example, when zinc combines with ethylene diamine there is at any time an intermediate in which zinc is attached to only one nitrogen and the other nitrogen is free before it comes around and forms a bond. I am sure those are two separate rate phenomena, but whether we can ever separate them or not I do not know. The ethylene diamine molecule in water solution in this particular case is surely not running around already poised to pop onto the zinc in two places simultaneously.

DR. SCHMIDT: I don't know whether this might not be so in this case.

DR. CALVIN: I think there are two successive steps but that the second one is so fast that we never see it.

DR. SCHMIDT: Then there is no example known where one has an intermediate in chelate complex formation?

DR. CALVIN: I think that Dr. Smith was mentioning some this morning.

DR. E. SMITH: I don't know of any for the metal chelates, but they haven't been looked for yet. Carboxypeptidase is not a metal enzyme, although we used to think it was. Among the metal peptidases I don't know of any examples where we have such intermediates, but they are only beginning to be sought.

DR. ANFINSEN: There is one example in biology that has always been puzzling to me, and that is the old yeast carboxylase. Perhaps Dr. Calvin can straighten us out on that. This was a system in which, if you added magnesium before you added diphosphothiamine, the maximum rate of decarboxylation of pyruvate was obtained at once. However, if you added diphosphothiamine first and then magnesium there was quite a delay—as I remember it, of the order of 10 minutes. Can this be interpreted in terms of chelate reactions, which, as I understand, are fairly rapid reactions?

DR. CALVIN: There are all possible sorts of explanations for this, so I think it would be futile to offer any.

DR. E. SMITH: There are several examples of that type of phenomena, such as arginase and some of the phosphatases. What Dr. Schmidt was asking about concerned the combination of a fully-formed enzyme with the substrate. What I have reference to is the leucine aminopeptidase, which I will mention later. If you take the protein without the metal and then add metal and substrate simultaneously, you get a very long lag period; but if you preincubate protein with the metal first and then add substrate the hydrolysis goes very rapidly, so that there is a slow interaction of the metal with the protein. All you can say is that it is probably not a simple metal complex formation, because such reactions are generally pretty rapid, so that this may involve a reorientation of the molecule or a stepwise reaction at several points on the protein surface.

DR. HAMMETT: There is a question that has bothered me quite a bit, and I wonder if Dr. Calvin would like to say something about it—with respect to the effect of the size of a ring on the stability of the chelates. One of the very striking things — and I think it has some bearing on this question of enzyme activity—is why it is that you get extremely stable oxalate or ethylene diamine complexes, but unstable complexes with malonate or with 1, 3-propylene diamine. These aren't strains in the sense of bending valence bonds. Maybe some of them could be accounted for by eclipsed or staggered hydrogen configurations. This doesn't take care of oxalate and malonate.

DR. CALVIN: Yes. Oxalate and malonate are special cases. There the two groups are right on each other, and you can then have the electronic interaction between the two oxygen atoms in the case of oxalate which you can't have in malonate, so there is something quite new in the oxalate which is not present in malonate at all. However, it is worth looking at a series in which you don't have this kind of complication, the stability of the polymethylene diamines with copper as measured by Pfeifer just before he died several years ago. He measured a whole series of them, I believe, up to 10 methylene groups, and, curiously enough, there is some alternation in the stability constant after you get past the first one.

DR. HAMMETT: You were referring to diamine tetra acetic acid?

DR. CALVIN: You can leave off the tetra acetic acid and still get the same picture if you consider a series in which the number of methylenes attached to the nitrogen is varied and in which a longer and longer polymethylene chain is added to the nitrogen. The one with two methylene groups is, as I said before, of course the most stable. I don't know why I say " of course," but it is. As you increase the length of the chain there is a certain amount of fluctuation which looks as though it goes with odd and even numbers of carbon atoms. The changes are small and monoatomic.

DR. HAMMETT: Then the general tendency is down?

DR. CALVIN: Yes, it goes down. I think if you examine the configuration possibilities when you bind the two ends together you do find some such fluctuations alternating with the number of carbon atoms on the various bases that you are suggesting, but they are small things compared to the difference betweeen oxalate and malonate—that's a big difference.

DR. HAMMETT: Does the difference between ethylene diamine and 1, 3-propylene diamine go down?

DR. CALVIN: Yes, that goes down; but there, you see, there is quite a ring difference. In the case of propylene diamine you can't get the square planar configuration you get with copper, so that it's a case of strain on the bond angles—at least, you can't get it as easily as you can with ethylene diamine. Beyond that number of methylene groups this factor is not very great, but in the case of propylene diamine it is.

DR. EYRING: I just want to ask what is this chelate compound between sodium and metabolite which pumps sodium and so accounts for the potential across cell membranes thus making nerve action possible.

DR. CALVIN: That's a very nice question. This same question is being asked actively by the plant physiologists in the root pump mechanism, and they are looking for compounds of the pyrophosphate—that is, of the ADP-ATP type—at the moment. Whether they'll have any success with that or not I don't know. I remember at the symposium last year one of the talks was addressed to this very question. At least, this question was raised and it wasn't answered, and it still has not been answered. I don't know of any specific compound which would explain these phenomena.

DR. KIRKWOOD: In connection with what you said about the ethylene diamine, would you be willing to say that increase in stability can be accounted for on the basis of the entropy of internal rotation?

DR. CALVIN: I certainly believe this is a contributory effect if not the entire one.

DR. KIRKWOOD: This may account for the alternation. We are dealing with a gaseous system, so perhaps solvent water plays a part.

DR. KOSHLAND: I would just like to say that metal ion catalysis of the hydrolysis of phosphate esters and acyl phosphates is known to occur in the absence of enzymes. The metal ions in the phosphate transfer reactions may, therefore, catalyze the enzymatic reactions by causing electronic shifts as well as by binding the substrate to the enzyme surface.

DR. RITTENBERG: I wonder whether Dr. Calvin would comment some more about what he called the model for hydrogenase action. What is the mechanism of action of the pyridine catalyst for this?

DR. CALVIN: That is a good question. You have to have a pyridine or quiniline base as the salt. Some recent investigations have gone much further than we did in this, trying different bases. I suspect that it has to do with the energy level of two electrons that are left on the cuprous compound. The cuprous compounds are diamagnetic for the most part, but I suspect that when the paramagnetic resonance method is called upon to investigate the distribution of the electrons in this cuprous complex it will be found that the electrons are not all in the 3-d shell of the cuprous complex but some have been promoted out, although the net compound is diamagnetic; and it takes the extra pairs from the base—the pyridine or the quiniline or various other bases that were used—in order to promote the electrons out of the 3-d shell of the cuprous complex so that they will be available for bonding to molecular hydrogen. This is as far as I have gone with it, except that I know you need different basic pairs. I know that the compound is diamagnetic when measured by the mass susceptibility method, but it has never been put into the microwave resonance machine.

DR. RITTENBERG: Do they catalyze the ortho to para conversion of hydrogen?

DR. CALVIN: It does, but not by the magnetic group. It does, by this same route that it catalyzes H_2-D_2 reactions. Of course, in this way if you start out with para hydrogen you come out with ortho hydrogen. This is not just an inversion of the nuclear spins as you have in the homogeneous magnetic field of the rare earth ions.

DR. LEHNINGER: I would like to ask Dr. Calvin a question concerning a set of facts that is widely familiar among enzyme chemists but on which there has been very little speculation concerning the physical chemical aspects. I think it is best to ask this by citing a few examples. These pertain to different kinds of metal specificity encountered with different kinds of metallo-enzymes. If you take the case of arginase, for instance, this enzyme requires manganese for activity, but it will also act in the presence of neighboring metals in that transition series but is not activated by Mg^{++} or any other metals. Now, to an amateur chemist like myself this seems rather reasonable, because these metals have certain similarities of size—even though they differ somewhat in electronic configuration. There is another case, for example the leucyl peptidase which has been studied by Dr. Smith and Dr. Johnson. This enzyme requires manganese for activity. No other neighboring transition series metal will suffice to activate this reaction, but it can be activated by magnesium, which is somewhat removed from it in the periodic table. To take a third case, I think that there are one or two enzymes known that are activated by manganese but by no other transition metals and are *not* activated by magnesium. I am just pulling these out of the hat, so to speak, as instances to illustrate this rather peculiar metal ion specificity. Obviously these specificities must have their basis on the properties of the metal and also on the properties of the bases with which they chelate. I was wondering if you could see an underlying pattern and, furthermore, whether you might speculate on whether it is profitable at this stage of the game to use this basic information about the properties of the metals and their complexes to work out or predict the nature of the active spots on the enzyme which are furnishing the other claw of the double chelate complex, which we presume is the actual form of the enzyme-substrate complex in the metallo-enzyme systems.

DR. CALVIN: Well, I would certainly say that it is profitable to speculate.

I would be the last to discourage speculation. Whether you could make any money out of it or not I don't know. In the contrasting cases that you mentioned, presumably leucyl peptidase involves just a hydrolysis, but I assume you could write the arginase reaction as simply a hydrolysis also. In the latter case we could also formulate it as an oxidation-reduction reaction with the same net result, but in this case the available orbitals of the transition elements are used, whereas in the case of peptidase, only the charge and the radius are involved, so that magnesium and manganese, being similar in the latter respects, would function. We can consider the arginase action as involving a movement of electrons involving the 3-d orbitals of Mn^{++}, while in the case of the peptidase these would not be involved.

DR. LEHNINGER: It is not certain that it is true, but it sounds reasonable.

DR. CALVIN: I think it would be very worthwhile to lay out, if possible, as many such cases in as orderly a fashion as you can and see what turns up. This refers to only the two cases you mentioned. If we consider more cases perhaps such a pattern will emerge. I looked in *Phosphorous Metabolism*, Volume I. I believe there was a list there of metals activating enzymes. This is the list I used in gathering some of the information which I presented.

THERMODYNAMIC AND MOLECULAR PROPERTIES OF SOME METAL-PROTEIN COMPLEXES

IRVING M. KLOTZ

Department of Chemistry,
Northwestern University, Evanston

IN A SYMPOSIUM on the mechanism of enzyme action, a discussion of the properties of metal-protein complexes should be directed primarily toward an elucidation of the role of metal ions in these catalytic systems. Much thought and effort have been devoted to this problem, and various phases have been reviewed recently by Lehninger (38), Martell and Calvin (40) and Schubert (53). Nevertheless, except for the heme proteins, little is yet known about the environment of the metal ion within the protein complex or about the effects of these cations on the state and configuration of the macromolecule. The question of the influence of the metal in enzymes thus lies largely in the realm of speculation.

In this paper certain aspects of metal-protein interactions will be examined with the following questions as primary guides: (1) Which groups on protein molecules are involved in bond formation with metallic ions? (2) Which metals form complexes with proteins and what factors determine the affinities observed? (3) Which observed modes of interaction between metals and proteins may be of significance in biological function, particularly enzymatic catalysis? A review of these problems has led to some suggestions which may clarify the role of metals in some enzymatic systems.

LIGAND GROUPS OF PROTEINS

Amino acids in themselves form complexes with a wide variety of metals by coordination through the carboxyl and amine groups (I).

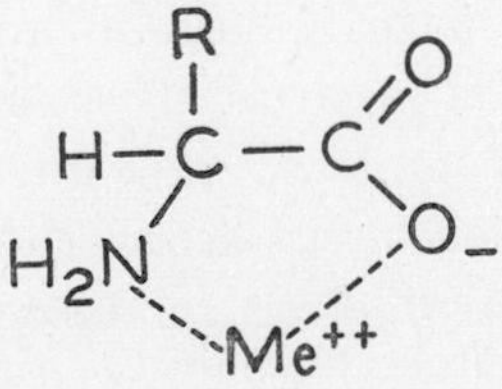

(I)

Within the protein molecule, however, it is the R group which is of primary importance, since the carboxyl and amine substituents are linked in peptide bonds. Polar side-chains, R, which might act as ligands in the formation of protein complexes with metals are listed in Table 1.

TABLE 1

POLAR SIDE CHAINS IN PROTEINS

		APPROXIMATE pK
PHOSPHORIC	$-O-P\overset{O}{\underset{OH}{\parallel}}{}^{OH}$	2, 7
CARBOXYL	$-C\overset{O}{\underset{OH}{<}}$	4
IMIDAZOLIUM	$\begin{array}{c}H\\-C-N^+\\ \parallel \quad CH\\HC-N\\H\end{array}$	6
α-AMMONIUM	$-NH_3^+$	6–8
ϵ-AMMONIUM	$-NH_3^+$	10
PHENOLIC	⬡—OH	10
SULFHYDRYL	$-SH$	10
GUANIDINIUM	$-N\overset{H}{-}C\overset{NH_2^+}{\underset{NH_2}{<}}$	12
ALCOHOLIC	$-\overset{\mid}{C}-\overset{\mid}{C}-OH$	$\gtrsim 14$
AMIDE	$-C\overset{O}{\underset{NH_2}{<}}$	$\gtrsim 14$

Except for the guanidine, aliphatic hydroxyl, and amide groups, strong evidence exists that each of these side-chains is involved in complex formation with at least some metals. The exclusion of the three groups mentioned emphasizes one of the most important factors in the formation of these complexes — competition of hydrogen ions. The dissociated form of each of these three groups is such a strong base (cf. pK's of acids in Table 1) that protons cannot be displaced from the acid by metal ions, except, perhaps, in solutions of very high pH.

Procedures to differentiate between side-chains as possible participants in bond formation with metals fall into several general categories: (1) stoichiometric; (2) chemical modification; (3) pH dependence; and (4) optical. Illustrations will be given of each of these experimental approaches.

Stoichiometric analysis. In some cases the number of metal ions bound shows a sharp break as the unbound cation concentration is increased. If the uptake corresponds precisely to the number of free groups of a given type, this observation may be accepted as strong evidence of the involvement of the side-chain indicated.

TABLE 2

STOICHIOMETRY OF CH_3HgI BINDING BY MERCAPTALBUMIN (Hughes)

Excess CH_3HgI	pH	Bound CH_3HgI
6%	9.7	(1.00)
20	9.7	1.00
7	7.3	0.98
16	7.3	0.97
23	7.3	0.97

An excellent example of this case is the interaction of the sulfhydryl group of serum albumin with metals. It has been shown by Hughes (27, 28) that the combination of mercurials with mercaptalbumin gives a sharp break at one mole of metal ion (Table 2). Benesch and Benesch (6) reported corresponding results with Ag^+. Agents which are highly specific for $-SH$ groups, such as p-chloromercuribenzoate ion, block the attachment of metal to the protein. Likewise the metal may be removed from the albumin by small molecules, such as cysteine, which form competing mercaptides. These results, coupled with the observation that no thiol groups are liberated when mercuric albumin is denatured by guanidine, indicate clearly that Hg^{++} and Ag^+ are bound in a 1 : 1 complex with albumin through the single available –SH group.

Simple stoichiometry alone may not be adequate, however, to establish the nature of the side-chains involved. Thus it has been known for some time that siderophilin and conalbumin each combine with two moles of iron or of copper (3, 16, 34, 50-52, 60, 61). The establishment of the specific sites involved, however, has required extensive measurements of the pH-dependence of binding as well as comparisons of optical properties (61), some details of which will be described below.

When the stoichiometric relationships exceed small integers, much more uncertainty exists in the assignment of the metal affinity to particular side-chains of the protein. Thus in investigations of zinc interactions with human serum albumin, Gurd and Goodman (21) have found that the binding data fit a mass-law equation based on sixteen available sites, a number which corresponds to the content of histidine residues in this protein (11). Further, the intrinsic affinity constant agrees well with that for simple zinc-imidazole complexes. Nevertheless, in the very same concentration range, there is strong evidence that zinc-binding by bovine albumin also involves the thiol group (32). The difference may be due to species differences in the albumins, but in any event uncertainties in interpretation are evident.

Chemical modification. The general principle of this technique is to expose the protein to chemical reagents which act specifically on a particular type of group and convert it into another type. Again, most reliable results are obtained when the side-chain of interest occurs in only a small proportion.

In copper-albumin interactions, for example, it has been found (32) that an absorption peak appears, under certain conditions, at $375 \, m\mu$ (Fig. 1). It has been possible to prove by three experiments that a copper-sulfhydryl interaction is responsible. (a) Addition of one mole of Hg^{++} per mole of protein completely abolishes this absorption peak. (b) Addition of one mole of Ag^+ removes the band almost completely. (c) Addition of one mole of salyrganic acid, an organic mercurial that reacts with thiol groups (7), completely abolishes the peak. Since the single –SH group of albumin reacts with mercurials and with silver ion before other side-chains

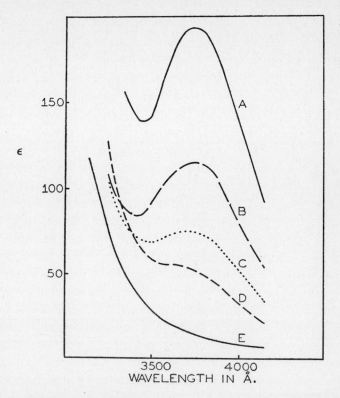

FIG. 1. Effect of various metallic ions on absorption of copper-albumin complex; A, 0.003 M Cu^{++} and 0.0003 M bovine serum albumin, pH 6.0; B, same as A but with 0.003 M Zn^{++}; C, same as A but with 0.003 M Cd^{++}; D, same as A but with 0.003 M Pb^{++}; E, same as A but with 0.0003 M Hg^{++}. Solution A was made up to 0.2 ionic strength with sodium nitrate; the peak is slightly lower if sodium acetate is used. Solutions B to E were made up to 0.2 ionic strength with sodium acetate. The molecular extinction coefficients, ϵ, were calculated from the equation: log $I_o/I = \epsilon c d$, where I_o is the intensity of the light emerging from the pure protein solution, I the intensity of the light emerging from the metal ion-protein solution, c the molar concentration of the metal ion, and d the cell thickness in centimeters.

do (6, 28), it is clear that the cupric ion must be displaced from a mercaptide linkage when the 375 mμ band disappears.

In the preceding example, definitive results were possible largely because only a single sulfhydryl site was involved. When a large number of sites of a given type are available, interpretation of observations is more difficult, for the net charge of the protein molecule may be changed, and the specificity of the chemical reagent is not always complete. Nevertheless, much interesting information has been obtained.

Many years ago Northrop and Kunitz (45) showed that deaminization of gelatin did not reduce the extent of binding of calcium ions by the protein. More recently, Abels (1) found similar results upon deaminizing egg albumin. It seems, therefore, that Ca^{++} uptake does not occur appreciably at the amino side-chains of these protein molecules. Such behavior of the binding sites on the protein is in line with the affinity constants of isolated complexing groups; for Ca^{++}, in contrast to Cu^{++}, the affinity for amine nitrogen is less than for carboxyl groups (33). It seems reasonable, therefore, to assume that the sites on gelatin and on ovalbumin with an attraction for Ca^{++} are predominantly carboxyl groups.

Modification of side chains has been used also as indirect evidence to substantiate the participation of histidine residues in zinc-binding at pH's near 7. Thus Gurd and Goodman (21) found that conversion of ammonium groups of lysine to guanidinium groups did not affect zinc uptake other than through the change in net electrostatic charge on the serum albumin molecule. Conversion of a few $-COO^-$ to $-COOCH_2CONH_2$ groups produced changes in binding attributable to the removal of a small number of negative charges rather than of specific sites of attachment.

In a similar fashion the participation of carboxyl groups in chromium fixation by collagen is indicated by the observation that uptake of the metal is markedly decreased in a sample of protein in which the carboxyl groups have been converted to their methyl esters (10, 22).

pH dependence. Again, if used with caution and in conjunction with other evidence, the dependence of binding upon pH may give good indications of the nature of the groups involved. Thus Warner and Weber (13) have found that conalbumin takes up iron or copper, from citrate complexes, in a pH range corresponding to the ionization of lysine or tyrosine groups. The trailing of the uptake curve to very high pH's pointed preferentially to phenolic groups; convincing confirmation, however, required additional spectroscopic evidence.

For many metals uptake by serum albumin becomes appreciable only above the isoelectric point, i. e., at pH's above 5. Since this region corresponds to that of the ionization of imidazolium groups, it has been concluded that histidine side-chains must be involved in the binding of metals such as zinc, cadmium, and lead (21, 57) (Fig. 2). However, if such a criterion were to be used alone, it

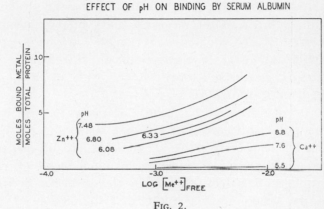

EFFECT OF pH ON BINDING BY SERUM ALBUMIN

FIG. 2.

would lead to a similar conclusion for calcium, whose uptake by albumin also increases rapidly above pH 5 (29) (Fig. 2), whereas evidence from stability constants makes such a conclusion highly unlikely. Similarly, it has been shown in this Laboratory that cupric ion interactions with the thiol group of serum albumin occur at pH's from 5 upward (Fig. 3). In the absence of the evidence described above (32), one might have concluded erroneously that the thiol group must be ruled out, since its pK is so much greater than 5.

On reflection it becomes evident why pH profiles may sometimes be misleading. It is necessary first to recognize that many proteins change from positive to negative net charge in the pH region 5 to 7. This increase in negative charge would, of course, increase the attraction for metallic cations and may be just sufficient, when added to the intrinsic affinity, to produce an observable uptake of metal ion. An additional difficulty is introduced sometimes by the very strong affinity of a metal for a particular side-chain or site composed of a constellation of side-chains.   In such a situation the proton may be displaced in a pH region far below that which is normally characteristic of the group.

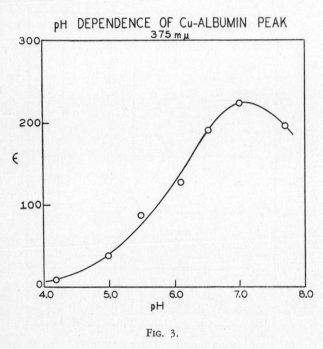

FIG. 3.

Optical methods. When they can be applied, spectroscopic methods are to be preferred, for they introduce no significant perturbations into the metal-protein complex.   They are usually severely limited, however, by two factors: the metal ion must be colored, and the spectra of its complexes with small molecules containing the functional groups of interest (Table 1) must be sufficiently distinctive to allow differentiation.

Copper-albumin complexes are an example in which under appropriate conditions both of these requirements are fulfilled. Thus COO · · · Cu⁺⁺ complexes exhibit absorption peaks near 700 mμ whereas — N · · · Cu⁺⁺ complexes have maxima near 600 mμ (except when the number of coordinated groups is only one or two). Thus it is evident (Fig. 4) that the uptake of copper by albumin at pH 9 must be through nitrogen linkages.

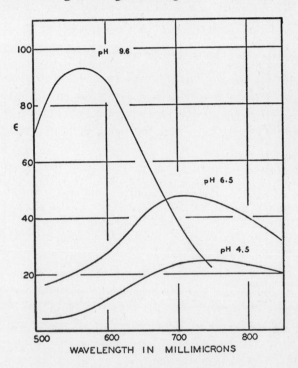

FIG. 4. Cu⁺⁺-albumin spectra.

Similar observations were carried out by Warner and Weber (61) to verify the involvement of phenolic side-chains in metal complexes of conalbumin. The copper-protein in this case is yellow (rather than blue as is copper-albumin); yellow copper complexes, with absorption maxima in the neighborhood of 400 mμ are obtained with compounds such as o-dihydroxybenzene.

The limitations of the optical approach can occasionally be overcome by application of competition techniques. For example, it has been shown in a preceding section that copper-mercaptide interaction in serum albumin is expressed by an absorption peak at 375 mμ. Other metals can then be added to the solution, and the disappearance of the band may be used as an indicator for the detection of other protein mercaptides. By this procedure, it has been found (32) that Fe^{++}, Zn^{++}, Pb^{++}, and Cd^{++}, for example, form mercaptides with serum albumin.

Comparison of Metals

Small number of available sites. In any comparison of metal affinities for proteins it is necessary at the outset to make clear distinctions with respect to the type of protein. The heme proteins form a special category, in that the metal is bound to a prosthetic

TABLE 3

Metal	Log K for Conalbumin (WARNER AND WEBER)	pK$_{S.P.}$ for Hydroxides
Fe^{+++}	30	38
Cu^{++}	17	20
Zn^{++}	< 17	17

group which in itself can be detached from the protein. The binding of the metal to the protein involves largely the porphyrin ring. Progress in understanding the structure and function of the heme proteins has been reviewed frequently (39, 58, 62), and this paper has nothing to contribute to this field.

In addition to the heme proteins there are a number of proteins which possess a few sites of unusually high affinity for certain metals. For example, conalbumin shows a marked affinity for iron, copper, and zinc (3, 16, 50, 60, 61), in each case two metal ions combining with one mole of protein and carrying along two moles of bicarbonate. In this series the order of affinity $Fe^{+++} > Cu^{++} > Zn^{++}$ has been reported (61). It is of interest that this is also the order of complexing ability of these metals with OH$^-$ ions (Table 3), as measured by the concentration of hydroxide ion at the onset of precipitation (9). Warner and Weber have indicated that the phenoxide ion ^-O—⟨⟩— of tyrosine is the basic element in the site of attachment. If this interpretation is correct and if the mercuric ion can be made available in solution at the required pH's, one would predict that Hg^{++} should also be bound by conalbumin, with an affinity of the order of that of Fe^{+++}.

Another series in which an order of affinity of metals has been determined under comparable conditions is that with the sulfhydryl group of serum albumin (32). Here affinity decreases in the order: $Hg^{++} > Ag^+ > Pb^{++} > Cd^{++} > Zn^{++} > Ca^{++}, Mg^{++}$. It is of interest that this is the order of the solubility products of the metal sulfides (Table 4).

TABLE 4

Metal	$pK_{S.P.}$ for Sulfide
Hg^{++}	53
Ag^+	51
Cu^{++}	38
Pb^{++}	29
Cd^{++}	28
Zn^{++}	24
Mg^{++}	—
Ca^{++}	—

Large number of available sites. Since almost all proteins have side-chains with carboxyl groups and basic nitrogen atoms, it is not surprising that they are capable of forming complexes of moderate stability with many metals except when electrostatic or environmental factors (e. g., type of buffer) are especially unfavorable. For purposes of this discussion it may be convenient to divide metals into three classes: (a) those which may be bound very strongly and by several possible functional groups; (b) those bound weakly and primarily at charged sites; and (c) those which do not ordinarily form stable complexes with proteins.

In the first group we may include transition metals, typified by mercury, silver, copper, or zinc. These metals may be bound to any of several side-chains in a protein. Although no really extensive quantitative comparison of the affinity of a protein for a series of metals has been made, certain relationships are evident from available data. Thus from an examination of polarographic experiments (57) the following approximate order emerges: $Cu^{++} > Zn^{++} > Cd^{++} > Pb^{++}$; from dialysis investigations (15, 21, 30) $Cu^{++} > Ni^{++} > Co^{++}, Zn^{++}$. This order parallels that observed in many simple systems of metal complexes with small molecules, including the amino acids (2, 42, 44) (Table 5). Thus to a certain extent proteins

TABLE 5

RELATIVE ORDER OF METAL AFFINITIES

FOR SERUM ALBUMIN

$$Cu^{++} > Zn^{++} > Cd^{++}, Pb^{++} \quad \text{(POLAROGRAPHY)}$$
$$Cu^{++} > Ni^{++} > Co^{++}, Zn^{++} \quad \text{(DIALYSIS)}$$

FOR AMINO ACIDS

$$Cu^{++} > Ni^{++} > Zn^{++} > Pb^{++} > Co^{++} > Cd^{++}$$

FOR PTERIDINES

$$Cu^{++} > Ni^{++} > Zn^{++}$$

behave toward the transition metals in a very non-specific fashion in which a large number of side-chains act as they would if they were independent of the macromolecule.

The alkaline-earth metals, of which calcium is the prime example, stand a notch below the transition group in their affinity for proteins. As has been pointed out above, calcium seems to be bound primarily at the carboxylate side-chains of proteins such as ovalbumin and gelatin. Strong binding of alkaline earths is also exhibited by casein, which possesses a large number of anionic phosphate groups (18). In view of the known ability of calcium to form complexes with simple phosphate ions, it seems likely that its interaction with caseins, or other phosphorylated proteins, involves this anionic group as well as carboxyl side chains.

Numerous studies have also been made with the alkali metal ions Na^+ and K^+, which give little evidence of protein combinations, except possibly at very high pH's. Early investigators were unable to detect any binding of sodium by blood serum (for citations of original literature consult ref. 33). Similar results have also been reported for solutions as high as 10 per cent in concentration of gelatin (45), as well as for concentrated solutions of serum albumin (49), casein (43), crystalline hemoglobin or hemerythrin (5). Recent electrometric measurements with permselective membranes (12) indicate some lowering of the activity of Na^+ in solutions of casein at high pH. It is of interest to note that alkali metals ions form practically no complexes with common organic or inorganic small ions or molecules. On the other hand, Na^+ and K^+ ions are immobilized by many anionic polymeric electrolytes, natural or synthetic (33). It seems possible, therefore, that under conditions where they acquire a large negative charge, proteins too may be capable of binding alkali metal ions. If the analogy with other polyelectrolytes can be carried over, then it follows also that alkali metal ions could have a profound effect on the shape and size of highly anionic proteins. It is perhaps through a mechanism of this type that these small ions are capable of influencing the biological function of certain proteins.

Metals as bridge linkages. When a metallic ion can form a complex with a protein alone or with some small molecule alone, the juxtaposition of all three components may produce either of two results. One effect is typified by the action of glycine on copper-albumin complexes (31), where the protein and amino acid compete for the metal. The same type of result is evident in the many buffer effects which have demonstrated removal of metal from the protein. On the other hand, under suitable conditions, the three components may act cooperatively to give a ternary complex.

It has been shown recently that uncharged organic molecules are bound only slightly (below pH 7) by serum albumin and not to any significant extent by any of the other proteins examined (e. g., pepsin). In the presence of certain metal ions, however, the interaction of a neutral molecule, such as pyridine-2-azo-*p*-dimethylaniline (II), is markedly changed, substantial quantities of dye being bound by each of several proteins. In the presence of zinc, for example, the affinity of pepsin for (II) (Fig. 5) exceeds several fold that of albumin for many anions or neutral molecules. That

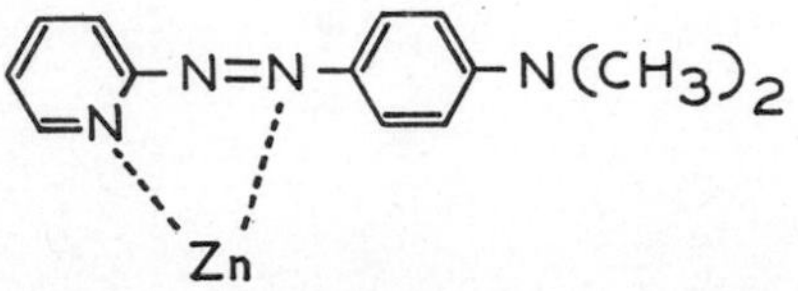

(II)

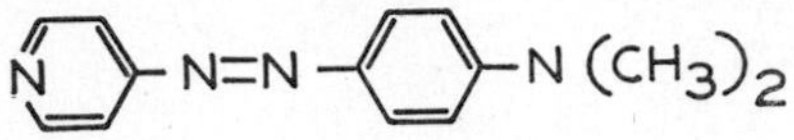

(III)

the metal serves actually as a bridge in the formation of the ternary complex, rather than merely as a source of perturbation of the configuration of the protein, is indicated by experiments with pyridine-4-azo-*p*-dimethylaniline (III). This compound is not bound by pepsin even in the presence of zinc, nor does it form a complex with zinc ions.

Having established the role of the metal as that of mediator between the protein and small-molecule "substrate," we felt it would be of interest to compare, among other things, the abilities of a variety of metals to act as bridge linkages. Among the metals examined, Hg^{++}, Cu^{++}, Ag^+, Ni^{++}, Zn^{++}, Co^{++}, and Mn^{++} can serve as a bridge between pepsin and the azopyridine dye (II). Ca^{++} and Mg^{++}, however, are inactive.

Separate measurements have been made of the chelate formation constants of some of these metals with the dye (II) in the absence

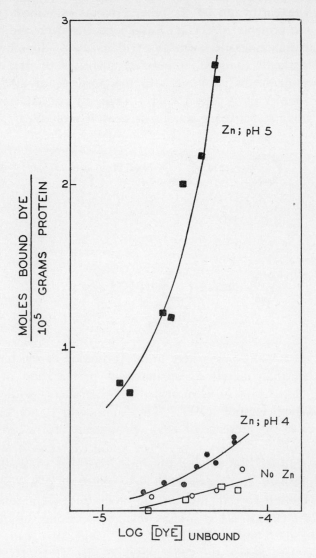

FIG. 5. Binding of Dye (II) by Pepsin.

of any protein. The values determined are assembled in Table 6. It is of interest to note first that the affinity of the azopyridine compound for either Ca^{++} or Mg^{++} is essentially zero. The reason for the inability of these alkaline earth metals to act as mediators thus becomes obvious.

Among those metals which do combine with the " substrate " are some (e. g., Cu^{++} and Ni^{++}) which tend to form square-planar complexes, others (e. g., Hg^{++} and Zn^{++}) which prefer tetrahedral coordi-

TABLE 6

STABILITY CONSTANTS FOR METAL–DYE (II) CHELATES pH $\sim$ 6

Metal	K_1 (x 10^{-3})
Cu^{++}	133
Hg^{++}	83
Ni^{++}	17.2
Co^{++}	2.14
Zn^{++}	0.229
Mn^{++}	0.005
Mg^{++}	0.000
Ca^{++}	0.000

TABLE 7

Metal	P–Me–D Me_{TOTAL}
Cu^{++}	0.43
Co^{++}	0.05
Zn^{++}	0.017
Mn^{++}	0.0005
Ca^{++}	0.0000

nation, and still others (e. g., Co^{++} and Mn^{++}) which are usually in an octahedral configuration. All of these can act as bridge between small molecule and protein. It is thus clear that the type of coordination arrangement preferred by the metal cation is not a primary factor in determining its ability to act as a mediator.

Nevertheless, there are striking differences in the mediating effectiveness of these coordinating metals. Their relative efficiencies may be compared on the basis of the fraction of total metallic ion which is bound in the form of the ternary complex (Table 7). It is of interest that the order observed, $Cu^{++} > Co^{++} > Zn^{++} > Mn^{++}$, is the same as that of the chelate stability constants (Table 6) of the azopyridine dye with these metals. Evidently the extent of formation of the protein-metal-dye complex depends largely on the affinity of the metal for the small molecule. It should also be mentioned that the affinity of the protein for the metals listed probably also falls in the same order (see preceding section), so that the net effect is to accentuate the chelate-metal preference.

Despite the relative simplicity in the relationships described so far, there are a number of observations of the mediating effects of these metals which point to influences which have not been fully

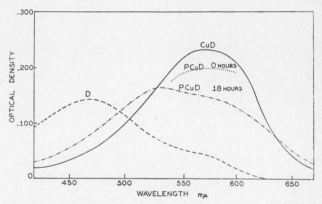

FIG. 6. Change of pepsin-copper-dye (II) spectra with time.

appreciated in the past. The position of Hg^{++} in Table 6 is unexpected, since in general this cation stands at the head of the list in complex-forming ability. Even more surprising is the *decrease* found in the affinity constant as the pH is raised from 5.8 to 6. At first glance one would expect a slight increase, if any change at all, since there would be a slight increase in the uncharged form of (II) as the last fraction of its acidic cationic form dissociates.

Anomalous behavior was observed also for the copper complex at various stages. In contrast to Zn^{++}, the spectrum of the Cu^{++} chelate of (II) shows some change with pH. Furthermore, when pepsin is added to the copper chelate, a very slow change occurs in the spectrum (Fig. 6); with zinc (and Co^{++}, Ni^{++}, and Mn^{++}) the effect of the protein is instantaneous.

The unexpected behavior of Hg^{++} and Cu^{++} parallels one of the major properties in which these two metals differ from the others studied — their hydrolytic equilibria.   Copper and mercury have a much greater affinity for hydroxyl ion, as is illustrated in Fig. 7.

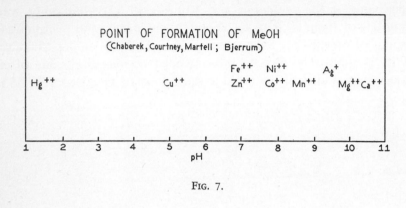

FIG. 7.

As a result, at pH's between 5 to 7, which were used in the current studies, the equilibrium (IV) is shifted strongly to the right for Cu^{++}

$$D{\small\bigcirc}Me\!\!<^{OH_2}_{OH_2} \;+\; OH^- \;\rightleftharpoons\; D{\small\bigcirc}Me\!\!<^{OH_2}_{OH} \;+\; H_2O$$

AT   pH   6 - 7

Zn ⟵

Cu ⟶

(IV)

(or Hg^{++}) but not for metals such as Zn^{++}.   With Hg^{++}, in fact, higher hydroxides probably compete with the dye (chelate) for metal ion, since the formation constant of $Hg(OH)_2$ is known to be very large (26).   Consequently the stability constant for the mercury chelate drops with increased hydroxide concentration.

The slow formation of the ternary complex when copper is the mediating metal is also probably a reflection of the hydrolytic equilibria (V). The replacement of H_2O on the metal by OH^- is likely to be a rapid exchange, since it can occur by a proton transfer from the aquo molecule. However, if we may judge from corresponding phenomena in inorganic complex-ion chemistry (4), it is quite likely that the displacement of one or more OH^- ligands by the combining side-chains of the protein is a slow process. Likewise other substitutions of ligands on metal complex ions may require substantial periods of time (4). This behavior is of particular interest because of its possible relevance to the extended activation periods often observed in studies of metal-catalyzed enzymatic reactions (24, 55).

$$D\subset Me\begin{subarray}{l}\diagup OH_2 \\ \diagdown OH_2\end{subarray} \qquad\qquad\qquad + H_2O$$

$$+\ P \longrightarrow D\subset Me\subset P$$

$$D\subset Me\begin{subarray}{l}\diagup OH \\ \diagdown OH\end{subarray} \qquad\qquad\qquad + OH^-$$

(V)

METAL-PROTEIN INTERACTIONS AND STATE OF ENZYME

In the light of the properties of metal-protein complexes described and referred to in the preceding discussion, it is of interest to consider some of the ways that such interactions might influence enzymatic activity. These modes may be grouped, to some extent arbitrarily, into three categories (Fig. 8) on the basis of the component

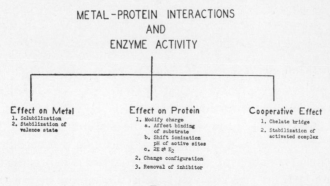

FIG. 8.

to which one attributes the major effect: (a) primary effect on properties of metal; (b) primary effect on the characteristics of the enzyme protein; (c) metal and protein participate cooperatively.

Effect on metal. Examples of the first group are to be found to a great extent among the iron and copper oxidation-reduction enzymes. The former will not be considered further, since the porphyrin prosthetic group plays a major role in determining the behavior of the metal. The copper proteins in nature were discussed in the first of the McCollum-Pratt symposia (41) and reviewed in detail somewhat earlier by Dawson and Mallette (13). An obvious function of the protein in these enzymes is to keep the copper in solution, for cupric ion and certainly cuprous ion are not water-soluble at physiological pH's. The protein may also contribute to the stability of the lower valence state and thereby facilitate the shuttling of electrons in the oxidation-reduction process. However, it must be emphasized that neither of these two effects account for the unique behavior of the copper enzyme; for Dr. W. L. Riedeman in this Laboratory has prepared water-soluble cupric and cuprous complexes of serum albumin which do not have unusual catalytic properties in oxidation reactions. It is evident that the natural copper enzyme contains the metal in some special linkage or perhaps near another site which has an appreciable affinity for the substrate in the oxidation reaction.

Effects on protein. From the known behavior of protein complexes, a number of ways can be visualized in which combination with a metal may profoundly influence the activity of an enzyme. Some of these mechanisms seem to be recognizable in several well-known systems.

When a metal combines with a protein molecule, it is obvious that the net charge of the complex differs from that originally on the protein. This modification in charge may change directly the affinity of the enzyme for the substrate on purely electrostatic grounds. The electrostatic effect may also operate in more indirect ways. The titration curves of proteins are markedly affected by combination with metals. As a result of combination, groups involved in the catalytic activity may have their dissociation curves shifted markedly along the pH axis. In essence, the pH-activity curve of the enzyme may be shifted so that measurements of activity in a restricted pH range would be markedly influenced by the presence of metallic ions. Thirdly, the electrostatic effect of bound metal may influence a monomer-dimer equilibrium of an enzyme:

$$2\ E \rightleftharpoons E_2$$

If, for example, E is negatively charged, the formation of E_2 would be favored on electrostatic grounds if combination with a cationic metal can occur. If E_2 is the enzymatically active species, the presence of metal would increase activity. It is possible that an influence of this last type is operative in the effect of divalent cations on the activity of trypsin and chymotrypsin (8, 19, 20). The monomer-dimer equilibrium of chymotrypsin has been well established (54).

A metal may also affect the configuration of a protein for reasons other than modification of charge. As was pointed out above, a variety of metals form mercaptides with the sulfhydryl groups of proteins. If the thiol is involved directly in the enzymatic action, inhibition is of course to be expected. However, the –SH group may play a role in maintaining a particular configuration of a protein molecule. With hemoglobin, for example, Riggs (48) observed that blocking of the thiol group with a mercurial had a marked effect on the oxygenation curve; for the purposes of the present discussion, the sizable increase in uptake of oxygen in the low-pressure region (Fig. 9) is particularly noteworthy. While the mechanism of this effect with hemoglobin is still not understood, the most interesting feature to note from our viewpoint is that an added metal may have a profound effect on an enzymatically-active site even though the added metal is not directly involved in the makeup of the site and may, in fact, be very far removed on a molecular scale. It follows, therefore, that experimental observations of increased uptake of substrate upon addition of metal, even if demonstrated by more direct methods than increased rate of enzymatic activity, do not necessarily imply that the metal acts as a bridge between enzyme and substrate. Likewise it is perhaps worth mentioning that enzymatic inhibition by mercurials and other thiol-blocking agents does not necessarily imply that the –SH group is a member of the active site of the enzyme.

Finally, mention should be made of another indirect mechanism by which a metal may activiate an enzyme — removal of an inhibitor. A possible example is Warburg's experiments with zymohexase (59),

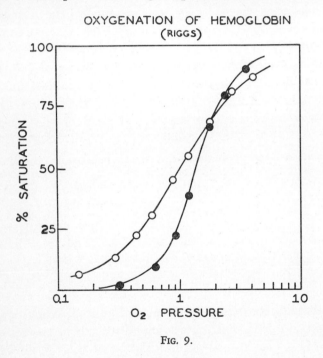

FIG. 9.

in which the inactivating effect of several metal-complexing agents can be counteracted by addition of suitable metal ions. In the same connection it is of interest to point to the reversal of Be^{++}-inhibition of alkaline phosphatase when Mn^{++}, Co^{++}, or Ni^{++} is added to the medium (14).

Cooperative effects.   As has been shown above, metals may actually serve as bridges in the formation of a complex between protein and small molecule.   Such a mechanism has indeed been postulated for some time for many metal-activated enzyme reactions, in particular decarboxylations (35, 36, 56) and hydrolyses (24, 55). Details of the mechanism of decarboxylations have been outlined convincingly by Steinberger and Westheimer (56). Among hydrolytic reactions, specific sites for the metal bridging have been described by Hellerman (24) and by Smith (55) for arginine in arginase activity and for various peptides in peptidase systems. Particular emphasis has been placed in the latter systems on the formation of a chelate between metal ion and substrate as a requirement for enzymatic activity.

A number of questions have been raised in the past (38, 40) in regard to the details of the chelate-formation picture of metal-activated enzymatic hydrolyses. It has been our feeling that the fol-

TABLE 8

Log K_1 for Metal–Amino Acid Complex Formation (Monk)

	Glycine	Alanine	Glycylglycine
Cu^{++}	8.62	8.51	6.05
Ni^{++}	6.18	5.96	4.49
Zn^{++}	5.52	5.21	3.80
Pb^{++}	5.47	5.00	3.23
Co^{++}	5.23	4.82	3.49
Mn^{++}	3.44	3.02	2.15
Mg^{++}	3.44	1.96	1.06

lowing questions are actually the most troublesome in connection with this picture. (a) The most commonly occurring activators are Mn^{++} and Mg^{++}, yet these are at the bottom of the list in chelating ability (Table 8) (44). (b) The products of peptide hydrolyses are usually stronger chelating agents than the initial reactants. Thus it has been shown by Kroll (37) that leucine complexes much more strongly with Mn^{++} ions than does leucinamide. It is difficult to see, therefore, why leucineaminopeptidase, which is activated by Mn^{++}, should dissociate the product, leucine, of the hydrolytic cleavage of leucineamide. (c) Finally, formation of a chelate should stabilize the ground state of a substrate-metal-enzyme complex; a mechanism which made it clearer how the metal might stabilize an activated state would be more satisfying. It is not always realized that the formation of a metal complex with an organic molecule may inhibit the rate of a reaction (47), as well as speed it up.

In our experience with metal bridging of dye-protein complexes, one of the most illuminating observations was that the metals with greatest chelating ability toward substrates did not necessarily function most effectively as bridges to the protein. Their strong complexing ability favored competing reactions. These results, coupled with the fact that the poorest complexing metals (Mn^{++} and Mg^{++}) are most often encountered as activators of hydrolyzing enzymes, have led us to adopt a rather modified viewpoint of the role of metals in these enzymatic processes. The scheme to be described discounts the chelate-forming ability of the cation. By drawing attention instead to the activated or intermediate state in the hydrolysis process, it suggests an alternative role for the metal ion which permits a broader unification of the behavior of seemingly diverse systems.

If the mechanism of basic hydrolysis of simple esters (17) may be transposed to amides and peptides (46), the reaction course may be represented by (VI).

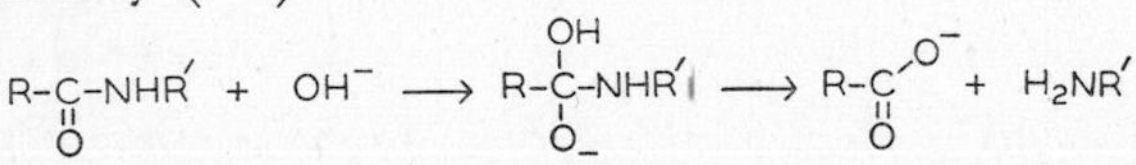

$$R-\underset{O}{\underset{\|}{C}}-NHR' + OH^- \longrightarrow R-\underset{O_-}{\underset{|}{\overset{\overset{\textstyle OH}{|}}{C}}}-NHR' \longrightarrow R-\overset{O^-}{\underset{O}{\overset{\nearrow}{\underset{\|}{C}}}} + H_2NR'$$

(VI)

The most significant feature from our viewpoint is the nature of the intermediate complex (VI). A cationic metal on a suitable protein could favor the formation of this activated form in two ways. First, the metal would stabilize the transition state by the formation of the complex (VII).

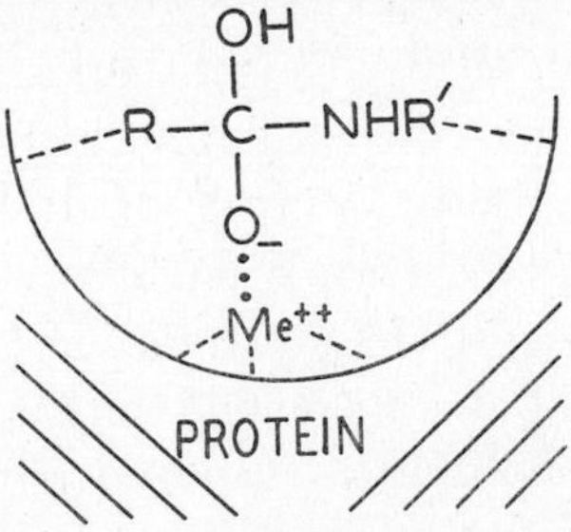

(VII)

Secondly, the cationic Me^{++} would increase the local concentration of OH^-. Both of these factors would make the local environment in the neighborhood of the sensitive bond more "basic" and hence speed up the hydrolysis.

In this picture it is assumed that R and R', the substituents that determine the specificity of the hydrolyzing enzyme, are bound directly to the enzyme, rather than by a chelate linkage to the metal. Assumption of chelation of the substrate to the metal has been omitted on several grounds. The primary function of such an assumption has been to provide a basis for some of the specificities observed among the peptidases. Invariably, though, certain aspects of specificity behavior, particularly differences between stereoisomers, require one to fall back onto the configuration of the protein. It seems just as well, then, to place responsibility for specificity in general on the interaction of R and R' groups with the apoenzyme directly. From this viewpoint it is also much easier to reconcile enzymatic behavior with our observations on protein-metal-dye complexes and to understand the outstanding positions of Mn^{++} and Mg^{++} as activators of the peptidases. Metals which form complexes with great avidity are not likely to have any open coordination positions, particularly at pH's as high as 8-9, at which these enzymatic reactions have been studied. At pH's above 7, most of the divalent cations having open coordination positions will bind OH^- ions strongly. If R includes an $-NH_2$ group, it is conceivable that this group might replace an OH^- from the metal coordination sphere; it is very difficult to believe, however, that the very weakly-complexing

$$\overset{\text{O}}{\overset{\|}{-\text{C}-}}$$ or $-NH-$ groups of the amide could displace a second strongly bound OH^- to form a chelate. On the other hand, with the assumption that they cannot do so, it becomes quite clear why metals such as Mn^{++} and Mg^{++} are the common activators. These metals, being among the weakest coordinators, still have open coordination bonds. Even at pH's 8–9 their interaction with OH^- ions is weak. As a result they are in a state in which they can stabilize the intermediate complex (VII) by formation of a link with the negatively-charged $C-O^-$ group.

On the basis of the picture (VII) it is also easier to understand the effect of hydrolysis products on the activity of the peptidases. The splitting of the amide bond produces a carboxyl and an amine group, which coordinate only weakly with Mn^{++} or Mg^{++}. This weak bond which might be formed with the metal is counterbalanced by the loss of a point of anchorage of the amino acid, as compared to the parent peptide, to the apoenzyme directly. Thus the products might be bound slightly to the enzyme but are hardly likely to have a high affinity for the active site.

With a picture of metal stabilization of an intermediate complex in an hydrolysis reaction, it is a simple matter to extend the inter-

(VIII)

pretation to the observed behavior of arginase (24), without assuming the formation of unlikely ring structures in order to have a chelate. Our interpretation requires only a slight extension of the general ideas of Hellerman and Perkins (23) and Hellerman and Stock (25). The sensitive bond in the arginase system is of the same general type as in the amides and esters. In this case, as has been suggested by Hellerman and Perkins (23), the metal ion may first destroy the resonance stabilization of the guanidinium group by displacing a hydrogen ion. From our viewpoint, it is in the next step, the stabilization of the intermediate complex (VIII), that the metal plays its critical role, for it facilitates the opening of the C=NH bond and the simultaneous introduction of the OH^- ion.

From this viewpoint some of the differences between arginase and the peptidases also seem reasonable. With the former enzyme, a hyrogen ion is displaced from the amidinium $=NH_2^+$ group before the activated complex (VIII) is formed. This displacement can be brought about by a metal having some tendency to complex with nitrogen groups. On the other hand too strong an affinity for ligands would keep the metal complexed with OH⁻ ions so avidly that displacement by =NH groups would not be significant. On this basis it seems reasonable that Ni^{++}, Co^{++}, Fe^{++}, and Mn^{++} should be the activators for arginase; Mg^{++} has a much weaker affinity for nitrogens; Cu^{++}, Fe^{+++}, and Hg^{++} have too strong an affinity for hydroxyl ions. It is also of interest in connection with this interpretation that the activating effects of metals on arginase are more pronounced at pH 7.5 than at 9.5 (23), i. e., at pH's where metal complexing with OH⁻ is decreased by the reduced hydroxyl concentration.

(IX)

The appearance of Mn^{++} and Mg^{++} as primary activators in phosphatase action suggests that the role of metals in these hydrolyses is analogous to those described above. Again one may visualize an intermediate (IX) stabilized by metal coordination. Likewise among the phosphate-transferring enzymes, the occurrence of Mn^{++} and Mg^{++} activators suggests the desirability of writing a mechanism which emphasizes stabilization of a charge-separated type of activated state. For some of these systems the metal may function simultaneously as an agent for increased binding of the substrate to the enzyme. Where such a role is a significant one, it seems likely that metals that form stronger complexes than Mn^{++} or Mg^{++} should also appear as activators.

Conclusion

With the increased availability of purified, crystallized proteins, studies of interactions with metal ions have become more amenable to interpretation and understanding in terms of the behavior of these cations in simple solutions. As investigations of the effects of metals on non-enzymatic proteins have expanded, it has become evident that the influence of metals on enzymatic systems may occur through an ever-larger number of mechanisms. Extensive information, therefore, may be necessary to ascertain which mechanism or group of mechanisms is operative in a particular case, and only grudgingly slow progress may be made in this field. It is encouraging, on the other hand, that more and more similarities between non-enzymatic and enzymatic metal-protein systems are being discovered. There is thus some basis for anticipation of the reproduction of biological catalysis by essentially artificial systems.

REFERENCES

1. Abels, J. C., *J. Am. Chem. Soc.*, 58, 2608 (1936).
2. Albert, A., *Biochem. J.*, 47, 531 (1950); 50, 690 (1952).
3. Alderton, G., W. H. Ward, and H. L. Fevold, *Arch. Biochem.*, 11, 9 (1946).
4. Basolo, F., B. D. Stone, and R. G. Pearson, *J. Am. Chem. Soc.*, 75, 819 (1953).
5. Battley, E. H., and I. M. Klotz, *Biol Bull.*, 101, 215 (1951).
6. Benesch, R., and R. E. Benesch, *Arch. Biochem.*, 19, 35 (1948).
7. Benesch, R., and R. E. Benesch, *Arch. Biochem. and Biophys.*, 38, 425 (1952).
8. Bier, M., and F. F. Nord, *Arch. Biochem. and Biophys.*, 33, 320 (1951).
9. Bjerrum, J., *Metal Ammine Formation in Aqueous Solution*, p. 75. P. Haase and Son, Copenhagen (1941).
10. Bowes, J. H., and R. H. Kenten, *Biochem. J.*, 44, 142 (1949).
11. Brand, E., *Ann. N. Y. Acad. Sci.*, 47, 187 (1946)
12. Carr, C. W., and L. Topol, *J. Phys. & Colloid Chem.*, 54, 176 (1950).
13. Dawson, C. R., and M. F. Mallette, *Advances in Protein Chem.*, 2, 179 (1945).
14. DuBois, K. P., K. W. Cochran, and M. Mazur, *Science*, 110, 420 (1949).
15. Fiess, H. A., *J. Am. Chem. Soc.*, 74, 3539 (1952).
16. Fraenkel-Conrat, H., and M. Cooper, *J. Biol. Chem.*, 154, 239 (1944).
17. Frost, A. A., and R. G. Pearson, *Kinetics and Mechanism*, pp. 5-7. J. Wiley and Sons, New York (1953).
18. Gordon, W. G., W. F. Semmett, R. S. Cable, and M. Morris., *J. Am. Chem. Soc.*, 71, 3293 (1949).
19. Gorini, L., *Biochim. et Biophys. Acta*, 7, 318 (1951).
20. Green, M. M., J. A. Gladner, L. W. Cunningham, and H. Neurath, *J. Am. Chem. Soc.*, 74, 2122 (1952).
21. Gurd, F. R. N., and D. S. Goodman, *J. Am. Chem. Soc.*, 74, 670 (1952).

22. Gustavson, K. H., *J. Am. Chem. Soc.*, 74, 4608 (1952).
23. Hellerman, L., and M. E. Perkins, *J. Biol. Chem.*, 112, 175 (1935).
24. Hellerman, L., *Physiol. Rev.*, 17, 454 (1937).
25. Hellerman, L., and C. C. Stock, *J. Biol. Chem.*, 125, 771 (1938).
26. Hietanen, S., and L. G. Sillen, *Acta Chem. Scand.*, 6, 747 (1952).
27. Hughes, W. L., Jr., *J. Am. Chem. Soc.*, 69, 1836 (1947)
28. Hughes, W. L., Jr., *Cold Spring Harbor Symposia Quant. Biol.*, 14, 79 (1950).
29. Katz, S., and I. M. Klotz, *Arch. Biochem. and Biophys.*, 44, 351 (1953).
30. Klotz, I. M., and H. G. Curme, *J. Am. Chem. Soc.*, 70, 939 (1948).
31. Klotz, I. M., and H. A. Fiess, *J. Phys. & Colloid Chem.*, 55, 101 (1951).
32. Klotz, I. M., J. M. Urquhart, and H. A. Fiess, *J. Am. Chem. Soc.*, 74, 5537 (1952).
33. Klotz, I. M., in *Modern Trends in Physiology and Biochemistry* (E. S. G. Barron, ed.), p. 427. Academic Press, New York (1952).
34. Koechlin, B. A., *J. Am. Chem. Soc.*, 74, 2649 (1952).
35. Kornberg, A., S. Ochoa, and A. Mehler, *J. Biol. Chem.*, 174, 159 (1948).
36. Krebs, H. A., *Biochem. J.*, 36, 303 (1942).
37. Kroll, H., *J. Am. Chem. Soc.*, 74, 2034 (1952).
38. Lehninger, A. L., *Physiol. Rev.*, 30, 393 (1950).
39. Lemberg, R., and J. W. Legge, *Hematin Compounds*, Interscience, New York (1949).
40. Martell, A. E., and M. Calvin, *Chemistry of the Metal Chelate Compounds*, Chapter 8. Prentice-Hall, New York (1952).
41. McElroy, W. D., and B. Glass, eds., *Copper Metabolism*, The Johns Hopkins Press, Baltimore (1950).
42. Mellor, D. P., and L. Maley, *Nature*, 159, 370 (1947); 161, 436 (1948).
43. Miyamoto, S., and C. L. A. Schmidt, *J. Biol. Chem.*, 99, 335 (1933).
44. Monk, C. B., *Trans. Faraday Soc.*, 47, 297 (1951).
45. Northrop, J. H., and M. Kunitz, *J. Gen. Physiol.*, 7, 25 (1924-25); 9, 351 (1925-26); 11, 481 (1927-28).
46. Pearson, R. G., priv. com.
47. Pedersen, K. J., *Acta Chem. Scand.*, 3, 676 (1949).
48. Riggs, A. F., *J. Gen. Physiol.*, 36, 1 (1952).
49. Scatchard, G., I. H. Scheinberg, and S. H. Armstrong, Jr., *J. Am. Chem. Soc.*, 72, 535, 540 (1950).
50. Schade, A. L., and L. Caroline, *Science*, 100, 14 (1944).
51. Schade, A. L., and L. Caroline, *Science*, 104, 340 (1946).
52. Schade, A. L., R. W. Reinhart, and H. Levy, *Arch. Biochem.*, 20, 170 (1949).
53. Schubert, J., in *Memoirs of the University Laboratory of Physical Chemistry Related to Medicine and Public Health of Harvard University*, Number 3, Academic Press, New York (in press).
54. Schwert, G., and S. Kaufman, *J. Biol. Chem.*, 190, 807 (1951).
55. Smith, E. L., *Proc. Nat. Acad. Sci. U. S.*, 35, 80 (1949).
56. Steinberger, R., and F. H. Westheimer, *J. Am. Chem. Soc.*, 73, 429 (1951).
57. Tanford, C., *J. Am. Chem. Soc.*, 74, 211 (1952).
58. Theorell, H., *Advances in Enzymol.*, 7, 265 (1947).
59. Warburg, O., *Heavy Metal Prosthetic Groups and Enzyme Action*, translated by A. Lawson, Chap. 19, Clarendon Press, Oxford (1949).
60. Warner, R. C., and I. Weber, *J. Biol. Chem.*, 191, 173 (1951).
61. Warner, R. C., and I. Weber, *J. Am. Chem. Soc.* (in press).
62. Wyman, J., Jr., *Advances in Protein Chem.*, 4, 407 (1948).

DISCUSSION

DR. HELLERMAN: I think I will ask Dr. Hughes if he would care to say a few words about the mercaptalbumins in relation to Dr. Klotz's talk.

DR. HUGHES: The only thing that I would like to emphasize is the matter of specificity, which I think Dr. Klotz has already discussed. No interaction is absolutely specific. For example, mercurials have been used as very specific agents for thiol groups, but they are not necessarily absolutely specific. They can be made specific, though. You will note in the slide that Dr. Klotz used showing stoichiometry of methyl mercury binding, specificity holds for small excesses of this mercurial. In the case of methyl mercury iodide, the specificity was enhanced by the strong competing effect of the iodide ion, which shows a very strong affinity for mercury. If one uses other mercury salts, the specificity can vanish fairly completely. For example, with methyl mercury hydroxide extremely large numbers of mercurial groups can be bound to serum albumin.

DR. HELLERMAN: Was this around neutral pH?

DR. HUGHES: This was between pH 6 and 7. For example, when methyl mercury hydroxide is added to albumin there is almost complete binding of the mercurial until 15 to 20 mols have been bound, followed by a gradual increase in the amount of free mercurial as larger amounts are added. I haven't reached the maximum yet, but we have obtained as much as 100 mols of the mercurial bound per mol of albumin. This is at a point where the free mercurial is around 0.01 molar. The hydroxide is weakly dissociated (pK = 9.5), so that the actual concentration of the methyl mercury ion is very much lower. I think this serves to emphasize that it is very important to check the specificity of the reagent that you use. This excess binding must mean that the mercurial is combining not only with the SH groups but also with the carboxyl, as well as with the amino groups.

DR. GUNSALUS: I should like to give another example of an enzyme which may involve metal catalysis, and involves a carbon-carbon cleavage rather than a C–N cleavage of the hydrolytic type which Emil Smith discussed for us. I should like to get an opinion from some of the physical chemists as to how much energy is involved. In our laboratory Mr. Gillespie, using *Streptococcus faecalis*, and Dr. Marianne Manago, using *E. coli*, are studying an enzyme which splits citrate to acetate and oxalacetate. This system is activated by approximately 0.001 M manganese ion. The reaction does not require CoA, and goes essentially to completion in the direction of acetate and oxalacetate. This reaction is the reverse of the reaction catalyzed by Ochoa's condensing enzyme, so far as the carbon skeletons, acetic and oxalacetic acids are concerned, but it forms acetate, not acetyl-CoA; thus the difference in equilibrium and the suggestion that another enzyme—a citrate desmolase—is involved.

I just asked Dr. Ochoa about the energy of this bond in citrate. I believe Dr. Kaplan calculated it at about 5000 calories. The value could be calculated from Stadtman's, and Ochoa and Stern's data on the equilibria of the acetyl-phosphate-acetyl-CoA, and the acetyl-CoA plus oxalacetate-citrate reactions, assuming an accurate energy value can be assigned to the anhydride bond of acetyl-phosphate. The question I had in mind was suggested by Dr. Smith's discussion of the activation of hydrolytic cleavages. Can we also consider manganese, in the same way, to be the catalyst for activation of the citric acid splitting reaction which I have just drawn on the board? In other words, is this another example of a carbon-carbon cleavage which we could put into the category of the general series of metal chelates?

DR. E. SMITH: The decarboxylases are also essentially splitting carbon-carbon bonds, one of the model systems which Dr. Westheimer has studied.

DR. GUNSALUS: Then you think that one might say, in view of the fact that we found manganese as a co-factor for the citrate desmolase that we need not look farther for other co-factors?

DR. E. SMITH: I don't think that is necessarily true.

DR. GUNSALUS: Do you think it's unreasonable to expect the energy of activation to come from the formation of a manganese complex with citrate and enzyme?

DR. E. SMITH: No.

DR. DOUDOROFF: I was going to ask whether there is a plague on the monovalent ions. Nothing has been said about sodium or potassium as activators of hydrolytic enzymes.

DR. CALVIN: Are they?

DR. DOUDOROFF: At least in one very peculiar case reported by Cohn and Monod, where the same enzyme was activated by sodium in the hydrolysis of nitrophenol galactoside, and by potassium in the case of lactose—that is, with the same enzyme—two different metals catalyze the reaction on two different substrates.

DR. HELLERMAN: Is this a specific effect, or a general effect?

DR. DOUDOROFF: This is a specific effect.

DR. HELLERMAN: Dr. Boyer, would you care to comment on the function of potassium in the pyruvate kinase reaction?

DR. BOYER: I should point out that the experiments of Cohn and Monod have been investigated further by Dr. Lardy's group, and Monod's data do not seem to hold up.

DR. BONNER: Did Lardy use the same strain as Cohn and Monod, because there seem to be some differences.

DR. DOUDOROFF: I have seen the experiments, and they look very good.

DR. BONNER: There is a distinct potassium activation of the lactase in the coli strains that Monod used. We have done this in our laboratory.

DR. BOYER: The question raised is not one of potassium activation, but one of a change in metal requirement depending upon the nature of the substrate. Have you found that?

DR. BONNER: No.

DR. BOYER: It is nothing unusual for potassium to activate lactase or a great number of enzymes.

DR. DOUDOROFF: Then do you think this is merely a charge effect in the case of these ions? Can you construct nice pictures like some of these that have been drawn on the board for the action of these metals?

DR. BOYER: The difference between potassium and sodium in this case I don't think is something that we need to worry about until it is further established to be right. It wasn't a question of whether it's potassium activation alone, but whether one can obtain potassium activation in one reaction and sodium activation in another reaction using the same enzyme.

DR. DOUDOROFF: I have seen the experiments, and they look good to me.

DR. KLOTZ: I think the reason people seem to try to avoid answering this question—and I think I shall do likewise—is that there are practically no systems known which will form complexes with sodium or potassium. There are a couple of unusual ones, like uramil di-acetate, which will form complexes with potassium and sodium, and if you use your imagination you might think that these mimic the purine structure; but you have to have a lot of imagination to see that, so that no one is able to see any simple analogy which we would consider as a satisfactory explanation. The only mechanism which I can see is that sodium and potassium will combine with a long-chain polyelectrolyte, and perhaps with certain proteins if they have a very high negative charge, and there might be some specificity in these cases. There might also be some change in configuration of the protein due to the neutralization of the charge. Perhaps that has something to do with it, but this is pretty speculative.

DR. HELLERMAN: I think one of Dr. Calvin's slides said something about sodium or potassium ion.

DR. CALVIN: That was the missing one.

DR. HELLERMAN: Oh, was that on one of the missing slides? I thought I saw it on one that wasn't missing.

DR. CALVIN: As Dr. Klotz said, there are one or two cases in which sodium and potassium complexes can actually be isolated. In these cases it looks as though the sodium and potassium ions are exhibiting four coordinate linkages.

DR. KLOTZ: They have a low stability.

DR. CALVIN: Oh, they are very unstable. They hydrolyze instantly in water and must be isolated in non-aqueous systems. It could be that inside the protein one might have something like this. The case I have in mind that Dr. Hellerman brought up was a contrast between sodium and copper which was very easy to account for and carries a very great difference in the nature of the compound.

DR. RITTENBERG: When I finished my Ph. D. around 20 years ago, Urey took me aside and said, " My boy, physical chemistry is a sterile field. It hasn't done anything in the past 20 years, and it won't do anything in the next 20 years, so get out." I took his advice, and if there are any objections to what I say now I think that the objection ought to be directed to Chicago. In fact, we have today all been carefully avoiding the central problem, and that is: What is the role of the protein in these catalytic effects? Since I don't have a slide with me I wonder if Dr. Klotz would let me use his slide number 7? I believe it illustrates our difficulty. There is no doubt that the proteins have a role other than that of giving geometrical specificity. They must have some role in the activation process. Whatever explanation we offer must take into account that proteins are part of the whole system. I now wish to offer a model for enzyme action which explains why you need proteins. I don't think Dr. Klotz will mind if I say that in his slide he might just as well have left the protein out. There is no indication of the part the specific protein plays in the reaction.

DR. KLOTZ: He neglected to notice that you have a dotted line to the protein.

DR. RITTENBERG: Yes, but this hemispherical device really has nothing to do with chemistry but more nearly with psychiatry, I think. I don't believe that the reaction goes that way with the addition of the hydroxyl group, because if you try the effect of chymotrypsin on carbobenzoxy phenylalanine in the presence of O^{18} waters you find that there is a substitution of hydroxyl from the medium into the carboxyl group. If you do it with the amide and recover the amide, you find no O^{18} in the amide. If you do it chemically—that is, by acid hydrolysis—you do find O^{18} unhydrolyzed amide, so there is some evidence that the chemical and enzymatic reactions are different. Now, if nobody will ever hold me responsible for what I say, I would like to suggest the following as a mechanism. Instead of drawing the protein as a hemisphere, let me draw it as a wiggly line. If a molecule of the following composition:

$$\overset{\displaystyle O}{\underset{\displaystyle RC-X}{\|}}$$

approaches the surface of the protein molecule, we can envision the reaction which occurs as follows. In each peptide bond there is one free pair of electrons, which could be written as follows:

$$\begin{array}{c} \text{X} \\ \cdot\cdot \\ \text{R}:\text{N}:\text{C} \\ \uparrow\downarrow \end{array}$$

What I want to do is to uncouple these two electrons so that their spins are parallel. I want now to get rid of the electrons from this particular spot in the protein. I now need a big protein so that I can smear out these two electrons over the whole structure. If you look at the nitrogen in the peptide of the protein you don't find two electrons there, but you find less than two electrons there—not zero, but less than two. If you look at all the other peptide bonds at every nitrogen you find less than two there, and the sum of all the deficiencies is going to make up two electrons, I am now essentially denying that there are active centers on the protein. I admit that there are centers which are geometrically more favorable than others, but I am essentially denying active spots. I would think that the active spot can arise wherever the substrate approaches the protein. If now the substrate molecule approaches any of the protein nitrogens in the molecule, it is possible for the two electrons associated with the carbon-oxygen bond to eliminate the deficiency, and with the cooperation of a hydroxyl ion in solution we get hydrolysis. We tried to test this experimentally by investigating whether chymotrypsin does indeed have paramagnetic properties while it's hydrolyzing protein. These measurements gave negative results. Our procedure, however, was rather insensitive.

DR. HELLERMAN: I wish we had two hours for discussion. Perhaps we can continue this at another time.

DR. RITTENBERG: I apologize for taking so much of your valuable time with a theory.

DR. HELLERMAN: We want a theory of enzyme action, even if it doesn't work.

DR. EYRING: I would like to say a word about something I thing everybody knows. There is a sizable industry in Utah for separating potassium chloride from sodium chloride by flotation using straight-chain amines. This emphasizes the big difference between the affinities of potassium and sodium chloride crystals for straight-chain amines.

DR. KLOTZ: I just want to make one remark. I don't think that this discourse of Dr. Rittenberg has convinced me that physical chemistry has made more progress in the last two minutes than in the last 20 years. I take it from his viewpoint that synthetic polyglycine should also work like chymotrypsin if you say all we need is peptide bond to give a localization of the unpaired electrons, and to my knowledge it doesn't.

THE SPECIFICITY AND MODE OF ACTION OF TWO METAL-PEPTIDASES *

EMIL L. SMITH, NEIL C. DAVIS, ELIJAH ADAMS,** and
DARREL H. SPACKMAN †

*Laboratory for Study of Hereditary and Metabolic Disorders, and Departments of
Biological Chemistry and Medicine,
University of Utah College of Medicine, Salt Lake City*

SEVERAL YEARS AGO, in an attempt to explain the specificity of the metal-peptidases, it was suggested that the metal ion acts as a ligand in forming a coordination complex with both the substrate and the enzyme (29–33). It was also recognized that the side-chain specificity exhibited by the substrates of certain peptidases could be explained by assuming a van der Waals interaction between the protein portion of the enzyme and the side chains of the substrates (36, 37). Although certain first applications of the metal-ligand hypothesis were, perhaps, somewhat overenthusiastic, the main features of the theory still seem to be the simplest way of explaining the experimental facts concerning these and other metal-activated enzymes.

One criticism, raised earlier, is that most of the enzymes for which the theory seemed most reasonable were available only in a crude or partially purified form and that the characteristics and individuality of the enzymes were uncertain. This is, indeed, a valid criticism and one which we have been endeavoring to overcome for some years. Unfortunately, although the intracellular peptidases are highly active, they are present only in low concentrations in animal tissues and are highly labile. It has been an exceedingly laborious task to obtain these enzymes in a highly purified state.

No attempt will be made at present to survey the whole field and its history. Lehninger (15) has recently reviewed the situation with

* The original work of the authors has been supported by research grants from the National Institutes of Health, United States Public Health Service.
** Present address: National Institutes of Health, Bethesda, Maryland.
† Predoctorate Fellow of the National Cancer Institute, U. S. Public Health Service.

respect to the metal-enzymes in general, and a survey of the peptidases has also been given (33). In this discussion, the present status of two metal-peptidases will be described: prolidase, which has been highly purified and obtained as poorly defined crystals, and leucine aminopeptidase, which also has been extensively purified but which has not yet been prepared in a physically homogeneous state.

PROLIDASE

In 1937, Bergmann and Fruton (5), working with extracts of intestinal mucosa, ascribed the hydrolysis of glycyl-L-proline to a new enzyme which they named prolidase. Since that time, the enzyme has been obtained from many animal tissues, and the main features of its specificity have been delineated (2, 9, 28, 35). The specificity of this peptidase is unique. At the present time, it is the only known enzyme which can bring about the rapid hydrolysis of substrates in which the sensitive peptide bond involves the imino nitrogen of proline or hydroxyproline.[1] Glycyl-L-proline is a typical substrate for prolidase.

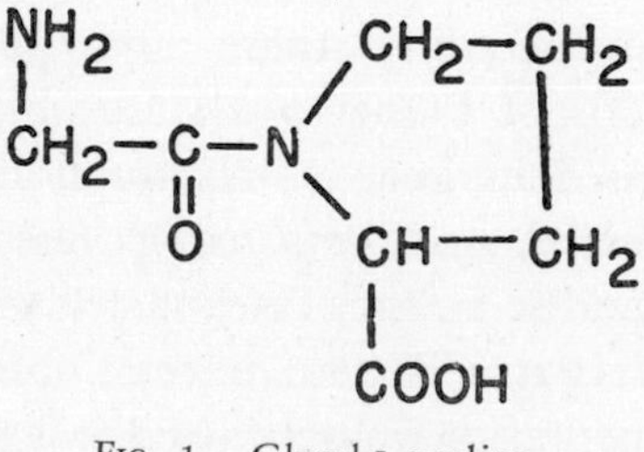

$$\begin{array}{cc} NH_2 & \\ | & CH_2{-}CH_2 \\ CH_2{-}\underset{\underset{O}{\|}}{C}{-}N & | \\ & CH{-}CH_2 \\ & | \\ & COOH \end{array}$$

FIG. 1.   Glycyl-L-proline.

These peptides lack the peptide hydrogen ordinarily found at the peptide bond, as in the general structure –CONH–. Purified prolidase does not attack any compounds with the normal peptide bond, and no enzyme other than prolidase attacks the imide peptide linkage. We are in the curious position that purification has, thus far, taught

[1] Carboxypeptidase has an extremely weak action on carbobenzoxy-L-tryptophyl-L-proline (33).

us little more concerning the specificity of this enzyme than we knew from studies on much cruder preparations.

The most convenient source of prolidase is swine kidney, and from this tissue the enzyme has been purified about 12,000-fold, as judged by the activity per mg. soluble protein N in the crude and purified preparations. Enzyme activity is estimated as the first-order rate constant (K_1) expressed in minutes and decimal logarithms from hydrolytic experiments at a substrate concentration of 0.05 M. Specific activity is given by the proteolytic coefficient $C_1 = K_1/E$ where E is the enzyme concentration in mg. of protein N per ml. The crude extract of swine kidney has a C_1 of 0.01, whereas our best preparation has a C_1 greater than 120. The method of purification will not be described in detail at the present time; however, the main features of the procedure, which will be described soon (7), depend on the solubility of the enzyme in 45 per cent ethanol, its resistance to denaturation in this mixture by chloroform, and on subsequent fractionation with ammonium sulfate and with acetone. The enzyme is greatly stabilized by Mn^{++}, the activating ion, and by sulfhydryl compounds, such as cysteine and glutathione. Thus, in the last steps of purification, Mn^{++} and glutathione were always added, and the enzyme was isolated in the active state.

The best preparations of kidney prolidase obtained thus far are more than 90 per cent homogeneous electrophoretically and in the ultracentrifuge. The electrophoretic component identified as the enzyme has been separated in the Tiselius cell and exhibits all the activity of the preparation. The main peak observed in the ultracentrifuge has a sedimentation constant of about 6.4 Svedberg units, which indicates a molecular weight in excess of 100,000. More definitive physical studies are required, but these will have to await more knowledge of the properties of the enzyme and will depend on the availability of more material. The present yield of the 90 per cent pure material is about 100 mg. from 30 kilos of fresh swine kidney.

Prolidase exhibits a typical protein absorption spectrum in the ultraviolet. Examination of a hydrolysate on a two-dimensional paper chromatogram shows all the usual amino acids.

The enzyme, which may be obtained from various animal tissues, requires for its maximal activity the presence of divalent manganese. In the absence of this ion, carefully treated preparations show either low or negligible levels of activity. The metal activation is specific; none of the other common biologically active divalent cations has the slightest activating effect whatsoever (2, 7, 35). Pyrophosphate, versene, and other chelating agents are strong inhibitors of the crude enzyme when no Mn^{++} has been added (2). Preparations of prolidase from which the Mn^{++} has been removed by various procedures can be reactivated by addition of this ion. There appears to be little doubt that the Mn^{++} is an essential component of the active enzyme.

As already noted, prolidase is greatly stabilized by Mn^{++} and glutathione; this suggested the presence in the enzyme of an essential sulfhydryl group. It was subsequently found that prolidase is strongly inhibited by p-chloromercuribenzoate whether Mn^{++} is present or not, and this inhibition can be reversed by the addition of glutathione or cysteine. The action of iodoacetamide on the enzyme is somewhat different. When prolidase has been fully activated by Mn^{++}, iodoacetamide has little or no inhibitory effect. However, when Mn^{++} is not present, iodoacetamide produces a strong inhibition, as shown by the negligible activity after the subsequent addition of Mn^{++}. These results suggest that Mn^{++} is bound to a sulfhydryl group in the enzyme and that this binding protects the –SH group from reaction with iodoacetamide but not with p-chloromercuribenzoate. It should be noted that prolidase is completely inhibited by low concentrations of metal ions, such as Zn^{++}, Pb^{++}, Hg^+ and Cd^{++}, which react readily with sulfhydryl groups (2).

There is no question that Mn^{++} is bound directly to the protein. The effect of this ion on both activity and stability indicates a specific binding. It has also been found that the electrophoretic mobility of kidney prolidase is diminished in the presence of Mn^{++}. This indicates a smaller net negative charge on the alkaline side of the isoelectric point of the protein, but part of this effect may be due to non-specific binding. In addition, the activation of the enzyme by Mn^{++} is slow but is accelerated by the addition of small amounts of glutathione. The time-reaction between the metal and the protein indicates that the interaction cannot be entirely electrostatic, since such processes require no activation energy. Such time-reactions to form active enzymes were first observed with leucine aminopeptidase (41, 44), and later with arginase (12, 21), phosphatase (25), and other metal-activated enzymes (33).

The data for the effect of Mn^{++} on the activity of erythrocyte pro-

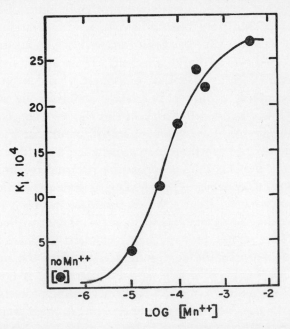

FIG. 2. Activity of erythrocyte prolidase as a function of Mn^{++} concentration. The solid line represents the mass law equation, $K_a = $ [active enzyme]/$[Mn^{++}]$ [inactive enzyme] where $K_a = 2.1 \times 10^4$. The data are those of Adams and Smith (2).

lidase may be described by the mass-law expression for the participation of one Mn^{++} in the activity of each active center (Fig. 2) (2). Such a study has not yet been performed with the highly purified kidney enzyme. However, similar results have been obtained for less highly purified preparations of other peptidases (33), and for the Mg^{++} and Mn^{++} activation of crystalline enolase (19, 44). The apparent association constants (K_a) for several of the metal-enzymes are given in Table 1. It is striking that for all these enzymes, the simple mass-law relationship for one metal ion per active center

TABLE 1

Association Constants and Free Energies of Binding for Some Metal–Enzymes

Enzyme	Source	Metal	pH	Temp. C.	K_a	$\Delta F°$
						calories
Leucine aminopeptidase (27)	Swine Intestine	Mn^{++}	8.0	40°	2.5×10^4	-6300
Glycylglycine dipeptidase (29)	Rat Muscle	Co^{++}	7.8	40°	3.6×10^4	-6600
Glycylleucine dipeptidase (29a)	Swine Intestine	Mn^{++}	7.8	40°	5.6×10^3	-5400
Prolidase (2)	Equine Erythrocytes	Mn^{++}	7.8	40°	2.1×10^4	-6200
Enolase (activity) (19)	Yeast	Mn^{++}	6.8	?	2.3×10^4	
" (binding) (19)	"	Mn^{++}	6.8	4°	5×10^4	-6000
" (activity) (44)	"	Mg^{++}	7.3	20°	1.6×10^3	-4300
" (44)	"	Mg^{++}	6.4	20°	2.7×10^3	-4600

appears to be the case, and that the K_a and $\Delta F°$ values for the binding are not too different. It is highly probable that similar chelate forces are concerned in the metal-binding of all these proteins. Moreover, as also noted by Malmström (19), the binding appears to be much stronger than that observed with amino acids or simple peptides. For enolase Malmström has compared the activation curve given by Mn^{++} and the binding curve determined by the equilibrium-dialysis technique. His results show that the two sets of measurements give K_a values of the same order of magnitude.

Specificity. As already mentioned, the highly purified prolidase obtained from swine kidney (7) and the partially purified preparation from equine erythrocytes (2) show no detectable action on

TABLE 2

Action of Prolidase on Various Compounds

C_1 is the proteolytic coefficient at pH 7.8 and 40° C.

Compound	C_1 Erythrocyte prolidase (2)	C_1 Kidney prolidase (7)
Glycyl-L-proline	0.43	126
Glycylhydroxy-L-proline	0.031	15
L-Phenylalanylhydroxy-L-proline	0.068	15
L-Prolyl-L-proline	0.11	
L-Prolylhydroxy-L-proline	0.018	
β-Alanyl-L-proline	0.0009	0.2
Dehydrophenylalanyl-L-proline	0	0
Glycylglycyl-L-proline	0	0
Glycyl-L-prolylglycine	0	0
Carbobenzoxyglycyl-L-proline	0	0

peptides or peptide derivatives which possess the usual peptide bond –CONH–. This has been tested with a large variety of dipeptides, such as prolylglycine, glycylglycine, leucylglycine, glycylleucine, etc., all of which are substrates for other peptidases, as well as with tripeptides, acyl dipeptides, acyl dipeptide amides, and proteins.

Prolidase is a dipeptidase since both amino and carboxyl groups alpha to the sensitive bond are required. The enzyme has no measurable action on the tripeptides, glycyl-L-prolylglycine and glycylglycyl-L-proline, or on the acyl derivatives, carbobenzoxyglycyl-L-proline or carbobenzoxyglycylhydroxy-L-proline (Table 2). β-

Alanyl-L-proline is hydrolyzed at an extremely slow rate when compared with the α-amino compound, glycyl-L-proline (2, 7, 9). Moreover, it is noteworthy that dehydrophenylalanyl-L-proline is completely resistant to the enzyme.

These data clearly delineate the main features of the specificity of prolidase. We may readily interpret these findings in terms of the aforementioned hypothesis that Mn^{++} acts as a ligand in the formation of the enzyme-substrate complex. The combination may be pictured according to the diagram shown below.

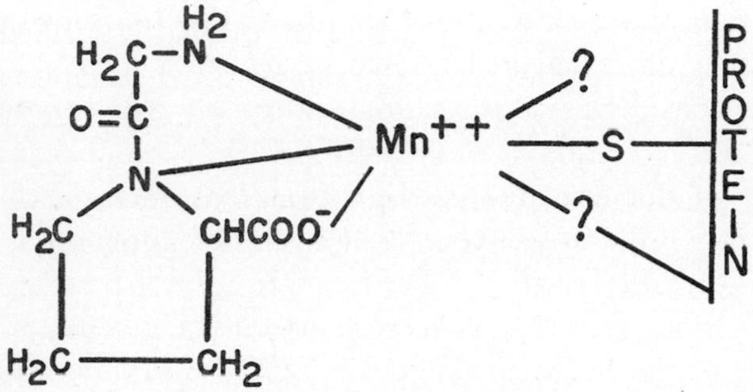

Fig. 3. Postulated coordination of glycyl-L-proline with prolidase.

The data indicate that the uncharged amino and the ionized carboxyl groups are essential points of attachment, and we assume that this occurs through the Mn^{++}. If this is the case, it is clear that the metal ion must have a third point of attachment in consonance with the well-known tendency of such ions to form chelates with five-membered rings. If the third point of attachment occurred through the peptide carbonyl, a five-membered and a seven-membered ring would result. It is more likely that two five-membered rings are formed as indicated in the diagram. This is also suggested by the exceedingly slow hydrolysis of β-alanyl-L-proline in which a 6-membered ring would have to be formed. Interestingly enough, the high sensitivity of L-prolyl-L-proline (2) indicates that a primary α-amino group is not required, provided that a five-membered ring can be formed.

As already mentioned, a sulfhydryl group of the protein is implicated in the metal binding and this is shown. Mn^{++} usually forms hexacoordinate complexes, and we have indicated that we have no direct evidence at present whether the two additional coordination places involve groups on the protein. However, to explain the stability of the metal-protein complex and the slow interaction by the metal and protein in forming the active enzyme, it is necessary to assume some type of chelate binding of the metal with the protein. It should be noted that the optimal action of this enzyme on glycyl-L-proline is near pH 8, a relation which suggests that if all the coordination places of the Mn^{++} are unfilled by the substrate and the protein, they are probably occupied by hydroxyl ions.

Before considering further implications of the enzyme-substrate complex indicated above, some additional important features of the specificity of this enzyme must be considered. The enzyme is optically specific; only 50 per cent of the racemic compound, glycyl-DL-proline is hydrolyzed (5). Furthermore, glycyl-L-proline is about ten times more sensitive than glycylhydroxy-L-proline. The lesser sensitivity of the hydroxy compound might be explained as due to a difference in bond strength of the two glycyl peptides, since it is known that the imino nitrogen of proline is much more basic than that of hydroxyproline. An alternative explanation is that the lesser susceptibility of the hydroxyproline compound depends on a steric interference by the hydroxyl group in the formation of the enzyme-substrate complex, since the γ-carbon of the pyrrolidine ring is optically active in hydroxyproline.

In an attempt to distinguish between these effects, glycylmethoxy-L-proline and glycylallohydroxy-L-proline were synthesized (1). The former is, of course, prepared from the O-methyl ether of naturally occurring hydroxyproline. The allo compound retains the optical configuration of natural hydroxyproline at the α-carbon atom but has the inverted configuration at the γ-carbon. In the methoxy compound, the large grouping on the γ-carbon would be expected to increase a steric interference and increase the basicity of the ring nitrogen by suppressing the effect of the free hydroxyl group. In the allo compound, a change in configuration of the hydroxyl at the γ-position would not be expected to influence strongly the basicity of the peptide nitrogen but would be expected to have a different steric effect than the diastereoisomeric compound. As shown in Table 3, the results indicate a steric effect. The rate of hydrolysis of the methoxy compound is very slow, whereas the rate of hydrolysis of glycylallohydroxy-L-proline is greater than that of the diastereoisomer, glycylhydroxy-L-proline.

TABLE 3

ACTION OF PROLIDASE ON CERTAIN DIPEPTIDES

The experimental conditions were the same as in Table 2. The data are those of Adams, Davis, and Smith (1).

Peptide	C_i Erythrocyte prolidase	C_i Kidney prolidase
Glycyl-L-proline	0.07	126
Glycylhydroxy-L-proline	0.0043	15
Glycylallohydroxy-L-proline	0.022	40
Glycylmethoxy-L-proline	0.00008	0.2
Glycylsarcosine		11

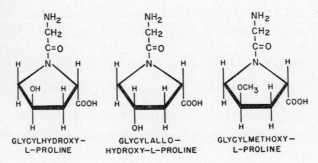

FIG. 4. Structure of prolidase substrates.

Hudson and Neuberger (11, 22) have shown that the carboxyl and hydroxyl groups are *trans* to one another in naturally occurring hydroxy-L-proline, whereas these groups are *cis* in the allo compound (see Fig. 4).

The binding of the carboxyl of the substrate to the metal ion in glycylhydroxy-L-proline should not be hindered by a hydroxyl in the *trans* position nor facilitated by this group in the *cis* position. Indeed, one would have expected the opposite to occur. We must, therefore, conclude that the pyrrolidine ring of the substrate must interact directly with some portion of the surface of the protein by a van der Waals interaction. Thus, we must postulate, as has been previously suggested for other metal peptidases, that the binding of the polar groups of the substate by the metal ion is insufficient to explain the relative specificity of the enzyme; we must also invoke other portions of the substrate as sites of interaction.

If the sole specificity requirements were for a dipeptide with an imide bond, we should expect that glycylsarcosine, which lacks a peptide hydrogen, would be rapidly hydrolyzed by prolidase. Bergmann and Fruton (5) long ago tested crude preparations of prolidase from intestinal mucosa and failed to observe any hydrolysis. With the purified kidney enzyme, there is a significant action of prolidase on glycylsarcosine (Table 3). Nevertheless, the fact that the rate is only about 10 per cent of that observed with glycylproline indicates that the pyrrolidine ring is an important feature of the most sensitive substrates of prolidase.

Since the type of chelation indicated for prolidase and its substrates would be expected to occur with other peptides—indeed, other peptidases also utilize Mn^{++} as the ligating ion—one must suppose that the fruitful combination involves a simultaneous or prior binding of the pyrrolidine ring structure to the protein. Once such a fruitful combination occurs, we can easily picture a sequence of events which would lead to rupture of the peptide bond.

If we assume that the point of metal combination is at the nitrogen of the peptide bond, this would lead to an electron displacement from the peptide carbonyl carbon to the nitrogen. This would render the carbonyl carbon more electropositive and would result in a strong hydroxyl-ion attraction. The subsequent events would then be the usual type of catalysis by hydroxyl-ion attack. Alternatively, if the point of metal attachment is to the carbonyl oxygen, this would lead to an electron displacement towards the carbonyl oxygen, again resulting in a more electropositive carbonyl carbon; the end result would be a hydroxyl-ion attack just as in the first instance. As mentioned above, however, we favor the metal-nitrogen binding as more probable since two five-membered rings would result. In either case, the metal ion of the enzyme is acting as an acid in promoting an attraction of electrons. This catalytic effect serves to facilitate a conventional type of hydroxyl-ion attack. Thus, the mechanism may be regarded as a conjoint type of acidic and basic catalysis.

LEUCINE AMINOPEPTIDASE

Several investigations (8, 33, 37-39) have shown that the hydrolysis of many amino acid amides and peptides is due to an aminopeptidase which was originally named leucyl peptidase by Linderstrøm-Lang (17, 18), and subsequently called leucine aminopeptidase (4). A useful substrate for the assay of this enzyme is L-leucinamide. The enzyme appears to be present in all animal tissues, as well as in plants and microorganisms, and is strongly activated by Mn^{++} or Mg^{++} (13, 33).

Crude aqueous extracts of intestinal mucosa have a proteolytic coefficient (C_1) of about 0.02 for L-leucinamide, and purification to a level of about 3.1 has previously been reported (35, 37). A richer and more convenient source of this enzyme is swine kidney. Crude extracts have a proteolytic coefficient of about 0.1 and purification of the kidney enzyme has given preparations with a coefficient of more than 85 or a purification of 850-fold from this source (41). Such preparations are still heterogeneous electrophoretically, and present estimates, from a tentative identification of the active enzymatic component, indicate a purity of about 40 per cent. On this basis, the pure aminopeptidase will have a coefficient of about 200 on leucinamide, as compared with 130 for prolidase and 14 for crystalline pancreatic carboxypeptidase on the most sensitive of their known substrates. Although such comparisons are only approximations, they do indicate the high specific activities of the intracellular peptidases. It should be noted that the activity of the proteinases on their best synthetic simple substrates is much weaker, the proteolytic coefficient for the action of papain, the most active proteinase, on benzoyl-L-argininamide being about 1.2 (14).

The best preparations of the aminopeptidase are strongly activated by Mn^{++}, the action of Mg^{++} being very weak, and that of other metal ions being negative or inhibitory. It is noteworthy that the stability of the crude or purified enzyme is decreased by Mn^{++} (26, 35) but is greatly enhanced by Mg^{++} (41). The stabilization produced by Mg^{++} has helped greatly in the extensive purification of this enzyme.

Action on amino acid amides. The action of the aminopeptidase on various amino acid amides has been followed during the course

TABLE 4

Hydrolysis of Amino Acid Amides by Leucine Aminopeptidase of Swine Kidney

Several aminopeptidase preparations [C_1 (leucinamide) $= 50$ to 85] were used for these studies. The value for leucinamide is given as 100 and for the other amides as the relative rate. In all experiments, pH $= 8.0$, t $= 40°$ C and $[Mn^{++}] = 0.002$ M in the final test solution. Substrate concentration $= 0.05$ M (0.1 M for racemic compounds). The data are from Spackman and Smith (41).

Substrate	Relative rate	Substrate	Relative rate
L-Leucinamide	100	L-Phenylalaninamide	26
DL-Norleucinamide	90	L-Tryptophanamide	17
DL-Norvalinamide	70	L-Tyrosinamide	12
DL-a-Amino-n-butyramide	30	L-Isoglutamine	3
L-Alaninamide	3.5	L-Aspartic diamide	4.5
Glycinamide	0.1	L-Lysinamide	1
L-Valinamide	8	L-Prolinamide	0.4
L-Isoleucinamide	9	Hydroxy-L-prolinamide	0.5
L-Serinamide	1		

of the purification, and it now appears, as suggested earlier (37), that the hydrolytic action is a very general one. The amino acid amides may be regarded as having the general structure R_1CHNH_2-$CONH_2$. It is evident from the data in Table 4 that the rate of hydrolysis is a function of the nature of the side chain R_1. It may be stated that there has been no significant change in the relative rate of hydrolysis of most of the tested substrates at various levels of purification from $C_1 = 3$ to $C_1 = 85$ for leucinamide. This provides substantial evidence that one enzyme is responsible for all these actions. It has already been noted (36, 37) that the rates of hydrolysis of the straight-chain aliphatic compounds appear to depend on the magnitude of a van der Waals interaction with the protein, and the data shown in Table 4 are consistent with this view.

For the aliphatic compounds which are branched at the β-carbon, isoleucinamide and valinamide, the rate of hydrolysis is much slower than that expected for the relative size of the side chains (39). This suggests the influence of a steric factor which influences the rate. It is important to note that a corresponding slow rate of hydrolysis is also observed with acidic or basic hydrolysis of isoleucyl and valyl peptides (16, 42), these two amino acids always being the most difficult to liberate during the acidic hydrolysis of proteins (10, 24, 40). The parallelism between the enzymatic action and that of the hydrogen or hydroxyl ion catalysis provides additional evidence that the actual catalysis of the peptide bond of the substrate when linked in the enzyme-substrate complex is mediated by a conventional type of ionic catalysis, the more likely possibility being basic catalysis.

The very slow action of the aminopeptidase on lysinamide, isoglutamine, and aspartic acid diamide suggests that the presence of ionic or polar groups in the side-chains of these substrates hinders normal enzyme-substrate combination.

The data in Table 4 also show that the action of the aminopeptidase on the amides of the aromatic amino acids is much slower than on the larger aliphatic amino acid amides, e. g., leucinamide. It is noteworthy that the reverse situation is the case for carboxypeptidase (23, 33) and chymotrypsin (23), that is, with these enzymes aromatic compounds are more susceptible than the aliphatic ones. If our supposition is correct that van der Waals forces are responsible for the binding of the side-chains of the substrates by these enzymes, the results on the three enzymes mentioned suggest that different groups in these proteins are involved. As a first approximation, one might assume that like binds like most strongly. If so, the evidence would implicate as the R binding groups of these enzymes a leucyl side chain in the aminopeptidase and tryptophyl or phenylalanyl side chains in carboxypeptidase and chymotrypsin.

If we assume that the role of the metal ion is to form a ligand with substrate and protein, then the coordination must be pictured as occurring with the essential free amino group and the peptide or amide nitrogen of the substrate. It should be noted that the amino-peptidase has no esterase action; that is, it does not attack compounds like L-leucine ethyl ester, hence it is unlikely that the carbonyl group is involved in the metal binding.

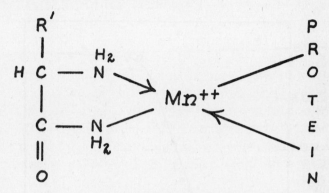

FIG. 5.   Postulated coordination of L-leucinamide with the aminopeptidase.

The coordination picture indicates that the metal ion is bound to two sites on the substrate and must be bound to at least two sites on the protein. Mn^{++} is tightly bound to the enzyme at the region of optimal activity, above pH 8 (Fig. 6), although the metal is readily removed by dialysis on precipitation of the protein at pH 6. The stability of the metal-protein complex in alkaline solutions and the slow reaction of the metal with the protein (33, 39) both indicate that in the active enzyme there is a stable chelate combination which must involve two or more coordination sites. Remaining coordination places may be occupied by hydroxyl ions.

Unlike prolidase, the aminopeptidase is not inhibited by sulfhydryl reagents like p-chloromercuribenzoate or iodoacetamide, and there is no direct evidence as to the nature of the groups in the protein which bind the metal. Nevertheless, there is good indirect evidence from the nature of the pH-activity curve and from the aforementioned observations of the pH lability of the metal-protein complex. The data of the pH activity curve may be fitted by the titration curves of two ionic groups whose pK^1 values are at pH 6.8 and 7.6. These values would be consistent with a binding of the metal to the protein through an un-ionized imidazole group and an un-ionized terminal α-amino group in peptide linkage, or with two imidazole groups of different pK values (39).

The observations that a sulfhydryl group is involved in the Mn^{++}

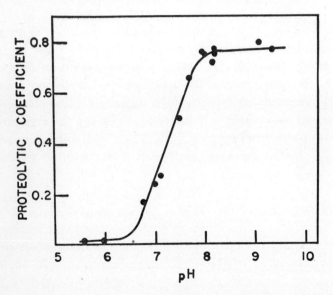

FIG. 6. The effect of pH on the hydrolysis of L-leucinamide by leucine aminopeptidase at 40° C. The protein was preincubated with Mn^{++} at pH 8.0. (From Smith, Spackman, and Polglase (39)).

binding of prolidase and that such a group cannot be concerned in the metal binding of the aminopeptidase suggest that the metal-binding groups may be different in the various metal enzymes. It may be recalled that, in contrast to hemoglobin, myoglobin shows no Bohr effect, an observation which has led to the inference that in these iron porphyrin proteins, as well as in peroxidase and catalase, different groups of the proteins are coordinated with the iron atoms (43).

Action on dipeptides. The action of the aminopeptidase on dipeptides of the general structure

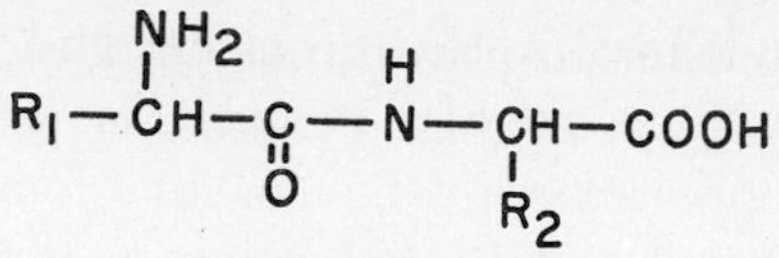

$$R_1 - \underset{\underset{\text{O}}{\|}}{\overset{\overset{\text{NH}_2}{|}}{\text{CH} - \text{C}}} - \underset{\underset{R_2}{|}}{\overset{\overset{\text{H}}{|}}{\text{N} - \text{CH}}} - \text{COOH}$$

FIG. 7. Dipeptide substrates of the aminopeptidase.

is of some interest. The enzyme is optically specific. With amino acid amides and dipeptides the residue bearing R_1 must be of the L-configuration; there is no action whatsoever on D compounds (Table 5). We have studied the action of the enzyme on a number of L-leucyl dipeptides of this structure, and the general findings may be summarized very briefly. If the residue bearing the free carboxyl group is optically inactive, e. g., glycine or β-alanine, the rate of hydrolysis is almost the same as that of L-leucinamide (Table 5).

TABLE 5.

HYDROLYSIS OF SOME DIPEPTIDES BY LEUCINE AMINOPEPTIDASE OF SWINE INTESTINE

These tests were made with a partially purified preparation of swine intestinal mucosa [C_1 (leucinamide) $= 1.5$); C_1 (Leucylglycine $= 2.1$)]. The data are mainly from Smith, Spackman, and Polglase (39).

Substrate	Relative activity	Substrate	Relative activity
L-Leucylglycine	105	L-Leucyl-D-alanine	3
L-Leucyl-L-leucine	100	L-Leucyl-D-leucine	0.7
L-Leucyl-L-isoleucine	80	L-Leucyl-D-phenylalanine	0.45
L-Leucyl-L-valine	65	L-Leucyl-D-isoleucine	0
L-Leucyl-L-alanine	60	L-Leucyl-D-valine	0
L-Leucyl-L-phenylalanine	22	D-Leucylglycine	0
L-Leucyl-L-tyrosine	15	D-Leucyl-L-tyrosine	0
L-Leucyl-β-alanine	95		

With C-terminal residues of the L configuration, there is only a small influence on the rate of hydrolysis and the L-leucyl derivatives are hydrolyzed in the order glycine $=$ L-leucine $>$ L-isoleucine $>$ L-valine > L-alanine > L-phenylalanine > L-tyrosine (39). With C-terminal residues of the D configuration, the L-leucyl derivatives are hydrolyzed in the order D-alanine > D-leucine > D-phenylalanine (39). There is no detectable hydrolysis of L-leucyl-D-isoleucine and L-leucyl-D-valine.

These findings suggest that the enzyme combination with the dipeptides is similar to that already postulated for the amides, namely, metal binding to the free amino group and the peptide nitrogen, but the possibility of a carboxyl binding with the peptides in which both residues are of the L configuration cannot be excluded. It is also likely that the major influence on the rate of hydrolysis of

TABLE 6

HYDROLYSIS OF SOME PEPTIDES AND PEPTIDE AMIDES BY LEUCINE AMINOPEPTIDASE

Substrate	Relative activity	
	Swine Intestine ($C_{LA} = 3.1$) (37)	Swine Kidney ($C_{LA} = 70$) (41)
Leucinamide	100	100
Glycyl-L-leucinamide	55	35
Glycyl-L-leucine	11	10
L-Alanyl-L-leucinamide	260	305
L-Alanyl-L-leucine	190	135
Diglycyl-DL-leucylglycine	5.5	2.5
Glycylglycine		1.0

the L-leucyl peptides of the L–L type represents steric effects. Likewise, the variations in rate with peptides in which the C-terminal amino acid is of the D configuration probably represent a steric interference of the R_2 side-chain with the metal binding to the peptide nitrogen, this interference being least with the relatively small methyl side-chain of D-alanine and greatest with the branched side-chains of D-valine and D-isoleucine residues (39).

The aminopeptidase has an additional specificity which is extremely interesting. Although glycyl-L-leucine is a relatively poor substrate for the enzyme, one bond of glycyl-L-leucinamide is rapidly hydrolyzed, followed by the slow hydrolysis of a second bond (Table 6). Evidence has been presented earlier that the initial attack is at the terminal amide bond and is then followed by the slower hydrolysis of the liberated peptide (37, 38).

Glycyl-L-leucinamide → NH₃ + glycyl-L-leucine → glycine + leucine

Other dipeptide amides are also susceptible to the action of the enzyme (37), but in some cases both susceptible bonds are attacked very rapidly, e. g., L-alanyl-L-leucinamide, and the sequence of events has not been demonstrated. It should be noted that this type of specificity, first observed with the cruder preparations of enzyme from intestinal mucosa, is also found with the highly purified prepa-

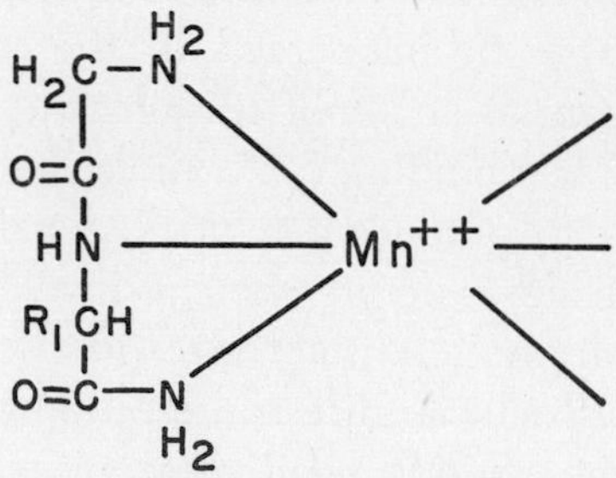

FIG. 8. Postulated coordination of glycyl-L-leucinamide with the aminopeptidase.

rations from swine kidney. In view of the presence of the various specificities in the different preparations, their similar response to Mn⁺⁺ activation, and like behavior under other conditions, there appears to be little reason to doubt that one enzyme is concerned.

The action of the aminopeptidase on the dipeptide amides must involve a different type of chelation than that postulated for the amino acid amides or dipeptides. It is likely that the metal must bind with the free amino group which is essential, and with the amide nitrogen at the susceptible bond. If these were the only bindings, one would have to assume the formation of an exceedingly weak and improbable 8-membered ring. It is more probable that the Mn⁺⁺ forms an additional bond to the peptide nitrogen. This would yield two 5-membered rings in which the strength of the bonds is increased by the formation of the bidentate ring structures as shown in the diagram for glycylleucinamide.

It is noteworthy that the tetrapeptide, diglycylleucylglycine, is attacked at the slow rate to be expected for the primary liberation of the N-terminal glycine residue followed by secondary hydrolysis of other bonds.

Although an aminopeptidase is usually defined as an enzyme which hydrolyzes a peptide bond adjacent to a free amino group, it is evident that the leucine aminopeptidase can attack a peptide bond one residue further removed from the free amino group. In a sense, this resembles an endopeptidase action. However, this is not a true endopeptidase action, since acyl dipeptides, acyl dipeptide amides, and acyl tripeptides or their amides are completely resistant (38).

Thus, to summarize the main facts of the present position concerning the mechanism of action of this enzyme, we must assume an essential van der Waals binding of R_1 directly to the protein. This must occur in order to produce a fruitful metal chelation with the substrate. Once chelation occurs, we can invoke precisely the same mechanism of a hydroxyl ion attack already discussed for prolidase.

It must be emphasized that direct interaction of the metal ion and the groupings at the peptide bond, carbonyl oxygen, or nitrogen, would be too weak to have any effect on the peptide bond (20). This interaction is made possible only because van der Waals interaction and the stronger metal interactions with the carboxyl and amino groups favor the formation of a mono or bidentate ring structure. As emphasized earlier (31), chelation is a necessary feature of the catalytic action of metal-peptidases and, we feel, of other metal-enzymes as well. In essence, chelation of the substrate with the metal in the metal-enzymes must be regarded as only one example of the more general proposition that enzymes interact with multiple sites on the substrate. From this viewpoint, studies of enzyme specificity are studies of the number and kinds of interactions involved in the formation of enzyme-substrate complexes. This is simply a restatement in general terms of the polyaffinity theory of Bergmann (3, 6).

There are some weaknesses in the present position with respect to the two peptidases which have been described here. It is obvious that kinetic studies at a single arbitrary level of substrate concentration

(0.05 M) cannot yield completely unequivocal information. Fortunately, however, most of the effects we have been studying thus far have depended on all-or-none information or large quantitative changes in rate, and much has been learned about these enzymes from such experiments. We have not felt that precise kinetic studies on grossly impure enzymes are desirable or that much could be gained by such investigations; the difficulties involved in kinetic studies are great enough even with relatively homogeneous enzymes. Nevertheless, we are now in a position to perform such kinetic investigations with prolidase and, we hope, soon with leucine aminopeptidase.

REFERENCES

1. Adams, E., N. C. Davis, and E. L. Smith, unpub.
2. Adams, E., and E. L. Smith, *J. Biol. Chem.*, 198, 671 (1952).
3. Bergmann, M., *Harvey Lectures*, 31, 37 (1935-36).
4. Bergmann, M., *Advances in Enzymol.*, 2, 49 (1942).
5. Bergmann, M., and J. S. Fruton, *J. Biol. Chem.*, 117, 189 (1937).
6. Bergmann, M., L. Zervas, J. S. Fruton, F. Schneider, and H. Schleich, *J. Biol. Chem.*, 109, 325 (1935).
7. Davis, N. C., and E. L. Smith, *Federation Proc.*, 12, 193 (1935); and unpub.
8. Dekker, C. A., S. P. Taylor, Jr., and J. S. Fruton, *J. Biol. Chem.*, 180, 155 (1949).
9. Hanson, H. T., and E. L. Smith, *J. Biol. Chem.*, 175, 833 (1948).
10. Harfenist, E. J., and L. C. Craig, *J. Am. Chem. Soc.*, 74, 4216 (1952).
11. Hudson, C. S., and A. Neuberger, *J. Org. Chem.*, 15, 24 (1950).
12. Hunter, A., and C. E. Downs, *J. Biol. Chem.*, 155, 173 (1944).
13. Johnson, M. J., and J. Berger, *Advances in Enzymol.*, 2, 69 (1942).
14. Kimmel, J. R., and E. L. Smith, unpub. studies on crystalline papain.
15. Lehninger, A. L., *Physiol. Rev.*, 30, 393 (1950).
16. Levene, P. A., R. E. Steiger, and A. Rothen, *J. Biol. Chem.*, 97, 717 (1932).
17. Linderstrøm-Lang, K., *Z. physiol. Chem.*, 182, 151 (1929); 188, 48 (1930).
18. Linderstrøm-Lang, K., and M. Sato, *Z. physiol. Chem.*, 184, 83 (1929).
19. Malmström, B. G., *Nature*, 171, 392 (1953).
20. Martell, A. E., and M. Calvin, *Chemistry of the Metal Chelate Compounds*, Prentice-Hall, New York (1952).
21. Mohamed, M. S., and D. M. Greenberg, *Arch. Biochem.*, 8, 349 (1945).
22. Neuberger, A., *Advances in Protein Chem.*, 4, 325 (1948).
23. Neurath, H., and G. W. Schwert, *Chem. Rev.*, 46, 69 (1950).
24. Paulson, J. C., F. E. Deatherage, and E. F. Almy, *J. Am. Chem. Soc.*, 75, 2039 (1953).
25. Roche, J., Nguyen-Van-Thoai, and M. Roger, *Arch. intern. physiol.*, 54, 209 (1946).
26. Schwimmer, S., *J. Biol. Chem.*, 154, 361 (1944).
27. Smith, E. L., *J. Biol. Chem.*, 163, 15 (1946).
28. Smith, E. L., *J. Biol. Chem.*, 173, 553 (1948).

29. Smith, E. L., *J. Biol. Chem.*, 173, 571 (1948).
29a. Smith, E. L., *J. Biol. Chem.*, 176, 9 (1948).
30. Smith, E. L., *J. Biol. Chem.*, 176, 21 (1948).
31. Smith, E. L., *Federation Proc.*, 8, 581 (1949).
32. Smith, E. L., *Proc. Nat. Acad. Sci. U. S.*, 35, 80 (1949).
33. Smith, E. L., *Advances in Enzymol.*, 12, 191 (1951).
34. Smith, E. L., and M. Bergmann, *J. Biol. Chem.*, 138, 789 (1941).
35. Smith, E. L., and M. Bergmann, *J. Biol. Chem.*, 153, 627 (1944).
36. Smith, E. L., and R. Lumry, *Cold Spring Harbor Symposia Quant. Biol.*, 14, 168 (1950).
37. Smith, E. L., and W. J. Polglase, *J. Biol. Chem.*, 180, 1209 (1949).
38. Smith, E. L., and N. B. Slonim, *J. Biol. Chem.*, 176, 835 (1948).
39. Smith, E. L., D. H. Spackman, and W. J. Polglase, *J. Biol. Chem.*, 199, 801 (1952).
40. Smith, E. L., and A. Stockell, unpub. studies on the amino acid composition of carboxypeptidase.
41. Spackman, D. H., and E. L. Smith, unpub.
42. Synge, R. L. M., *Biochem. J.*, 39, 351 (1945).
43. Theorell, H., *Advances in Enzymol.*, 7, 265 (1947).
44. Warburg, O., and W. Christian, *Biochem. Z.*, 310, 384 (1942).

DISCUSSION

DR. HELLERMAN: In my role as chairman I don't feel that I should take time to discuss here my own views concerning the mode of action of metal ions in enzyme systems. I can only say that I respect the speculations of Drs. Klotz and Smith with regard to the role of the metal ion. I respect those views tremendously. With regard to everything else they said in their papers, I believe every word; but I don't agree with all of their speculations on the mode of action of these metal ions. My own point of view is reflected, in part, in several papers published some years ago (for example, *J. Biol. Chem.*, 125, 771 [1938]; 134, 237 [1940]).

I should like now to call on Dr. Klotz for a brief comment, if he wishes to give one, on Dr. Smith's mechanism versus Dr. Klotz's mechanism.

DR. KLOTZ: I think the points which Dr. Smith has stressed today are points with which I would agree wholeheartedly—that is, he has paid particular attention to the interactions involving the R group and has emphasized the interaction as occurring at the protein end, and I feel the same way; so there is no disagreement on that point whatsoever. With respect to this structure (the chelate drawn on the board by Dr. Smith) I would say exactly what I said when I started. Among other things, I don't see why other metals wouldn't work here. Furthermore in this case which we have before us manganese combines the leucyl amide undetectably. Manganese does combine however with leucine. Not only does it combine, but it combines by a factor of 10^2 or 10^3 greater. I don't see why, then, this amino acid shouldn't be an extremely strong inhibitor. That was the essence of the two points that I made. From then on I think it's a matter of choice of what picture you like better.

I did make one or two notes concerning some minor comments. One of these I should mention, because maybe Dr. Smith felt this had some implications with respect to some of the things I was saying. He pointed out that the K for association for the manganese prolidase system was larger than in amino acids. I think it was about 10^4, wasn't it?

DR. E. SMITH: It was roughly that.

DR. KLOTZ: Well, for amino acids it's about 10^3, and I suspect that means that it isn't really larger, because this K is calculated for a protein with a pH of 7 to 8 or so. Since this protein carries a negative charge, you have to make a correction in calculating that K for the effect of these negative charges on the manganese. That could readily amount to 1,000 calories from what I have seen, so I think it would put the two values in the same order of magnitude. Even if it were larger, I don't think it would be a critical factor, because there might be some other kind of system really involved here. The same kind of comment would apply to the analysis of the titration curve that you showed in connection with the leucine amino peptidase, where perhaps there are two pK's; but I think that, before I believe it, the fact that this curve was kind of squeezed inward also makes me think that it is squeezed inward because of the increased negative charge when you change the pH, making for stronger binding—in other words (perhaps I should explain it to the non-physical chemists) I would expect the pH titration curve to be expanded over a range of about 2 units in the absence of any electrostatic interaction. If it's expanded over a greater range, then there's some repulsive action. If it's sort of compressed, that means there's a cooperative interaction. The fact that you are changing the charge on the protein surely is a cooperative or helpful interaction, so maybe that ought to be looked into.

DR. E. SMITH: There is just one very minor point as to the reason why we have drawn the type of chelation we have. After the discovery by Dr. Neurath and his collaborators of the esterase action of the proteinases and of carboxypeptidase, we looked very carefully to see whether leucine aminopeptidase had any esterase action. Those experiments were reported some 4 or 5 years ago. At that time we could not detect any esterase action whatsoever. We felt that this ought to be checked into again, and recently we wasted another two weeks trying to find esterase action on the part of this enzyme, and it still isn't there. Now, with the type of interaction suggested by Dr. Klotz we would have to postulate an esterase hydrolysis, because if the oxygen is not involved in the metal interaction we should get exactly the same situation as with a proteinase or with carboxypeptidase. Since the esters are completely resistant to the enzyme action, we would think that the amide linkage is the important one. I would like to make one point perfectly clear: The mechanism which I have postulated is based on the information of what we know the enzyme does and what we can postulate as a consistent hypothesis to explain the specificity. If the protein does something strange with the metal so that it binds stronger with leucine amide than it does with leucine, that is in essence the problem of enzyme chemistry for which we are seeking the solution. I don't think that we can explain everything about the action of this enzyme with this simple picture. The other thing that I wanted to say about these titration curves is that I agree with Dr. Klotz that perhaps this does represent that sort of effect, but we are not measuring here general manganese binding; we are measuring the manganese effect on activity.

DR. KLOTZ: But it would depend on the binding.

DR. E. SMITH: It would depend on the binding at this one site. With a K value of 10^4 we like to think that perhaps a chelate bound with two groups is involved, and conveniently this works out. It may be entirely wrong—I don't know.

DR. HELLERMAN: These remarks make me feel better about the speculations.

DR. KLOTZ: I can't explain the lack of esterase activity.

DR. E. SMITH: Of course, I should add that prolidase cannot have esterase activity, and we should be consistent in considering the mechanism of the metal dipeptidases and aminopeptidases. They would all appear to have the same kind of mechanism of action.

DR. CALVIN: Just a word in support of Dr. Smith. In connection with the unique specificity with respect to the optical activity of the leucyl residues, I would like to amplify your suggestion here that what is bound to the manganese in the form of protein affects the nature of what it can bind afterwards very, very pronouncedly. Now, there is a very nice example of this in a simple case where one doesn't have to speculate. This is the case in which one determines the nature of the complex formed when one uses a mixture of L- and D-amino acids together with either cobalt or manganese to produce octahedral coordination complexes involving six coordinate linkages. Now, this complex with manganese or cobalt is itself essentially asymmetric only if it is chelated. That asymmetry arises from the fact that these ligands are bound together. When they are not bound together there is no potential asymmetry. It seems to me that herein lies an additional bit of evidence in support of the suggestion that the manganese octahedron is bound to three points on the peptide and that the nature of that binding is dependent on what groups from the protein are also bound to it. For example, if you make a complex of mixed D- and L-amino acids you find that the complex is not D- and L- mixed but all D- or all L-. They don't mix up, so that it's a very highly specific sort of combination that occurs.

DR. HELLERMAN: Dr. Calvin, will you comment on the suggestion that manganous manganese is only happy when you have the octahedral configuration with six coordinate bonds? I mean, could we conceivably have in the metallo-enzyme the configuration with only four bonds?

DR. CALVIN: Oh, yes.

DR. HELLERMAN: I wondered about that statement. One other thing, Dr. Calvin, concerning coordination with sulfhydryl sulphur.

DR. CALVIN: What about it?

DR. HELLERMAN: This isn't to discredit Dr. Smith's hypothesis, but here is something I want to know. Will the sulfhydryl group ever enter into hydrogen bonding with another donor?

DR. CALVIN: Mercaptans are very much like alkanes in terms of their general properties and not like alcohols at all, which is quite surprising.

DR. HAMMETT: It could be because the sulphur does not want to accept the protons.

DR. CALVIN: Yes.

DR. HAMMETT: I wouldn't be surprised if the hydrogen bonded to a basic ion. But between SH and SH there would be very little bonding.

DR. CALVIN: I agree with you. What I mean is that the SH groups do not act the way that alcohols or hydroxylic groups do.

DR. HAMMETT: I would like to make a point with respect to Dr. Klotz's mechanism—namely, this: that if you are going to hydrolyze an amide you have to do two things. You have to bring up the oxygen, and you have to get rid of the nitrogen. The nitrogen is going to go off with the bonding pair. With respect to the two parts of that process having a positive charge in the neighborhood, it is helpful for bringing up the oxygen, but it's harmful with respect to getting away with the other part, so that you're in one of these situations where you never can make any prediction about what the net effect is going to be. In order to get that reaction you have to get the nitrogen away, and a positive charge in the neighborhood is going to hold it. On the other hand, if you have the amine in the neighborhood of the nitrogen, then that helps in both effects—namely, to get in the hydroxyl and to get rid of the nitrogen.

DR. NEURATH: I would like to ask a few questions of an experimental nature. First of all, is the manganese activation reversible; and, secondly, in the determination of the pH dependence did you take into account the dependence of the substrate concentration on the pH? In other words, was there an effect of pH on the ionization of the substrate?

DR. E. SMITH: I will give you the answer to the second question first. As far as the substrate is concerned, the substrate used for this particular study was leucine amide, which has the pK of its amino group at about 7.8, which means that you would expect to find, if the substrate concentration were rate limiting, a rise in the rate until a pH value of 9 was reached— in other words, we would reach a maximum at the place where the substrate is completely dissociated. However, the maximal activity of the enzyme is reached at pH 8 so substrate ionization has no effect above this pH value.

DR. NEURATH: So it could be an effect of pH on the substrate.

DR. E. SMITH: Yes, that's right, below pH 8 there could be an effect. For the other substrates we have measured them only at the optimum. The same optimum holds for all of the substrates. Concerning the question of whether the manganese reaction is reversible with leucine aminopeptidase, the manganese activation is completely reversible. You can bring the enzyme to pH 6 and dialyze out the manganese and then bring the activity right back again by adding manganese at pH 8. With prolidase the problem of reversibility is a difficult one. With crude preparations it is completely reversible. With the highly purified preparations it is not entirely reversible. When we take the manganese out we can't reactivate completely, we get some denaturation. In crude preparations apparently the enzyme is stabilized by the various protein impurities there. That is why I showed the manganese activation curve with the erythrocyte enzyme rather than with the kidney enzyme, which we haven't been able to do over as great a range of manganese concentrations.

DR. HELLERMAN: Dr. Smith, do you regard the manganous manganese as an integral part of this enzyme? It's rather loosely bound, isn't it? In other words, there's quite a bit of manganese involved in the reaction, isn't there?

DR. E. SMITH: It depends on what you call loosely bound. This is a relative question. Here we have a dissociation constant of 10^4. I would rather have Dr. Klotz answer that.

DR. HELLERMAN: You can dialyze the metal away very rapidly.

DR. E. SMITH: At the right pH. But then you have changed the association constant enormously in going from pH 8 down to pH 6, and that's all we think we are measuring here.

DR. WAGNER-JAUREGG: Dr. Klotz, you mentioned that probably a hydroxyl-group is bound to the metal in the chelate systems which you discussed. What is your opinion about the possible influence of such a chelate on hydrolytic reactions which are catalyzed by OH ions? I am interested in this question because we found that certain copper chelates are very active catalysts of the hydrolysis of diisopropyl fluorophosphate.

DR. KLOTZ: I think that you could not replace an OH group by—let us say—an amide oxygen or an amide nitrogen, but I feel certain that you could replace an OH group by a strong chelate. That's obvious from the fact that if you take copper hydroxide you can redissolve it by adding glycine. I think that if you have strong enough chelating groups for the copper the OH groups will be displaced.

DR. HELLERMAN: Dr. Lehninger, would you like to comment on the metal specificities described here in connection with your previous question?

DR. LEHNINGER: I am glad to hear that the magnesium effect on leucyl amino peptidase must be a function of the impurity of the preparation of the type studied earlier. However, there are still a lot of other enzymes known which do have a dual specificity for Mn^{++} and Mg^{++}.

DR. M. COHN: In connection with Dr. Lehninger's question about specificity, I would like to ask Dr. Calvin what he thinks of this idea. Manganese is the only divalent ion with a half-filled 3-d shell, and such a structure is intermediate, in a way, between something like magnesium (which has a filled shell) and something like cobalt (which has a partially filled shell). In those enzymatic reactions in which manganese behaves like magnesium you have an enzyme which can be satisfied by the half-filled shell or by the filled shell. When manganese behaves like cobalt and iron, the enzyme involved forms bonds which can be satisfied by a half-filled shell or by a partially filled shell. In those cases in which only manganese will work it is probably because it is the only divalent ion which has the unique property of having a half-filled 3-d shell.

DR. CALVIN: I think that manganese is almost ideal, because it has this great versatility.

DR. MALLETTE: I wonder if Dr. Smith has tried magnesium as an inhibitor or activator in the case of some of the poor substrates. Would it work any better there than it did with the good substrates?

DR. E. SMITH: I don't think we tried that with the purified enzyme. We tried it with the partially purified stuff, but I don't know what that means; and I would rather do it over again with the cleaner preparations.

DR. HELLERMAN: A final word, Dr. Klotz?

DR. KLOTZ: No, except that I am not so upset now that I finally understand what Dr. Hammett said. I think it might be necessary for some slight modifications to be made, but I still think everything else I said holds. I just took the particular picture that I did, because I accepted the organic chemists' viewpoint on the mechanism of base catalyzed hydrolysis. If you want to change it slightly I can still take that mechanism and put it right into the scheme which I have proposed without having to change the essential part of what I have said.

DR. HAMMETT: I won't argue any more about that point.

Part IV

THE MECHANISM OF ELECTRON AND HYDROGEN TRANSPORT

" ONE–ELECTRON " AND " TWO–ELECTRON " OXIDATION–REDUCTION REACTIONS IN INORGANIC AND ORGANIC CHEMISTRY

F. H. WESTHEIMER

Department of Chemistry, University of Chicago

INTRODUCTION

OXIDATION-REDUCTION reactions are among the most important biochemical transformations. A partial elucidation of the mechanism of these reactions has been supplied by the knowledge of the essential coenzymes involved. For example, the discovery that diphospho-pyridine nucleotide is required for the oxidation of alcohol to acetaldehyde, or that riboflavin functions in the reduction of cyto-chrome c, represents considerable progress toward an understanding of the mechanism of a biochemical oxidation-reduction reaction. But many questions of detail remain. How is DPN^+ reduced? What intermediates, if any, occur? Behind these questions is a funda-mental one for each individual oxidation-reduction study: does the reaction proceed by way of a one-electron or by way of a two-electron transfer?

In 1931, Haber and Willstätter (41) suggested that many oxi-dation-reduction reactions occur by way of one-electron transfer, and somewhat later Michaelis (73) proposed " the hypothesis that any oxidation (or reduction) has to proceed in successive univalent steps." Since almost all stable organic compounds contain an even number of electrons, the concept of compulsory univalent steps clearly implies that the reactions are of a free radical nature. Outside the field of oxidation-reduction, the reactions of organic chemistry fall, in general, into two mechanistic catagories: free radical reactions and polar reactions. It has been inferred from the publications of Michaelis, and of Haber and Weiss (40, 97), that only one of these categories is represented in oxidation-reduction processes. The concept of compulsory univalent oxidation has been supported by the quantum-mechanical argument that chemically, as well as photo-chemically, the probability of simultaneous transfer of two electrons is vanishingly small.

However, the latter argument does not apply to most chemical reactions, and even where it might be applicable, it is obscured by the question of the meaning of "simultaneous." If, during a chemical reaction an atom (for example a hydrogen or an oxygen atom) is transferred from one molecule to another, then the transfer of this atom can be accompanied by the transfer of two valence electrons, or of one, or of none. The reaction is presumably adiabatic, but the motion of electrons is so fast compared to that of the atom that the question of "simultaneous" transfer of electrons loses its meaning. The theoretical objection to two-electron reactions therefore does not apply in those cases of oxidation-reduction where an atom is transferred as an essential part of the process. Since most ions in solution are solvated, and since solvent molecules may be transferred during an oxidation-reduction reaction from oxidant to reductant (or vice versa), perhaps there is no theoretical ground for objecting to any two-electron transfer between ions in a polar solvent.

Nevertheless, occasionally it has been argued that all oxidation-reduction reactions do proceed by way of one-electron changes, but that two such changes may occur in rapid succession. The distinction between one-electron and two-electron processes is a practical dichotomy, not a rigid distinction. However, it is convenient to apply the following classification: If a molecule with an even number of electrons is oxidized or reduced to form another molecule with an even number of electrons, the process will be considered a two-electron transfer unless a species is produced which contains an odd number of electrons and which has a half-life, during the reaction, longer than 10^{-11} seconds. This essentially means that a free-radical intermediate, to be considered, must survive long enough to break out of the "solvent cage" in which it is formed, so that it may react with some compound other than those surrounding it at the moment of its creation.

Many one-electron oxidation-reduction reactions are known. In the light of Michaelis' hypothesis, it is pertinent to ask whether any reactions are known which should be classified as two-electron transfer reactions. The answer to this question is emphatically in the affirmative. There are several examples where it is highly probable that a two-electron exchange has accompanied the transfer of an atom during an oxidation-reduction reaction. Of course, the statement that a reaction is fundamentally a series of one-electron processes, or, alternatively, that it is a two-electron process, is a conclusion from the experimental data, and not a direct observation. It then has the feature of any theory in chemistry (e. g., the atomic theory) that it can never be proved, but only made increasingly probable.

The present paper is divided into the following sections: I. One-electron oxidation-reduction reactions in inorganic chemistry; II. One-electron oxidation-reduction reactions in organic chemistry; III. Two-electron oxidation-reduction reactions in inorganic chemistry; IV. Two-electron oxidation-reduction reactions in organic chemistry; V. Biochemical oxidation-reduction reactions.

I. ONE-ELECTRON OXIDATION-REDUCTION REACTIONS IN INORGANIC CHEMISTRY

Since there is little question that many oxidation-reduction reactions in inorganic chemistry proceed by way of one-electron transfer, the examples presented here have been chosen arbitrarily, and do not represent any attempt to present a comprehensive review of the subject.

Exchange reactions

Among the cleanest examples of one-electron oxidation-reduction systems are the "virtual," or exchange, reactions which can be studied by means of radioactive tracers. For example (1, 18, 91) the reaction

$$Fe^*(CN)_6^{-4} + Fe(CN)_6^{-3} \rightleftarrows Fe^*(CN)_6^{-3} + Fe(CN)_6^{-4} \qquad (1)$$

is too fast to measure (the "labeled" atoms here and subsequently are marked with an asterisk). The virtual reaction shown (equation 1) almost certainly proceeds as a one-electron oxidation-reduction reaction.

Another example of a one-electron oxidation-reduction process is supplied by the work of Lewis, Coryell, and Irvin (64). They examined the reaction

$$Co^*(en)_3^{++} + Co(en)_3^{+++} \rightleftarrows Co^*(en)_3^{+++} + Co(en)_3^{++} \qquad (2)$$

where " en " stands for $H_2NCH_2CH_2NH_2$, and Co^* stands for Co^{60}. The reaction is first order in the cobaltous ion complex, approximately first order in the cobaltic ion complex, and the rate is independent of the concentration of added excess ethylenediamine. When the concentrations of the reagents were about 0.1 molar, the half-time for the reaction (at 45° C. and an ionic strength of 1) was around 20 hours. Since the reaction rate is independent of the concentration of added ethylenediamine, it is clear that there cannot be a rapid equilibrium, such as

$$Co(en)_3^{+++} \rightleftarrows Co(en_2)^{+++} + en \qquad (3)$$

prior to the rate-controlling step. The kinetic reaction is then identical with the stoichiometric one (equation 2); the process must be a slow one-electron transfer between the cobalt complexes. There are, however, details of mechanism about this reaction which are not yet understood.

The reaction (equation 4) between the ammonia complexes of cobalt is also slow. When the two reagents are at 0.1 molar concentrations the half-time for the reaction (at 45° C. and an ionic strength of 1) is 80 days.

$$Co^*(NH_3)_6^{++} + Co(NH_3)_6^{+++} \rightleftarrows Co^*(NH_3)_6^{+++} + Co(NH_3)_6^{++} \qquad (4)$$

Since one-electron oxidation-reduction reactions are generally taken for granted, such a detailed analysis of individual examples is perhaps unnecessary. However, the examples will serve as background in later discussions of two-electron transfer processes.

Theories of exchange reactions

It is informative to consider the possible reasons why reactions such as (2) and (4) are slow. A number of theories have been advanced. Perhaps all of these theories are (in part) correct, and an oxidation-reduction reaction will proceed rapidly unless several conditions have been met, i. e., unless several factors contribute to the free energy of activation. First, when ions of like sign react, their charges cause an electrostatic repulsion which greatly diminishes the reaction rate (37). Certainly the activation-free energy for reaction (4) must contain a large positive electrostatic term. But clearly this electrostatic interaction between ions of like sign is not in itself sufficient to guarantee a slow reaction, since the rates of the reactions between ferricyanide and ferrocyanide ions, between manganate and permanganate ions (12, 52), and between mercuric and mercurous ions (60, 105), are too great to measure. For these reactions, the free energy of activation must be less than 18 kcal./mole.

Second, the rates of these oxidation-reduction reactions in aqueous solution may be influenced by a factor which has been suggested by James Franck, and discussed in some detail by Libby (65). In aqueous solution, there are several layers of water oriented around each ion, and the extent of this solvation depends on the charge upon the central ion. For example, the solvation shell around a triply positive ion will be larger than that around a doubly charged positive ion.

At the instant of reaction, the divalent ion gives up an electron and becomes trivalent, while the trivalent ion acquires an electron and becomes divalent. Provided that the electronic transfer is very rapid compared to the movement of the solvent molecules, the reaction could lead to the products in an unfavorable state of solvation. If reaction occurs between ions surrounded by their proper solvation sphere, then immediately after the electronic transfer, the solvent around the new divalent ion will be oriented in the manner appropriate to a trivalent ion; too much solvent, therefore, is oriented near the divalent ion to correspond to its lowest energy state. An analogous situation obtains at the site where the divalent ion has become trivalent. More probably, fluctuations in position of the solvent molecules may produce an atmosphere around the ions which is intermediate between the best (i. e., energetically lowest) configuration of solvent for the reactants and the best configuration for the products.[1] But clearly the free energy required to produce this intermediate configuration of the solvent will contribute to the free energy of activation for the oxidation-reduction process. A sort of modified Franck-Condon principle applies, then, to an instantaneous electronic transfer between solvated ion in solution. Although this effect is undoubtedly real, its magnitude is still uncertain.

Third, the rate of electron transfer cannot be independent of the coordinating agent involved and its charge (if any), since these must affect the energy levels of electrons in the outer orbitals of the ions. Thus ammonia shields cobaltous and cobaltic ions better than ethylenediamine does (64), and water shields ferrous and ferric ions better than cyanide ions do (i. e., the ferric-ferrous ion exchange (66, 89) is slow compared to the ferricyanide-ferrocyanide reaction.) It is not altogether clear why there are such large differences in rate depending upon different ligands in the first coordination sphere, but probably both the charge and the detailed chemical structure of the ligand is important.

As a matter of fact, the one-electron transfer reactions between ferrous and ferric ions (66, 89), between cerous and cerric ions (39, 51), and between europous and europic ions (70) all take place at measurable rates. The relative importance of charge—charge repulsions, the modified Franck-Condon principle, and the chemistry of the first coordination shell, in contributing to the free energies of activation is uncertain. However, all three factors probably contribute to slowing down the rates of exchange.

[1] H. Taube, H. Meyers and R. Rich (*J. Am. Chem. Soc.*, 75, 4118 (1953)) have recently demonstrated that the oxidation of Cr^{++} by $Co(NH_3)_5 Cl^{++}$ takes place by way of an activated complex in which the chlorine acts as a bridge between the cobalt and chromium atoms. All the metal complexes (reactants and products) have a net charge of $+ 2$, and all probably have octahedral configurations about the metal atoms. The reaction, therefore, will not be impeded by large and unfavorable changes in the solvation of the ions. Further, in this particular reaction, the chlorine atom is transferred directly from cobalt to chromium during the oxidation-reduction process. It remains to be seen how general such atom transfers, during one electron oxidation-reduction processes, will prove to be.

Chain reactions

In addition to one-electron oxidation-reduction reactions between stable ionic species, there are numerous reactions of inorganic chemistry which proceed by way of unstable free radicals or radical-ions (95). Among the more important chain reactions which involve inorganic free radicals are the reduction of hydrogen peroxide by ferrous ion (3, 71, 98) and the autoxidation of bisulfite (2). Similar chain reactions, involving organic free radicals, are discussed in Section II. Further consideration of inorganic free radicals will be omitted here.

Equi-valence change

Several reactions have been classified by Shaffer (87) as examples of two-electron transfer reactions. His classification was based on an examination of the rates of many inorganic oxidation-reduction reactions. Some one-electron transfer reactions (see above) are rapid. Shaffer found that some reactions (e. g., those between Tl^{+3} and Sn^{++}, or between Tl^{+3} and H_2SO_3), which may prove to be two-electron transfer reactions, are also fast. But the reaction between ceric and thallous ions

$$2Ce^{+4} + Tl^+ \rightarrow 2Ce^{+3} + Tl^{+3} \tag{5}$$

is slow, despite the fact that both the ceric-cerous and the thallic-thallous systems are rapidly reversible at an electrode of an electrolytic cell. Shaffer noted that the only stable valence states are 3 and 4 for cerium, 1 and 3 for thallium, and suggested that the low rate of reaction (5) arises because there is a strong tendency for Ce^{+4} to enter chemical reactions as a one-electron acceptor, whereas Tl^+ is preferentially a two-electron donor. Shaffer found numerous examples similar to that shown in equation (5) and generalized them in the principle of "equi-valence change." According to this principle, there will be a rapid reaction between two-electron acceptors and two-electron donors, or between one-electron acceptors and one-electron donors; reactions such as (5), between one-electron acceptors (or donors) and two-electron donors (or acceptors) will be slow. Although Shaffer's principle (83) may contain an element of truth, it cannot be the whole truth, and certainly is unproved. The simple one-electron virtual reactions between Ce^{+4} and Ce^{+3}, and between $Co(NH_3)_6^{+2}$ and $Co(NH_3)_6^{+3}$ are slow (see above). The two-electron virtual reaction

$$(Tl^*)^+ + Tl^{+++} \rightleftharpoons (Tl^*)^{+++} + Tl^+ \tag{6}$$

is slow (46, 82). The reasons why such reactions may be slow have already been discussed and include electrostatic repulsion, the detailed chemistry of the first coordination shell of the ions, and solvation effects. Perhaps the reaction between thallous and thallic ions actually requires the transfer (24) of an oxygen atom (or hydroxyl group) as well as two electrons:

$$Tl^*(OH)^{++} + Tl^+ \rightarrow (Tl^*)^+ + Tl(OH)^{++}; \tag{7}$$

perhaps the reaction takes place by way of an unstable intermediate of Tl^{++}.

Shaffer (87) further found that the reaction between ceric ion and thallous ion is strongly catalyzed by Mn^{++}, by other ions which exhibit numerous stable valence states, and by some quinone-type organic dyes. He suggested that the dye (or Mn^{++}) acts as a " shuttle " between ceric and thallous ions. Many organic dyes can be reduced to form free radicals (semiquinones; see below) intermediate in oxidation state between the dye and its leuco base. If the dye functions as a " shuttle," it must oxidize thallous ion in a two-electron reaction, and then reduce ceric ion in two successive one-electron processes. However, this interpretation of the data is by no means required. Johnson and Winstein (56, 57) examined the catalysis by 2-hydroxy-3-aminophenazine (and other dyes) of the reaction (equation 8) between iodine and Ti^{+3}, but were unable

$$I_3^- + 2Ti^{+3} \rightarrow 3I^- + 2Ti^{+4} \tag{8}$$

to conclude from their kinetic data that the " shuttle " mechanism is correct. It is therefore apparent that a demonstration of two-electron transfer reactions will require more extensive evidence than that which is so far available from the principle of equi-valence change. Such evidence is presented in Sections III and IV.

II. One-Electron Oxidation-Reduction Reactions in Organic Chemistry

Triphenylmethyl

The most obvious one-electron reactions in organic chemistry are those which involve the formation or destruction of stable organic free radicals. The reaction between triphenylmethyl and iodine, for example, most probably proceeds by way of the reactions:

$$(C_6H_5)_3C\cdot + I_2 \rightarrow (C_6H_5)_3C–I + I\cdot \tag{9}$$

$$(C_6H_5)_3C\cdot + I\cdot \rightarrow (C_6H_5)_3C–I. \tag{10}$$

Similarly, the reaction between NO and triphenylmethyl presumably occurs by way of the reaction

$$(C_6H_5)_3C\cdot + NO \rightarrow (C_6H_5)_3CNO. \tag{11}$$

The evidence that reactions (9), (10), and (11) require the triphenylmethyl radical is clear: the over-all rate of the reaction between hexaphenyl ethane and iodine (108) proceeds at the same rate as does the reaction between the ethane and NO (109); the reaction rates are independent of the concentrations of iodine and the partial pressure of NO respectively; and both proceed, at least as a first approximation, at the same rate as does the dissociation of hexaphenylethane:

$$(C_6H_5)_3C–C(C_6H_5)_3 \rightarrow 2(C_6H_5)_3C\cdot \tag{12}$$

as measured colorimetrically in the absence of either I_2 or NO. Of course, a skeptic might suggest that the reaction between triphenylmethyl and iodine could occur by the termolecular reaction

$$(C_6H_5)_3C\cdot + I_2 + \cdot C(C_6H_5)_3 \rightarrow 2(C_6H_5)_3C–I, \tag{13}$$

but a corresponding explanation for the reaction between $(C_6H_5)_3C\cdot$ and NO would be hard to find. Almost certainly, the oxidations of triphenylmethyl by I_2 and NO proceed by one-electron transfers.

When hexaphenyl ethane is oxidized by oxygen, the product is the peroxide, $(C_6H_5)_3C–O–O–C(C_6H_5)_3$. The rate of the oxidation depends upon the partial pressure of oxygen, and somewhat exceeds that for the oxidation of hexaphenyl ethane by iodine or by NO (108, 109); therefore the rate of oxidation exceeds the rate of the dissociation of hexaphenyl ethane into radicals. The quantitative data are roughly consistent with the kinetic equation derived from the set (14)-(17):

$$(C_6H_5)_3C-C(C_6H_5)_3 \rightarrow 2(C_6H_5)_3C\cdot \tag{14}$$

$$(C_6H_5)_3C\cdot + O_2 \rightarrow (C_6H_5)_3C-O-O\cdot \tag{15}$$

$$(C_6H_5)_3C-O-O\cdot + (C_6H_5)_3C-C(C_6H_5)_3 \rightarrow$$
$$(C_6H_5)_3C-O-O-C(C_6H_5)_3 + (C_6H_5)_3C\cdot \tag{16}$$

$$(C_6H_5)_3C\cdot + (C_6H_5)_3C-O-O\cdot \rightarrow (C_6H_5)_3C-O-O-C(C_6H_5)_3. \tag{17}$$

In this set of equations, reaction (14) represents the chain-initiating step, reaction (17), the chain-terminating step and reactions (15) and (16), the chain-propagating steps in the production of the peroxide. Further evidence for the function of radicals in autoxidations is supplied by Ziegler's discovery that hexaphenyl ethane, but not the stable peroxide, promotes the autoxidation of aromatic aldehydes (107); some unstable active agent must therefore be formed from hexaphenyl ethane; either $(C_6H_5)_3C\cdot$ or $(C_6H_5)_3C-O-O\cdot$ must attack the aldehyde to form an intermediate which then can react with oxygen. The autoxidation of aldehydes in the presence of hexaphenylethane is a free radical process similar to that (discussed above) for the autoxidation of hexaphenylethane itself, and to that (discussed below) for the autoxidation of tetralin.

Semiquinones

Another example of stable free radicals has been supplied by Michaelis (72, 75) and his coworkers. The electrometric titration of many hydroquinones leads not only to the corresponding quinone, but also to a stable monomeric free radical (28, 31), or semiquinone. For example in alkaline solution the reduction of duroquinone (76) yields the semiquinone anion

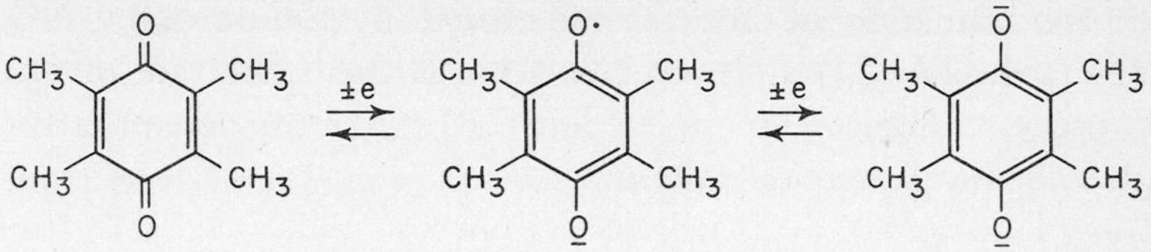

(18)

as a monomeric radical. The monomeric radical is presumably stabilized by resonance, principally between structures like

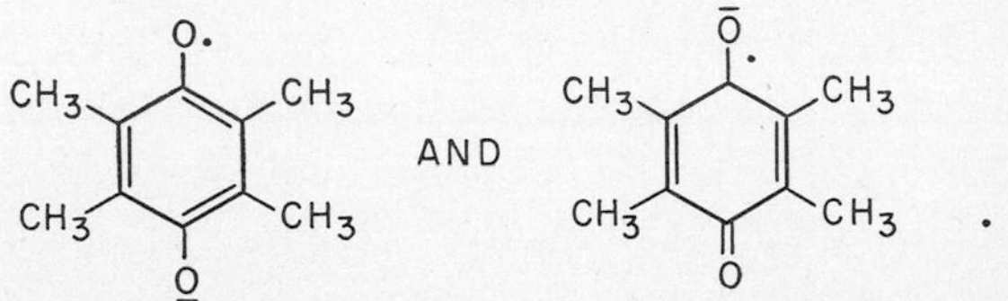

AND

.

That a radical is in fact formed during the reduction of duroquinone has been unambiguously proved, since the paramagnetic susceptibility of the reaction mixture increases during the reduction of the quinone by glucose (76). The same phenomenon has been observed for the reduction of phenanthroquinone-3-sulfonic acid (74).

Although semiquinones are formed in equilibrium with quinones and hydroquinones, it does not necessarily follow that a semiquinone is always an intermediate in the oxidation of a hydroquinone (or in the reduction of a quinone) by a particular chemical reagent. For example, in the reduction of duroquinone by glucose, a semiquinone is certainly formed, and therefore somewhere in the reaction process a one-electron transfer has occurred. But in the absence of kinetic data, it is not safe to assume that the oxidation of glucose occurs, by way of free radicals, in two one-electron steps. The data are open to the interpretation that glucose is oxidized in a two-electron reaction, with concomitant reduction of duroquinone to durohydroquinone. Then in a subsequent step, excess duroquinone could react with durohydroquinone to yield the semiquinone.

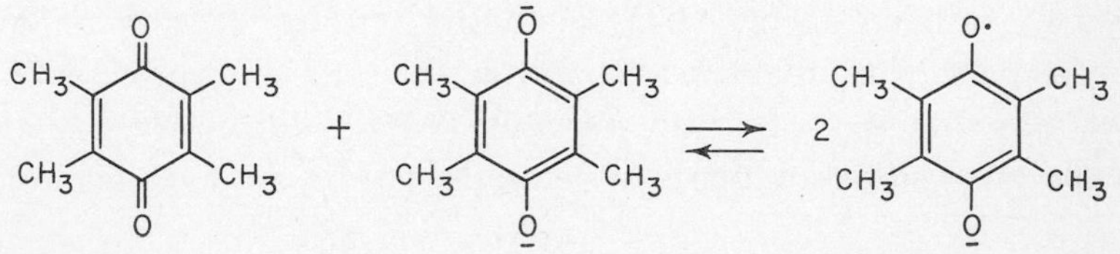

(19)

In one particular process (the autoxidation (55, 67) of durohydro-quinone), available kinetic evidence does in fact point to a free-radical process. Similar kinetic evidence is of course necessary for each new chemical reaction examined.

Although it cannot be concluded, from the presence of a free radical in solution, that it is necessarily an intermediate in the reaction under consideration, it is likewise true that failure to obtain magnetic or electrometric titration evidence for a free-radical inter-mediate does not preclude the possibility that an oxidation-reduction reaction may take place by way of this radical. In fact, there are many reactions where kinetic or other indirect evidence strongly supports the postulate of transitory free-radical intermediates in oxidation-reduction reactions.

Chain processes

The photochemical chlorination of aliphatic hydrocarbons (85), the photochemical addition of chlorine to olefins (85), the poly-merization of olefins (9) initiated by Fenton's (27) reagent (Fe^{++} + H_2O_2), and the autoxidation of aldehydes (108), olefins (26), and other hydrocarbons (21) are examples of free-radical chain processes.

Oxidation of tetralin by O_2

The autoxidation of tetralin is almost certainly an example of a free-radical chain-reaction. The product of the oxidation process is tetralin hydroperoxide (47)

$$\text{(20)}$$

The oxidation is autocatalytic, and shows a marked induction period, but this induction period can be eliminated by the addition of a variety of oxidizing agents (84), including tetralin hydroperoxide (69). In particular, the reaction follows a smooth course when benzoyl peroxide is used as an initiator (35). Numerous studies of the decomposition of benzoyl peroxide (6, 16, 48, 79), and of the reactions (including polymerization) which can be initiated by its decomposition, have led to the conclusion that the peroxide undergoes a thermal, homolytic fission to form free radicals.

$$C_6H_5CO_2-O_2CC_6H_5 \rightarrow 2C_6H_5CO_2 \cdot \qquad (21)$$

The rate of decomposition of benzoyl peroxide (35) in tetralin at 110° C. is the same as the rate of its decomposition in chlorobenzene, where the validity of equation (21) was established. Now, in the presence of the peroxide, the autoxidation of tetralin is fast, and more than 200 molecules of the hydrocarbon are consumed for each molecule of peroxide which is decomposed. In order to fit these facts, it is therefore assumed that a free radical from the decomposition of benzoyl peroxide initiates a reaction between tetralin and oxygen. A reasonable chain process can be formulated as follows:

Chain initiation:

where R· is a free radical formed in the decomposition of dibenzoyl peroxide.

Chain propagation:

Although a careful kinetic study (35) has been carried out on the reaction, no altogether satisfactory chain-terminating steps have been postulated, but presumably reactions such as

$$(25)$$

can end the chains.

The chain process represented by equations (23) and (24) parallels that for the autoxidation of hexaphenyl ethane. When no dibenzoyl peroxide is present, tetralin hydroperoxide itself can undergo thermal decomposition to supply free radicals as initiators (84). Various polyvalent metal ions (e. g., Cu^{++}) (36) can initiate the autoxidation, presumably by a one-electron process. The catalytic effect of finely divided solids on the autoxidation has been traced to the presence, in these solids, of subanalytical amounts of transition elements (32) which can start (and stop) the reaction chains. Finally, the autoxidation is sensitive to inhibition by β-naphthol; it resembles in this way many other free-radical chain processes.

III. Two-Electron Oxidation-Reduction Reactions in Inorganic Chemistry

Oxidation of iodine by H_2O_2

One of the best examples of a two-electron oxidation in inorganic chemistry is the reaction between hydrogen peroxide and potassium iodide

$$H_2O_2 + 2H^+ + 2I^- \rightarrow I_2 + 2H_2O. \qquad (26)$$

The rate of this reaction is given by kinetic equation (27).

$$-d(H_2O_2)/dt = k(H_2O_2)(I^-)(H^+) + k'(H_2O_2)(I^-) \qquad (27)$$

Noyes and Scott suggested that hypoiodite (78) is an intermediate in reaction 26.

$$H^+ + H_2O_2 + I^- \rightarrow H_2O + IOH \qquad (28)$$

$$H^+ + IOH + I^- \rightarrow I_2 + H_2O \qquad (29)$$

If equation (28) is correct, the first step in the over-all process (equation 26) is the transfer of an oxygen atom from hydrogen peroxide to an iodide ion; this reaction is effectively a two-electron process. Alternatively, it might a priori be supposed that equation (30)

$$H_2O_2 + H^+ + I^- \rightarrow I\cdot + H_2O + \cdot OH \qquad (30)$$

or some equivalent one-electron process could produce iodine atoms as intermediates in the reaction.

The best evidence that iodine atoms are *not* produced during reaction (26) has been advanced by Taube (90). The photochemical oxidation of oxalates by iodine (38) presumably does occur by way of iodine atoms.[2]

$$I_2 + h\nu \rightarrow 2I\cdot \qquad (31)$$

$$I\cdot + C_2O_4^= \rightarrow I^- + C_2O_4^- \qquad (32)$$

$$C_2O_4^- + I_2 \rightarrow 2CO_2 + I^- + I\cdot \qquad (33)$$

Equations (32) and (33) represent a chain process for the oxidation of oxalate by iodine. Taube proposed to use the reaction between iodine atoms and oxalate ions as a diagnostic test for the presence of these atoms during an oxidation-reduction reaction. If iodine atoms are produced, they will initiate a chain decomposition of oxalate. Further, from the rate constants obtained in the photochemical work, and those obtained in a chemical oxidation, it is possible to calculate the fraction of the reaction which proceeds by way of iodine atoms. When iodide was oxidized by persulfate, according to equation (34)

$$S_2O_8^= + 2I^- \rightarrow 2SO_4^= + I_2 \qquad (34)$$

in the presence of oxalate, an induced oxidation of oxalate was observed. It therefore follows that at least a part[3] of the reaction proceeds by way of iodine atoms. But when iodide is oxidized by hydrogen peroxide (equation 26) in the presence of oxalate, no

---

[2] Probably $I\cdot$ is complexed with I^- as $I_2\cdot^-$. This will not, however, affect the nature of the argument.

[3] H. Taube (private communication) now calculates that only a few per cent of this reaction proceeds by a path which produces iodine atoms.

induced oxidation of the oxalate could be observed. It therefore follows (90) that the reaction between hydrogen peroxide and iodide ions does *not* take place by way of free iodine atoms. Of course, these facts cannot prove that the mechanism of equations (28) and (29) is necessarily correct. But the evidence at least strongly suggests that such is the fact.

Oxidation of sulfite by ClO_3^-

The reaction between chlorate and sulfite provides another example of a two-electron transfer in inorganic chemistry:

$$ClO_3^- + 3H_2SO_3 \rightarrow Cl^- + 3H_2SO_4 \tag{35}$$

The reaction proceeds according to the rate law (77)

$$-d(ClO_3^-)/dt = k(ClO_3^-)(H_2SO_3) \tag{36}$$

and is accompanied by the transfer of oxygen (42) atoms from the chlorate to the sulfite. The oxygen transfer was demonstrated by carrying out the reaction in water enriched in H_2O^{18}; sulfite exchanges oxygen with the solvent, but chlorate and sulfate do not. The sulfate produced in reaction (35) contained excess O^{18}. The reaction kinetics show that reaction (35) must occur in steps, and presumably both chlorite and hypochlorite are intermediates in the complete reduction of the chlorate to chloride. The oxygen exchange is not quite complete (i. e., only about 2.3 of the three oxygen atoms of the chlorate are transferred to the sulfate). Taube and his coworkers have presented convincing evidence that there is a complete oxygen transfer in the first, rate-controlling, step of the process, and that the incomplete transfer occurs in the last step (reduction of hypochlorite). The second-order reaction, with oxygen transfer, probably takes place either by way of equation (37), or by way of equations (38) and (39).

$$
\begin{array}{c}
H \\
O \\
.. \\
O:S: \\
.. \\
O \\
H
\end{array}
+
\left[
\begin{array}{c}
O^* \\
.. \\
*O:\overset{..}{C}l:O^* \\
..
\end{array}
\right]^-
\rightarrow
\begin{array}{c}
H \\
O \\
.. \\
O:S:O^* \\
.. \\
O \\
H
\end{array}
+
\left[
\begin{array}{c}
O \\
.. \\
:\overset{..}{C}l:O^* \\
..
\end{array}
\right]^-
\tag{37}
$$

$$2H^+ + \begin{bmatrix} O \\ \cdot\cdot \\ O:\overset{\cdot\cdot}{S}:O \\ \cdot\cdot \end{bmatrix}^= + \begin{bmatrix} O* \\ *O:\overset{\cdot\cdot}{C}l:O* \\ \cdot\cdot \end{bmatrix}^- \rightleftarrows H_2O + \begin{bmatrix} O \quad\quad O* \\ \cdot\cdot \quad\quad \cdot\cdot \\ O:\overset{\cdot\cdot}{S}:O*:\overset{\cdot\cdot}{C}l:O* \\ \cdot\cdot \quad\quad \cdot\cdot \end{bmatrix}^- \quad (38)$$

$$\begin{matrix} O \quad\quad O* \\ \cdot\cdot \quad\quad \cdot\cdot \\ O:\overset{\cdot\cdot}{S}:O*:\overset{\cdot\cdot}{C}l:O* \\ \cdot\cdot \quad\quad \cdot\cdot \end{matrix} + H_2O \rightarrow SO_3O*^= + 2H^+ + (ClO_2*)^- \quad (39)$$

The first pathway (equation 37) is a direct oxygen exchange, the second (equations 38 and 39) is a reaction by way of a mixed anhydride of sulfurous and chloric acids. Since sulfite exchanges oxygen with water, whereas chlorate does not, it is reasonable to suppose that anhydride formation would occur (as in equation 38) with loss of an oxygen from sulfite, not from chlorate. If such a reaction actually takes place in the manner indicated, then it represents " two-electron " oxidation of sulfite by chlorate.

If a one-electron reduction of chlorate occurred, the product would be ClO_2, or something similar to it. Chlorine dioxide, a species containing an odd electron, easily oxidizes sulfite to sulfate. But this reaction proceeds (42, 50) according to the kinetic equation

$$-d(ClO_2)/dt = k(ClO_3)^2(H_2SO_3). \quad (40)$$

The mechanism for this reaction is not known, but the rate law shows that the slow step is not a simple one-electron reaction between ClO_2 and sulfurous acid.

Oxidation of sulfite by H_2O_2

When hydrogen peroxide reacts with sulfite in aqueous solution, both the oxygen atoms of the peroxide are transferred (43) to the sulfate formed. Furthermore, the reaction is a poor initiator for the oxidation of sulfite by oxygen. The latter process certainly proceeds by way of free radical chains (2, 44) and is extremely sensitive to small quantities of initiators; the acceleration due to 10^{-9} m./l. of Cu^{++} can easily be detected (92). It is therefore extremely unlikely that the reaction between sulfite and peroxide produces more than a trace of the radicals which are intermediates in the autoxidation of sulfite. In particular, the OH radical is probably excluded from the reaction path, since this radical exchanges its oxygen with the solvent (29). The rather remarkable fact that two oxygen atoms from the peroxide are incorporated into the sulfate formed suggests that the reaction proceeds as follows:

$$HO*O*H + H_2SO_3 \rightleftarrows H_2O + HO-\overset{\overset{\displaystyle O}{\|}}{S}-O*-O*-H \qquad (41)$$

$$HO-\overset{\overset{\displaystyle O}{\|}}{S}-O*-O*-H \rightarrow H_2SO_2O_2*. \qquad (42)$$

If this pathway is correct, the over-all reaction involves transfer of oxygen atoms accompanied by a two-electron change.

Oxidation of arsenite by CrO_3

The reduction of chromic acid can probably proceed either by one-electron or by two-electron processes. Since chromic acid, on reduction to chromic ion, accepts three electrons per chromium atom, and since most reducing agents can supply only one or two electrons per molecule, it follows that the reduction of chromic acid to chromic ion must take place by way of unstable intermediates of pentavalent chromium, or of tetravalent chromium, or of both (100). It has been possible in some instances to determine with high probability that the reactions occur with an initial two-electron transfer.

For example, chromic acid in dilute mineral acid solution quantitatively oxidizes arsenite to arsenate

$$2HCrO_4^- + 3H_3AsO_3 + 8H^+ \rightarrow 2Cr^{+++} + 3H_3AsO_4 + 5H_2O. \qquad (43)$$

The reaction follows (22, 100) the rate law

$$-d(CrO_3)/dt = k(H_3AsO_3)(HCrO_4^-)(H^+)^2. \qquad (44)$$

If manganous ion is added to the reaction mixture of arsenite and chromic acid, the formation of MnO_2 accompanies the oxidation of the arsenite (61); if sodium iodide is added to the reaction mixture, the formation of elementary iodine accompanies the oxidation (22).

Neither the oxidation of I^- or of Mn^{++} by chromic acid alone occurs under the experimental conditions where these oxidations can be " induced " by arsenite; in fact, the direct oxidation of Mn^{++}

to MnO_2 by chromic acid alone in dilute aqueous acid is thermo-dynamically impossible (62). It must then be inferred that these induced oxidations are caused by the unstable intermediates of Cr^{+4} or of Cr^{+5}, or both, which are produced during the reduction of chromic acid by arsenite.

The induced oxidation which yields MnO_2 was studied in some detail by Lang and Zwerina (61), who found that the maximum amount of MnO_2 which can be obtained corresponds to one mole for every two moles of arsenite oxidized. This fact suggests (see below) that the induced oxidation requires Cr^4. A mechanism (but not the only possible mechanism) which will account for the facts can be expressed schematically (100) as follows: In the absence of manganous ion,

$$Cr^6 + As^3 \xrightarrow{\text{slow}} Cr^4 + As^5 \qquad (45)$$

$$Cr^6 + Cr^4 \rightarrow 2Cr^5 \qquad (46)$$

$$Cr^5 + As^3 \rightarrow Cr^3 + As^5 \qquad (47)$$

and in the presence of manganous ion,

$$Cr^4 + Mn^2 \rightarrow Cr^3 + Mn^3 \qquad (48)$$

$$2Mn^3 \xrightarrow{\text{fast}} Mn^2 + Mn^4. \qquad (49)$$

Although chromic acid is thermodynamically incapable of oxidizing manganous ion to MnO_2, it can of course oxidize I^- to I_2. However, in dilute aqueous acid, the latter reaction is slow. The induced oxidation is, however, fast, and a maximum of two moles of iodine are produced for each mole of arsenite oxidized. DeLury (22) demonstrated that in the presence of iodide the over-all rate of disappearance of chromic acid is unchanged, although the rate of oxidation of arsenite is diminished to one-third of its initial value. These facts are consistent (100) with equations (45), (46), and (47), for the oxidation of arsenite in the absence of iodide, and the additional equation

$$Cr^5 + 2I^- \rightarrow Cr^3 + I_2 \qquad (50)$$

in the presence of iodide. The over-all reaction path (equations 45, 46, and 50) accounts for the fact that two moles of iodine are formed for every mole of arsenite consumed, and for the fact that the rate of disappearance of chromic acid is unchanged. The over-all schemes for the induced oxidation of manganous ion and of iodide are essentially the same, except that it is assumed that the induced oxidation of iodide is caused by pentavalent, that of manganous ion by tetravalent chromium.

Although it is impossible to prove that these reaction schemes are the correct ones, it is certainly true that they are consistent with kinetics for a large number of other chromic acid oxidations and specifically with the postulated mechanism for the chromic acid oxidation of isopropyl alcohol (see section below on two-electron oxidations in organic chemistry). At least no mechanism without any two-electron transfers has yet been suggested to explain these induced oxidations. As a matter of fact, a convincing argument can be made (100) to the effect that the induced oxidation of iodide (equation 50) involves the direct oxidation of iodide to hypoiodite, and not to iodine atoms.

IV. Two-Electron Oxidation-Reduction Reactions in Organic Chemistry

Bromination of stilbene

Most known reactions of organic chemistry proceed without the transitory intervention of free radicals. Some of these which are not ordinarily classified as oxidation-reduction reactions should be so regarded. The bromination of trans-stilbene is a good example. In methanol solution, two products (54) are formed:

$$C_6H_5CH = CHC_6H_5 + CH_3OH + Br_2 \rightarrow$$
$$C_6H_5CHBr - CHOCH_3C_6H_5 + H^+ + Br^- \qquad (51)$$

$$C_6H_5CH = CHC_6H_5 + Br_2 \rightarrow C_6H_5CHBr - CHBrC_6H_5 \text{ (meso)} \qquad (52)$$

The reaction kinetics (7) show that the active halogenating agent is Br_2, and not CH_3OBr or $CH_3OBr + H^+$. The formation of the methoxybromide (equation 51) may therefore take place in steps. An increase in the concentration of bromide ion increases the yield of meso α,α'-dibromodibenzyl at the expense of the methoxybromide.

The kinetics and product analyses are consistent with the following mechanism:

$$C_6H_5CH = CHC_6H_5 + Br_2 \rightarrow C_6H_5\underset{\underset{Br^+}{\diagdown\diagup}}{CH - CH}C_6H_5 + Br^- \qquad (53)$$

$$C_6H_5\underset{\underset{Br^+}{\diagdown\diagup}}{CH - CH}C_5H_5 + Br^- \rightarrow C_6H_5CHBr-CHBrC_6H_5 \qquad (54)$$

$$C_6H_5\underset{\underset{Br^+}{\diagdown\diagup}}{CH - CH}C_6H_5 + CH_3OH \rightarrow C_6H_5CHBr-CHOCH_3C_6H_5 + H^+. \quad (55)$$

The bromonium ion intermediate (44, 53) explains the fact that trans-stilbene yields the mesodibromide (99); this stereochemical result follows, provided that the bromide ion attacks the cyclic intermediate (equation 54) with "Walden" inversion. The mechanism also accounts for the fact that the methoxybromide is the principal product, even though the active brominating agent is molecular bromine.

Although the data are thus consistent with an ionic mechanism, it is worthwhile specifically pointing out the reasons why it is improbable that the reaction occurs by way of free radicals. The addition of bromine to carbon-carbon double bonds by a bromine-atom and free-radical mechanism has been realized. For example, the addition of bromine to stilbene in carbon tetrachloride solution (10) is strongly accelerated by light, and is quite irreproducible in the dark.

In general, oxygen inhibits both the photochemical (104) addition of halogen to olefins and the thermal addition by way of bromine atoms (8, 13); furthermore, oxygen is often absorbed during the addition (11). By way of contrast, the addition of bromine to styrene in methanol proceeds at a reproducible rate in the dark, and the rate is not materially affected by excluding or adding oxygen (7).

The addition of bromine to stilbene is then an example of a polar reaction, and really represents a type of "two-electron" oxidation. If, however, it is argued that there has been no net oxidation in the formation of the dibromide, then it is possible to consider its subsequent hydrolysis. This can be accomplished with potassium acetate in acetic acid solution (30).

$$C_6H_5CHBr\text{--}CHBrC_6H_5 + 2KOAc \rightarrow$$
$$C_6H_5CHOAcCHOAcC_6H_5 + 2KBr \quad (56)$$

In the over-all process (equations 52 and 56) the hydrocarbon has been oxidized to hydrobenzoin diacetate and the bromine reduced to bromide ion. Although the kinetics of this displacement reaction (equation 56) have not been worked out, it seems very probable (44, 53) that it is an ionic process. Since the formation of the dibromide is also an ionic process, the over-all oxidation has occurred without the intervention of any free-radical intermediates.

Oxidation with hydroxylamine

Another example of an organic oxidation-reduction process which occurs without free-radical intermediates is the oxidation of an aldehyde by hydroxylamine to an acid; the NH_2OH is reduced to NH_3.

For example:

$$C_6H_5CHO + H_2NOH \rightarrow C_6H_5CH\text{=}NOH + H_2O \quad (57)$$

$$C_6H_5CH\text{=}NOH \rightarrow C_6H_5C\text{≡}N + H_2O \quad (58)$$

$$C_6H_5C\text{≡}N + 2H_2O + HCl \rightarrow C_6H_5CO_2H + NH_4Cl. \quad (59)$$

The reaction by which the oxime is formed is almost certainly of an ionic nature (4, 20, 80). Although the mechanism for the dehydration of the oxime is not known with certainty, the reagents (45) for the dehydration (e. g., acetic anhydride) are those for ionic reactions. Finally, the hydrolysis of the nitrile (44, 53) is almost certainly an ionic reaction. It isn't altogether obvious where the oxidation-reduction has occurred. However, in the over-all process,

$$C_6H_5CHO + NH_2OH + HCl \rightarrow C_6H_5CO_2H + NH_4Cl, \quad (60)$$

benzaldehyde has been oxidized and hydroxylamine reduced, and nowhere in the reaction pathway have free radicals been formed.

Oxidation of isopropyl alcohol by CrO₃

A more conventional oxidation-reduction reaction is the conversion of isopropyl alcohol to acetone by aqueous chromic acid.

$$3CH_3CHOHCH_3 + 2HCrO_4^- + 8H^+ \rightarrow$$
$$3CH_3COCH_3 + 2Cr^{+++} + 8H_2O \qquad (61)$$

The mechanism of this reaction is necessarily complex, since the chromium atom decreases in valence from six to three, whereas the net oxidation of isopropyl alcohol constitutes only a two-electron transfer. It has, however, been possible to show (49,100) that the reaction proceeds in steps; the first two steps are probably:

$$CH_3CHOHCH_3 + HCrO_4^- + H^+ \underset{}{\overset{fast}{\rightleftharpoons}} (CH_3)_2CHOCrO_3H + H_2O \quad (62)$$

$$(CH_3)_2CHOCrO_3H + H_2O \rightarrow (CH_3)_2CO + H_3O^+ + HCrO_3^-. \qquad (63)$$

The further reactions of the postulated intermediate, $HCrO_3^-$, have not been elucidated in detail, but they may parallel those postulated (in equations 46 and 47) for the reactions of Cr^4 produced in the oxidation of arsenious acid (100).

$$Cr^4 + Cr^6 \rightarrow 2Cr^5 \qquad (46)$$

$$Cr^5 + CH_3-CH-CH_3 \rightarrow Cr^3 + CH_3COCH_3 + 2H^+ \qquad (64)$$
$$\overset{|}{OH}$$

The evidence in favor of this mechanism consists of two parts: (a) the evidence that isopropyl chromate is an intermediate in the process; and (b) the evidence that reaction (63) produces acetone and a compound of tetravalent chromium, rather than a free radical (viz., $CH_3-\overset{\cdot}{C}-CH_3$) and a compound of pentavalent chromium.
$$\overset{|}{OH}$$

(a). The reaction kinetics (49, 103) show that one molecule of isopropyl alcohol, one acid chromate ion and (in dilute solution) one hydrogen ion enter the activated complex. The formation of diisopropyl chromate (49) is rapid under the experimental conditions of the reaction; the unstable yellow neutral ester can be extracted into benzene. It therefore follows that the formation of the monoester is likewise rapid. These facts do not prove that the ester is an intermediate in the oxidation-reduction process. However, the probability is high that the ester is in fact an intermediate, since the decomposition of the ester in benzene (63) shows many points of similarity to the over-all oxidation process in water. For example, 2-deuteropropanol-2 $CH_3–CD–CH_3$ is oxidized by chromic acid only

$$\underset{\displaystyle OH}{|}$$

a seventh as fast as is $CH_3–CH–CH_3$ (19, 102), and a similar

$$\underset{\displaystyle OH}{|}$$

difference has been observed for the rates of decomposition of the corresponding chromic acid esters (63) in benzene. Such large differences between the rates of reaction of compounds substituted with deuterium rather than with hydrogen have been observed in many other instances (94). The rate difference arises because of a difference in the zero-point vibrational energies of the C–H and C–D bonds. Both theory and experiment agree that the smaller rate of reaction of the deuterium compound can arise only if the C–H or C–D bond is broken in the rate-controlling step of the reaction (94, 102). It therefore follows that the secondary hydrogen atom of $CH_3CHOHCH_3$ is removed during the rate-controlling step of the oxidation of isopropyl alcohol in aqueous solution, and of diisopropyl chromate in benzene. Furthermore, it is probable that this hydrogen atom is removed as a proton, since both the decomposition of diisopropyl chromate in benzene and the oxidation of isopropyl alcohol in aqueous solution at pH 2-3 are accelerated by pyridine (49); the experimental evidence strongly suggests that the pyridine functions as a base. These facts are consistent with the decomposition of the ester as postulated in equation 63.

(b). When manganous salts are added to the reaction mixture of isopropyl alcohol and chromic acid, MnO_2 is produced by the induced oxidation (103) of Mn^{++}. The detailed study of this reaction, carried out by Watanabe (96), showed that no more than one mole of MnO_2 could be produced for each two moles of isopropyl alcohol consumed, (cf. the oxidation of Mn^{++} induced by arsenious acid) and that the rate at which chromic acid is consumed is diminished by a factor of approximately two. These factors are consistent with the reaction scheme (62), (63), (46), (64) in the absence of manganous ion, and the scheme (62), (63), (48), (49) in the presence of manganous ion.

$$CH_3CHOHCH_3 + HCrO_4^- + H^+ \rightleftharpoons (CH_3)_2CHOCrO_3H + H_2O \quad (62)$$

$$(CH_3)_2CHOCrO_3H + H_2O \rightarrow (CH_3)_2CO + H_3O^+ + HCrO_3^- \quad (63)$$

$$HCrO_3^- \text{ (i. e. } Cr^4) + Mn^2 \rightarrow Cr^3 + Mn^3 \quad (48)$$

$$2Mn^3 \xrightarrow{\text{fast}} Mn^2 + Mn^4. \quad (49)$$

The set of equations (62), (63), (46), (64) constitutes a chain of chain-length 2. According to this reaction path, whenever one acid chromate ion is consumed, an unstable intermediate is produced which causes another acid chromate ion (equation 46) to react. If the unstable intermediate of Cr^4 is swept from solution (equation 48) before it can react with acid chromate, then the over-all rate of disappearance of chromic acid will be diminished by a factor of 2.

The mechanism here presented accounts for the following experimental facts: the rate law, the seven-fold diminution of the rate for $CH_3CDOHCH_3$, the pyridine catalysis, the amount of MnO_2 formed in the induced oxidation of Mn^{++}, the two-fold diminution of the rate when Mn^{++} is present, and the similarity between the oxidation of isopropyl alcohol in water and the decomposition of diisopropyl chromate in benzene. Now, the pathway here presented requires that at least part of the oxidation of isopropyl alcohol to acetone shall occur (by way of equations 62 and 63) without the intervention of any organic free-radical intermediates. In order to establish this mechanism with reasonable assurance, it is necessary to inquire whether an alternative free-radical path cannot be advanced which will account for the same set of facts. Of course, such an alternative is always a possibility, but so far no such scheme has been advanced. In an attempt to investigate other paths, Watanabe and Westheimer (96) examined all the reactions which they could construct between the species Cr^6, Cr^5, Cr^4, Cr^3, Cr^2, $CH_3CHOHCH_3$, $CH_3-C(OH)CH_3$, CH_3COCH_3, and $HO\cdot$, subject to the restrictions that the reactions must be bimolecular (not counting H^+), that only one variety of any particular unstable intermediate can be formed, and that no two unstable intermediates react with one another to the exclusion of reaction with a stable species present in the solution. Furthermore, the pathways have been examined which can be constructed by adding, to the reactions of the species listed above, the following reactions of manganese salts:

$$Mn^2 + Cr^5 \rightarrow Mn^3 + Cr^4 \tag{65}$$

$$Mn^2 + Cr^5 \rightarrow Mn^4 + Cr^3 \tag{66}$$

$$Mn^2 + Cr^4 \rightarrow Mn^3 + Cr^3 \tag{48}$$

$$Mn^2 + Cr^4 \rightarrow Mn^4 + Cr^2 \tag{67}$$

$$Mn^2 + Cr^6 \rightleftarrows Mn^3 + Cr^5 \tag{68}$$

$$Mn^3 + Cr^6 \rightarrow Mn^4 + Cr^5 \tag{69}$$

$$2Mn^3 \rightarrow Mn^2 + Mn^4. \tag{49}$$

A large number of reaction paths was therefore constructed. With the assumptions presented, and within the set of reactions examined, the only reaction paths which will satisfy the experimental facts are those closely related to the scheme of equations (62), (63), (46), (64). In particular, all satisfactory pathways require a two-electron transfer in the rate-controlling step.

Of course, the species and reactions listed above may not include all those which should be considered, and of course some of the assumptions on which the analysis is based, although reasonable, may not be correct. But an intensive examination of numerous possibilities has so far failed to reveal any alternative to a two-electron transfer in the oxidation of isopropyl alcohol to acetone by chromic acid.

Reduction by LiAlH₄

Reactions in which an organic compound is reduced by an inorganic reagent may proceed by way of the transfer of a hydrogen atom with its electron pair (i. e., by way of a hydride ion transfer). In particular, most reductions with lithium aluminum hydride or with sodium borohydride (14) are probably of this nature. Plattner and his coworkers (81) investigated the reduction of β-cholesterin oxide acetate with LiAlH₄, and found that the principal product[4] was 3β,6β-dihydroxycholestane; the oxide is opened with inversion about one of the carbon atoms of the three membered ring.

The stereochemistry is that which would be predicted (44, 53) for a reaction which proceeds by a displacement mechanism; those reagents which open an oxide ring with nucleophilic attack on carbon invert the configuration of one of the carbon atoms of the ring. On the other hand, it is by no means certain that a free radical, if one were formed, would react to yield only the products obtained. Other types of evidence suggest a hydride ion transfer reaction. Primary halides are reduced by lithium aluminum hydride more rapidly than are secondary halides, whereas tertiary halides are not reduced at all (93). The order of reactivity parallels that for most ionic displacement reactions (44, 53). The reduction of alkyl tosylates with lithium aluminum hydride yields aliphatic hydrocarbons and *p*-toluene sulfonates (86), whereas catalytic reduction (58) yields alcohols and *p*-toluene sulfinic acid. These facts suggest (59) that the reactions of lithium aluminum hydride require the transfer of hydride ion, rather than the transfer of a hydrogen atom. Finally when reaction (71) is carried out with levoratatory *a*-chloroethyl benzene,

$$4C_6H_5CHClCH_3 + LiAlD_4 \rightarrow LiCl + AlCl_3 + 4C_6H_5CHDCH_3 \quad (71)$$

a levorotatory (25) monodeutero-hydrocarbon is obtained. If the reaction had proceeded by way of an organic radical, it is unlikely that an asymmetric configuration (88) around the *a*-carbon atom would have survived.

---

[4] The other product was 3β, 5-dihydroxycoprostane; since position 6 is no longer asymmetric, the formation of this compound is not stereochemically significant for the argument presented here.

Other hydride ion processes

Similarly, the Meerwein-Pondorff-Verley reduction probably involves the transfer of a hydride ion (23, 106) from an aluminum alkoxide molecule to a molecule of ketone.

The reaction discovered by Bartlett, Condon, and Schneider (5)

$$(CH_3)_3CCl + (CH_3)_2CHC_2H_5 + AlBr_3 \rightarrow$$
$$(CH_3)_3CH + (CH_3)_2CBrC_2H_5 + AlBr_2Cl \qquad (72)$$

occurs in less than 0.001 second at room temperature, and is almost certainly an ionic, and not a free-radical reaction. Presumably it proceeds by way of the following steps:

$$(CH_3)_3CCl + AlBr_3 \rightarrow (CH_3)_3C^+ + AlBr_3Cl^- \qquad (73)$$

$$(CH_3)_3C^+ + (CH_3)_2CHC_2H_5 \rightarrow (CH_3)_3CH + (CH_3)_2C^+-C_2H_5 \quad (74)$$

$$(CH_3)_2C^+-C_2H_5 + AlBr_3Cl^- \rightarrow (CH_3)_2CBrC_2H_5 + AlBr_2Cl. \qquad (75)$$

(In these equations, it is assumed that the carbonium ions are not free, but exist at all times as ion pairs with ions of the type AlX_4^-, where X represents a halogen atom.[5]) This mechanism does not allow for the existence of free radicals at any time; the second step (equation 73) represents the transfer of a hydrogen atom with its electron pair from one hydrocarbon residue to another.

Finally, it should be reiterated that no attempt has been made here to record all or even most of the two-electron oxidation-reductions in organic compounds. Rather a few representative examples have been selected for discussion.

V. Biochemical Oxidation-Reduction Reactions

Michaelis' hypothesis of compulsory one-electron oxidation-reduction reactions does not apply to inorganic or to organic chemistry. The hypothesis has so far been neither proved nor disproved for reactions in biochemistry. Even the question of the reactions promoted by iron-porphyrin complexes is far from settled (15, 17, 33, 34). The mechanisms of reactions which require diphosphopyridine

[5] For the purposes of this discussion the mechanism shown in equations (73), (74), and (75) cannot be distinguished from a concerted ternary reaction.

nucleotide (DPN^+) or triphosphopyridine nucleotide are even less clear. The demonstration (101) that deuterium is transferred from dideuteroethanol to DPN^+ (to form monodeutero-reduced DPN^+, or DPND)

$$CH_3CD_2OH + DPN^+ \xrightarrow[\text{dehydrogenase}]{\text{alcohol}} DPND + CH_3CDO + H^+ \quad (76)$$

does not in any way prejudice the question of whether a deuterium atom or a deuteride ion is transferred. In a recent paper, Mackinnon and Waters (68) claimed that the experiment with deuterated alcohol " strongly supports the view " that a one-electron transfer has occurred. They illustrate a possible one-electron process by the equation:

$$(FeOH)^{++} + CH_3CD_2OH \rightarrow (Fe, HOD)^{++} + CH_3\dot{C}DOH. \quad (77)$$

Subsequently the intermediate, viz., $(Fe, HOD)^{++}$, is assumed to transfer its deuterium atom to a free-radical form of the coenzyme to yield DPND. Since Mackinnon and Waters offered these equations merely to give a concrete example of a one-electron process, it is unnecessary to point out that no iron compounds are involved in the reaction catalyzed by yeast alcohol dehydrogenase, or that a compound such as $(Fe, HOD)^{++}$ cannot be an intermediate in the reaction, since it would exchange hydrogen with the solvent. But it should be emphasized that the detailed mechanism for the reactions of DPN^+ simply have not yet been elucidated. In order to establish the mechanism of reaction (76) or of any other particular oxidation-reduction reaction in biochemistry, the same standards of rigor must be applied as those demanded in organic and in inorganic chemistry.

REFERENCES

1. Adamson, A. W., *J. Phys. Chem.*, 56, 858 (1952).
2. Alyea, H. N., and H. L. S. Bäckström, *J. Am. Chem. Soc.*, 51, 90 (1929).
3. Barb, W. G., J. H. Baxendale, P. George, and K. R. Hargrave, *Trans. Faraday Soc.*, 47, 462 (1951).
4. Barrett, E., and A. Lapworth, *J. Chem. Soc.*, 93, 85 (1908).
5. Bartlett, P. D., F. E. Condon, and A. Schneider, *J. Am. Chem. Soc.*, 66, 1531 (1944)

6. Bartlett, P. D., and K. Nozaki, *J. Am. Chem. Soc.*, 69, 2299 (1947).
7. Bartlett, P. D., and D. S. Tarbell, *J. Am. Chem. Soc.*, 58, 466 (1936).
8. Bauer, W. H., and F. Daniels, *J. Am. Chem. Soc.*, 56, 2014 (1934).
9. Baxendale, J. H., M. G. Evans, and G. S. Park, *Trans. Faraday Soc.*, 42, 155 (1946).
10. Berthoud, A., and J. Béraneck, *J. chim. phys.*, 24, 213 (1927).
11. Bockemüller, W., and L. Pfeuffer, *Ann. Chem. Justus Liebigs*, 537, 178 (1939).
12. Bonner, N. A., and H. A. Potratz, *J. Am. Chem. Soc.*, 73, 1845 (1951).
13. Brown, R. F., and F. Daniels, *J. Am. Chem. Soc.*, 62, 2820 (1940).
14. Brown, W. G., *Organic Reactions*, VI, p. 469, John Wiley & Sons, New York (1951).
15. Cahill, A. E., and H. Taube, *J. Am. Chem. Soc.*, 73, 2847 (1951).
16. Cass, W. E., *J. Am. Chem. Soc.*, 68, 1976 (1946).
17. Chance, B., in Edsall's *Enzymes and Enzyme Systems*, Harvard University Press (1951).
18. Cobble, J. W., and A. W. Adamson, *J. Am. Chem. Soc.*, 72, 2276 (1950).
19. Cohen, M., and F. H. Westheimer, *J. Am. Chem. Soc.*, 74, 4387 (1952).
20. Conant, J. B., and P. D. Bartlett, *J. Am. Chem. Soc.*, 54, 2881 (1932).
21. Criegee, R., *Fortschr. chem. Forsch.*, 1, 508 (1950).
22. deLury, R. E., *J. Phys. Chem.*, 7, 239 (1903); 11, 54 (1907).
23. Doering, W. von E., and R. W. Young, *J. Am. Chem. Soc.*, 72, 631 (1950).
24. Dodson, R. W., *J. Am. Chem. Soc.*, 75, 1795 (1953).
25. Eliel, E. L., *J. Am. Chem. Soc.*, 71, 3970 (1949).
26. Farmer, E. H., H. P. Koch, and D. A. Sutton, *J. Chem. Soc.*, 541 (1943).
27. Fenton, H. J. H., *J. Chem. Soc.*, 65, 899 (1894)
28. Fieser, L. F., and W. Y. Young, *J. Am. Chem. Soc.*, 54, 4095 (1932).
29. Forchheimer, O. L., and H. Taube, *J. Am. Chem. Soc.*, 74, 3705 (1952).
30. Forst, C., and Th. Zincke, *Ann. Chem. Justus Liebigs*, 182, 246 (1876).
31. Friedheim, E., and L. Michaelis, *J. Biol. Chem.*, 91, 355 (1931).
32. George, P., *Trans. Faraday Soc.*, 42, 210 (1946).
33. George, P., *Advances in Catalysis*, 4, 367 (1952).
34. George, P., *Nature*, 169, 612 (1952).
35. George, P., *Proc. Roy. Soc. (London)*, A, 185, 337 (1946).
36. George, P., and A. Robertson, *Trans. Faraday Soc.*, 42, 217 (1946).
37. Gorin, M. H., *J. Am. Chem. Soc.*, 58, 1787 (1936).
38. Griffith, R. O., A. McKeown, and A. G. Winn, *Trans. Faraday Soc.*, 29, 369, (1933).
39. Gryder, J. W., and R. W. Dodson, *J. Am. Chem. Soc.*, 71, 1894 (1949).
40. Haber, F., and J. Weiss, *Naturwissenshaften*, 20, 948 (1932).
41. Haber, F., and R. Willstätter, *Ber. deut. chem. Ges.*, 64, 2844 (1931).
42. Halperin, J., and H. Taube, *J. Am. Chem. Soc.*, 74, 375 (1952).
43. Halperin, J., and H. Taube, *J. Am. Chem. Soc.*, 74, 380 (1952).
44. Hammett, L. P., *Physical Organic Chemistry*, McGraw-Hill (1940).
45. Hantzsch, A., *Ber. deut. chem. Ges.*, 24, 13 (1891).
46. Harbottle, G., and R. W. Dodson, *J. Am. Chem. Soc.*, 73, 2442 (1951).
47. Hartmann, M., and M. Seiberth, *Helv. chim. Acta*, 15, 1390 (1932).
48. Hey, D. H., and W. A. Waters, *Chem. Rev.*, 21, 169 (1937).
49. Holloway, F., M. Cohen, and F. H. Westheimer, *J. Am. Chem. Soc.*, 73, 65 (1951).
50. Holst, G., *Svensk Kem. Tidskr.*, 56, 369 (1944).
51. Hornig, H. C., and W. F. Libby, *J. Phys. Chem.*, 56, 869 (1952).

52. Hornig, H. C., G. L. Zimmerman, and W. F. Libby, *J. Am. Chem. Soc.*, 72, 3808 (1950).
53. Ingold, C. K., *Structure and Mechanism in Organic Chemistry*, Cornell University Press (1953).
54. Jackson, E. L., *J. Am. Chem. Soc.*, 48, 2166 (1926).
55. James, T. H., and A. Weissberger, *J. Am. Chem. Soc.*, 60, 98 (1938).
56. Johnson, C. E., Jr., and S. Winstein, *J. Am. Chem. Soc.*, 73, 2601 (1951).
57. Johnson, C. E., Jr., *J. Am. Chem. Soc.*, 74, 959 (1952).
58. Kenner, G. W., and M. A. Murray, *J. Chem. Soc.*, S 178 (1949).
59. Kenner, G. W., and M. A. Murray, *J. Chem. Soc.*, 406 (1950).
60. King, E. L., *J. Am. Chem. Soc.*, 71, 3553 (1949).
61. Lang, R., and J. Zwerina, *Z. anorg. Chem.*, 170, 389 (1928).
62. Latimer, W. M., *Oxidation Potentials*, Prentice-Hall, New York (1952).
63. Leo, A., and F. H. Westheimer, *J. Am. Chem. Soc.*, 74, 4383 (1952).
64. Lewis, W. B., C. D. Coryell, and J. W. Irvine, Jr., *J. Chem. Soc.*, S 386 (1949).
65. Libby, W. F., *J. Phys. Chem.*, 56, 863 (1952).
66. Linnenbom, V. J., and A. C. Wahl, *J. Am. Chem. Soc.*, 71, 2589 (1949).
67. LuValle, J. E., and A. Weissberger, *J. Am. Chem. Soc.*, 69, 1567 (1947).
68. Mackinnon, D. J., and W. A. Waters, *J. Chem. Soc.*, 323 (1953).
69. Medwedew, S. S., *Acta Physicochim. U.R.S.S.*, 9, 395 (1938).
70. Meier, D. J., and C. S. Garner, *J. Phys. Chem.*, 56, 853 (1952).
71. Merz, J. H., and W. A. Waters, *J. Chem. Soc.*, S 15 (1949).
72. Michaelis, L., *Chem. Rev.*, 16, 243 (1935).
73. Michaelis, L., *Cold Spring Harbor Symposia Quant. Biol.*, 7, 33 (1939).
74. Michaelis, L., G. F. Boeker, and R. K. Reber, *J. Am. Chem. Soc.*, 60, 202 (1938).
75. Michaelis, L., and M. P. Schubert, *Chem. Rev.*, 22, 437 (1938).
76. Michaelis, L., M. P. Schubert, R. K. Reber, J. A. Kuck, and S. Granick, *J. Am. Chem. Soc.*, 60, 1678 (1938).
77. Nixon, A. C., and K. B. Krauskopf, *J. Am. Chem. Soc.*, 54, 4606 (1932).
78. Noyes, A. A., and W. O. Scott, *Z. physik. Chem.*, 18, 118 (1895).
79. Nozaki, K., and P. D. Bartlett, *J. Am. Chem. Soc.*, 68, 1686 (1946).
80. Ölander, A., *Z. physik. Chem.*, 129, 1 (1927).
81. Plattner, Pl. A., H. Heusser, and M. Feurer, *Helv. Chim. Acta.*, 32, 587 (1949).
82. Prestwood, R. J., and A. C. Wahl, *J. Am. Chem. Soc.*, 71, 3137 (1949).
83. Remick, A. E., *Record Chem. Prog. (Kresge-Hooker Sci. Lib.)*, 9, 95 (1948).
84. Robertson, A., and W. A. Waters, *Trans. Faraday Soc.*, 42, 201 (1946).
85. Rollefson, G. K., and M. Burton, *Photochemistry and the Mechanism of Chemical Reactions*, Prentice-Hall, New York (1942).
86. Schmid, H., and P. Karrer, *Helv. Chim. Acta*, 32, 1371 (1949).
87. Shaffer, P. A., *Cold Spring Harbor Symposia Quant. Biol.*, 1, 50 (1939).
88. Shriner, R. L., R. Adams, and C. S. Marvel, in Gilman's *Organic Chemistry*, 2nd ed., Vol. I, p. 383, John Wiley & Sons, New York (1943).
89. Silverman, J., and R. W. Dodson, *J. Phys. Chem.*, 56, 846 (1952).
90. Taube, H., *J. Am. Chem. Soc.*, 64, 161 (1942).
91. Thompson, R. C., *J. Am. Chem. Soc.*, 70, 1045 (1948).
92. Titoff, A., *Z. physik. Chem.*, 45, 641 (1903).
93. Trevoy, L. W., and W. G. Brown, *J. Am. Chem. Soc.*, 71, 1675 (1949).
94. Urey, H., and G. K. Teal, *Rev. Mod. Physics*, 7, 34 (1945).
95. Uri, N., *Chem. Rev.*, 50, 375 (1952).
96. Watanabe, W., and F. H. Westheimer, *J. Chem. Phys.*, 17, 61 (1949).
97. Weiss, J., *Nature*, 133, 648 (1947).

98. Weiss, J., *Ann. Repts on Progr. Chem.* (*Chem. Soc. London*), 44, 60 (1947).
99. Weissberger, A., *J. Am. Chem. Soc.*, 67, 778 (1945).
100. Westheimer, F. H., *Chem. Rev.*, 45, 419 (1949); Errata, *ibid.* (June 1950).
101. Westheimer, F. H., H. Fisher, E. Conn, and B. Vennesland, *J. Am. Chem. Soc.*, 73, 2403 (1951).
102. Westheimer, F. H., and N. Nicolaides, *J. Am. Chem. Soc.*, 71, 25 (1949).
103. Westheimer, F. H., and A. Novick, *J. Chem. Phys.*, 11, 506 (1943).
104. Williams, G., *Trans. Faraday Soc.*, 37, 749 (1941).
105. Wolfgang, R. L., and R. W. Dodson, *J. Phys. Chem.*, 56, 872 (1952).
106. Woodward, R. B., N. L. Wendler, and F. J. Brutschy, *J. Am. Chem. Soc.*, 67, 1425 (1945).
107. Ziegler, K., and L. Ewald, *Ann. Chem. Justus Liebigs*, 504, 162 (1933).
108. Ziegler, K., L. Ewald, and P. Orth, *Ann. Chem. Justus Liebigs*, 479, 277 (1930).
109. Ziegler, K., P. Orth, and K. Weber, *Ann. Chem. Justus Liebigs*, 504, 131 (1933).

DISCUSSION

DR. BALL: It is always interesting to an oldster like myself to see the scientific pendulum swing. I remember coming to Baltimore in the fall of 1929 to work with Bill Clark on oxidation-reduction reactions. In those days the very idea of a one-electron change in organic systems was almost taboo. However, I do recall Keith Cannan coming to the laboratory in those early days and listening in on the conversation between him and Bill Clark about the titration curves Keith Cannan had obtained on the bacterial pigment pyocyanine. The potentials showed that the darn thing behaved as though only one electron at a time was going on. Only a few years later Michaelis and Elema managed to get similar data published which they had obtained on pyocyanine. I say managed because it was not easy for them to convince the editors to accept their paper in which they advanced their one-electron transfer theory. Then, as you know, the pendulum swung so that one-electron transfers were the order of the day. I am very glad to see that Dr. Westheimer is now helping to push the pendulum back a little in the other direction. As you have seen, it is perhaps harder to prove that a reaction proceeds two electrons at a time than by one-electron transfer. I think that Dr. Westheimer is to be congratulated on the fine job he has done. Now enough from the chairman. Who would like to discuss this paper?

DR. McELROY: I wasn't quite clear on the bromination. In this case is the bromine ion just as effective as the alcohol?

DR. WESTHEIMER: The major product of the reaction in methanol solution is in fact the methoxybromide; the dibromide is a minor product. However, the yield of dibromide increases with increasing bromide concentration. The bromide ion is more effective mol for mol than is methanol in opening the bromonium ion ring, but of course the concentration of the bromide is much less than that of the solvent.

I am in a very poor position to comment on Dr. Chance's presentation. I can only say that it is quite clear that the type of intensive study you are carrying out is completely consistent with the type of intensive studies of oxidation-reduction reactions that have been carried out in the fields of organic and inorganic chemistry. I am glad to see all the possibilities carefully inspected, and the contrast brought out between possible one-electron and possible two-electron mechanisms. I simply don't know enough about the field to make any reasonable decisions at the present time, and it is of course possible that all the data are not available and that the decision simply cannot yet be made.

DR. KAUZMANN: I would like to point out that there are several more very well-known cases of two electron transfer in inorganic chemistry. One of them is simple $H_2 + I_2$, which react to give 2HI on a simple collision. The other is the electrolytic deposition of metals. For example, in the deposition of a metal like divalent zinc there seems to be no evidence of a one-electron intermediate. Monovalent zinc doesn't seem to be involved.

DR. WESTHEIMER: I am very glad to have you bring out these other examples. I certainly did not make a comprehensive study of two-electron oxidation-reduction reactions, but I tried to present some of the examples which I think are now well understood.

DR. COLOWICK: In connection with the question brought up by Dr. Westheimer, as to whether or not the reduction of DPN proceeds by way of a free radical intermediate, I would like to describe some experiments being carried out by Mr. Michael Yarmolinsky, in our laboratory. These experiments concern the nature of the yellow compound (Y) which is known to occur as a transient intermediate under the conditions commonly used for the reduction of DPN by dithionite (hydrosulfite) in bicarbonate solutions:

$$\text{DPN} \xrightarrow{\text{I}} \text{Y} \xrightarrow{\text{II}} \text{DPNH}$$

It is known from studies in Euler's laboratory that when the reaction is carried out in sodium hydroxide instead of bicarbonate solution, step II does not take place, so that compound Y accumulates. After the destruction of excess dithionite by oxygenation, step II can be brought about by lowering the pH to a value around 7. Since, under the conditions employed by the Euler group, the yield of DPNH from Y never exceeded 50 per cent, it has been generally assumed that Y is a free radical which is stable in alkali and which undergoes a dismutation in neutral solution to form equal amounts of DPNH and DPN. However, Mr. Yarmolinsky has found that, under appropriate conditions, Y can be converted to DPNH in yields as high as 90 per cent. This finding makes it appear unlikely that Y is a free radical and has led us to the view that Y is a compound formed by the addition of dithionite (or one of its derivatives) to the pyridine ring of DPN.

Addition reactions of this type are known to occur. For example, Meyerhof and his collaborators have described the reaction of DPN with cyanide and with bisulfite, and I believe that Dr. Kaplan will mention some other examples this afternoon. In all such cases, the addition appears to be of the following type:

$$\text{(pyridinium-CONH}_2\text{)} + XH \xrightarrow{\ I\ } \text{(dihydropyridine with H, X-CONH}_2\text{)} + H^+$$

The addition can be written in the para position, at least in the case of Y, because of recent evidence, which I will mention this afternoon, that reduction of DPN occurs in this position.

According to this view, compound Y would be an addition compound of the above type, but would differ from the others in that it could undergo hydrolytic cleavage to form DPNH:

$$\text{(H, X-CONH}_2\text{ dihydropyridine)} + H_2O \xrightarrow{\ II\ } \text{(H, H-CONH}_2\text{ dihydropyridine)} + XOH$$

In order to test this hypothesis, some experiments were carried out using heavy water. When step I was carried out at pH 11 in normal water and the resulting Y, after destruction of excess dithionite, was converted to DPNH at pH 7.5 in heavy water, the DPNH was found to contain deuterium in the expected amount. When the reverse procedure was used, i. e., step I in heavy water at pH 11 and Step II in normal water at pH 7.5, the DPNH contained no appreciable amount of deuterium. These results are compatible with the view that Y is an addition compound which yields DPNH upon hydrolysis.

The question of the composition of the addition compound remains to be considered. There are several reasons for believing that dithionite itself is not the substance which adds to DPN. It seems more likely that the dithionite ion first undergoes a hydrolytic cleavage to form sulfite and sulfoxylic acid:

$$S_2O_4^= + H_2O \rightarrow SO_3^= + H_2SO_2$$

and that sulfoxylic acid then adds to DPN:

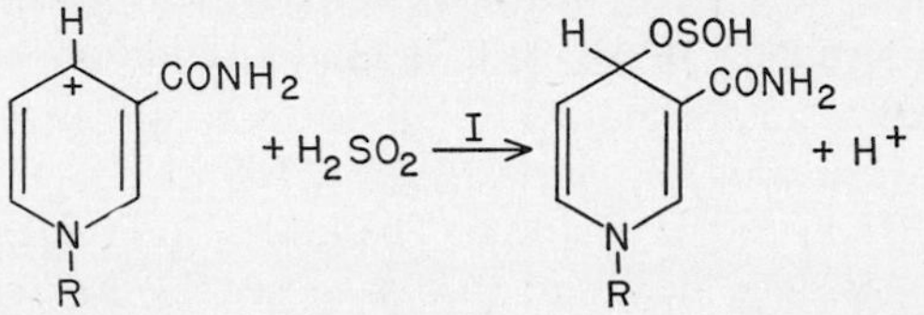

Among the reasons for believing that Y is a DPN-sulfoxylate, rather than a DPN-dithionite compound are the following: (a) Dithionite is known to react with aldehydes to yield sulfoxylate addition compounds, which, like Y, are stable toward oxygen. The aldehydic character of DPN is apparent from its reactions with cyanide and with bisulfite. (b) We have found that a yellow compound, similar to, if not identical with Y, is formed on adding formaldehyde sulfoxylate to DPN at pH 10 or above, and that, upon neutralization, this compound gives rise to DPNH in good yield. (c) The manometric data of Warburg suggest that of the three hydrogen ions released in the reduction of a DPN molecule by dithionite, at least one results from the formation of Y, while release of the remaining hydrogen ions accompanies the conversion of Y to DPNH. If Y were a DPN-dithionite addition compound, no hydrogen ions would be released in its formation. On the other hand, if Y is formed from H_2SO_2, which is probably an extremely weak acid, one hydrogen ion would be liberated in bicarbonate solution.

There is some question as to whether the addition compound of DPN and sulfoxylic acid should be written as a sulfoxylate as shown $(-\overset{|}{C}-OSOH)$,

or as a sulfinic acid $(-\overset{|}{\underset{|}{C}}-S\overset{OH}{\underset{O}{\diagdown}})$. The former is tentatively preferred

because of its weaker acid properties, which appear to fit better with the manometric data, and which provide a more reasonable explanation for the effect of pH on the stability of compound Y. One may assume that at high pH values the sulfoxylate is dissociated $(-C-OSO^-)$ and compound Y is stable, while at lower pH values, at which the sulfoxylate is undissociated, hydrolysis occurs as follows:

In summary, we would like to propose that DPN reduction by dithionite does not proceed through a free radical intermediate, but rather through a sulfoxylate addition compound which undergoes hydrolytic cleavage. The studies on this reaction may provide a useful model for the enzymatic reduction of DPN in certain systems. There is a close analogy between the mechanism demonstrated here and that proposed by Racker for the triosephosphate dehydrogen system, in which he suggests that reduction occurs by " aldehydolysis " of a DPN-enzyme addition compound.

DR. WESTHEIMER: Dr. Colowick's demonstration of the nature of the yellow intermediate is so good that perhaps additional evidence is not necessary; but I would like to add that Mr. David Mauzerall in our laboratory carried out the hydrosulfite reduction of the iodide salt of N-propyl nicotinamide in Professor C. Hutchinson's microwave spectroscopy apparatus, but was unable to detect the presence of any free radicals during the reduction process.

HYDROGEN TRANSPORT AND STERIC SPECIFICITY IN REACTIONS CATALYZED BY PYRIDINE NUCLEOTIDE DEHYDROGENASES

BIRGIT VENNESLAND and F. H. WESTHEIMER

Departments of Biochemistry and Chemistry, The University of Chicago

THE CELLULAR oxidation of most " food-stuff " metabolites has been shown to consist of a linked sequence of oxidation-reduction reactions, rather than a direct attack of oxygen on the metabolite itself. One particularly well-known respiration sequence involves the participation, in turn, of a pyridine nucleotide dehydrogenase, a flavoprotein, and a series of cytochromes, with cytochrome oxidase carrying out the eventual reduction of oxygen. Toward the end of this chain of reactions, the chemistry apparently requires electron transfer from reduced to oxidized iron porphyrins. At any rate, no hydrogen transfer seems to be involved in the oxidation-reduction reaction. At the beginning of the reaction sequence, however, the substrate of the pyridine nucleotide dehydrogenase loses hydrogen on oxidation, and the pyridine nucleotide gains hydrogen on reduction.

Though Wieland (47) suggested as early as 1912 that hydrogen " activation " and transfer might occur in organic oxidation-reduction, his views were not supported by conclusive experimental evidence (10). A unified theoretical treatment of the *equilibria* of oxidation-reduction reactions was achieved by defining them as electron transfer, with or without the participation of oxygen and hydrogen atoms. This theoretical treatment probably enhanced the tendency among biochemists to think of the *mechanism* of the biological oxidation sequence also in terms of electron transfer; any loss or gain of hydrogen, required by the stoichiometry, was obtained by expelling ions into, or taking them up from, the solvent. The application of deuterium as a tracer, however, has made it possible to show that some of the pyridine nucleotide dehydrogenase reactions require an actual transfer of hydrogen (or deuterium) atoms between substrate and coenzyme. For these reactions, at least, simple electron transfer is not a correct explanation of the facts. The present paper is largely concerned with the tracer experiments carried out in our laboratories at the University of Chicago by Harvey Fisher, Eric Conn, Peter Ofner, and Frank Loewus. The original tracer problem was this: Is the extra hydrogen atom which appears in the enzymatically reduced pyridine nucleotide derived from the substrate or from the aqueous medium in which the reaction takes place? The feasibility of the experimental approach was demonstrated by showing that reduced diphosphopyridine nucleotide (DPN) prepared with sodium hydrosulfite in a medium of D_2O contains one atom of non-exchangeable deuterium per molecule. (This reduced deutero DPN will be designated by the symbol DPND.)

Two enzymes were selected for initial study: alcohol dehydrogenase from yeast, and lactic dehydrogenase from heart muscle. The choice of these enzymes was based largely on the practical fact that simple and easily reproducible procedures were available (37, 40) for their purification. It seemed desirable to work with purified enzymes in order to avoid, as far as possible, interference by side reactions. Furthermore, the two enzymes show an interesting difference. Yeast alcohol dehydrogenase is very sensitive to sulfhydryl reagents, whereas lactic dehydrogenase is not (1, 3, 32), though both enzymes catalyze similar reactions: the oxidation of a primary alcohol to an aldehyde, in one case, and the oxidation of a secondary alcohol to a ketone in the other.

DEUTERIUM TRANSFER WITH ALCOHOL DEHYDROGENASE AND LACTIC DEHYDROGENASE

The first experiments with alcohol dehydrogenase gave an immediate answer to the original question (46, 9). The data, summarized in Table 1, show that all of the extra hydrogen in enzymatically reduced DPN is derived from the α-position of the ethanol.

There is no indication that any of the hydrogen has been derived from the medium. The accuracy of the analyses are not sufficient,

TABLE 1

DEUTERIUM TRANSFER WITH ALCOHOL DEHYDROGENASE

Reaction	Substance analyzed	Atoms D per molecule*
$CH_3CH_2OH + DPN^+ \rightleftarrows CH_3CHO + DPNH + H^+$ D_2O	DPNH	0.02 (3)
$CH_3CD_2OH + DPN^+ \rightleftarrows CH_3CDO + DPND + H^+$ H_2O	DPND	1.01 (2) 0.99 (2)**
	CH_3CDO	1.00 (1)

* Numbers in parenthesis represent the numbers of separate determinations.
** Prolonged incubation.

however, to rule out exchange to the extent of about one or two per cent of the total reaction.

$$CH_3CD_2OH + DPN^+ \xrightleftharpoons[\text{dehydrogenase}]{\text{alcohol}} CH_3CDO + DPND + H^+ \quad (1)$$

In these experiments, the reduction of DPN by dideuteroethanol was carried out with a large excess of dideuteroethanol to counteract the somewhat unfavorable position of the equilibrium shown in equation (1). The final end-point of the reaction, (i. e., maximum reduction of the DPN) was approached relatively slowly, so that by the time the reaction was terminated, many molecules of DPN had had the opportunity to react more than once. In the experiment (Table 1) marked with two asterisks, such equilibration was deliberately sought, by using a large excess of enzyme and by allowing an extra incubation period before heat inactivation prior to isolation of the DPND.

There were grounds for anticipating that, on longer incubation, extra deuterium might be introduced into the reduced DPN. One hydrogen atom is already present at the site of reduction in oxidized DPN; a second is introduced upon reduction. When reduced DPN is reoxidized by acetaldehyde, either hydrogen or deuterium might be transferred from coenzyme to substrate. If hydrogen were transferred, the monodeuteroethanol formed would be insignificant in amount relative to the large excess of dideuteroethanol which was present; but any monodeuterated, oxidized DPN would be reduced again, to form dideutero DPN. This process might lead to the eventual incorporation of nearly two atoms of deuterium per molecule of reduced DPN. The fact that the deuterium content of the reduced DPN did not exceed a value of one atom of D per molecule first suggested that the enzymatic reduction was stereospecific for the DPN.

STEREOCHEMISTRY OF REDUCED DPN

The two possible diastereomers of monodeutero reduced DPN are shown in Fig. 1. The reduction is here shown to occur at position 4 of the pyridine ring, in accordance with the recent evidence of Pullman, San Pietro, and Colowick (7, 36). (The arguments regarding the stereospecificity hold regardless of the site of reduction.)

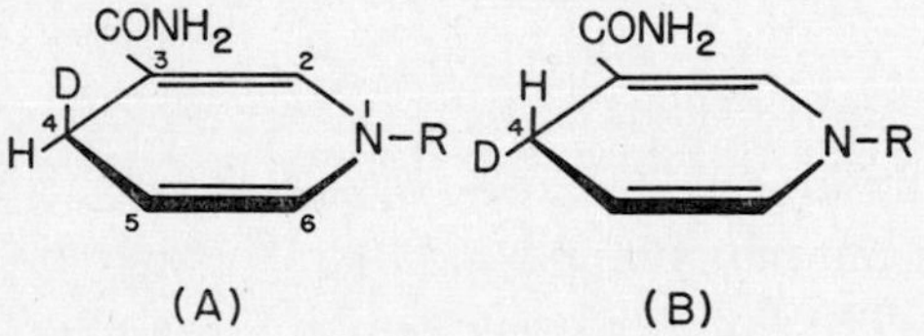

(A)   (B)

FIG. 1.

When reduced DPN was reoxidized enzymatically with acetaldehyde, the results shown in Table 2 were obtained. In reaction (2),

$$H^+ + DPND + CH_3CHO \overset{\textit{alcohol}}{\underset{\textit{dehydrogenase}}{\rightleftharpoons}} DPN^+ + CH_3CHDOH, \quad (2)$$

all of the deuterium is removed from the enzymatically reduced DPND. The large preference for deuterium over hydrogen cannot arise as an isotopic fractionation factor, and therefore clearly shows that enzymatically reduced DPND consists of only one of the diastereomers of Fig. 1. When chemically reduced DPND was reoxidized (equation 2) somewhat more than half of the deuterium was removed from the DPN; therefore chemically reduced DPND consists of a mixture of the diastereomers, with a slight preponderance of the one which is formed enzymatically.

Oxidation of the enzymatically reduced DPND was also carried out with pyruvate in the presence of lactic dehydrogenase (22). In this case, the lactate formed was converted to the solid ester, phenacyl lactate, which could be analyzed for deuterium with greater precision

TABLE 2

OXIDATION OF DPND WITH ALCOHOL DEHYDROGENASE

Type of DPND	Atoms D per molecule of DPN$^+$
Enzymatically reduced DPND	0.00
Chemically reduced DPND	0.44

TABLE 3

DEUTERIUM TRANSFER WITH LACTIC DEHYDROGENASE

Type of DPND	Atoms D per molecule of lactate*
Enzymatically reduced DPND	1.00
	0.95
Chemically reduced DPND	0.62
	0.54

* Isolated and analyzed as phenacyl lactate.

than is possible with DPN. The results are shown in Table 3. Enzymatically reduced DPND transferred one atom of deuterium to each molecule of pyruvate to form lactate, whereas chemically reduced DPND transferred somewhat more than half an atom of deuterium per molecule of lactate formed.

Stereospecificity of Dehydrogenases

These results show that lactic dehydrogenase causes a direct transfer of hydrogen from coenzyme to substrate, just as does alcohol dehydrogenase. They also demonstrate that the enzymatic reactions of DPN with alcohol dehydrogenase and with lactic dehydrogenase are stereospecific for the DPN. Furthermore, both enzymes transfer hydrogen to and from the same side of the pyridine ring. In the case of lactic dehydrogenase it was known that the enzyme is likewise stereospecific for lactic acid, i. e., the heart muscle enzyme, like the skeletal muscle enzyme (19), acts only with L(+)-lactic acid, and not at all with the D isomer (22, 32).

Of course, this does not preclude the possibility that another, different lactic dehydrogenase might react with D- rather than with L-lactic acid. Recently Lehninger and Greville (20) discovered a DPN-linked dehydrogenase which acts on *d-β*-hydroxybutyryl-coenzyme A, and not on the corresponding *l*-compound. This enzyme is quite distinct from the DPN-linked dehydrogenase previously described (11, 24), which acts specifically on *l-β*-hydroxybutyric acid, and not at all on *d-β*-hydroxybutyric acid.

But a search of the literature has failed to reveal any example of a pyridine nucleotide dehydrogenase which has been demonstrated not to show some steric specificity for the substrate. In addition to the examples already cited, we may list glutamic dehydrogenase, which has been shown to act only on L-glutamic acid (38), malic dehydrogenase and the " malic enzyme " for the Ochoa reaction, which react only with L-malic acid (33), and α-glycerophosphate dehydrogenase, which reacts only with L-α-glycerophosphate (38). Not all known dehydrogenases have been fully investigated with regard to steric specificity. Apparently no direct studies of the steric specificity of phosphogluconic dehydrogenase have been made. It has been reported that α-glycerophosphate dehydrogenase will act on the naturally occurring L-propanediol-1-phosphate (29), as well as with its usual substrate. Though D-propanediol-1-phosphate has not been tested, it is reasonable to assume it would be inactive, in view of the demonstrated specificity of the enzyme for L-a-glycero-phosphate. Similarly, the reduction of hydroxypyruvic acid with muscle lactic dehydrogenase (28, 39) probably gives L-, and not D-glyceric acid.

The reasonable assumption is often made that if only one of the possible isomers of the substrate occurs in the tissue from which the enzyme is derived, this isomer and only this isomer is acted on by the enzyme. However, when the asymmetry of the substrate can be affected by several different enzymes, such an assumption is not necessarily valid. Thus Strecker and Harary (13) have found evidence that acetoin and diacetyl are reduced by DPN-linked enzymes. The stereospecificity of these reactions (which has not been investigated) cannot necessarily be determined from a study of the configuration of any acetoin and 2, 3-butylene glycol accumulating in the tissue, since this configuration might be influenced also by the nature of the reaction in which acetoin is formed from other precursors.

It has been stated frequently that isocitric dehydrogenase acts only on d-isocitric acid. Since there are two dissimilar asymmetric carbon atoms in isocitric acid, there are four possible stereoisomers, and it is assumed that the enzyme acts on only one of these, which is, of course, the "naturally occurring" isocitrate (45). Since 50 per cent of the synthetic isocitrate is active with the enzyme, it is assumed that synthetic isocitrate contains only one of the two possible racemates. But the four individual isomers themselves have not been prepared in pure form, nor have we been able to find evidence that anyone has tested the action of the enzyme on both of the two different racemic mixtures (25). Although it seems highly probable that the conclusions drawn regarding the stereospecificity of isocitric dehydrogenase are correct, it seems appropriate also to point out that complete stereospecificity for the carbon atom which is actually oxidized does not necessarily imply stereospecificity for all the asymmetric centers in the molecule. An illustrative example is provided by liver sorbitol dehydrogenase, studied by Blakley (4). This enzyme catalyzes the oxidation of D-sorbitol to D-fructose, as shown in equation (3). The reaction is reversible;

$$
\begin{array}{c}
\text{CH}_2\text{OH} \\
| \\
\text{H–C–OH} \\
| \\
\text{HO–C–H} \\
| \\
\text{H–C–OH} \\
| \\
\text{H–C–OH} \\
| \\
\text{CH}_2\text{OH}
\end{array}
\qquad
\underset{\text{DPN}}{\rightleftharpoons}
\qquad
\begin{array}{c}
\text{CH}_2\text{OH} \\
| \\
\text{C}=\text{O} \\
| \\
\text{HO–C–H} \\
| \\
\text{H–C–OH} \\
| \\
\text{H–C–OH} \\
| \\
\text{CH}_2\text{OH}
\end{array}
\qquad\qquad (3)
$$

D-sorbitol   D-fructose

D-fructose oxidizes reduced DPN in the presence of the enzyme. It was found initially that L-sorbose also oxidized reduced DPN. Though the possibility that a separate enzyme might here be involved was not excluded, there seemed to be a strong implication that D-sorbitol was oxidized both at the 2 and the 5 positions. However, if we regard the –CH₂OH groups next to the 2 and the 5 positions as equivalent groups in these two reactions, then carbon 2 and carbon 5 actually have opposite configurations. Further investigation showed, however, that D-sorbitol was never converted to L-sorbose. Instead the enzyme preparation was found to catalyze reaction (4) as well as reaction (3), i.e., L-sorbose is reduced reversibly to L-iditol. The enzyme has no action on D-iditol, D-mannitol,

$$
\begin{array}{c}
\text{CH}_2\text{OH} \\
| \\
\text{H–C–OH} \\
| \\
\text{HO–C–H} \\
| \\
\text{H–C–OH} \\
| \\
\text{HO–C–H} \\
| \\
\text{CH}_2\text{OH}
\end{array}
\qquad
\underset{\text{DPN}}{\rightleftharpoons}
\qquad
\begin{array}{c}
\text{CH}_2\text{OH} \\
| \\
\text{C}=\text{O} \\
| \\
\text{HO–C–H} \\
| \\
\text{H–C–OH} \\
| \\
\text{HO–C–H} \\
| \\
\text{CH}_2\text{OH}
\end{array}
\qquad\qquad (4)
$$

L-iditol   L-sorbose

or on dulcitol. The substrate must have the same configuration as D-sorbitol at carbon 2 and carbon 4, but the configuration at carbon 5 is immaterial. The effect of a change of configuration at carbon 3 has not been tested.

The β-hydroxysteroid dehydrogenase recently studied by Talalay and his collaborators (43, 44) provides another example of stereospecificity with an entirely different type of substrate. An adaptive enzyme from certain species of *Pseudomonas* causes the DPN-linked reversible interconversion of 3-β- and 17-β-hydroxysteroids and their corresponding keto steroids. This enzyme catalyzes the reaction shown in equation (5). It does not act at all on the α-epimer of

TESTOSTERONE   ANDROST − 4 − ENE − 3,17 − DIONE   (5)

testosterone, i. e., the OH must be in the β position. It is interesting that the same enzyme will apparently act on the molecule in the 3 as well as in the 17 position. Thus it will also catalyze reaction (6), though more slowly. Again, however, it acts only on the β isomer, not on the α form. It is not necessary to have a β-hydroxyl

DEHYDROEPIANDROSTERONE   ANDROST − 4 − ENE − 3,17 − DIONE   (6)

group at position 3, however, in order to have a reaction at position 17; the removal of the hydroxyl group from position 3 gives a substrate which can still be oxidized by the enzyme at position 17.

There are other interesting aspects of this work with β-hydroxysteroid dehydrogenases which merit attention, but sufficient examples have probably been given to illustrate the point we wish to make: that to our knowledge all known pyridine nucleotide dehydrogenases which have been properly examined appear to show complete stereospecificity for the asymmetric carbon atom of the substrate which is oxidized in the enzymatic reaction.

THE ENANTIOMORPHS OF ETHANOL-1-D

The fact that steric specificity is the rule in the reduction of carbonyl groups to secondary alcohols with other pyridine nucleotide dehydrogenases suggested that the enzymatic reduction of acetaldehyde to ethanol might also be stereospecific. This possibility was investigated by preparing deuteroethanol both from ordinary acetaldehyde and enzymatically reduced DPND, and also from deuteroacetaldehyde (CH_3CDO) and DPNH (23). The two enantiomorphs of deuteroethanol thus prepared were individually distilled off from their respective reaction mixtures, but were available only in aqueous solution. There was not a sufficient quantity of either to determine its optical rotation (the expense of the DPN was a limiting factor for large-scale preparations); but the enantiomorphs were identified by observing the products of their enzymatic reoxidation.

The method used to prepare and to analyze one of these enantiomorphs is shown in Table 4. The analytical results on which our conclusions are based are also included in the table.

The essential parts of the reaction sequence involve a reduction of acetaldehyde with enzymatically reduced DPND, separation of the ethanol by distillation, and reoxidation of this ethanol with purified oxidized DPN. The acetaldehyde formed in the last step was isolated as the dimedon derivative, and found to be completely free of deuterium, whereas the reduced DPN obtained in the same reaction contained approximately as much deuterium per molecule as the ethanol from which it was formed. The zero value for the deuterium content of the acetaldehyde is highly significant. It indicates that no racemization of the ethanol occurred. Our deuterium analyses were sufficiently accurate so that two per cent racemization could certainly have been detected.[1]

TABLE 4

PREPARATION OF ETHANOL-1-D

Sequence I		Substance analyzed	Atoms D per molecule	
			Exp. A	Exp. B
H H		DPND*		0.88
CH₃–C=O + DPND + H⁺ → CH₃–C–OH + DPN⁺		CH₃CHDOH	0.51	0.48
(D, distill)				
H H		DPND	0.41	0.54
CH₃–C=O + DPND + H⁺ ← CH₃–C–OH + DPN⁺		DPND*	0.31	0.42
(D)		CH₃CHO	0.00	0.00

* Atoms of D transferred enzymatically to lactate.

The method used to prepare and analyze the other isomer of ethanol-1-D, and the analytical results, are summarized in Table 5.

[1] There is one unexplained and significant discrepancy in the present work. In the experiments carried out at the beginning of this investigation, enzymatically prepared DPND was reoxidized with acetaldehyde in the presence of alcohol dehydrogenase. The DPN⁺ obtained from this oxidation contained no excess deuterium. (This result has been independently confirmed, by similar but not identical experiments, by Pullman, San Pietro and Colowick.) It was in part on the basis of these experiments that the conclusion has been drawn that the reduction of DPN is stereospecific with respect to the reduced carbon atom of the pyridine ring. More recently, these earlier experiments have been successfully repeated. Nevertheless, the DPN⁺ formed in the first reaction of Table 4 was found to contain 0.3 atoms of D per molecule. It appears that the particular alcohol dehydrogenase used in this set of experiments contained, as an impurity, an enzymatic system which can exchange the positions of hydrogen and deuterium (e. g., by a racemization about the reduced carbon atom of DPND). This reaction, however, seems to be a secondary one which is not a necessary part of the oxidation-reduction actually under investigation. At least, the difficulty only appears severe when DPN and DPND have been incubated for long periods with alcohol dehydrogenase.

Despite the obvious importance of the discrepancy, the conclusions concerning stereospecificity appear valid. The reasoning behind this conclusion may be summarized as follows.

The discrepancy was first discovered because the deuteroethanol prepared by the oxidation of DPND by acetaldehyde contained only 0.5 atom of D per molecule

Here acetaldehyde labeled with deuterium was reduced with ordinary DPNH, and the ethanol so formed contained, as expected, approximately one atom of deuterium per molecule.

The ethanol-1-D of sequence II was reoxidized enzymatically with DPN, and this time the reduced DPN contained no deuterium whatever, whereas the acetaldehyde contained approximately one atom of deuterium. The somewhat low value for the deuterium content of the acetaldehyde may have been due to some contamination of the dimedon derivative, since the amount of material available was too small to permit recrystallization prior to analysis. In this experiment, as in the previous one, the most significant figure is the value

---

(Table 4) instead of 1 atom as expected. (It should be noted that the deuteroethanol so produced consisted of one pure enantiomorph; the stereospecificity about the alpha carbon of ethanol is not in question). The DPND used to produce the deuteroethanol was analyzed, and found to contain 1 atom of D per molecule as previously reported. When this same DPND was used to reduce pyruvate, the lactate formed contained 0.88 atom of D per molecule. Nevertheless, when the same DPND was reoxidized with acetaldehyde, in the experiment shown in Table 4, the DPN$^+$ formed contained 0.3 atom of D per molecule. However, when the experiment was repeated on a small scale with precautions to keep the incubation time as brief as possible, the DPN$^+$ (formed from the same DPND) then contained 0.15 atom of D per molecule. This value is compatible with the analysis of 1 atom of D per molecule, and a transfer of 0.88 atom of this D to pyruvate to form lactate. Apparently some exchange of D and H had occurred during the large scale preparation of the DPND, and further exchange to about the same extent occurred in the large scale preparation of deuteroethanol. This is not exchange of D with H of the medium, however, but rather, exchange with H in the DPN molecule itself.

The possibility that the value of 0.5 atoms of D per molecule of ethanol might arise, at least in part, from exchange with the medium during oxidation was tested directly and disproved. DPNH was oxidized with ordinary acetaldehyde in D_2O; the ethanol formed was isolated as usual as the p-nitrobenzoate and analyzed for deuterium. The ester contained no more than 0.02 atoms of D per molecule. This experiment served to show that neither exchange with H of the medium nor enolization of the acetaldehyde occurs to a significant extent during the oxidation-reduction process.

Except for the value of 0.5 atom of D per molecule of ethanol-1-D formed from DPND and acetaldehyde, the remaining analytical results shown in Table 4 display no serious discrepancies. The reduced DPND formed from ethanol-1-D was analyzed directly, and was also used to transfer deuterium to lactate. The lactate values are the more accurate, and the difference between the values before and after transfer to lactate are not unreasonable in view of the possible errors in the direct analysis of the DPN. The fact that the lactate values are lower than the value for the ethanol is also not unreasonable. The ethanol consists of a mixture of ordinary ethanol and monodeuteroethanol, and under these circumstances there may be an isotopic discrimination effect, with ordinary ethanol reacting more rapidly than deuteroethanol.

of zero; in Sequence II, this value applies to the excess deuterium content of the DPNH. This analysis shows again, with relatively high accuracy, that no racemization of the ethanol occurred during the enzymatic process.

TABLE 5

PREPARATION AND INVERSION OF ETHANOL-1-D

Sequence II and Inversion	Atoms D per molecule	
$$\begin{array}{ccc} D & & D \\ \| & & \| \\ CH_3\!-\!C\!=\!O + DPNH + H^+ & \rightarrow & CH_3\!-\!C\!-\!OH + DPN^+ \\ & & \| \\ & & H \end{array}$$ distill	CH₃CDO	1.04
	CH₃CDHOH	0.96
$$\begin{array}{ccc} D & & D \\ \| & & \| \\ CH_3\!-\!C\!=\!O + DPNH + H^+ & \leftarrow & CH_3\!-\!C\!-\!OH + DPN^+ \\ & & \| \\ & & H \end{array}$$	CH₃CDO	0.77
	DPNH	0.00
$$\begin{array}{c} D \quad O \\ \| \quad \| \\ CH_3\!-\!C\!-\!O\!-\!S\!-\!C_6H_5CH_3 \\ \| \quad \| \\ H \quad O \end{array}$$		0.87
$$\begin{array}{ccc} H & & H \\ \| & OH^- & \| \\ CH_3\!-\!C\!=\!O + DPND + H^+ & \leftarrow & CH_3\!-\!C\!-\!OH + DPN^+ \\ & & \| \\ & & D \end{array}$$	DPND	1
	DPND*	0.6
	CH₃CHO	0.00

* Atoms of D transferred enzymatically to lactate.

STEREOCHEMICAL INVERSION

Confirmatory evidence that the two enantiomorphs of ethanol-1-D have, in fact, been synthesized, was obtained by converting one to the other by a stereochemical (i. e., "Walden") inversion. The ethanol formed in Sequence II was treated with p-toluenesulfonyl chloride to form the tosyl ester. This ester was analyzed for deuterium, and a sample was then hydrolyzed in strong alkali. The ethanol obtained from the hydrolysis was then submitted to enzymatic reoxidation, and the oxidation products analyzed for deuterium.

The over-all process (formation of the tosyl ester, followed by alkaline hydrolysis of the ester) inverts one enantiomorph of ethanol-1-D into the other. The equations for these transformations, and the appropriate deuterium analyses, are presented in Table 5; and a summary of the data, which identify the two enantiomorphs of ethanol-1-D before and after inversion, are assembled in Table 6. For convenience in assessing the results, the deuterium content of the products, shown in the latter table, has been calculated on the basis of the deuterium content of the monodeutero-ethanol used.

TABLE 6

IDENTIFICATION OF THE ENANTIOMORPHS OF ETHANOL-1-D
BEFORE AND AFTER INVERSION

Sequence	Source of Monodeuteroethanol	Products of Oxidation of Monodeuteroethanol Atoms D per molecule*		
		Acetaldehyde	Reduced DPN	
			Direct	Transferred to lactate
I	$CH_3CHO + DPND$	0.00 0.00	0.8 1.1	0.61 0.88
II	$CH_3CDO + DPNH$	0.81	0.00	
Inversion	Inverted product from Sequence II	0.00	1	0.7

* Atoms D per molecule/atoms D per molecule of monodeuteroethanol, i. e., atoms D per molecule based on the monodeuteroethanol used.

Tables 5 and 6 show that, before stereochemical inversion the monodeuteroethanol of sequence II yielded CH_3CDO and DPNH on enzymatic reoxidation; after inversion the monodeuteroethanol yielded CH_3CHO and DPND on enzymatic reoxidation. Although the deuterium analyses in these experiments are not very accurate, because of the necessary high dilution of the samples, there can be no question of the presence of deuterium in the enzymatically reduced position of the DPND (obtained at the end of the " Inversion Sequence ") in approximately the amount expected. The zero value of the excess deuterium content of the acetaldehyde (obtained by oxidation of the inverted alcohol) is highly significant, for here again, as in Sequence I, two per cent racemization could easily have been detected. The results clearly show that both enantiomorphs of ethanol-1-D have been prepared, and that neither of the enantiomorphs is appreciably contaminated with the other.

The chemistry of the "Inversion Sequence" warrants a few comments. It was assumed, as usual (12, 14, 18, 35), that the formation of the tosyl ester from p-toluenesulfonyl chloride and alcohol occurs without stereochemical change at the asymmetric carbon atom of the alcohol. The ethyl p-toluenesulfonate was hydrolyzed under conditions where the reaction can be inferred (16, 27, 30) to be bimolecular (i. e., the reaction occurs between the ester and hydroxide ions). Under similar experimental conditions, the displacement reactions of derivatives of secondary alcohols proceed with stereochemical inversion. The entering hydroxyl group attacks the asymmetric carbon atom on the tetrahedral face opposite the carbon-oxygen bond which is broken. It has often been assumed that displacement reactions of primary alcohols likewise occur in similar fashion; now, in one case, it has been possible to prove it. The assumption has similarly been substantiated by the independent investigations of Streitwieser (42), who has synthesized butanol-1-D by chemical means, and has established the stereochemical inversion of the corresponding bromide.

DISCUSSION

Our results exclude from consideration all suggested mechanisms of action of alcohol and lactic dehydrogenases which require or allow hydrogen to exchange with the medium during the oxidation-reduction reaction. They provide no information, however, about whether the reduction occurs as a one-step transfer of a hydride ion, or as a transfer of a hydrogen atom and an electron, in separate steps, with the intermediary formation of a free radical. For more detailed discussion, the case of lactic dehydrogenase may be considered first. We have referred to our results as a " direct transfer of hydrogen atoms between substrate and coenzyme." This phrase implies that the hydrogen is donated from one molecule to the other without intermediary transfer to any other group. The possibility must be considered that hydrogen is transferred reversibly from the substrate to the enzyme protein, and then from enzyme protein to coenzyme. It seems unlikely, however, that the protein should be reduced in such a way as to contain non-exchangeable deuterium. In particular, there appears to be little reason to consider the possible participation of sulfhydryl groups in the reaction, since this enzyme is not inhibited by sulfhydryl reagents (1, 3, 32).

The direct hydrogen transfer, and the stereochemical specificity, of lactic dehydrogenase may be pictured schematically as shown in

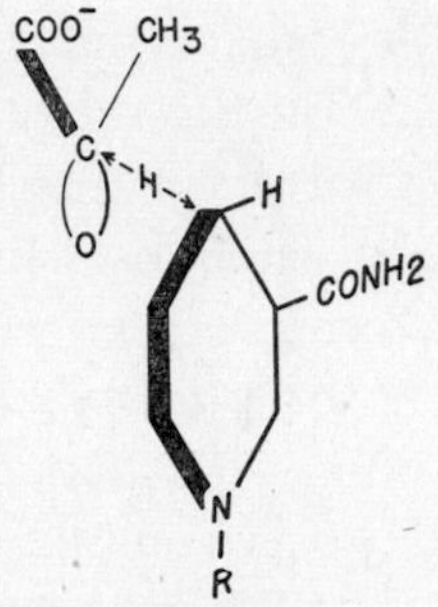

FIG. 2.

Fig. 2. The diagram is not intended to represent actual mechanism. For example, the carbonyl oxygen atom of pyruvate may be bonded during the reaction, but such bonding has not been indicated in Fig. 2, in view of our ignorance of the nature or location of the possible binding group. The diagram furthermore should not be understood to represent absolute configuration or to imply a choice of any particular one of the possible spatial arrangements of the molecules. The figure is designed only as a visual aid in picturing both substrate and coenzyme in adjacent positions at the active site of the protein, with a high degree of spatial orientation, so that hydrogen can be transferred directly from (or to) one side only of the pyridine ring, to (or from) one side only of the carbonyl group of pyruvate. The specificity of the enzyme has been studied by Meister

(28), who has shown that many α-keto acids, including glyoxylic acid, may be substituted for pyruvate. It follows that the methyl group is not critical for enzymatic activity. Nielands (32) and Chance and Nielands (6) have studied the kinetics of this reaction and obtained spectrophotometric evidence for the formation of a complex between the enzyme and reduced DPN. Our studies confirm and extend their findings.

Yeast alcohol dehydrogenase is very sensitive to -SH inhibition, and Barron (1) has suggested that the sulfhydryl of the protein participates as an intermediary in the reduction of DPN by ethanol.

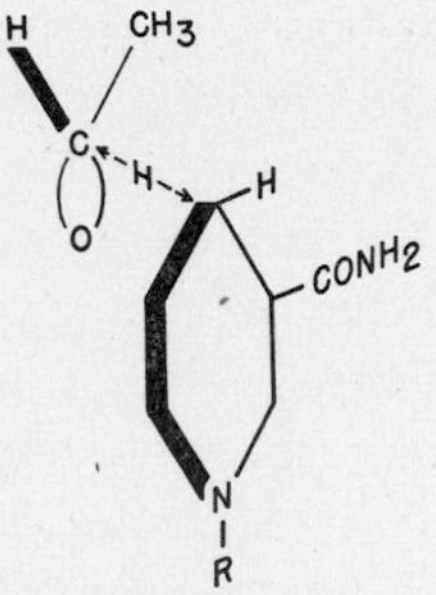

FIG. 3.

However, deuterium attached as a sulfhydryl (S-D) group would almost certainly exchange with the solvent, unless it were protected in some very special way from the protons of the medium; it is therefore improbable that this sulfhydryl group can serve as a hydrogen donor or acceptor in the reaction. The sulfhydryl group may, of course, participate in the enzymatic reaction in some other manner.

It should be pointed out, however, that if some component of the enzyme itself is oxidized and reduced during the reaction, one might expect the enzyme to cause an oxidoreduction between the oxidized and reduced form of the pyridine nucleotides in the absence of ethanol. Kaplan, Colowick, and Neufeld (15) have studied this possibility for alcohol dehydrogenase and found no evidence for it. The reaction catalyzed by alcohol dehydrogenase is pictured in Fig. 3, in a diagram analogous to that used for lactic dehydrogenase. Again, the diagram is intended to illustrate only the direct transfer of hydrogen, and the steric specificity of the hydrogen transfer reaction. Since the ethanol-1-D obtained in Sequences I and II was optically pure, it follows that the position of the hydrogen atom and methyl group are fixed, and that no oxidation-reduction can occur with an acetaldehyde molecule where the positions of these substituents are reversed. Analogously, in the reaction catalyzed by lactic dehydrogenase, the relative positions of the carboxyl and methyl groups must be fixed, since only L-lactic acid is in fact formed. It is not unreasonable to suppose that the highly polar carboxyl and carbonyl groups of pyruvic acid are bound to particular sites on the protein, and such binding can account for the steric specificity observed. But it is a little more difficult to account for the steric specificity observed in the reaction catalyzed by alcohol dehydrogenase. The carbonyl group of acetaldehyde (or the hydroxyl group of ethanol) is highly polar, and can easily be held by the protein at a particular site. However, in order to account for the formation of only one enantiomorph of ethanol-1-D in the Sequence I, for example, either the methyl group or the hydrogen atom must also be held at a specific site on the enzyme surface. Although the methyl group may be held to the protein by van der Waals attractive forces, these forces are in general weak. A more important factor in the orientation of the methyl group may be supplied by the cohesive forces of the water molecules; the methyl group may be "squeezed" out of solution, and into a favorable site on the protein, by the surrounding solvent. Very crude calculations indicate that the cohesive forces of the water probably are sufficient to account for the degree of orientation of the methyl group which has been observed (i. e., for the formation of each enantiomorph of ethanol-1-D contaminated by no more than 2 per cent of its enantiomorph). However, it is still possible that the enantiomorphs of ethanol-1-D will prove to be of even higher optical purity. If such is the case, it may be necessary to assume that the methyl group is forced, by steric repulsions, out of all possible positions except that in which it is properly oriented on the enzyme surface. An interpretation involving both attractive and repulsive forces between enzyme and substrate is consistent with the fact that isopropyl alcohol (5) and methanol (2) react only very slowly with DPN in the presence of yeast alcohol dehydrogenase. In other words, if a methyl group is substituted for the hydrogen atom in acetaldehyde, the reaction rate becomes very much slower, and likewise, if a hydrogen atom is substituted for the methyl group of acetaldehyde, the reaction again takes place with much diminished velocity. Barron and Levine (2) have shown further, that only a little lengthening of the hydrocarbon chain can be tolerated. In a study of the specificity of yeast alcohol dehydrogenase they have shown that allyl alcohol is as good a substrate as ethanol and that propanol-1, butanol-1 and pentanol-1 all act with the dehydrogenase, but with decreasing effectiveness. Presumably with these larger molecules, steric hindrances come into play at the site of the binding of the alkyl group.

The geometric picture adopted here is not new. First of all, the concept of the formation of an enzyme-substrate complex is sufficiently familiar to require no documentation. In early kinetic studies of yeast alcohol dehydrogenase, Negelein and Wulff (31) assumed a combination between the enzyme and its substrates, and measured the apparent dissociation constants of these compounds. The more recent, elegant spectrophotometric studies of Chance and Theorell and their collaborators have provided convincing evidence in some cases for the existence of such compounds. Although some of the early assumptions used in interpreting the significance of the enzyme-substrate dissociation constants have been shown to be wrong, the concept that the enzyme combines with the substrate has been strengthened rather than weakened. The specificity of many enzyme reactions has likewise been recognized. The full significance of the stereochemistry was sometimes overlooked, however, until Ogston (34, see also 26, 48) discussed it in terms of what he called a three-point landing.

PROJECTED APPLICATIONS

It is entirely feasible to extend the study of hydrogen transfer to all other pyridine nucleotide enzymes. In some cases the method could probably not be used to demonstrate direct hydrogen transfer, since the extra hydrogen on the reduced substrate would be expected to exchange rapidly with the medium. These cases include pyridine nucleotide reactions with (a) disulfides and sulfhydryl compounds (viz., glutathione and lipoic acid), (b) quinones, and (c) flavoproteins. Among the latter are included diaphorases, cytochrome reductase, and probably nitrate and nitrite reductase. With all of these enzymes, however, it should be possible to study the steric specificity of the reaction with respect to the pyridine nucleotide.

The large group of pyridine nucleotide dehydrogenases which oxidize alcohols to carbonyl groups, (as well as the related reaction catalyzed by glutamic dehydrogenase) are certainly all open for study, both of direct hydrogen transfer and of steric specificity for DPN or TPN. Here in every case the reduced form of the substrate contains an extra atom of non-exchangeable hydrogen. Another large family of pyridine nucleotide dehydrogenases causes the oxidation of aldehydes to carboxyl groups or to a variety of acyl derivatives. Formic dehydrogenase might be included in this group. Here again, there is a non-exchangeable hydrogen atom on the aldehyde group, and the possibility of direct hydrogen transfer can certainly be investigated. Though it is apparent that the enzymes of the latter group may show stereospecificity for the reduced pyridine nucleotide, it might seem at first glance that the oxidation of aldehydes cannot show stereospecificity with respect to the substrate. This is not, however, necessarily the case. Consider, for example, the reaction catalyzed by glucose dehydrogenase. It has been shown by Strecker and Korkes (41) that the reaction product is the δ-lactone of gluconic acid, and the conclusion has been drawn that the corresponding pyranose ring form of the sugar is the actual substrate of the enzyme. Cori and Lipman (8, 21) have come to similar conclusions regarding the substrate for glucose-6-phosphate dehydrogenase. The pyranose sugar may have either the α- or β-configuration at carbon atom one, and it is quite possible that the enzyme can act only on one of these isomers (see discussion).

All oxidations of aldehydes may be formulated in a similar fashion, as shown in Fig. 4. The reaction may involve the addition of HOH, HSR, or $HOPO_3^=$ to a carbonyl group, followed by a removal of hydrogen from the carbonyl carbon atom and from the OH group of the addition compound. If some group in the enzyme itself first forms the addition compound, as is likely to be the case, the situation is still quite analogous to that for the oxidation of

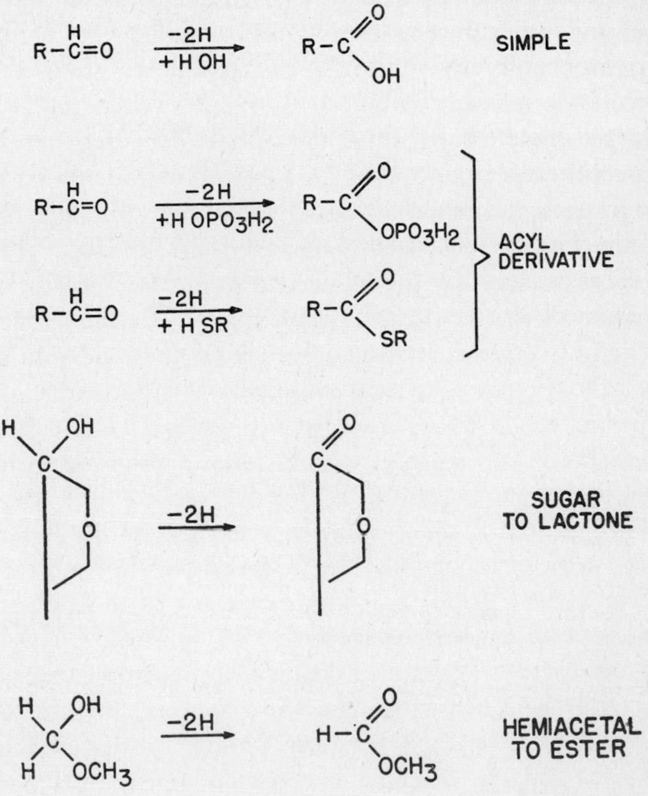

FIG. 4.

alcohols. In every case there is at least a theoretical possibility of stereospecificity.

The last equation of Fig. 4 represents a reaction studied by Kendal and Ramanathan (17). They found that, in the presence of DPN, liver aldehyde mutase preparations convert a mixture of methanol and formaldehyde to methyl formate. This reaction was relatively insensitive to iodoacetate. The mutase consists of a mixture of alcohol and aldehyde dehydrogenase. The latter enzyme is relatively sensitive to iodoacetate inhibition, whereas the former is not. Kendal and Ramanathan therefore suggested that the hemiacetal of methanol and formaldehyde served as a substrate for the alcohol dehydrogenase. In view of the similarity of the reaction to other aldehyde dehydrogenase reactions, it seems more reasonable to us to group the reaction with aldehyde oxidations rather than with alcohol oxidations. The lack of sensitivity to iodoacetate suggests that the methanol, in adding to the aldehyde, may perform a function otherwise carried out by an SH group of the enzyme.

In conclusion, it should be emphasized that this discussion has been limited to only one aspect of a large problem. Some of the very interesting results obtained in other laboratories have been presented, as discussion, by other members of the symposium.

REFERENCES

1. Barron, E. S. G., *Advances in Enzymology*, 11, 201 (1951).
2. Barron, E. S. G., and S. Levine, *Arch. Biochem. and Biophys.*, 41, 175 (1952).
3. Barron, E. S. G., and T. P. Singer, *J. Biol. Chem.*, 157, 221 (1945).
4. Blakley, R. L., *Biochem. J.*, 49, 257 (1951).
5. Burton, K., and T. H. Wilson, *Biochem. J.*, 54, 86 (1953).
6. Chance, B., and J. B. Nielands, *J. Biol. Chem.*, 199, 383 (1952).
7. Colowick, S. P., pers. com.
8. Cori, O., and F. Lipmann, *J. Biol. Chem.*, 194, 417 (1952).
9. Fisher, H. F., E. E. Conn, B. Vennesland, and F. H. Westheimer, *J. Biol. Chem.*, 202, 687 (1953).
10. Gillespie, L. J., and H. T. Liu, *J. Am. Chem. Soc.*, 53, 3969 (1931).
11. Green, D. E., J. G. Dewan, and L. F. Leloir, *Biochem. J.*, 31, 934 (1937).
12. Hammett, L. P., *Physical Organic Chemistry*, Chapter VI. McGraw-Hill, N. Y. (1940).
13. Harary, I., pers. com.
14. Ingold, C. K., *Mechanism and Structure in Organic Chemistry*, Cornell University Press, Ithaca, N. Y. (1952).
15. Kaplan, N. O., S. P. Colowick, and E. F. Neufeld, *J. Biol. Chem.*, 195, 107 (1952).
16. Karlsson, K. G., *Z. anorg. Chem.*, 145, 47 (1925).
17. Kendal, L. P., and A. N. Ramanathan, *Biochem. J.*, 52, 430 (1952).
18. Kenyon, J., H. Phillips, and V. P. Pittman, *J. Chem. Soc.*, 1935, 1072 (1935).
19. Kubowitz, F., and P. Ott, *Biochem. Z.*, 314, 94 (1943).
20. Lehninger, A. L., and G. D. Greville, *J. Am. Chem. Soc.*, 75, 1515 (1953).
21. Lipmann, F., *Phosphorus Metabolism*, Vol. I (W. D. McElroy and B. Glass, eds.), p. 158. Johns Hopkins Press, Baltimore (1951).

22. Loewus, F. A., P. Ofner, H. F. Fisher, F. H. Westheimer, and B. Vennesland, *J. Biol. Chem.*, **202**, 699 (1953).
23. Loewus, F. A., F. H. Westheimer, and B. Vennesland, *J. Am. Chem. Soc.*, (in press).
24. Magnus-Levy, A., *Arch. exptl. Path. Pharmakol.*, **45**, 389 (1901).
25. Martius, C., and F. Lynen, *Advances in Enzymol.*, **10**, 167 (1950).
26. Martius, C., and G. Shorre, *Ann. Chem. Justus Liebigs*, **570**, 140, 143 (1950).
27. McCleary, H. R., and L. P. Hammett, *J. Am. Chem. Soc.*, **63**, 2254 (1941).
28. Meister, A., *J. Biol. Chem.*, **184**, 117 (1950); **197**, 309 (1952).
29. Miller, O. N., C. G. Huggins, and K. Arai, *J. Biol. Chem.*, **202**, 263 (1953).
30. Morgan, M. S., and L. H. Cretcher, *J. Am. Chem. Soc.*, **70**, 373 (1948).
31. Negelien, E., and H. J. Wulff, *Biochem. Z.*, **284**, 289 (1936).
32. Nielands, J. B., *J. Biol. Chem.*, **199**, 373 (1952).
33. Ochoa, S., *The Enzymes* (J. B. Sumner and K. Myrbäck, eds.) Vol. II, Part 2, p. 929. Academic Press, New York (1952).
34. Ogston, A. G., *Nature*, **162**, 963 (1948).
35. Phillips, H., *J. Chem. Soc.*, **123**, 44 (1923).
36. Pullman, M. E., and S. P. Colowick, *Federation Proc.*, **12**, 255 (1953).
37. Racker, E., *J. Biol. Chem.*, **184**, 313 (1950).
38. Schlenk, F., *The Enzymes* (J. B. Sumner and K. Myrbäck, eds.) Vol. II, Part 1, p. 250. Academic Press, New York (1951).
39. Schwert, G., and M. T. Hakala, reported at the Federation meeting, 1953.
40. Straub, F. B., *Biochem. J.*, **34**, 483 (1940).
41. Strecker, H. J., and S. Korkes, *Nature*, **168**, 913 (1951).
42. Streitwieser, A., *J. Am. Chem. Soc.* (in press).
43. Talalay, P., and M. M. Dobson, unpub.
44. Talalay, P., M. M. Dobson, and D. F. Tepley, *Nature*, **170**, 620 (1952).
45. Vickery, H. B., *Science*, **113**, 314 (1951).
46. Westheimer, F. H., H. F. Fisher, E. E. Conn, and B. Vennesland, *J. Am. Chem. Soc.*, **73**, 2403 (1951).
47. Wieland, H., *Ber. deut. chem. Ges.*, **45**, 482 (1912).
48. Wilcox, P. E., C. Heidelberger, and J. R. Potter, *J. Am. Chem. Soc.*, **72**, 5019 (1950).

DISCUSSION

DR. KAUZMANN: Was the optical activity of the enantiomorphs of ethanol determined?

DR. VENNESLAND: No, there wasn't enough material on hand to do this. In experiments of this sort, the cost of the DPN is a limiting factor.

DR. HORECKER: In the experiment in which you failed to get the one atom of D in the alcohol, was it possible that the enzyme was contributing small amounts of alcohol which would dilute the isotope?

DR. VENNESLAND: Well, we worried about all the reagents that we were using. The thing that bothered us here was that, when we used the same reagents for the other enantiomorph and we thought that we should have gotten the same dilution in that case, we didn't get it.

DR. HORECKER: Was it the same enzyme preparation?

DR. VENNESLAND: No, it wasn't; so it is possible this might account for the results. At least, it hasn't been excluded as a possibility. However, we haven't been able to show that there is alcohol in the enzyme.

DR. HORECKER: In our laboratory we have found that there is enough alcohol left in some enzyme preparations to give a reaction with DPN without addition of substrate.

DR. VENNESLAND: That did not appear to be the case with these enzyme preparations.

DR. E. SMITH: I would just like to make a statement. I don't see that there is any difficulty in expecting the methyl group of the alcohol to be bound to alcohol dehydrogenase. We know that amino acids like alanine show complete optical specificity in the case of the amino acid oxidases, and with peptidases. One must postulate some sort of interaction with the methyl group there. I would think that a type of interaction like van der Waals forces might be involved. This should be perfectly possible with the alcohol dehydrogenase.

DR. WESTHEIMER: Complete optical specificity can be obtained in any enzymatic reaction where there are three appropriate points of attachment for the substrate, or substrate and coenzyme, on the enzyme surface. There are always three or more strongly polar groups in any peptide, and therefore the alkyl side chains (although they certainly are important) need not be involved in determining optical specificity. However, a somewhat different situation obtains for the stereospecific reduction of acetaldehyde. The reduced position of the coenzyme is one fixed point on the enzyme surface; the position of the highly polar carbonyl group is a second. But to specify the third fixed position (and thus to insure the optical specificity of the reduction) the position of the methyl group of acetaldehyde must also be fixed. Van der Waals forces between the methyl group and the enzyme are unlikely to be sufficiently large to account for the observed optical specificity.

We can, however, suggest two explanations for the observed specificity. One of these explanations accounts for the observations as the result of steric hindrance. In other words, large groups on the enzyme surface are assumed to interfere with the methyl group, whenever it occupies any position other than the preferred one. A second alternate explanation is based on the cohesive forces in water, which were discussed, during the first day of this conference, by Professor Kirkwood and Professor Eyring. If there is a "hole," (a preferred position, surrounded by the hydrocarbon portion of the protein side chains) for the methyl group, then the water molecules in the surrounding medium can "squeeze" the methyl group of the acetaldehyde into this "hole." We have carried out a crude calculation of the potential effect of the cohesive forces of water on the stereospecificity of the reduction of acetaldehyde, and are convinced that the effect is large enough to account for our observations.

DR. COLOWICK: I would like to mention briefly our reasons for believing that reduction of DPN occurs in the para position rather than in the ortho position, as previously supposed. The experiments which I will describe were carried out by Dr. Pullman and Dr. San Pietro in this laboratory.

The approach used was based on the experiments of Vennesland and Westheimer and their collaborators, who showed that when DPN was reduced by dithionite in heavy water and then reoxidized enzymatically by means of acetaldehyde and yeast alcohol dehyrogenase, the resulting DPN contained about 0.5 atom of deuterium per molecule. We have prepared deuterium labeled DPN in this manner, and also in the reverse manner; that is, by enzymatic reduction with dideuteroethanol and yeast alcohol dehydrogenase, followed by chemical reoxidation with neutral ferricyanide. A third method was also used, namely chemical reduction with dithionite in heavy water, followed by chemical reoxidation with neutral ferricyanide.

Having obtained deuterium-labelled DPN by any one of these methods, the position of the deuterium in the pyridine ring was determined as follows: the labelled DPN was treated with *Neurospora* DPN-ase, and the resulting nicotinamide was isolated and treated with CH_3I to give N^1-methylnicotinamide. The latter was oxidized by alkaline ferricyanide, a procedure which Dr. Pullman has found to yield approximately equal amounts of the isomeric ortho pyridones, the structures of which have been established unequivocally. Deuterium analyses showed that none of the deuterium had been removed in the formation of either the 2- or the 6-pyridone of N^1-methylnicotinamide. It, therefore, seems unlikely that reduction of DPN (enzymatically or chemically) occurs at either ortho position. Since reduction in the meta position can be ruled out from considerations of electron structure, we have concluded that reduction occurs in the para position. The experiments with deuterium-labelling may thus be summarized as follows:

The widely held view that reduction of DPN occurs at one of the ortho positions is based on the studies of Warburg and Karrer, who used reduced N^1-methylnicotinamide as a model compound. Their conclusion that this compound is an ortho dihydro derivative was based on comparisons of such properties as color, fluorescence, reducing power and crystallizability with those of other dihydro pyridine derivatives of established structure. We are planning to use the deuterium technique just described, in order to determine whether or not the reduced model compound gives the same results as reduced DPN. It is possible that the model compounded and DPN are reduced at different sites.

DR. SAN PIETRO: I should like to discuss some work carried out with Dr. Kaplan and Dr. Colowick, concerning the nature and stereospecificity of the bacterial transhydrogenase reaction. They have shown that the enzyme, transhydrogenase, of *Pseudomonas fluorescens* catalyzes a reaction between reduced pyridine nucleotide and oxidized pyridine nucleotide. Several reactions of this nature are:

$$
\text{(1)} \quad \text{TPNH} + \text{DPN} \quad \overset{\text{ad. } a}{\rightleftharpoons} \quad \text{TPN} + \text{DPNH}
$$

$$
\text{(2)} \quad \text{TPNH} + \text{desTPN} \longrightarrow \text{TPN} + \text{desTPNH}
$$

$$
\text{(3)} \quad \text{DPNH} + \text{desDPN} \overset{\text{ad. } a}{\longrightarrow} \text{DPN} + \text{desDPNH}
$$

$$
\text{(4)} \quad \text{DPNH} + \text{DPN}^{\bullet} \overset{\text{ad. } a}{\longrightarrow} \text{DPN}^{\bullet}\text{H} + \text{DPN}
$$

Reaction 1, the oxidation of reduced TPN by DPN, proceeds in the forward direction in the absence of adenylic a (2'-adenylic acid); but no appreciable reversal of this reaction takes place unless adenylic a is present. TPN is known to inhibit reaction 1 in both directions; that is, even in the reverse reaction where it should serve as substrate, moderate concentrations of TPN are strongly inhibitory. Since TPN is known to contain the adenylic a moiety, it appears likely that, in this case, the action of adenylic acid a is due to its competitive action in overcoming the inhibitory effect of TPN. Reactions 3 and 4 similarly show a requirement for adenylic a, and this is suggestive of a possible direct requirement for the a grouping, since no competition with an inhibitory a nucleotide can be invoked in this case. These equations, 3 and 4, represent the same reaction, namely, an exchange reaction between the oxidized and reduced form of DPN, except that chemical labeling of the purine moiety is used in reaction 3 and isotopic labeling of the nicotinamide moiety in reaction 4. No requirement for adenylic a has been shown for reaction 2. It is possible that either the TPNH or desamino TPN can supply the necessary a grouping in this reaction, and that neither of these nucleotides is inhibitory.

In contrast to the results with bacterial transhydrogenase, adenylic *a* has no effect on any of the transhydrogenase reactions catalyzed by the animal enzyme. Another point of contrast is the apparent predominance of the exchange reaction (equations 3 and 4) in certain animal tissues, namely, brain and liver, in which reactions 1 and 2 do not occur at appreciable rates.

Studies of the nature of the products from the reaction between TPNH and C^{14} labeled DPN, which was found to proceed as follows:

$$(5) \quad TPNH + DPN^{\bullet} \rightarrow TPN + DPN^{\bullet}H$$

established that either an electron or hydrogen transfer was involved in reaction 1. The possibility of a phosphate or nicotinamide moiety transfer was ruled out by this experiment.

The possibility that a direct hydrogen transfer was involved was suggested by the work of the Chicago group reported at this meeting by Dr. Vennesland. As she pointed out, they have demonstrated that a direct hydrogen transfer from alcohol to DPN is catalyzed by yeast alcohol dehydrogenase. They have also shown that yeast alcohol dehydrogenase and beef heart lactic hydrogenase are stereospecific in that they can only act on one side of the pyridine ring. We have found that the bacterial transhydrogenase also catalyzes a direct hydrogen transfer, but that it exhibits a lack of stereospecificity, that is, the transhydrogenase can place hydrogen on either side of the pyridine ring.

The reaction studied with the bacterial enzyme was the oxidation of chemically reduced deutero-TPN by DPN.

$$(6) \quad TPND + DPN \rightarrow DPND + TPN$$

The resulting reduced deutero-DPN was oxidized either chemically or enzymatically, and the deuterium content of the total DPN fraction was determined. The experimental procedures used were similar to those just reported here by Dr. Colowick. With chemical oxidation, the expected amount of deuterium was found, assuming no stereospecificity for the chemical oxidation or reduction, and no reversal of reaction 6, since adenylic acid *a* was omitted. After enzymatic oxidation, using acetaldehyde and yeast alcohol dehydrogenase, the same amount of deuterium was found in the total DPN fraction as for the chemical oxidation. If the transhydrogenase were stereospecific, then the deuterium content of the total DPN fraction, following enzymatic oxidation, should be either zero or approximately twice the amount of deuterium found with chemical oxidation. It, therefore, appears that a direct hydrogen transfer is involved and that the enzyme shows a lack of stereospecificity.

We have investigated this same reaction, using enzymatically reduced deutero-TPN. Using a catalytic amount of TPN, deutero-reduced TPN was continuously generated by the isocitric dehydrogenase system from pig heart in heavy water. (The mechanism whereby deuterium enters the reduced TPN in this reaction is being investigated. The possibility that the action of aconitase is responsible for this incorporation is being considered.) The resulting TPND was oxidized continuously by excess DPN and bacterial transhydrogenase. The resulting reduced deutero-DPN was analyzed for deuterium as previously described. The results were the same, whether chemically reduced deutero-TPN or enzymatically reduced deutero-TPN was used as the starting material.

In summary, the bacterial transhydrogenase has been shown to catalyze a direct hydrogen transfer between reduced and oxidized pyridine nucleotides. Furthermore, this enzyme appears to show a lack of stereospecificity in contrast with the studies on the dehydrogenases so far investigated which appear to be stereospecific.

DR. VENNESLAND: I haven't thought it out too carefully, but I was just wondering about the possibility that the TPN and the DPN might alternately exchange their sites of combination on the enzyme. This might account for the apparent lack of stereospecificity—that is, you have two pyridine nucleotides operating in this case, and the hydrogen might be transferred either to corresponding sides or to the opposite sides. If the two substrates could alternate their positions — that is, if each on the enzyme could bind either TPN or DPN — you might get the result which was found. As I say, I haven't thought it out carefully.

DR. BENTLEY: I think another case of stereospecific hydrogen transfer is to be found with the enzyme notatin (glucose dehydrogenase) which has FAD as its prosthetic group. Here the primary reaction is a conversion of glucose to gluconic acid lactone, and the reaction has been shown to be specific for beta glucose. Alpha glucose is not oxidized until after mutarotation takes place.

DR. ANFINSEN: I just happened to think that it might be possible to conceive of an animal enzyme which could act like the *Pseudomonas* transhydrogenase. I am referring to the glutamic dehydrogenase of animal tissues. To prove it would require the help of Velick and others, since we don't know in this case whether nucleotide is bound as it is in the case of triose phosphate dehydrogenase for example. If one were to find multiple binding sites and could show that perhaps DPN and TPN were simultaneously bound, then in the presence of ketoglutarate and ammonia you would have a sort of synthetic model for the transhydrogenase reaction.

DR. KAPLAN: We have tried using dehydrogenases, but find that it has no transhydrogenase activity.

DR. ANFINSEN: Was this done with deuterium?

DR. KAPLAN: No. We havn't done it with deuterium. We have done it with C^{14} labelled nicotinamide present in the oxidized DPN. The exchange of this labelled compound with reduced DPN is not catalyzed by dehydrogenases.

DR. ANFINSEN: What I was thinking of was binding deuterium labelled TPN to a partially saturated glutamic dehydrogenase.

DR. KAPLAN: Saturated with what? With substrate?

DR. ANFINSEN: No. With ketoglutarate and DPN, assuming that the enzyme binds the nucleotides. We don't know that, but if it did then it might be feasible to investigate whether there was a transfer of deuterium from TPND to DPN in the presence of ketoglutarate.

DR. KAPLAN: Well, if you have substrate present—that is, ketoglutarate + ammonia—then you would get the transfer. The exchange reaction that I mentioned between oxidized and reduced pyridine nucleotides was carried out without the substrate. I might add that addition of small amounts of ketoglutarate does not promote exchange between TPNH and DPN by glutamic dehydrogenase.

DR. MEHLER: Dr. Vennesland's explanation for the randomization brought about by a stereospecific transhydrogenase is quite adequate if two assumptions are made. One, that the reaction always transfers hydrogen from one site of the donor nucleotide to the opposite position on the acceptor; and two, that the reduced product of the reaction can be used subsequently by the enzyme to transfer a hydrogen atom to a new acceptor. Then in each cycle of oxidation and reduction of a pyridine ring there would be an inversion at the site of reduction, and all possible combinations of deuterium and hydrogen should be formed at that site.

DR. KAPLAN: I would like to discuss some experiments which may have bearing on the mechanism of dehydrogenase action. Dr. Vennesland has pointed out that dehydrogenase activity involves a direct transfer of hydrogen from substrate to pyridine nucleotide. One might postulate several mechanisms by which this transfer might occur. A possible scheme is that the substrate hydrogen may go directly to protein, forming reduced protein; the hydrogen from the reduced protein could then be transferred directly to the pyridine nucleotide. We have found that using C^{14}-nicotinamide-labelled DPN, that dehydrogenases such as yeast alcohol dehydrogenase, lactic dehydrogenase, and triosephosphate dehydrogenases do not catalyze an exchange between oxidized and reduced forms of pyridine nucleotides. Since this exchange is not promoted, it is not likely that a reduced enzyme is an intermediate in dehydrogenase action.

A second possible mechanism might involve DPN-substrate compound as an intermediate. A scheme involving such a mechanism is as follows, where E represents the enzyme and RH the substrate:

Step (1) $DPN + E \rightarrow E \cdot DPN$

Step (2) $E \cdot DPN + RH \rightarrow E \cdot DPN \cdot HR$

Step (3) $E \cdot DPN \cdot HR \rightarrow E \cdot DPNH + R$

Step (4) $E \cdot DPNH \rightarrow E \cdot + DPNH$

The hypothesis proposes that there is first a binding of the coenzyme to the protein (Step 1) which is then followed by a direct addition of substrate to the nicotinamide moiety of the nucleotide (Step 2). This addition complex is then split and results in the formation of reduced DPN and the oxidized substrate (Step 3). The final step would be a dissociation of the reduced DPN from the enzyme.

I would like to emphasize that the quaternary nitrogen in the nicotinamide moiety of DPN makes the molecule very susceptible to addition reactions. It has been found that cyanide, bisulfite, and hydroxyl ions will form addition compounds with DPN. Dr. Colowick spoke this morning of the hydrosulfite products forming an addition compound with DPN, which appears to be an intermediate in the formation of reduced DPN. Mr. Burton, in our laboratory, has demonstrated that dihydroxyacetone will add to pyridine nucleotides non-enzymatically. The compound which is formed gives an absorption spectrum identical with that of reduced DPN; however, the compound is not reduced DPN, since it is not oxidized by acetaldehyde with alcohol dehydrogenase.

The dihydroxyacetone DPN compound has recently been isolated by Mr. Burton and Dr. San Pietro. The compound, although not oxidized enzymatically, can be oxidized by ferricyanide, according to the following equation:

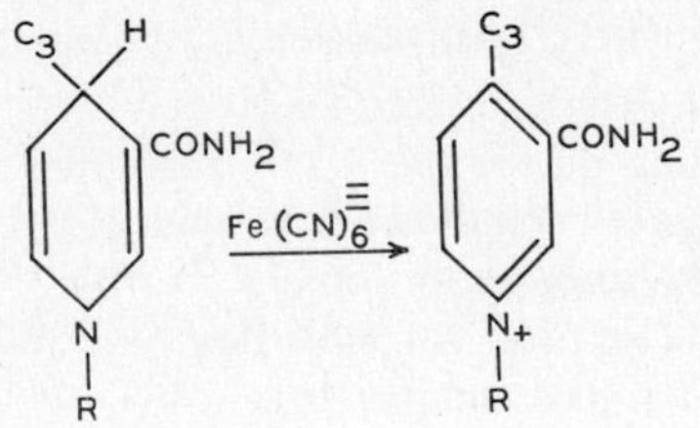

I have written the structure with a C_3 unit; as yet we are not certain as to what the nature of the linkage of the dihydroxyacetone to DPN is. The structure of the addition compound is now being investigated. The oxidized form is a compound with properties similar to the isonicotinic acid hydrazide analogue of DPN, which Dr. Zatman will discuss later.

All the above addition reactions of the pyridine nucleotides take place only with the oxidized forms and not with the reduced forms. It is possible that this great reactivity of the pyridine nucleotide may be related to the wide distribution of these coenzymes in dehydrogenase reactions.

Miss Ciotti and I have been able to obtain some evidence with horse liver alcohol dehydrogenase, that the DPN-substrate compound is an intermediate in the enzymatic reaction. This has been through the use of hydroxylamine which we have found to be a competitive inhibitor of ethanol in both the liver and yeast alcohol dehydrogenase systems. (Kaplan and Ciotti, *J. Biol. Chem.*, 201: 785 (1953)). In the case of the liver system, it was observed that preincubation of the enzyme with hydroxylamine and DPN resulted in a rate of reaction which was very much slower than when the reaction was started with DPN.

We have found that by incubating the enzyme with small levels of DPN and hydroxylamine we can obtain very strong inhibition even when a large excess of alcohol and DPN are added. The inhibition does not occur when either hydroxylamine or DPN alone are incubated with the enzyme. The inhibition is not only with the oxidation of alcohol, but also with reduction of acetaldehyde. The inhibitory complex appears to be very tightly bound, but after 48 hours of dialysis, the inhibition is removed and the full activity of the enzyme is returned. These dialyses experiments indicate that the hydroxylamine inhibition is reversible. I should like also to point out that reduced DPN cannot replace the oxidized coenzyme in promoting the hydroxylamine effect.

Recently we have been able to show that a reaction between DPN and hydroxylamine on the liver alcohol dehydrogenase does occur when large amounts of enzyme are used. The compound which is formed has a maximum absorption at 300 mμ. The millimolar extinction coefficient at this wave length is approximately 6. The amount of absorption formed depends on the level of enzyme used. Two moles of DPN react per mole of enzyme. Addition of more than 2 moles of DPN does not result in any further rise in absorption. I should emphasize that DPN does not react with hydroxylamine to yield any detectable complex. It is only in the presence of the three components, enzyme, hydroxylamine, and DPN, that the complex is formed. There is a decrease of the 260 mμ absorption of the pyridine nucleotide, as a result of the hydroxylamine reaction; this might be expected, since reduced DPN and the addition reactions of cyanide, bisulfite, dihydroxyacetone all result in a decrease of the 260 absorption. The hydroxylamine compound, therefore, appears to have all the properties of a DPN addition reaction.

Denaturation of the enzyme abolishes the absorption due to the hydroxylamine DPN compound. Oxidized DPN can be recovered after such treatment. Para chloromercuric benzoate also causes removal of the band associated with the complex. Reduced DPN which has been found by Bonnischen and Theorell to be bound to the enzyme is dissociated from the enzyme by the DPN-hydroxylamine complex. The complex appears to have a much greater affinity for the enzyme than either reduced DPN or the oxidized nucleotide.

I believe that these experiments with hydroxylamine are significant in that they demonstrate that the enzyme is acting either on DPN or hydroxylamine or on both substances to promote a complex formation. As I mentioned before, this complex does not occur except in the presence of the enzyme. The effect of hydroxylamine appears to be specific for alcohol dehydrogenases. I believe that since hydroxylamine competes with ethanol, that there is a good possibility that the initial step is actually in addition of the ethanol to the DPN, which is then followed by a splitting to reduced DPN and acetaldehyde. We are now further pursuing the relationship of the binding of pyridine nucleotides to the liver alcohol dehydrogenase with respect to the mechanism of action of the enzyme, and will publish the details of this investigation elsewhere.

ONE AND TWO ELECTRON REACTIONS
IN CATALASES AND PEROXIDASES [1]

B. CHANCE and R. R. FERGUSSON

*The E. R. Johnson Foundation for Medical Physics,
University of Pennsylvania*

WE HAVE SHOWN that catalase and peroxidase systems follow essentially similar reaction mechanisms that are adequately represented by an enlargement of the theory of Michaelis and Menten in which the first-order decomposition of ES is replaced by the second-order reaction of the enzyme-substrate complex and the donor molecule:

$$E + S \rightarrow ES \tag{1}$$

$$ES + AH_2 \rightarrow E + SH_2 + A \tag{2}$$

Our studies furnish no support for significant participation of chain reaction mechanisms (1).

Through the work of Keilin (2) and Theorell (3) and that carried on in this laboratory (4), four different types of enzyme-substrate compounds have been identified by spectroscopic and magnetometric methods (5). On the basis of rapid kinetic studies of these compounds, it has been possible to show that only one of the observed intermediates functions catalytically in catalase reactions (6). On the other hand, two compounds participate in peroxidase reactions (7).

We denote the three or four compounds resulting from the interaction of enzyme and substrate as enzyme-substrate compounds. Our studies show that only one of these compounds is rate-limiting in catalytic activity, complex I of catalase, and complex II of peroxidase. This particular complex is the one that fulfils the requirements of the Michaelis theory because it dominates the activity-substrate concentration relationship and is therefore termed the " Michaelis compound."

[1] This work has been supported in part by the National Science Foundation.

The Physical Properties of the Complexes

In Table 1 we present a summary of spectroscopic and magneto-metric data on the four types of enzyme-substrate compounds of catalases and peroxidases, and for comparison, we include data on their compounds with cyanide as well. Data on the compounds formed by ferrimyoglobin and peroxide are also presented.

The segregation of the complexes into the four types is based primarily upon the sequence in which these compounds are formed from peroxides; complex I appears first and is followed by complex II, which is converted into complex III or IV with excess peroxide. In the case of ferrimyoglobin, where no sequence exists, spectro-scopic and magnetometric data are used to classify the complex (5).

Complexes of type III are all relatively inactive, and so is catalase complex II. The activity of the latter towards ethanol is about 1/100,000 that of the active complex I (8). The magnetic properties of the catalase complex II and the ferrimyoglobin complex are rather similar, as are their very small catalytic activities. The highly active complexes are complexes I of catalase and peroxidase and complex II of peroxidase. The activity of these complexes is evaluated by direct measurements of the velocity constant for their reaction with donor molecules (see Table 1 for typical values). It is seen that the maximal activities of the active complexes reach about the same limits.

The chemical differences between catalase and peroxidase com-plexes are emphasized by the following reactions which we have studied spectroscopically:

(1) Excess peroxide is sufficient to convert catalase complex I into inactive complex II. The reaction is not accelerated by donors that react rapidly with complex I:

$$\text{Catalase complex I} \xrightarrow{\text{excess peroxide}} \text{Catalase complex II} \qquad (8)$$

(2) Peroxidase complex I requires a donor for the formation of complex II:

$$\text{Peroxidase complex I} \xrightarrow{\text{donor}} \text{Peroxidase complex II} \qquad (9)$$

TABLE 1

Spectroscopic and Magnetic Properties of Compounds of Hemoproteins and Peroxides

(Reaction velocity constants are in $M^{-1} \times$ sec.$^{-1}$ and in sec.$^{-1}$ and magnetic susceptibility in 10^6 c.g.s. e.m.u. Wavelengths are in mμ.)

Hemoprotein	Property	Compound					Gross Reaction Mechanism of Catalytic Function	Eq. Ref.
		Cyanide	Complex I	Complex II	Complex III	Complex IV		
Catalase (erythrocyte)	Nature of compound	inactive	active	inactive	inactive	unknown	$E + S \xrightarrow[k_2 < .02]{k_1 = 6 \times 10^6} ES_I$	(3) (18)
	Absorption bands	425 (20) 586 (16) 554 (16)	405 (4) 655 (4)	429 (5) 568 (16) 536 (16)	416 (4) 585 (16) 545 (16)	—	$ES_I + AH_2 \xrightarrow{k_4' = 1.8 + 10^7} E + SH_2 + A$	(4)
	Magnetic susceptibility	2,240 (5)	unknown	3,400 (5)	unknown	—		
Peroxidase (horse-radish)	Nature of compound	inactive	active	active	inactive	inactive	$E + S \xrightarrow[k_2 < 3]{k_1 = 9 \times 10^6} ES_I$	(5) (19)
	Absorption bands	420 (21) 580 (16) 538 (16)	410 (4) 665 (4)	418 (4) 555 (16) 527 (16)	416 (4) 583 (16) 546 (16)	405 (21) 670 (21)	$ES_I + AH \xrightarrow{k_7 \rightleftharpoons 70k_4} ES_{II} + A$	(6)[1a] (11)
	Magnetic susceptibility	2,970 (5)	6,500 (5)	5,040 (5)	unknown	14,300 (5)	$ES_{II} + AH \xrightarrow{10^1 < k_4 < 10^8} E + SH + A$ where $ES_{II} \rightleftharpoons (ESH)_I$	(7) (19)
Ferrimyoglobin (horse)	Nature of compound	inactive	unknown	unknown	inactive	unknown		
	Absorption bands	423 (22) 542 (27)	—	—	423 (17) 590 (17) 549 (17)	—		
	Magnetic susceptibility	unknown	—	—	3,500 (5)	—		

[1a] To show proper stoichiometry in Equation (6), ES_{II} may be considered to contain the hydrogen atom of AH.

(3) Catalase complex I reacts with donors such as alcohol to give the free enzyme:

$$\text{Catalase complex I} \xrightarrow{\ donor\ } \text{Free Catalase} \tag{10}$$

(4) Peroxidase complex II requires a reaction with a donor to release the free enzyme:

$$\text{Peroxidase complex II} \xrightarrow{\ donor\ } \text{Free peroxidase} \tag{11}$$

(5) Catalase II is relatively stable and accumulates in the presence of donors such as alcohols.

The active complexes I and II have a larger magnetic susceptibility than the inactive complexes of types II and III, in so far as experimental data are available.

TABLE 2

CORRESPONDENCE BETWEEN MAGNETIC SUSCEPTIBILITY AND UNPAIRED ELECTRONS

Number of unpaired electrons	1	2	3	4	5
μ_{eff}	1.73	2.63	3.87	4.90	5.92
χ_m (20° C.)	1,266	3,370	6,340	10,140	14,760

The number of unpaired electrons in the complexes is related to the magnetic susceptibility for "spin only" contributions, as shown in Table 2. However, it turns out that there are large deviations from the "spin only" values, as shown in Table 3, and it may be assumed that there are large "orbital contributions" [2] in the active peroxidase complex II. The compound whose structure is fairly certain is that of the cyanide compound—one of ferric iron and covalent bonds—and this shows a large "orbital contribution" (~ 0.7). Thus it is an open question as to how the results of the magnetic study should be interpreted in terms of bond type of the complexes. Neither do the magnetic data shed any light on whether higher valence states of the iron exist in the complexes because

[2] An alternative explanation to "orbital contributions" is discussed by Taube (9) on the basis of an equilibrium between two forms of the compound of nearly the same energy but of different electron configuration.

only ferric and ferrous compounds have been prepared for magneto-metric studies.

Titrations of complex I and complex II with one-electron donors. In a beautiful experiment using substrate quantities of peroxidase, Philip George (10) has titrated, with ferrocyanide, complex II formed from an exceptional preparation of horse-radish peroxidase.[3] It was found that complex II retains only one of the two oxidizing equivalents of peroxide. Proof that one oxidizing equivalent of complex I is lost in the transition to complex II in a second-order reaction of a donor molecule and complex I is afforded by further direct experimental data obtained in this laboratory (11).

TABLE 3

IRREGULARITIES IN "ORBITAL CONTRIBUTIONS" IN HEMOPROTEIN-PEROXIDE COMPOUNDS

Complex	Peroxidase I	Peroxidase II	Catalase II	Metmyoglobin III	Cyanide Compounds of Catalase, Peroxidase Hemoglobin
Nearest unpaired electron	3	2	2	2	1
Orbital contribution	0	0.6	0	0	~ 0.7

Attempts to detect free radicals in solutions of complexes I, II, and III. Through the kindness of Drs. Commoner, Thompson, and Weissman of Washington University, we were able to attempt a determination of the electronic resonance absorption of complexes I, II, and III. Using between 0.5 and 1×10^{-3} M solutions of the complexes I and II of peroxidase[4] and of complex III of ferri-myoglobin, we were unable to detect any evidence for a free radical having a value of g[5] in the range 1.7 to 2.3 when operating the apparatus at optimum sensitivity for aqueous solutions.

In order to increase the sensitivity further, and to obtain more

[3] Purified and assayed by Dr. A. C. Maehly, Miss M. Grenholm, and Mr. T. M. Devlin of this laboratory.

[4] Stabilized as described in ref. 11.

[5] For a discussion on the unwisdom of our attempting to define g here, see Darrow's recent review (12, 13).

quantitative results, freeze-dried samples of complexes I and II were prepared by Dr. Commoner.[6] Again substantially negative results were obtained, as shown in Fig. 1. With 4×10^{-7} moles of enzymes present, the maximal deflection that was obtained in the most favorable case corresponded to $\sim 2 \times 10^{-11}$ moles of free radical of $g \approx 2$, as determined by independent calibration. Our preliminary conclusion is that these complexes contain less than one part in 20,000 of a free radical that shows electronic resonance absorption.

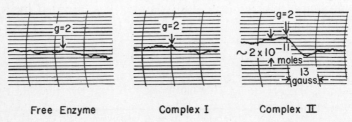

Free Enzyme   Complex I   Complex II

Fig. 1. Representative records of attempts to measure electronic resonance absorption of 4×10^{-7} moles of peroxidase in the form of the dried solids of the free enzyme, complex I, and complex II (Expt. 141).

Studies with heavy oxygen. Cahill and Taube (14) have studied the fractionation of isotopic oxygen in $H_2O_2{}^{18}$ during reduction by various inorganic ions and report a value for catalase obtained by J. P. Hunt (14) that leads them to suggest a one-electron reduction of H_2O_2; the reaction of catalase with H_2O_2 to form complex I would consist, for example, of two steps of one-electron reduction of H_2O_2, with consequent one-electron oxidation steps for the enzyme.

Our direct studies of the reaction of catalase and peroxidase with H_2O_2 show no detectable amount of a one-electron intermediate in the reaction. We have also determined experimentally that complex I has the two oxidizing equivalents of peroxide, and therefore may very likely be a simple hydrogen peroxide complex since there is no direct experimental evidence to the contrary.

Taube (pers. com.) indicates that the isotope fractionation ratio

[6] It is interesting to note that we could prepare green and red solids from complexes I and II. We are further studying the method and are proceeding to measure the magnetic susceptibility of these solid enzyme-substrate compounds.

may not clearly indicate in the case of catalase whether a one- or two-electron reaction occurs. First, a diffusion-limited reaction would show an isotope fractionation ratio characteristic of a one-electron reaction whether or not it is a one-electron reaction. And it is possible that catalase is a diffusion-limited reaction, since the energy of activation is less than 1400 cal. (15) for k_1 of Eq. (3) of Table 1. Secondly, the binding of peroxide to catalase in a special way, as in complex I, would render the isotopic fractionation value insensitive to whether a one- or two-electron process occurs.

Taube also points out that even if a one-electron reaction does take place with catalase, a reaction involving hydroxyl radicals,

$$Fe^{III} + H_2O_2 = Fe^{IV} + OH \cdot + OH^- \tag{12}$$

$$OH \cdot + H_2O_2 = HO_2 \cdot + H_2O \tag{13}$$

$$2\,HO_2 \cdot \quad\quad = H_2O + O_2 \tag{14}$$

does not take place according to the oxygen fractionation data, and a mechanism not involving the reaction of $HO \cdot$ and H_2O_2 must be formulated.

In summary, the more complex nature of the catalase reaction limits the usefulness of the isotope fractionation ratio in deciding whether catalase operates by a one- or two-electron mechanism. Perhaps the most useful result is that a particular one-electron mechanism has been proved not to occur.

The reaction mechanism on a kinetic basis. In our studies of catalase, the rate of formation of complex I and the rate of its reaction directly with the donor molecule are completely consistent with the amount of the enzyme-substrate complex present in the steady-state. We have therefore concluded that only one intermediate compound, complex I, can as yet be detected in this reaction. Even though Stern in 1936 (23) and more recently George (24) proposed a catalytic function for complex II, neither carried out kinetic studies essential to prove that complex II has the properties required of an enzyme-substrate compound acting according to an extension of the theory of Michaelis and Menten.

It would appear that this is a case of a two-electron one-step reaction, both reducing equivalents of the donor molecule being transferred to the enzyme-substrate complex simultaneously, in so far as we can determine.[7] We have written the reaction mechanism for the reaction of complex I with alcohol as follows:

$$\text{Fe}\cdot\text{HOOH} \xrightarrow{k_4} \text{FeHOH} + \text{H}_2\text{O} + \text{CH}_3 - \text{C} = \text{O} \qquad (15)$$

and believe that a similar reaction occurs with hydrogen peroxide

$$\text{Fe}\cdot\text{HOOH} \xrightarrow{k_4'} \text{Fe}\cdot\text{HOH} + 2\text{H}_2\text{O} + \text{O}_2 \qquad (16)$$

This scheme postulated by Chance (25) is in accord with the later isotopic studies of Dole (26) and Taube (14).

But in the case of peroxidase, complex I is observed only in the initial transient phases of the reaction; in the steady-state, complex II is present and complex I can scarcely be detected at all. Our kinetic data show that peroxidase and catalase reaction mechanisms start in the same way, namely, with the formation of complex I and its reaction with the donor (see Table 1, Equations 5 and 6). If a one-electron donor is used, then there is no reason for the reaction with complex I of peroxidase to proceed farther until collision with a second donor molecule occurs, as indicated by Equation 7 of Table 1, and these equations provide a satisfactory explanation of peroxidase activity towards one-electron donors.

But the vast majority of compounds with which peroxidase reacts are two-electron donors; this includes almost all the classical sub-

---

[7] Our rapid reaction methods cannot yet fulfill the criterion of simultaneity for a two-electron transfer reaction proposed here by Westheimer—that escape from the solvent cage shall not have occurred ($\sim 10^{-11}$ sec.). However, it is possible that the electron-transfer reaction at the surface of protein molecules may be somewhat slower and still be considered a two-electron reaction because the solvent cage may be replaced by a much more complex steric condition. Our kinetic data on catalase suggest that the two-electron transfer reaction occurs in $< 10^{-7}$ sec.

stances; the only exception of biological importance is ferrocyto-chrome-c. When a two-electron donor is used with peroxidase, the reaction of complex I with a two-electron donor does not proceed beyond the complex II stage, and collision of complex II with a fresh donor molecule is required to liberate the enzyme.

It is more difficult to write a reaction mechanism which explains how the reaction of peroxidase with two-electron donors occurs and which is compatible with our experimental finding that the formation of complex I, its transition to complex II, and the liberation of enzyme from complex II are pH-independent reactions. One must also consider that inappreciable amounts of free radicals are found in solution from peroxidase or catalase plus H_2O_2 (15a), and this is in accord with our electronic resonance absorption data on complexes I and II of peroxidase.

We can account for several aspects of the kinetics of peroxidase in the presence of a bivalent donor according to a reaction sequence in which the principal steps are outlined as follows:

Step I. Formation of the enzyme-substrate compound:

$$\underset{Peroxidase}{Fe^{+3}(H_2O)} + H_2O_2 \underset{k_3 < 3}{\overset{k_1 = 9 \times 10^6}{\rightleftharpoons}} \underset{Complex\ I}{Fe^{+3}(H_2O_2)} + H_2O \qquad (17)$$

Step II. Transition from I to II:

$$Fe^{+3}(H_2O_2) + AH_2 \xrightarrow{k_7 = 5 \times 10^4} Fe^{+3}(OH\cdot) + AH\cdot + H_2O \qquad (18)$$

Step III. Decomposition of II:

$$AH\cdot + Fe^{+3}(OH\cdot) + AH_2 \xrightarrow{k_4 = 2 \times 10^3} Fe^{+3}(H_2O) + A + AH_2 \qquad (19)$$

These reaction velocity constants were measured experimentally with $AH_2 = p$-aminobenzoic acid. The units are moles per liter and seconds.

It is very important to learn more of the whereabouts of the half-oxidized donor molecule of Equation (18); in some cases it may remain attached to the peroxidase protein until reaction with the second donor molecule occurs.

The chemical structure of complex II is not known, and several alternatives are possible; the form given here is the well-known trivalent iron and renders unnecessary the postulation of higher valence states of iron (quadri- and quinque-valencies) of which the existence is doubtful and for which no physical and chemical properties of iron are known. In addition, the reaction sequence is in accord with the observed effects of pH upon the reactions of Equations (17), (18), and (19).

REFERENCES

1. Chance, B., *Biological Antioxidants*, Trans. of the Fourth Conference, Josiah Macy, Jr. Foundation, p. 54 (1950).
2. Keilin, D., and E. F. Hartree, *Biochem. J.*, 49, 88 (1949).
3. Theorell, H., Heme-Linked Groups and Mode of Action of Some Hemoproteins, *Advances in Enzymol.*, 7, 265 (1947).
4. Chance, B., *Arch. Biochem. and Biophys.*, 41, 404 (1952).
5. Theorell, H., and A. Ehrenberg, *Arch. Biochem. and Biophys.*, 41, 442 (1952).
6. Chance, B., *Acta Chem. Scand.*, 1, 236 (1947).
7. Chance, B., *Arch. Biochem.*, 22, 224 (1949).
8. Chance, B., *J. Biol. Chem.*, 179, 1341 (1949).
9. Taube, H., *Chem. Rev.*, 50, 69 (1952).
10. George, P., *Biochem. J.*, 54, 267 (1953).
11. Chance, B., *Arch. Biochem. and Biophys.*, 41, 416 (1952).
12. Darrow, K. K., *Bell System Tech. J.*, 32, 82 (1953).
13. Darrow, K. K., *Bell System Tech. J.*, 32, 391 (1953).
14. Cahill, A. E., and E. Taube, *J. Am. Chem. Soc.*, 74, 2312 (1952).
15. Chance, B., and D. Herbert, *Biochem. J.*, 46, 402 (1950).
15a. Dainton, F. S., and P. Smith, cited by P. George in *Advances in Catalysis*, 4, 367 (1953).
16. Keilin D., and E. F. Hartree, *Biochem. J.*, 49, 88 (1951).
17. George, P., and D. H. Irvine, *Biochem. J.*, 52, 511 (1952).
18. Chance, B., D. S. Greenstein, and F. J. W. Roughton, *Arch. Biochem. and Biophys.*, 37, 301 (1952).
19. Chance, B., Enzyme-Substrate Compounds, *Advances in Enzymol.*, 12, 153 (1951).
20. Bonnichsen, R., Dissertation, Karolinska Institute, Stockholm (1948).
21. Chance, B., *Arch. Biochem.*, 21, 416 (1949).
22. Besnák, M., *Acta Chem. Scand.*, 2, 333 (1948).
23. Stern, K. G., *J. Biol. Chem.*, 114, 473 (1936).
24. George, P., Proceedings of the Biochemical Society, *Biochem. J.*, xix (1952).
25. Chance, B., *J. Biol. Chem.*, 179, 947 (1950).
26. Dole, M., R. DeForest, G. Muchow, and C. Compte, *J. Chem. Phys.*, 20, 961 (1952).
27. Unpublished data.

ENZYME MECHANISMS IN LIVING CELLS *

Britton Chance

The E. R. Johnson Foundation for Medical Physics
University of Pennsylvania, Philadelphia

Introduction

FOR SOME TIME we have been studying the mechanisms of enzyme action by means of direct spectroscopic measurements of the reaction kinetics of the enzyme-substrate complexes. We have obtained definite results in vitro with peroxidases from horse-radish, milk, leucocytes, and yeast, catalases from liver, erythrocytes, and bacteria (see ref. 8, Table I, p. 156), and DPN-linked alcohol dehydrogenase from liver (ADH) (45). In these systems we studied spectroscopically intermediate complexes of enzyme and substrate, determined the sequence of their formation and disappearance, and showed which complex is the rate-limiting or " Michaelis " complex for a particular set of conditions. Such studies. validated the use of the Michaelis-Menten theory for the representation of enzyme action and, more significantly, showed the detailed applicability of simple mechanisms in the explanation of catalysis involving enzyme-substrate compounds.

The reaction mechanisms that we employ are the simplest ones that give a satisfactory explanation of the experimental data. As technical improvements of our complex experimental techniques give more accurate data, we may test in detail more sophisticated reaction mechanisms which would be applied prematurely to our data at this time.

The much more vulnerable aspect of even the simpler reaction mechanisms is the extrapolation of in vitro mechanisms to in vivo systems, and we have begun to study the question intensively. In the

* This research was supported in part by a grant from the Division of Research Grants and Fellowships, United States Public Health Service, and in part from the Office of Naval Research.

399

case of peroxidase, Keilin's keen visual spectroscopic technique had already shown that peroxidase complex II could be formed by the addition of peroxide to extracts of horse-radish, but he could give no indication that the reaction sequence in vitro (31) applied to the actual situation in vivo. Nor was any evidence provided on the nature or amount of substrate or hydrogen donor present in the cell.

In the case of catalase, no enzyme-substrate complex had been found in vivo by ordinary methods, although the existence of a peroxide as a substrate for catalase-coupled oxidation in liver slices had been suggested by the work of Heppel and Porterfield (24).

By using the sensitive spectrophotometric methods developed for the study of the cytochromes in turbid heart-muscle preparations and in whole-cell suspensions (11), we have identified the primary catalase—hydrogen-peroxide complex as a normal component of aerobic cultures of *Micrococcus lysodeikticus* (12) and have further shown that natural hydrogen donors are present in the cell to react with the catalase complex in biological oxidations. In bakers' yeast, the addition of peroxide causes the rapid formation of the peroxidase complex II. This complex reacts readily with the reduced forms of the respiratory pigments and has a potential activity even greater than that of cytochrome oxidase. However, the peroxidase complex has not yet been positively identified as a natural component of the yeast cell.

The yeast glyceraldehyde-3-phosphate–dehydrogenase—DPN complex (37) can be identified in the aerobic, starved cell and can bind about one-fourth of the total DPN content of the cell. The action of this enzyme can be observed directly upon the addition of glucose to the starved yeast cell.

The spectroscopically distinct compound of DPNH and horse liver ADH (45) has not been found with yeast ADH in vitro (5, 19, 23a). The detailed mechanism of horse liver ADH action in vitro is reviewed here.

Intracellular enzyme systems consisting of sequences of many enzymes in the pathways from glucose or ethanol to oxygen are characterized by different levels of steady-state oxidation of the various enzymes involved. In the alcohol sequence in yeast cells:

$O_2 \leftarrow a_3 \leftarrow a \leftarrow c \leftarrow$ factor $\leftarrow$ diaphorase
"b"

$$DPNH \xleftarrow[ADH]{} \begin{array}{c} DPN \\ + \\ Ethanol \end{array} \qquad (1)$$

We have observed that DPNH levels of 30 per cent saturate the capacity of the respiratory system and at the same time cause a maximal steady-state concentration of a pigment spectroscopically similar to both cytochrome b and to peroxidase complex II. This pigment, denoted "cytochrome b," appears to limit the rate of oxygen uptake in the yeast cell, and has been indicated in Equation (1) by "b."

We have developed a method for calculating the reaction-velocity constants for the interaction of members of an enzyme sequence on the basis of the flux of electrons through the system and the steady-state concentration of the components. We have also shown how these calculations can be applied to the cytochrome components of the succinic oxidase system (11).

A cellular component on which no kinetic studies in vivo have been reported previously is DPNH. We have made a study of the kinetics of reduction of DPN when glucose or ethanol is added to aerated starved yeast cells. This potent tool for the investigation of pathways of metabolism in vivo already shows the action of alcohol dehydrogenase when alcohol is the substrate, or glyceraldehyde-3-phosphate dehydrogenase when glucose is the substrate. The interaction of the latter enzyme with what is deduced to be α-glycerol-phosphate dehydrogenase in a DPN-linked pair of dehydrogenases gives the first picture of such a "shuttle" of DPNH and DPN between two dehydrogenase systems in vivo. It is found that the interactions of such linked systems regulate the DPN/DPNH ratio to a considerably greater extent than do the respiratory enzymes, which reach half-maximal activity with about 15 per cent reduced DPN for the particular conditions of our studies.

This paper is largely a preliminary report on a broad series of studies on the reaction kinetics of intracellular enzymes and should serve as an indication of the potentialities of these methods. The actual physical apparatus has been recently described elsewhere (14).

Catalase

Catalase reaction mechanisms in vitro. In order to interpret the data that are presented on the action of catalase in the respiring bacterial cell, it is important to review briefly some characteristics of catalase action in vitro.

Keilin and Hartree's pioneer work on coupled oxidations of catalase in the presence of H_2O_2, continuously generated by an oxidase system such as glucose dehydrogenase (29), showed the possibilities of a biological function of catalase other than that as a scavenger of excess H_2O_2. The complete elucidation of the reaction mechanism, as presented here, provides pathways for the oxidation of hydrogen donors such as alcohol, formic and nitrous acids, as well as the decomposition of H_2O_2 into water and oxygen:

Step I   Formation of the enzyme-substrate complex:

$$\text{Catalase} + H_2O_2 \underset{k_2}{\overset{k_1}{\rightleftharpoons}} \text{Catalase-}H_2O_2 \tag{2}$$

Step II$_a$ Reaction of the enzyme-substrate complex with a hydrogen donor—a peroxidatic reaction:

$$\text{Catalase-}H_2O_2 + \text{HCOOH} \xrightarrow{k_4} \text{Catalase} + CO_2 + 2H_2O \tag{3}$$

Step II$_b$ Reaction of the enzyme-substrate complex with a second molecule of H_2O_2—a catalatic reaction:

$$\text{Catalase-}H_2O_2 + H_2O_2 \xrightarrow{k_4'} \text{Catalase} + O_2 + 2H_2O \tag{4}$$

The over-all reaction for Steps I and II$_b$ has a velocity constant k_1'

$$2H_2O_2 \xrightarrow{k_1'} 2H_2O + O_2 \tag{5}$$

that is readily measured by titration (6) or ultraviolet spectrophotometry (18).

We have obtained quantitative proof of the mechanism for catalase action by directly measuring k_1 by rapid spectrophotometric methods and by comparing this value with that computed from the over-all reaction rate (k_1') in terms of the following equation (16):

$$k_1 = \frac{k_1'}{8\,(1 - p_M/e)} \tag{6}$$

The term p_M/e is the maximal value of the catalase-H_2O_2 complex in the steady-state and may be conveniently referred to in terms of the number of catalase hematins bound to H_2O_2—1.6 out of 4 for bacterial catalase (18). The excellent agreement of the measured and computed values of k_1 has recently been made possible by an electric analog computer study (15) and the correlation of the calculated and observed values shown in Table 1 is consistent with the accuracy at present obtainable in measuring millisecond reactions with very dilute catalase solutions.

TABLE 1

A CORRELATION OF OVER-ALL AND ENZYME-SUBSTRATE KINETICS OF CATALASE (16)

Type of Catalase p_M/e		Experimental Values		Theoretical Values	
		$k_1' \times 10^{-7}$ $(M^{-1} \times \text{sec.}^{-1})$	$k_1 \times 10^{-7}$ $(M^{-1} \times \text{sec.}^{-1})$	$k_1 \times 10^{-7}$ $(M^{-1} \times \text{sec.}^{-1})$	$k_4' \times 10^{-7}$ $(M^{-1} \times \text{sec.}^{-1})$
Erythrocyte	$\dfrac{1.2}{4}$	3.5	0.5	0.62	1.5
Bacterial	$\dfrac{1.6}{4}$	5.3	2.0	1.1	1.7

The experimental data have been obtained from rapid spectrophotometric techniques. The theoretical values have been obtained by means of an electric analog computer study resulting in the solution of higher-order nonlinear differential equations which represent the enzyme action.

In studies of catalase in bacteria, we utilize the difference between the spectra of the catalase-H_2O_2 and the catalase-CH_3OOH compounds in order to determine whether the intracellular substrate for catalase is H_2O_2 or an organic peroxide. These spectral differences are illustrated by Fig. 1. With methyl hydrogen peroxide, a 4/1.6-fold larger optical density change is obtained because $p_M = e$; all the catalase hematins may be bound to CH_3OOH:

$$\text{Catalase} + 4CH_3OOH \underset{k_2}{\overset{k_1}{\rightleftharpoons}} \text{Catalase-}(CH_3OOH)_4 \qquad (7)$$

In such studies of the spectra of intracellular pigments, " difference spectra " are obtained; the difference of light absorption between one form of the enzyme and that of another—usually the reduced and oxidized forms but, in the case of catalase, the free enzyme and the enzyme-H_2O_2 compound. Such difference spectra for catalase are plotted in Fig. 1, *A* for ready comparison with the in vivo data.

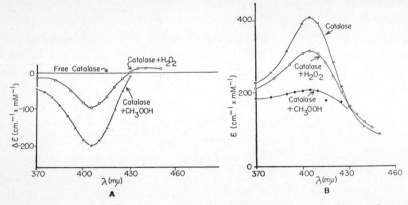

FIG. 1. In vitro data on catalase. *A*, The spectra representing the differences between free catalase and its hydrogen peroxide complex and its methyl hydrogen peroxide complex. *B*, The absolute spectra of free catalase, catalase hydrogen peroxide, and catalase methyl hydrogen peroxide (Expt. 144) (18).

Identification of the catalase—hydrogen-peroxide complex. Micrococcus lysodeikticus has been chosen for the study of intracellular catalase because this enzyme has already been crystallized from the cells (25) and because of their unusually high catalase content of 1 per cent (25). Our method of detecting the presence of the catalase-H_2O_2 complex is based upon Equation (3), the decomposition of the complex by a large excess of hydrogen donor. By using a sensitive recording spectrophotometer, we have plotted in Fig. 2 the difference spectrum obtained by adding excess formic acid to an aerobically respiring suspension of *M. lysodeikticus* (12). It is seen that the difference spectrum is very similar to that of Fig. 1. When the difference of signs is taken into account, Fig. I *A* represents the formation of the complex (a decrease in optical density at 405 mμ), and Fig. 2 represents the decomposition of the complex (an increase of optical density at 405 mμ). Thus a specific reaction caused by formate yields the difference spectrum of a catalase-hydrogen peroxide complex. If the respiration of the cell suspension is continued until the dissolved oxygen is exhausted, the absorption bands of the reduced cytochromes appear, as shown in Fig. 2.

In order to identify whether the physiological substrate is hydrogen peroxide or an organic peroxide, we have compared the optical density changes caused by the reaction of Equation (3) with that of Equation (7). If an organic peroxide is the physiological substrate, then we should obtain equal optical density changes but of opposite sign. Fig. 3, however, shows that unequal changes are measured

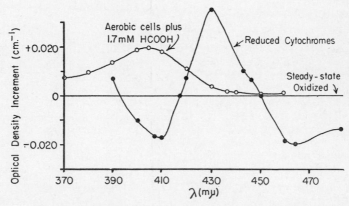

Fig. 2. In vivo data on catalase and cytochromes. Spectra representing the difference in optical density between an aerobic (steady-state oxidized) and anaerobic (reduced) suspension of *Micrococcus lysodeikticus*, and the difference between the aerobic suspension and the aerobic cells plus hydrogen donor (formate) (Expt. 924) (12).

and their inequality (1.3/4-to-1.4/4) corresponds fairly well to the value of 1.6/4 that would be expected if hydrogen peroxide were the physiological substrate.

Cyanide titration. It is possible to titrate intracellular catalase directly by adding cyanide to the anaerobic cells, and we have obtained agreement with the in vitro result that is within the experimental error (the dissociation constant is 2×10^{-5} M HCN) (18). Thus this property of the enzyme is the same in the state of nature as in the crystalline preparation.

It is fortunate that the cytochrome oxidase of *M. lysodeikticus* has a lower affinity for cyanide than catalase and that it is possible to titrate catalase to the end-point before the oxidase is titrated appreciably.

The catalase—methyl-hydrogen-peroxide complex. Titration of the free catalase of the anaerobic cells with methyl hydrogen peroxide is also possible, and in this case the apparent dissociation constants

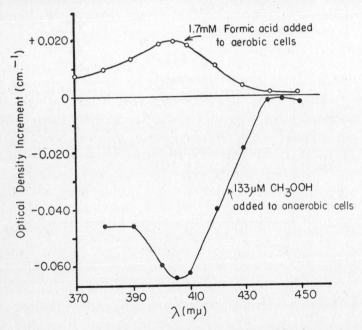

Fig. 3. Identification of hydrogen peroxide as the physiological substrate for catalase by a comparison of the optical density changes caused by adding formate to the aerobic cells to cause the reaction of Equation (3) or methyl hydrogen peroxide to the anaerobic cells to cause the reaction of Equation (7) (Expt. 924, 1-3).

in vitro and in vivo are $< 10^{-6}$ and 4×10^{-6} M respectively. The latter is to be regarded as a Michaelis constant because our kinetic data show the catalase-CH_3OOH compound to be unstable; when $k_4 a_0$ is calculated according to Equation (8) below, the in vivo turnover number of catalase is 0.09 sec.$^{-1}$ which is probably caused by endogenous hydrogen donors. Such a turnover lowers the affinity for peroxide and partially accounts for the observed decrease. This decrease would also be observed if the combination of intracellular catalase and methyl hydrogen peroxide proceeded more slowly in vivo than in vitro. This point is being studied further.

Addition of hydrogen donors such as nitrous or formic acids greatly increases the turnover number of the methyl hydrogen peroxide complex and by measuring the amount (p_m) and the life-time $(t_{\frac{1}{2}_{off}})$ of the complex, we can compute the velocity constant of Equation (3) for the initial donor concentration a_o:

$$k_4 = \frac{x_o}{p_m \, t_{\frac{1}{2} \, off} \, a_o} \tag{8}$$

Values of k_4 in the same range as those found in vitro are found in vivo and the larger value of k_4 for nitrous acid than for formic acid is substantiated in vivo. Thus the specificity of the intracellular enzyme is similar to that of the crystalline material.

A quantitative comparison of the data in vitro and in vivo is not yet possible because the reactive donor species is the free acid and the activity therefore depends upon the intracellular pH. Thus one would expect changes of the values of k_4 with metabolic states of the bacteria that alter the intracellular pH, and could quantify such changes of pH if desired.[1]

The catalase—hydrogen-peroxide complex. This complex is present in the aerobic cells as shown in Fig. 3. The kinetics of its disappearance are readily observed upon the cessation of respiration when the supply of peroxide is cut off due to exhaustion of the dissolved oxygen in the cell suspension. This is clearly shown by the recording obtained from our double-beam spectrophotometer shown in Fig. 4. The lower polarographic trace (platinum microelectrode) records the cessation of respiration as the oxygen concentration falls to zero. The 405 mμ trace shows an upward deflection

---

[1] For detailed studies, intracellular values of k_4 should first be measured with ethanol as a pH-insensitive donor and the true intracellular pH would be calculated:

$$\text{pH} = 7 + \log \left[\frac{175}{k_4 \text{ (in vivo, formic acid)}} \cdot \frac{k_4 \text{ (in vivo, ethanol)}}{13} \right]$$

where 175 is the value of k_4 found in vitro at pH 7 with formic acid and k_4 (in vivo, formic acid) is that value found at an unknown intracellular pH. The value for k_4 in vitro for ethanol is 13. In this way any systematic differences between the intracellular k_4 and that in solution would be eliminated.

(a decrease of optical density—compare Fig. 2) corresponding to a reduction of the cytochromes, followed by a slow increase of optical density caused by the disappearance of the catalase—hydrogen-peroxide complex (compare Figs. 1 and 2). By recording simultaneously at 418 mμ, a wavelength isosbestic for the reduced and oxidized cytochromes, we observe only the slow decomposition of the catalase–peroxide complex. From its rate of decomposition we

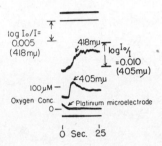

FIG. 4. A spectrophotometric and polarographic recording of the changes in a suspension of *Micrococcus lysodeikticus* which have become anaerobic due to their own respiration. The platinum microelectrode records the oxygen concentration. The double-beam spectrophotometer was set at 405 mμ and 418 mμ and records an increase of optical density as an upward deflection of the 418 mμ trace and a downward deflection of the 405 mμ trace (to avoid superposition). Cells suspended in a phosphate medium of pH 7.0 with 2.7 mM glucose present (Expt. 922a) (12).

compute according to the first-order equation the catalase turnover number ($k_3 = k_4 a_0$) to be 0.07 sec.$^{-1}$. Thus the catalase is supplied with H_2O_2 aerobically and with hydrogen donors as well that cause the intracellular function of this enzyme according to Equations (2), (3), and (4).

A calculation of the steady-state intracellular hydrogen peroxide concentration. If the experiment of Fig. 4 is repeated in the presence of added formic acid, the amount of catalase—hydrogen-peroxide complex recorded at 418 mμ will decrease due to the increased turnover number of the complex according to Equation (3). We have found that 2 mM formate causes a 50 per cent decrease of the steady-state concentration of the complex.

From our mechanism for catalase action the free hydrogen peroxide concentration (x_m) in the steady-state is (16).

$$x_m = \frac{k_4 a_o p_m}{k_1 e - (k_1 + k_4') p_m} \tag{9}$$

where the reaction velocity constants are defined by Equations (2), (3), and (4) and the values of the velocity constants k_1 and k_4' are given in Table 1 for bacterial catalase.

The average value of e is 0.8 μM on the basis of spectrophotometric data and p_m is observed to be 0.16 μM; a_o is 2 mM and k_4 is 200 $M^{-1} \times$ sec.$^{-1}$.

The average value of the peroxide concentration is calculated to be

$$x_m = \frac{200 \times 2 \times 10^{-3} \times 0.16 \times 10^{-6}}{2 \times 10^7 \times 0.8 \times 10^{-6} - (2 \times 10^7 + 1.7 \times 10^7) 0.16 \times 10^{-6}}$$
$$= 10^{-8} \, M \, H_2O_2.$$

At this level of hydrogen peroxide concentration, catalase is acting as we have suggested by a combination of the catalatic (Equation 4) and peroxidatic (Equation 3) pathways (see ref. 8, p. 186). In fact, the catalase of the bacterial cell utilizes as much H_2O_2 in peroxidatic reactions with endogenous hydrogen donors as it decomposes into water and oxygen in a catalatic reaction. Such action gives experimental support to the possibility that catalase acts both catalatically and peroxidatically in vivo (12). At higher levels of H_2O_2, catalase would provide its regulatory function and decompose more H_2O_2 into oxygen.

PEROXIDASE

Peroxidase reaction mechanism in vitro. In 1925 Thurlow (47) described the first coupled oxidation in vitro and showed how H_2O_2 produced from xanthine oxidase could be utilized by peroxidase in the oxidation of nitrous acid, but no demonstration in vivo of its activity was obtained. Keilin and Mann (31), who observed the formation of peroxidase-fluoride in slices of horse-radish roots, were able to observe the formation of the peroxidase-peroxide complex if they used a minced and concentrated cell extract. But no evidence of the formation of the peroxidase complex in the undamaged cell was observed.

The evidence for the presence of a peroxidase in yeast is based on the work of Altschul, Abrams, and Hogness (3), who purified an enzyme that has a high activity in catalyzing the reaction of H_2O_2 and ferrocytochrome c. For this reason, they called the enzyme cytochrome c peroxidase. Subsequent work has shown that this peroxidase has considerable activity towards usual hydrogen donors such as p-phenylenediamine and that activity towards ferrocytochrome c (9) is a general property of the four peroxidases that have been purified from plants, milk, leucocytes, and yeast (9).

Inasmuch as peroxidase is specific for ferrocytochrome c and could participate in intracellular coupled oxidations, this enzyme could provide an auxiliary path for biological oxidations. We have studied the kinetics of complex II of peroxidase in intact yeast cells and have found that the peroxidase, when adequately supplied with exogenous peroxide, can oxidize reduced cytochromes and pyridine nucleotides at a rate that exceeds the capability of the cytochrome oxidase system itself. We will present experimental evidence to support these conclusions.

If methyl hydrogen peroxide is added to yeast peroxidase in vitro, the spectrum of the secondary complex rapidly appears. The original data of Abrams et al. (3) are replotted in Fig. 5 as a difference spectrum with peaks at 427, 529, and 563 mμ that agree very closely with results on a recent preparation obtained in this laboratory.[2]

We have found that the yeast enzyme, in common with the other peroxidases, forms a primary complex before forming the secondary complex. In the yeast enzyme the transition from the primary to the secondary complex is very rapid even in the absence of added hydrogen donor. In these studies we would expect to observe only the secondary complex, the rate-limiting or "Michaelis" complex. The peroxidase reaction mechanism can therefore be simplified to include only Equations (10) and (12) as rate-determining reactions because *Step II* proceeds very rapidly.

---

[2] This work was ably carried out by Mr. T. M. Devlin, who prepared the enzyme in abundance.

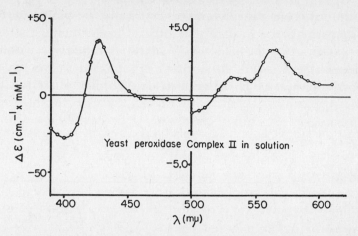

FIG. 5. Spectra representing the difference of absorption between methyl hydrogen peroxide complex II of yeast peroxidase and the free enzyme. The data have been replotted from an absolute spectrum of Altschul, Abrams, and Hogness (3).

Step I   Formation of the enzyme-substrate complex:

$$\text{Peroxidase} + H_2O_2 \underset{k_2}{\overset{k_1}{\rightleftharpoons}} \text{Peroxidase-}H_2O_2 \tag{10}$$

Step II   Transition from the primary to the secondary complex:

$$\text{Peroxidase-}H_2O_2 + AH \xrightarrow{k_7} \text{Peroxidase Complex II} + A \tag{11}$$

Step III   Liberation of the enzyme from complex II:

$$\text{Peroxidase Complex II} + AH \xrightarrow{k_4} \text{Peroxidase} + A + 2H_2O \tag{12}$$

As in the case of catalase, the turnover number of peroxidase, k_3, is readily calculated from the kinetics of complex II:

$$k_3 = k_4 a_0 = \frac{x_0}{p_m \, t_{\frac{1}{2} \, off}} \tag{13}$$

Spectrum of peroxidase complex II in yeast cells. If we add methyl hydrogen peroxide [3] to an aerobic starved suspension of bakers'

---

[3] We prefer to use methyl hydrogen peroxide to avoid the ambiguity introduced by using hydrogen peroxide; the latter is decomposed into water and oxygen by catalase;

yeast cells, we obtain the difference spectra that are plotted in Fig. 6. The similarity to the in vitro data of Fig. 5 is striking—the in vivo peaks lie at 428, 530, and 566 mμ, the agreement is within the experimental error, and the complex is identified as the secondary peroxidase complex. The concentration of complex is estimated as

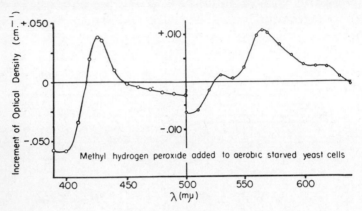

Fig. 6. The spectra representing the differences between the methyl hydrogen peroxide complex II of peroxidase and the free enzyme, as measured with an aerobic starved yeast cell suspension. 200 μM CH$_3$OOH. On the left the suspension is 130 mg./ml. and on the right it is 220 mg./ml. wet weight of yeast (Expt. 154).

the peak-to-trough difference in the Soret region of the spectrum as follows:

$$[p_m] = \frac{\Delta D_{428} - \Delta D_{400}}{62}\, mM\ (3). \tag{14}$$

We find 1 μM peroxidase in the sample used for the Soret band.[4] The peroxidase constitutes a few tenths of a per cent of the wet weight of the yeast.

From the size of the absorption band of reduced cytochrome c in the yeast cell, we compute that there is three times as much cytochrome c as peroxidase in these yeast cells.

the former is decomposed much more slowly, and only a very small part produces oxygen, even at very high catalase concentrations (46).

[4] This concentration of peroxidase and those given later for other intracellular pigments correspond to the concentration of a solution of the enzyme that is spectrophotometrically equivalent to the enzyme in the suspension of intact cells.

The kinetics of the peroxidase complex in the yeast cell. An example of our study of the kinetics of the peroxidase complex in the yeast cell is illustrated by the spectrophotometric tracings of Fig. 7. If methyl hydrogen peroxide is added to the aerated starved cell, we observe the rapid formation of the complex whose spectrum was plotted in Fig. 6. In this case we use a differential electronic circuit connection and take advantage of the fact that the optical density changes at 425 and 395 mμ are of the opposite sign. It is seen that the complex has a fairly short lifetime in vivo; the turnover number of the peroxidase in the starved aerobic cell is usually about 2 sec.$^{-1}$, as computed from Equation (13).

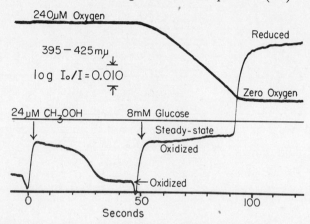

FIG. 7. The kinetics of the methyl hydrogen peroxide complex II of peroxidase are compared with the reaction kinetics upon the initiation of cellular respiration by the addition of glucose. ~ 0.3 μM peroxidase is present in this yeast cell concentration. 26° C. (Expt. 152-2).

After the peroxide has been used up, 8 mM glucose is added to initiate the respiration at the rate of 5.6 μM O_2/sec. The respiration continues until the dissolved oxygen is used up; then the absorption bands of the reduced cytochromes appear. The addition of glucose to the oxidized cells causes an optical density change of magnitude nearly equal to that caused by the addition of peroxide.

The turnover number of complex II in respiratory activity. After a control experiment to evaluate the complex II content of the yeast, we add glucose and then more peroxide to the yeast cell suspension, as in Fig. 8. We find much less complex is formed than without glucose and the maximum optical density change does not exceed that obtained in the cycle of complex II prior to the addition of glucose. If the turnover number is calculated from Equation (13), we obtain the very large value of 210 sec.$^{-1}$—about seventy times the rate without glucose. We find that the peroxidase turnover number

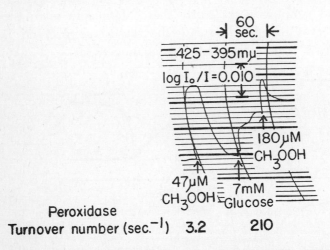

FIG. 8. The kinetics of the peroxidase complex II in the respiring cell: a comparison of the turnover numbers of peroxidase in the absence and in the presence of glucose. The values of the turnover numbers are computed from Equation (13). $\sim 0.6\ \mu M$ peroxidase is present in this yeast cell concentration (Expt. 153a).

increases with glucose concentration at least up to 8 mM glucose, as shown by the slope of the straight lines in Fig. 9. This we tentatively attribute to an increase in the concentration of reduced cytochromes caused by the increased activity of the dehydrogenases.

The effect of antimycin-a. In order to eliminate the possibility of a direct oxidation of reduced coenzymes (flavin and pyridine nucleotide) by complex II, we have inhibited the yeast cells with antimycin-a, which specifically blocks the reduction of cytochrome c, presumably by reacting with Slater's factor between cytochrome c and succinic dehydrogenase or diaphorase (2, 11, 36):

$$\text{O}_2 \leftarrow \text{a}_3 \leftarrow \text{a} \leftarrow \text{c} \leftarrow \text{factor} \leftarrow \text{diaphorase} \leftarrow \text{DPNH} \quad (15)$$

antimycin-a ↓ above, "b" below

$$\text{CH}_3\text{OOH} + \text{Peroxidase} \rightleftharpoons \text{Complex II}$$

The lower curve of Fig. 10 shows that the glucose no longer causes

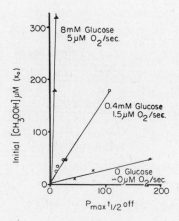

FIG. 9. The effect of glucose concentration upon the relationship between the initial methyl hydrogen peroxide concentration and the peroxidase turnover number. The experimental conditions are represented by Fig. 8 (Expt. 153a).

an appreciable increase of peroxidase turnover in the antimycin-a-inhibited yeast and lends support to our proposal that complex II reacts with ferrocytochrome c, as indicated in Equation (15).

We can also determine the nature of the peroxidase donor in vivo by observing what respiratory pigments are oxidized upon addition of methyl hydrogen peroxide to anaerobic yeast cells. As described later, we find reduced cytochrome c, flavoprotein, and pyridine nucleotide nearly fully oxidized. But, in addition, cytochrome a is largely oxidized. Thus we cannot single out ferrocytochrome c as the only electron donor in vivo for complex II and must keep cytochrome a under consideration as well.

The relative values of oxygen and peroxide utilization by yeast. In Table 2 the peroxide utilization is compared with the oxygen utilization of aerobic and anaerobic yeast. The peroxide exceeds the oxygen uptake by 1.5- to 3-fold, showing that peroxidase has greater activity than cytochrome oxidase in yeast cells.

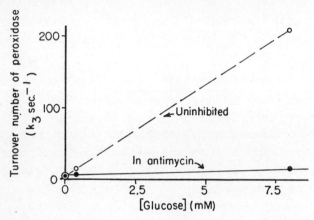

Fig. 10. Antimycin-a inhibition of the glucose effect on peroxidase turnover in yeast cells (Expt. 153b).

TABLE 2

Comparison of Peroxide and Oxygen Uptake Rates for Yeast Cell Suspensions

Cell condition	Aerobic			Anaerobic
Glucose concentration (μM)	0	0.4	8	8
Methyl hydrogen peroxide utilization (μM/sec.)	1.6	4.5	18	~ 30
Oxygen utilization (μM/sec.)	0	1.5	5	—
Ratio	—	3.0	3.6	6
Theoretical ratio for equal uptake rates ($O_2 \leftrightharpoons 2\ CH_3OOH$)	—	2	2	2
Observed/Theoretical	—	1.5	1.8	3.0

This result would be easy to understand if cytochrome c were considerably reduced in the steady-state of oxygen uptake; then the increased peroxidase turnover due to peroxide utilization would be explained by an increased oxidation of cytochrome c. We have at present some difficulty in accounting for simultaneous oxygen and peroxide utilization on this basis, but feel that further studies will show that the peroxidase activity all passes through cytochrome c.

The source of peroxide for the physiological function of peroxidase. Both carbon monoxide (51) and low azide concentrations (28) greatly inhibit the respiratory activity of yeast. The flavoproteins of the yeast cell that are not affected by these inhibitors are not autoxidized rapidly enough to play an important part in yeast respiration by either directly or indirectly producing H_2O_2 which could be utilized by intracellular peroxidase. These inhibitors do not prevent the peroxidase from utilizing added peroxide in the oxidation of the reduced cytochromes. But we cannot eliminate the possibility that peroxide is somehow produced by the cytochrome oxidase system and is utilized by the peroxidase. We do know that such a mechanism does not act in the succinic oxidase system prepared from homogenized heart muscle.

Summary. Direct spectroscopic studies of peroxidase in yeast cells show how the utilization of exogenous peroxide by this enzyme increases rapidly when cellular respiration is initiated by glucose. The utilization of peroxide by the respiring cell exceeds the oxygen rate by a factor of about two in the aerobic cell, and by an even larger factor in the anaerobic cell. The rapid peroxide utilization is probably caused by the intracellular reaction of the peroxidase complex II with ferrocytochrome c linked through the usual metabolic pathways to the substrate glucose. Support for our supposition that ferrocytochrome c is the physiological donor for the peroxidase reaction is provided by spectroscopic observation of the oxidation of intracellular ferrocytochrome c upon addition of peroxide, and also by the fact that antimycin-a, which inhibits ferrocytochrome c reduction in yeast cells, eliminates the rapid peroxide utilization in the presence of glucose.

Kinetic and spectroscopic studies of complex II of the yeast peroxidase show it to be the same complex II that we have studied in vitro and to have similar kinetic characteristics. The complex fulfils the requirements in vivo for a Michaelis-Menten enzyme-substrate complex. Based on measurements of the lifetime of the complex, we calculate the substrate-complex turnover of the peroxidase to be 2 sec.$^{-1}$ in the starved aerobic cell and as·high as 200 sec.$^{-1}$ in the rapidly respiring cell.

It is not yet proved that this peroxidase is supplied with peroxide during respiration of the yeast cells, although some data indicate that this may be so.

CYTOCHROME ACTION IN HEART MUSCLE HOMOGENATES AND IN RESPIRING YEAST CELLS

Considerably more complex than the reaction of the enzyme-substrate compounds of catalase and peroxidase are the reactions of the several cytochromes that transport electrons from succinate or from reduced diphosphopyridine nucleotides to oxygen. In this case the enzymes are bound to insoluble particles, and simple chemical isolation of the members of the reaction sequence, followed by a stepwise reconstitution of a system of the original activity, has not yet been possible. The succinic oxidase sequence is represented by Slater (39) as

$$O_2 \leftarrow a_3 \leftarrow a \leftarrow c \leftarrow \text{factor} \leftarrow b \leftarrow \text{succinic dehydrogenase} \leftarrow \text{succinate} \quad (15a)$$

$$\diagdown$$

$$\text{diaphorase} \leftarrow \text{DPNH}$$

Cytochromes a_3 and a have not been separated despite Smith's efforts (40). Cytochrome c was very early separated by Keilin (27), but has exhibited an activity in solution of less than 1/100 of its activity in the particulate system (38, 48). Slater's factor is unidentified spectroscopically and is known only by the BAL (2, 3-dimercapto-propanol-1), urethane, or antimycin-a sensitivity that defines Slater's factor. Cytochrome b and succinic dehydrogenase have been isolated (20), but there is no clear result regarding the extent to which the system can be reconstituted.

Many data indicate that a steric condition is responsible for the physiological activity of the particulate enzyme system, and consequently a reconstitution of the chemically isolated constituents in the proper orientation would be impossible. It is also possible that enzymes of an insoluble particle could act by physical reaction mechanisms not explainable by ordinary chemical collision theory (7). For these reasons, we began a few years ago to develop kinetic and spectroscopic methods for the study of the cytochromes on the particles of heart muscle and in intact cells of various types. One of the results of this study has been a critical evaluation of the nature of the dynamic equilibrium or steady-state of enzymatic function of the cytochromes, and the effect of inhibitors and environmental conditions upon this steady-state.

The steady-state of cytochrome action in the succinic oxidase system of heart muscle homogenates (11). A most satisfactory system

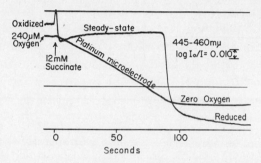

FIG. 11. The initiation of the steady-state in the succinic oxidase system of heart muscle particles and its termination upon the cessation of respiration. The micro-electrode is shown to record a constant rate of oxygen uptake, and both polarographic and spectrophotometric data are seen to be in agreement. pH 7.2, 0.15 M $PO_4^{\equiv}$ buffer (Expt. 222b).

for studies of this type is the heart muscle preparation of Keilin and Hartree (30), which gives a succinic oxidase activity corresponding to a Q_{O_2} of 400 or greater at 25° C. with no added cytochrome c. When excess succinate is added to this system, respiration starts rapidly, and the cytochromes are thrown into a constant steady-state level of activity that gives the characteristic constant respiration rate observed in Warburg manometers. We measure the disappearance of oxygen from solution by means of the platinum micro-electrode (21), and the concentration of the cytochromes by a sensitive spectrophotometer (11), as shown by Fig. 11. In the interval between the initiation of respiration by the addition of succinate and its termination upon the exhaustion of the oxygen dissolved in the solution, there is a steady-state which represents the level of activity of the cytochromes. This is no true equilibrium, and thermodynamic relationships should be applied to the steady-state with extreme caution. Upon the cessation of respiration, however, the steady-state is terminated and the cytochromes are reduced. Then thermodynamic relationships may be applied with usual discretion to the heart-muscle system.

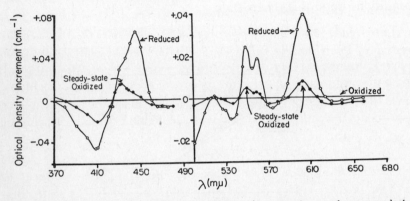

Fig. 12. The spectra representing the difference between the steady-state and the oxidized cytochromes of a succinic oxidase system of heart-muscle particles and also the difference between the reduced and the oxidized cytochromes. The base-line represents the oxidized cytochromes, and the succinate is added to give the " steady-state oxidized " curve. Upon cessation of respiration a second change in optical density occurs representing the reduction of the cytochromes ("reduced"). 0.15 M $PO_4^{\equiv}$ buffer, pH 7.7. The dilution factor for the Soret band is 12-fold and that for the visible is 3-fold (Expt. 937, 1, 4).

During the steady-state there is an interesting spectrum that represents the intensity of the catalytic action of the cytochromes. This spectrum can be much more readily obtained by our methods of sensitive recording than by visual spectroscopy because we can use comparatively dilute heart-muscle suspensions in which the steady-state lasts fairly long. A typical result for the visible and near ultraviolet region of the spectrum is shown in Fig. 12, and the cytochromes are identified at the wavelengths given below. The steady-state clearly shows the absorption bands of the reduced form of all the cytochrome components, except cytochrome a_3.

In order to calculate the extent of reduction of the cytochromes in the steady-state, we compare the steady-state spectrum with that of the reduced cytochromes as follows:

The procedure used earlier (10a) is extended to measure the relative amounts of the cytochromes from the differences in optical densities at a pair of wavelengths appropriate to each cytochrome; we can thus evaluate cytochrome a at 605-630 mμ, cytochrome b at 652-575 mμ, cytochrome c at 551-541 mμ, cytochrome a_3 at 444-470 mμ. On this basis, the percentage reduction of the cytochromes of this particular heart muscle preparation is 25, 26, 17, $<$ 14 for a, b, c, and a_3, respectively.[5] These values are characteristic of a heart-muscle preparation of slightly lower activity than usual. In preparations of higher activity, the percentage reduction of cytochromes b and c may approach 50 per cent. It is very probable that cytochrome a_3 is fully oxidized in the steady-state, because the pigment that appears at 444 mμ in the steady-state does not resemble cytochrome a_3 at all, and may well be due to cytochrome a.

This demonstration of the steady-state in succinic-oxidase action shows that the system is well-balanced; the components appear to have similar activities. But we may more incisively calculate their relative activities if we account for their relative concentrations, and thereby calculate the actual turnover numbers of the cytochromes, and finally the velocity constants with which they would interact according to the law of mass action.

The relative cytochrome content. Cytochromes c and b are sufficiently well purified that their molecular extinction coefficients are known and their concentrations are computed at a pair of wavelengths that are subject to a minimum interference from other components.

$$[c] = \frac{\Delta D_{551} - \Delta D_{541}}{19.1} \text{ mM} \quad (42) \tag{16}$$

$$[b] = \frac{\Delta D_{561} - \Delta D_{575}}{20} \text{ mM} \quad (4, 35) \tag{17}$$

---

[5] It should be observed that we give here steady-state reduction of the cytochromes while in a recent paper we gave steady-state oxidation values; in this case the latter values are 74, 75, 83, $\gg$ 86 for cytochromes a, b, c and a_3 respectively.

In the case of cytochrome a_3, we have recently carried out new determinations of the molecular extinction coefficient of its carbon monoxide compound and have deduced the following molecular extinction coefficient for use with a difference spectrum:

$$[a_3] = \frac{\Delta D_{445}}{110} \text{ mM} \quad (43).\tag{18}$$

The value for cytochrome a is based wholly upon an assumed analogy with verdoperoxidase (1, 9a):

$$[a] = \frac{\Delta D_{605} - \Delta D_{630}}{16} \text{ mM.}\tag{19}$$

On this basis we convert the actual values of the optical density changes (0.041, 0.023, 0.032, and 0.275 for a, b, c, and a_3, respectively, all calculated for the three-fold dilution of heart muscle) to concentrations: 2.6, 1.0, 1.5, and 2.5 μM for a, b, c, and a_3, respectively. Thus there are roughly equal concentrations of the cytochromes in these heart-muscle preparations. The somewhat smaller amounts of cytochromes c and b vary considerably, depending upon the details of the preparative procedure.

The turnover numbers of the cytochrome components. One of the criteria (K_4) (10) by which we evaluate the activity of our succinic-oxidase preparations is closely related to the turnover number of cytochrome a_3 where $K_4 = \mu M$ O_2/sec./ΔD_{444}. Since the oxygen equivalent of iron is 4 and since the value of the concentration of a_3 in millimoles of iron per liter is readily calculated from Equation (18) above;

$$T.N.a_3 = K_4 \times 4 \times 110 \times 10^{-3} = 0.44 \, K_4\tag{20}$$

For this particular preparation, $K_4 = 51$, and hence the turnover number of cytochrome a_3 is 22 sec.$^{-1}$.[6]

Since the turnover numbers of the other components are inversely

---

[6] An alternative calculation of less generality is:

the oxygen uptake rate is $K_4 \times \Delta D_{444} = 51 \times 0.275 = 14\mu M$ O_2/sec.

with a cytochrome a_3 concentration of 2.5 μM. Therefore the turnover number of cytochrome $a_3 = 4 \times 14/2.5 = 22$ sec.$^{-1}$.

proportional to their concentrations relative to cytochrome a_3, the sequence of relative contents given above can be used to calculate the sequence of turnover numbers as 26, 38, 56, and 22 sec.$^{-1}$ for cytochromes a, b, c, and a_3, respectively.[7]

In Table 3 we have summarized results for the turnover numbers of cytochrome components of several types of succinic-oxidase systems prepared from different sources. These values are recomputed from the values given previously (11), on the basis of the more accurate values for the molecular extinction coefficient for cytochrome a_3 in muscle and yeast.

TABLE 3

A COMPARISON OF THE CALCULATED VALUES OF TURNOVER NUMBERS OF THE CYTOCHROME COMPONENTS OF VARIOUS SUCCINIC OXIDASE PREPARATIONS AT 26° C. (UNITS ARE SEC.$^{-1}$)

Source	$K_4 = \mu M\ O_2/sec./\Delta D_{444}$	Turnover Numbers for Cytochromes				
		a_3	a	c	b	" factor "
Heart muscle (horse or pig)	80 (max.)	35	18	22	35	29
Pea seedlings	35	15	—	—	—	—
Flight muscle (sarcosomes)	25	11	7	3	3	—
Yeast cells (bakers')	220	77	29	9	22	—

The values of turnover numbers in Table 3 are based upon the total cytochrome content and not upon the content of the oxidized form of the cytochrome in the steady-state. However, the calculation of the velocity constants for the interaction of the cytochromes that is described below is a much more effective way of representing cytochrome activity.

Steady-state analysis. We can calculate the velocity constants with

---

[7] Turnover numbers for these cytochromes are calculated on the basis that their steady-state percentage reductions are compatible with the speeds of their oxidation and reduction. This has been found to be the case for cytochromes c, a, and a_3 and not to be the case for cytochrome b, which is reduced by succinate too slowly to account for the electron flux through the succinic oxidase system. The turnover number calculated for cytochrome b therefore more accurately describes the activity of the " succinic dehydrogenase + Slater's factor " complex and we assume that the value of 38 sec.$^{-1}$ applies directly to the latter complex. This assumption is in part validated by the fact that we find about as much of Slater's factor present in heart muscle as cytochrome b. However, we do not know the percentage oxidation of succinic dehydrogenase in the steady-state and assume arbitrarily a value of 50 per cent (see Table 4).

which the cytochromes would have to react to give the measured oxygen uptake and steady-state values if they were in a homogeneous solution. The applicability of such a calculation to the actual heterogeneous system involves rather bold assumptions, but serves a very useful purpose in clarifying our concepts on the possible modes of cytochrome action in the insoluble particle. Some of these assumptions will be explained more fully in a later paper.

If we represent the succinic oxidase system by a sequence of four enzymes, the velocity constants for the five reactions may be readily computed from the steady-state concentrations of the oxidized and the reduced forms of the cytochromes:

$$O_2 \xleftarrow{k_1} a_3 \xleftarrow{k_3} a \xleftarrow{k_5} c \xleftarrow{k_7} sd \xleftarrow{k_9} succinate \tag{21}$$

where " sd " represents succinic dehydrogenase plus Slater's factor.

If we represent the concentration of the oxidized and the reduced forms of the cytochromes as for example, a''' and a'', respectively, and the oxygen and succinate concentrations by x and y respectively, the values of the reaction velocity constants are computed as follows:

$$k_1 = \frac{a_3'''}{x} \cdot \frac{a''}{a_3''} k_3; \; k_3 = \frac{a'''}{a_3'''} \cdot \frac{c''}{a''} k_5; \; k_5 = \frac{c'''}{a'''} \cdot \frac{a''}{c''} k_7;$$

$$k_7 = \frac{sd'''y}{c''sd''} k_9; \; k_9 = \frac{1}{sd'''y}\left(-\frac{dy}{dt}\right) \tag{22}$$

We can solve for these velocity constants directly if we make the assumption that the cytochromes are uniformly distributed in a solution of average concentration equivalent spectrophotometrically to the optical density changes that we record for the actual turbid heart-muscle particles. Some data required for these calculations are tabulated in Table 4.

In order to calculate $k_9 y$ we use the turnover number of " succinic dehydrogenase " of 38 sec.$^{-1}$ as follows:

$$T.N._{sd} = \frac{1}{sd'' + sd'''} \cdot \left(-\frac{dy}{dt}\right) = \frac{1}{1.5} \cdot \left(-\frac{dy}{dt}\right) = 38 \text{ sec.}^{-1} \tag{23}$$

$$\therefore -\frac{dy}{dt} = 56 \; \mu M/\text{sec.}$$

$$k_9 y = \frac{1}{sd'''}\left(-\frac{dy}{dt}\right) = \frac{1}{0.75} \times 56 = 75 \text{ sec.}^{-1}$$

The k_7, k_5, and k_3 are calculated from the appropriate relationships and the values are summarized in Table 4. As is explained below, the values of k_3, k_5, and k_7 are to be divided by about 50 to represent the actual particulate system.[8]

The minimal rate constants (Table 4) for the "external" reactions with succinate and oxygen (k_9 and k_1, respectively) are best

TABLE 4

DATA REQUIRED FOR A CALCULATION OF THE REACTION VELOCITY CONSTANTS IN THE CYTOCHROME SYSTEM

Component	a_3	a	c	"succinic dehydrogenase"
Content (μM)	2.5	2.2	1.0	1.5
Turnover number based on total content	22	26	56	38
Percentage oxidation with steady-state	86	74	83	(50)
Oxidized form (μM)	2.1	1.6	0.83	(0.75)
Reduced form (μM)	0.4	0.6	0.13	(0.75)

Velocity constants $\times 10^{-6}$ ($M^{-1} \times$ sec.$^{-1}$):

$$O_2 \xleftarrow{10} a_3 \xleftarrow{40} a \xleftarrow{230} c \xleftarrow{100} \text{"succinic dehydrogenase"} \xleftarrow{0.1} \text{succinate}$$

computed from the Michaelis constants for succinate or oxygen, which we have determined in separate experiments. The procedure used in this calculation is described elsewhere (11). The calculation of velocity constants involves no assumptions as to the proximity of the cytochromes to one another, and only involves the assumption that the particulate enzymes are freely accessible to oxygen and succinate.

The effective concentration of the cytochromes in heart-muscle particles. On the other hand, the internal cytochromes must react with one another at a velocity largely dependent upon the proximity

[8] The reader should note that the values of k_3, k_5, and k_7 are different for the conditions of this calculation than for the previous calculation (11) because of the different steady-state levels of the cytochromes in this preparation. It is possible that such differences in the reaction velocity constants are caused by changes in the state of the particles which would bring about changes in the effective concentrations of the cytochromes relative to one another, as discussed below.

of one member of the reaction sequence to its neighbors. If, for example, the proximity of the cytochromes is such that their effective concentration exceeds that used in the calculations of Table 4, the values of the velocity constants k_3, k_5, and k_7 would be correspondingly smaller.

We have employed various methods of evaluating the effective concentration of the internal enzymes based upon measurements of particle size. Assuming the distribution of cytochromes to be uniform inside the particle, we find that the minimal concentrations for sarcosomes and heart-muscle particles are 40 and 70 μM. An upper limit of 5000 μM is set by assuming a molecular packing too close to permit access of substrate. Thus these values are considerably greater than those used in Table 4 and suggest that k_3, k_5, and k_7, which were calculated using $\sim 1 \mu M$, be greatly decreased.

The cytochromes are known to be attached to solid particles in the mitochondria and are insoluble under physiological conditions. If their mutual interactions are to occur by collision processes, as implied by the law of mass action, such collisions must be caused by thermal motions of the cytochromes about their points of attachment to the particle. Thus the internal enzymes would be separated by a distance of less than a molecular diameter and would be expected to be fastened to the particles in a sequential arrangement, with cytochrome a adjacent to cytochrome c, etc.

Since the relative content of the cytochromes in heart-muscle and yeast systems suggests that roughly equal numbers of components are present, it is conceivable that most of the cytochromes are located in oxidase "assemblies" that contain one each of the enzymes necessary for enzymatic function. Although no such assemblies have been identified in heart-muscle systems, very small particles are obtained from *Azotobacter vinelandii* (40) containing a complete bacterial succinic-oxidase system (52).

One consequence of such an "elementary assembly" theory is that cytochromes consisting of one assembly would have a small probability of reacting with the cytochromes of another assembly. Thus the solid angle of an internal cytochrome available for collision would be reduced by roughly 1/100, thereby reducing the effective concentration of 5000 μM to roughly 50 μM. Since we took $\sim$ 1 μM for the calculation of k_3, k_5, and k_7, we should divide the values given in Table 4 by 50 and obtain values for the velocity constants [9] on the order of 10^6 $M^{-1} \times$ sec.$^{-1}$ in the range form 0.2 to 4×10^6.

It is conceivable that processes similar to those in semiconductors account for electron transfer from succinate to oxygen, but the probability of reconstructing in vitro the activity of " solubilized " cytochrome oxidase towards soluble cytochrome c would seem unlikely according to such a mechanism. Nevertheless, active consideration of mechanisms other than collision processes is desirable.

The role of cytochrome b in heart muscle homogenates. While kinetic studies may not provide complete proof of a particular reaction mechanism, they can be used to eliminate specified reaction sequences. We have used this method to investigate the role of cytochrome b in heart muscle preparations. At low temperatures and in the presence of cyanide, we compared the rates of reduction of cytochromes by succinate with their estimated turnover numbers in the uninhibited oxidase activity and found satisfactory agreement for cytochromes a and c. But in the case of cytochrome b the reduction proceeds at only 2 per cent of the rate required for participation in the electron transport to oxygen. In addition, we have observed that the reduction of cytochrome b upon cessation of respiration of a heart muscle homogenate caused by exhaustion of the dissolved oxygen is prolonged after the reduction of the other cytochromes and even after the cessation of fumarate production. The latter effect also rules against the simple mechanism because, according to a general theorem we have developed regarding sequential enzyme systems, the time derivatives of the concentrations of the intermediate compounds must be zero when the time derivatives of the substrate (or product) concentrations are zero.

Slater has recently suggested that our results ignore the back

[9] In a previous paper (11) we arrived at the same conclusion by assuming that cholate-treated cytochrome oxidase should react with ferrocytochrome c in solution at the same rate as in the particulate system.

reactions in the sequential system (37a). The general theorem stated above, however, applies to systems in which there are back reactions. As a matter of fact we had already published an incisive experiment which can be interpreted to show that the back reaction does not significantly affect our measurements of the speed of reduction of cytochrome b over a 10-fold range of succinate concentration (see Table 2, reference 11), and we found only a two-fold increase of rate. Thus a more highly evolved formulation than that proposed by Slater is required to re-establish the role of cytochrome b in the main pathways of electron transport of heart muscle homogenates.

The studies of cytochrome b in whole yeast cells that are described below show that the nature and function of the pigment characterized spectroscopically as cytochrome b are by no means fully understood.

Summary. These preliminary efforts to quantify the reaction kinetics in an insoluble enzyme system will surely be greatly improved when more accurate data on the morphology of respiratory particulates become available, and when more of the cytochromes have been studied kinetically in solution. It is, however, of some interest to note that velocity constants for cytochrome interaction of nearly the same order as those observed for catalase and peroxidase reactions ($\sim 10^7 \; M^{-1} \times \text{sec.}^{-1}$) are large enough to explain the action of the insoluble system on the basis of a restricted collision mechanism and to permit a reasonable type of sequential enzyme structure in the intact cell.

The Steady-State in the Respiring Yeast Cell

If we add ethanol to an aerobic, starved yeast cell suspension we initiate the following reaction sequence:

$$O_2 \leftarrow a_3 \leftarrow a \leftarrow c \leftarrow \text{factor} \leftarrow \text{diaphorase}$$
$$\text{``b''}$$
$$\text{DPN}$$
$$\text{DPNH} \leftarrow\!\!\!\!\!\!\underset{ADH \quad \text{alcohol}}{\overline{\qquad\qquad}}\!\!\!\!\! + \qquad (1)$$

which represents steady-state action analogous to that observed with heart-muscle preparation on addition of succinate (as in Fig. 12).

Fig. 13 shows this steady-state spectrum and, in addition, the reduced spectrum obtained later upon exhaustion of the oxygen; the data are plotted in the same way as those for heart muscle (see Fig. 12), and, in addition, the ultraviolet region is included. The result is rather different from that obtained with heart muscle; the most distinctive pigment observed in the steady-state has absorption

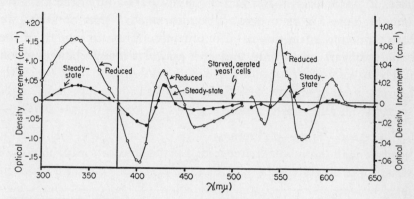

FIG. 13. The difference spectra of the steady-state and the reduced respiratory pigments of bakers' yeast. The starved, aerated suspension of yeast cells gives the base-line, addition of ethanol produces the "steady-state," and subsequent cessation of respiration the "reduced" curve. The yeast suspension is 2.9 more dilute in the region 300-500 mμ than in the region 500-650 mμ; the extracellular pH is 3.3, 0.1 M PO$^{4\equiv}$ (Expt. 172).

bands usually attributed to cytochrome b, the peaks in the spectrum lie at 428, 530, and 560 mμ. If this pigment were cytochrome b, the extent of reduction in the steady-state would be about 37 per cent (compare p. 421). Flavoprotein shows a similarly large reduction of 32 per cent. At 605 mμ we see about 20 per cent reduction of cytochrome a. There is less than 5 per cent reduction of cytochromes c and a$_3$. At 340 mμ the DPNH is 23 per cent reduced in the steady-state at the particular ethanol concentration employed (100 mM).

Since cytochrome b appears as the distinctive cytochrome in the steady-state of alcohol respiration, we have written "b" together with diaphorase in the reaction sequence of Equation (1).

The effect of ethanol concentration upon the oxygen uptake rate and upon the reduction of " cytochrome b " and DPN in the steady-state. In order to determine which respiratory pigment in yeast represents the " weakest-link " in the respiratory sequence causing alcohol oxidation, we have recorded a series of spectra similar to Fig. 13 for various ethanol concentrations. We have found that principally DPN and " cytochrome b " are reduced in the steady-state. In order to identify whether the respiration rate depends more upon the extent of reduction of " cytochrome b " than of DPN, we have plotted as a function of alcohol concentration in Fig. 14, *A* the initial oxygen uptake rate and the optical density changes upon

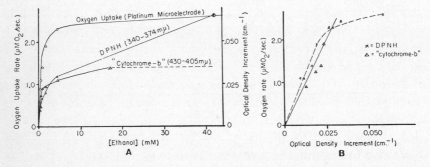

Fig. 14. The relationship between the oxygen uptake rate of yeast cells and the amount of reduced DPN and " cytochrome " for various ethanol concentrations. Yeast suspension 38 mg./ml. $M/20$ $PO_4^≡$ buffer, pH 4.7, 26° C. (Expt. 177b and 178a).

alcohol addition at wavelengths appropriate to the measurement of DPNH and reduced " cytochrome b." It is seen that the respiration increases roughly parallel to the increase in the reduction of these two pigments. In order to give a more incisive test of this relationship we have plotted the oxygen uptake rate directly against the pigment reduction in Fig. 14, *B.* Although the data now show the combined errors of both the measurements, we see that the respiration rate is proportional to the amount of DPNH or reduced " cytochrome b " for the lower alcohol concentrations. At higher alcohol concentrations it is possible to reduce still more DPN without increasing the respiration rate. The maximal rate was obtained with only a 30 per cent reduction of the DPN.

Thus both DPNH and " cytochrome b " are rate-limiting at low alcohol concentrations, but larger alcohol concentrations increase the DPN reduction without causing a corresponding increase in the reduction of " cytochrome b " or in the respiration rate. The rate-limiting step in the oxidation of the cytochromes is clearly the oxidation of reduced " cytochrome b," since even at large alcohol concentrations the other cytochromes are considerably more oxidized in the steady-state.

The result is inconsistent with current theories of cytochrome action—cytochrome b is not now recognized to be on the pathway of DPNH oxidation by cytochrome, and here we find a spectroscopically defined " cytochrome b " to be a rate-limiting intermediate in DPNH oxidation. Another reason for not expecting to find cytochrome b reduced in the steady-state is that very little succinate would be present in the starved yeast cell to which ethanol has just been added.

In order to determine whether succinate is involved, we have attempted to produce the result of Fig. 13 by the addition of excess succinate at low pH, but no effect has been observed, presumably due to the low permeability of the cell to dicarboxylic acids. We have also found that the pigment was likewise reduced by ethanol in yeast cells when we suspended them in 0.5 M malonic acid at pH 2.2.

We have further attempted to observe the slow reduction of " cytochrome b " due to a slow accumulation of succinate upon the addition of excess ethanol to aerated, starved yeast cells at 0° C. We found a rapid reduction of " cytochrome b " upon adding ethanol —a reaction that proceeded to completion just as fast as the reduction of DPN by the alcohol dehydrogenase. Such results make it unlikely that succinate is immediately involved in the spectral shift.

A comparison of the spectra of the steady-state reduced " cytochrome b " with that of the peroxidase-peroxide complex. It is now necessary to reconsider the similarity between the spectra of the steady-state reduced " cytochrome b " and the yeast peroxidase complex II. The two pigments are compared in Fig. 15.

In the region of the Soret band, there is close agreement of the spectra; the small differences could, to a considerable extent, be explained by the reduction of flavoprotein that causes the dip of the " cytochrome b " spectrum in the region of 430-480 mμ. In the visible region there are considerable differences, and it is apparent that the visible " cytochrome b " spectrum does not represent a single pigment. First, the 530 mμ band of " cytochrome b " is shifted to 525 mμ. Second, the 562 mμ band of the " cytochrome b "

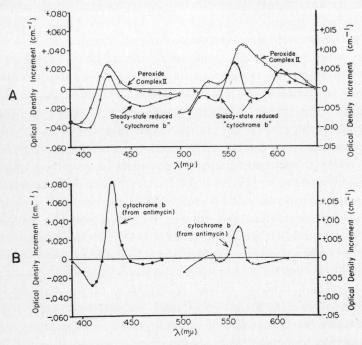

FIG. 15. A comparison of the difference spectra of peroxidase-peroxide complex with that of the steady-state reduced " cytochrome b " (A) and the difference spectrum of cytochrome b obtained by antimycin-a treatment of the yeast (B) (Expt. 154, 9, 11).

appears at 558-559 mμ. Third, there is a considerable absorption band at 605 mμ that may well be related to the trough at 580 mμ and, in addition, may contribute to the atypical position of the peak at 558-559 mμ.[10]

For comparison, we have included in Fig. 15 what may be defined

[10] We know, however, from purified cytochromes a + a$_3$ of heart muscle that no such trough at 580 mμ is associated with 605 mμ peak due to cytochrome a + a$_3$ (40).

as the true difference spectrum of cytochrome b in yeast cells, because we obtained this result by treating the cells with antimycin-a. This spectrum in the region of the Soret band does not agree too well with either that of complex II or of "cytochrome b"; the true cytochrome b absorption band is much sharper than that obtained in the steady-state of ethanol respiration or with peroxide addition. In the visible region, there is a fair agreement of the cytochrome b and the steady-state "cytochrome b" spectrum if the contribution of cytochrome a is taken into account.

We must also consider a pigment such as that studied by Kun (32a) or by Strittmatter and Ball (41b) that is involved in DPNH-linked cytochrome c reductase activity. Although their data show the peak of the Soret band lies at 426 mμ for a liver preparation, the analogous pigment in yeast could appear at 430 mμ.

In summary, we find that the steady-state of alcohol respiration of bakers' yeast is dominated by a pigment that shows certain spectroscopic similarities to cytochrome b, to yeast peroxidase complex II, and to a pigment observed in mammalian cytochrome c reductases, as well as certain differences from all three pigments. The known pathways of yeast respiration that can be set into operation in a few seconds are not likely to involve succinic dehydrogenase and cytochrome b in the same role with which we identify them in heart muscle. Thus evidence points to the hypothesis that the yeast peroxidase complex II is present in the steady-state respiring yeast cell and, based on our results with exogenous peroxide, this complex can participate actively in the respiratory activity of the cell.

This hypothesis rests upon a more direct proof of the existence of complex II in the respiring cell than spectroscopic data can afford at the present time. In the meantime, the steady-state reduced pigment will still be termed "cytochrome b."

THE ENZYME-COENZYME COMPOUNDS OF DEHYDROGENASES

Until fairly recently, the affinity of dehydrogenases for the reduced and oxidized forms of their pyridine nucleotide prosthetic groups had to be evaluated entirely as Michaelis-Menten enzyme-substrate affinities, and these affinity values were frequently confused with the true affinity of the enzyme for its coenzyme in the absence of substrate (33). There are now two excellent techniques for studying the nature of these enzyme-coenzyme compounds. One is the ultra-centrifugal method used extensively in the study of DPN-binding of triosephosphate and alcohol dehydrogenases (49, 23a), and the other is the spectrophotometric measurement of characteristic absorption bands of the enzyme-DPNH compound (44, 19) or of the enzyme-DPN compound (37). We shall emphasize the spectroscopic methods because they are also suitable for kinetic studies of the reactions of the enzyme-coenzyme complexes.

Not nearly so much is known of the details of the reaction mechanisms of the dehydrogenases as of the hemoproteins, where their more distinct absorption bands have permitted kinetic studies of the enzyme-substrate complexes for some time. On the other hand, some dehydrogenases offer a more challenging problem because not only oxidation-reduction but also phosphorylation and transfer reactions are catalyzed, as in the triosephosphate dehydrogenases. In addition, the alcohol dehydrogenases present an unusual opportunity for striking studies of the stereospecificity of enzyme action, as reported by Vennesland and Westheimer (50).

Spectra of the enzyme-coenzyme complexes. The original data of Theorell and Bonnichsen (44) on the horse liver alcohol-dehydrogenase–DPNH compound are replotted in Fig. 16 to show the absorption band that appears when added DPNH is bound to the ADH protein. The data are corrected for the absorption of unbound DPNH and protein. There is a peak in the spectrum at 325 mμ, and the value of the molecular extinction coefficient is 5.8 cm.$^{-1}$ $\times$ mM^{-1}.

In a similar type of experiment the DPNH compound of lactic dehydrogenase was found by Chance and Nielands (19), and the spectrum analogous to that of Theorell and Bonnichsen's is shown in Fig. 17. Again a similar peak is found, this time at 330 mμ.

In the case of the triosephosphate enzymes, the absorption band of the DPN compound can be obtained by adding the DPN directly to the yeast enzyme, which crystallizes without appreciable bound DPN, or to the charcoal-treated mammalian enzyme; and results obtained in this laboratory in collaboration with Dr. J. Harting are

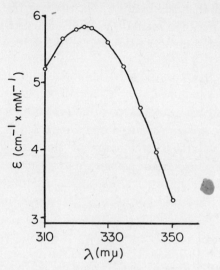

Fig. 16. The spectrum of the horse liver ADH–DPNH complex, according to Theorell and Bonnichsen, pH 7.0 (O-37) (44).

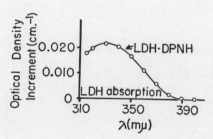

Fig. 17. An approximate spectrum of the LDH–DPNH complex. 12.7 μM LDH plus 21 μM DPNH, 25° C., pH 7.15, 0.15 M PO$_4^{\equiv}$ buffer (Expt. 949d-1) (19).

shown in Fig. 18. As described by Racker and Krimsky (37), the DPN compounds are spectroscopically distinct from the DPNH compounds already discussed, and have a very flat absorption band with a peak at about 360 mμ.

A somewhat more useful method for obtaining the spectra of these compounds is to add a large excess of DPN or DPNH to the protein and then add an SH specific reagent in order to split any enzyme complex that has formed. In this way the absorption of the large excess of pyridine nucleotide will not interfere with the detection of a small change on adding the splitting reagent, which should

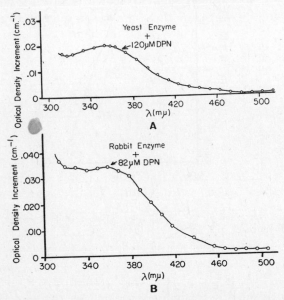

Fig. 18. The difference spectrum of the glyceraldehyde-3-phosphate dehydrogenase DPN compound obtained by adding DPN to the crystalline yeast enzyme (A) or to the charcoal-treated mammalian enzyme (B). The absorption of the protein has been subtracted from the absorption of the enzyme-coenzyme compound. The yeast enzyme was kindly supplied by Dr. E. G. Krebs. Concentrations are in micromoles per liter. (Expt. 16, 37e).

have negligible absorption in this region of the spectrum. This method was used by Racker and Krimsky (37), who split the triose-phosphate-dehydrogenase–DPN compound with iodoacetic acid. Of the various reagents that they used, we have found that hydrogen peroxide is the most satisfactory for this purpose because of its small absorption in the ultraviolet region (except at 230 mμ and below). By using this method we have been able to measure the difference spectrum of the mammalian triosephosphate-dehydrogenase–DPN compound in the region 232-450 mμ, as shown in Fig. 19. In these difference spectra the decreases of optical density are usually plotted upwards because the data then represent the absorption of the enzyme-DPN compound before the addition of the splitting reagent and are directly comparable with Fig. 18. The 240 mμ peak in this difference spectrum is suggestive of a thiol ester bond between DPN and the enzyme, but there are large quantitative differences

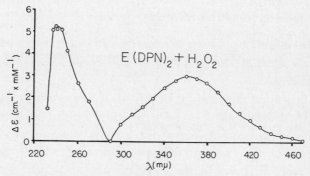

Fig. 19. The difference spectrum of the enzyme-DPN compound of the mammalian triosephosphate dehydrogenase as obtained by splitting with hydrogen peroxide (Expt. 121, 119a).

between this spectrum and that due to thiol esters in model compounds which must be explained, as well as the second point discussed below. The nature of the spectrum of the acetyl enzyme complex has recently been discussed by Harting and Chance (23).

So far the LDH–DPNH compound has appeared to be resistant to p-chloromercuribenzoate (pCMB) concentrations that rapidly split the horse-liver ADH–DPNH compound. But Neilands (33a) has recently found that pCMB reacts very slowly with LDH; an incubation time of 30 minutes is required at room temperature. Thus it is not surprising that the spectroscopic studies of the LDH–DPNH compound at 5° C. (19) showed no measurable effect of pCMB.

Spectrophotometric evidence for DPN- or DPNH-binding of other dehydrogenases has not been too successful; glutamic dehydrogenases (34) and yeast ADH do not yet show spectral shifts, and so far no horse liver ADH-DPN complex has been identified (13). On the other hand, Kaplan (26) reports that the horse liver enzyme forms a spectroscopically distinct DPN complex in the presence of excess hydroxylamine. In addition, Hayes and Velick (23a) report that yeast alcohol dehydrogenase binds DPN and DPNH on the basis of ultracentrifuge experiments.

We have summarized in Table 5 the known characteristics of the enzyme-coenzyme compounds. Although it is tempting to conclude that all enzyme-coenzyme compounds have distinctive absorption bands, we must observe the following points:

(1) Protein-binding of the coenzyme can occur without causing a detectable shift in the spectrum of DPN or DPNH (compare yeast ADH).

(2) When a spectral shift is observed, it has not been proved to be caused by direct binding of a sulfhydryl group because the yeast-ADH–DPN compound involves SH groups that do not cause a spectral shift of the two known types. However, SH groups may indirectly affect the bond between the enzyme and coenzyme.

(3) There are two distinct spectral types of complexes, the 320-330 mμ type and the 360 mμ type with either DPN or DPNH.

(4) A fuller explanation of these data requires more information on the number and type of chemical bonds that can exist between enzyme and coenzyme.

On the other hand, the spectroscopically distinguished coenzyme compounds are extremely useful tools in the elucidation of the mechanism of dehydrogenase action, as is illustrated by the kinetic study of the horse liver ADH-DPNH compounds.

The kinetics of the enzyme-coenzyme complexes: horse liver ADH. In order to avoid interference from DPNH in the measurement of the kinetics of the ADH-DPNH, we have developed a technique that records the difference of absorption at two wavelengths of equal DPNH absorption, for example, 328 and 353 mμ (45). Since the absorption of the ADH-DPNH is different at these two wavelengths, we can readily record the kinetics of the complex during the con-

TABLE 5

Compounds of Dehydrogenases with DPN or DPNH

Enzyme	Reactant	Number of Sites	Ultracentrifugal Evidence of Binding	Spectroscopic Evidence Peak (mμ)	$\Delta\epsilon$ [11a] (cm.$^{-1}$ × mM^{-1})	Sensitivity of Compound to SH Reagents	References
Horse liver alcohol dehydrogenase	DPNH	2	?	325	5.8	pCMB-sensitive	44, 45
"	DPN	?	?	negative result	—	—	13
"	DPN + NH$_2$OH	2	?	300	6	pCMB-sensitive	26
Yeast alcohol dehydrogenase	DPNH	4	yes	negative result	—	activity inhibited by pCMB	13, 23a
"	DPN	4	yes	negative result	—	"	13, 23a
Lactic dehydrogenase from heart muscle	DPNH	1	?	330	?	" [11b]	19
"	DPN	?	?	negative result	—	—	13, 19
Glutamic dehydrogenase	DPNH	?	some evidence that the enzyme crystallizes with nucleotide (41a)	negative result	—	—	34
Mammalian triose phosphate dehydrogenase	DPN	2-3	yes	360	∼3	pCMB-sensitive [11]	37, 49
"	DPNH	?	yes	related to that of DPN complex	—	"	13
Yeast triose phosphate dehydrogenase	DPN	2	yes	360	∼3	pCMB-sensitive	17, 49a
"	DPNH	?	?	?	—	—	13

[11] Velick (49b) reports that pCMB liberates DPN from the enzyme, whereas acetyl phosphate does not.

[11a] These are based on changes of absorption caused by adding the coenzyme.

[11b] Neilands (33a) finds pCMB inhibition of LDH activity.

version of DPNH to DPN, as shown by Fig. 20. The kinetics of formation and disappearance of this complex (*A*) together with the oxidation of DPNH by formaldehyde (*B*) are clearly demonstrated. Formaldehyde is used in this experiment to obtain a longer life-time of the intermediate complex. Similar kinetic studies have made it possible to compute the velocity constant for the following reactions which adequately represent the mechanism of action of horse liver ADH over the available range of experimental conditions.

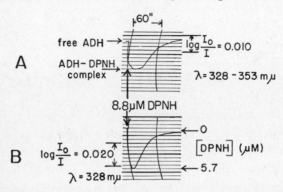

FIG. 20. The kinetics of formation and disappearance of the ADH–DPNH complex measured at 328-354 mμ (*A*) and the simultaneous disappearance of DPNH measured at 328 mμ (*B*). 1 cm. optical path flow apparatus. 1.17 μM ADH, 8.8 μM DPNH (initial), 66 μM HCHO, pH 7.0, 0.1 M PO$_4^\equiv$ (Expts. 7c-5) (45).

The velocity constants of the complex reaction sequence at pH = 7.0 are also measured experimentally.

$$\text{ADH} + \text{DPNH} \underset{k_2 \approx 0.4 \text{ sec.}^{-1}}{\overset{k_1 = 4 \times 10^6 \ M^{-1} \times \text{sec.}^{-1}}{\rightleftharpoons}} \text{ADH–DPNH} \qquad (24)$$

$$\text{ADH–DPNH} + \text{CH}_3\text{CHO} + \text{H}^+ \underset{k_6 \approx 10^3}{\overset{k_4 = 2 \times 10^5 \ M^{-1} \times \text{sec.}^{-1}}{\rightleftharpoons}}$$
$$\text{ADH–DPN}^+ + \text{CH}_3\text{CH}_2\text{OH} \qquad (25)$$

$$\text{ADH–DPN}^+ \underset{k_5 = 2 \times 10^6 \ M^{-1} \times \text{sec.}^{-1}}{\overset{k_3 = 45 \text{ sec.}^{-1}}{\rightleftharpoons}} \text{ADH} + \text{DPN}^+ \qquad (26)$$

A check on possible errors in our reaction velocity constants is provided by a computation of the equilibrium constant at pH = 7.0 from the kinetic data. Since the hydrogen ion concentration (10^{-7} M) was not taken into account in the velocity constants for Equation (25), it must be included below for a comparison of the data.

$$K = \frac{k_2 k_5 k_6 [H^+]}{k_1 k_3 k_4} = \frac{0.4 \times 2 \times 10^6 \times 10^3 \times 10^{-7}}{4 \times 10^6 \times 45 \times 2 \times 10^5} = 2 \times 10^{-12}$$

This is the first correlation of direct kinetic and equilibrium data on an enzyme reaction, and the agreement with Negelein and Wulff's value of 1.2×10^{-11} at pH 7.9 (33) is regarded to be satisfactory, in view of the possible errors in the six reaction velocity constants. And until more data are available, we would discourage others from attaching any fundamental significance to the discrepancy of the two results.

It is also of considerable interest that the speeds of break-down of any compounds of the enzyme with the substrates are not revealed as rate-limiting steps in this mechanism, and our results simply show that a hypothetical aldehyde-enzyme complex breaks down at a rate exceeding 45 sec.$^{-1}$ and an alcohol-enzyme complex breaks down at a rate exceeding 0.4 sec.$^{-1}$.

These results also underline the difference between the true equilibrium constants and Michaelis constants for intermediates in enzyme action. The Michaelis constants for DPN and DPNH are about the same, while the equilibrium constants differ by a factor of over one hundred. And the reaction sequence that gives perfectly satisfactory "Michaelis constants" for alcohol and aldehyde involves no enzyme-alcohol or enzyme-aldehyde intermediates at all. Now we do not doubt that such compounds can form, but we do emphasize that a "Michaelis constant" for the reaction does not prove the existence of an intermediate complex.

In this reaction sequence, Michaelis constants do not even bear a formal resemblance to dissociation constants; the dissociation constant for DPN is k_3/k_5, whereas the Michaelis constant is k_2/k_5 (45). Furthermore, the dissociation constant, usually regarded to be a lower limit to the Michaelis constant, can, in fact, be larger than the Michaelis constant.

Glyceraldehyde-3-phosphate dehydrogenase. The studies of the triosephosphate-dehydrogenase reaction have not been comparable to those of horse liver ADH. However, a few of the technical problems have been solved, and some preliminary results are at hand (17). It is relatively difficult to measure the kinetics of the triosephosphate-dehydrogenase-DPN complex in the presence of DPNH, but if one chooses a wavelength of 405 mμ or greater, the DPNH interferes very little, and the DPN complex is still measurable, as illustrated by Fig. 21. The decomposition of the enzyme-DPN complex by

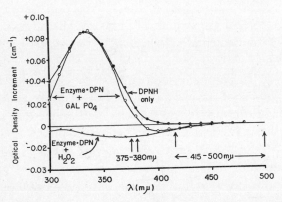

Fig. 21. Difference spectra of the triosephosphate dehydrogenase-DPN complex treated with hydrogen peroxide, the same complex treated with glyceraldehyde phosphate, and the absorption of an equivalent amount of DPNH only (Expt. 133d).

hydrogen peroxide gives the decrease in absorption shown. If glyceraldehyde phosphate is added to a fresh sample of the DPN complex, the disappearance of the enzyme-DPN complex is now noted only in the region 405-450 mμ where the DPNH formed does not interfere. Below 405 mμ the DPNH absorption resulting from the enzymatic action obliterates the absorption of the DPN complex. For comparison, the spectrum of DPNH alone is included.

In order to avoid errors in the measurement of the kinetics of DPN reduction in the presence of the enzyme-DPN complex, we record DPNH formation by the difference of optical densities at a pair of wavelengths (375-380 mμ, for example) close enough together so that there is no appreciable change due to the complex and yet a considerable change due to DPN reduction.

Studies of the kinetics of the yeast enzyme-DPN complex in the enzymatic reduction of DPN are illustrated by Fig. 22, *A* where we record at 415-500 mμ the rapid formation of the enzyme-DPN complex upon quickly mixing the enzyme with the coenzyme, the steady-state action of the complex, and its disappearance when the DPN is used up by the excess glyceraldehyde. In a separate experi-

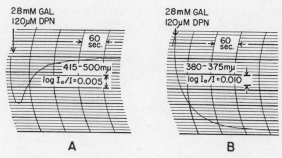

A   B

FIG. 22. A comparison of the kinetics of the yeast enzyme-DPN complex (*A*) and the kinetics of DPN reduction (*B*) in the presence of glyceraldehyde (*GAL*) (Expt. 135, 10c).

ment, the rate of formation of DPNH from DPN is recorded differentially in Fig. 22, *B* at a pair of wavelengths that are not appreciably influenced by the kinetics of the DPN complex as described above.

The degree of correlation of the kinetics of the DPN reduction and the enzyme-DPN complex is qualitatively encouraging, but quantitatively unsatisfactory at present for forming any conclusions that this complex is a rate-limiting or Michaelis intermediate in the action of the triosephosphate dehydrogenase.

The yeast triosephosphate-dehydrogenase complex in vivo. If iodoacetic acid is added to aerated starved yeast cells, we find a spectral shift very similar to that obtained with the DPN compound of the crystalline enzyme in vitro, as illustrated by the spectrum of Fig. 23. In the absence of any information on other iodoacetic-acid–sensitive compounds having this spectrum, we attribute the effect to the yeast enzyme-DPN compound.[12] If we compute the percentage of the yeast protein that is attributable to this enzyme on the basis of the molecular extinction coefficient of the DPN complex of 3 cm^{-1} × mM^{-1} at 360 mμ, we may obtain a value of about 10 per cent for our yeast samples. This value compares fairly well with the 5 per cent figure given by Krebs on the basis of the triosephosphate dehydrogenase content of proteins extracted from his

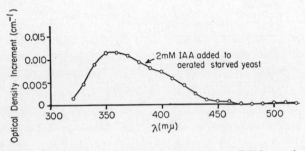

FIG. 23. Evidence for the triosephosphate dehydrogenase-DPN complex in aerated, starved yeast cells. The difference spectrum corresponds fairly closely to that obtained with iodoacetic acid and the enzyme-DPN complex in vitro. The kinetics of the IAA reaction is shown in the inset of Fig. 26, *A* (Expt. 171).

yeast (32). Such a simple and direct determination of triosephosphate dehydrogenase in vivo may turn out to be of importance in studying changes in the amount of this enzyme in response to various conditions.

In the next section, we describe our studies of DPNH in the yeast cell and compute the fraction of the total DPN content of the yeast cell that is bound to the triosephosphate dehydrogenase enzyme. We find about 20 per cent of the total DPN of the cell is so bound.

---

[12] We later show that the yeast ADH is unaffected by the concentration of IAA, and Stoppani *et al.* have recently showed that co-carboxylase reacts much more slowly with IAA (about 20 minutes are required) (41).

The Kinetics of the Oxidation and Reduction of the Pyridine Nucleotides in Intact Yeast Cells

With the development of sensitive spectrophotometers for the ultraviolet region of the spectrum, we have been able to observe the kinetics of oxidation and reduction by the pyridine nucleotide enzymes in yeast and bacterial cells. The pyridine nucleotides are, of course, much less specific than the cytochromes, which are believed to react only with their two neighbors in the cytochrome sequence. Pyridine nucleotides, however, can be involved with several enzymes of carbohydrate and intermediary metabolism without our being able to distinguish spectroscopically which enzyme is catalytically active. Since we cannot distinguish the dehydrogenases spectroscopically, we employ a kinetic approach in which we precipitously initiate carbohydrate or alcohol metabolism in the starved cell in order to observe the initial activities of various dehydrogenases in the reduction of pyridine nucleotides along the different pathways. After these initial phases are completed and the several pathways are operating, individual enzyme systems are obscured. A new transient in the cellular metabolism must then be initiated in order to define pathways kinetically. We find two transients particularly useful at this phase, one, the cessation of respiration due to the exhaustion of the dissolved oxygen available to the cell, the other, the changes brought about by the addition of a different substrate, or an inhibitor, or a shift of the intracellular pH.

In these transient phases of metabolism we may also observe in active operation a number of systems that are " dead ends " on a larger time scale, because in the starved cell there are many systems which must be brought into equilibrium with the main pathway of metabolism. The starved cell has metabolic reservoirs that are empty when the substrate is added and which will fill up to their equilibrium points at a rate dependent mainly upon the activity of the particular pathway and perhaps not at a rate indicative of the longer term flux of substrate through the cell. An equilibrium concentration of alcohol or glycerol, for example, may accumulate in the initial phases of glucose metabolism even though the main pathways to carbon dioxide are not through these products, but through pyruvate. Thus our studies are of especial interest because they focus our attention upon the capabilities of various pathways of metabolism in an emergency situation.

General characteristics of respiration initiated by alcohol or by glucose. If we add to the aerated, starved yeast cell suspension a large excess of ethanol, we observe, as in Fig. 24, at 340-374 mμ (a differential measurement to avoid interference from the triose-phosphate dehydrogenase-DPN complex) the fairly large and rapid

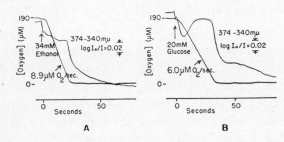

Fig. 24. The respiration of starved, aerated yeast cells initiated by the addition of ethanol (*A*) and by the addition of glucose (*B*). The respiration rate is determined polarographically and the level of DPNH spectrophotometrically using two wave-lengths which eliminate absorption of the enzyme-coenzyme complex. Cells suspended in *M*/20 PO₄≡, pH 4.5, 44° C. (Expts. 181, 31, 32).

reduction of DPN [13] to give a steady-state that persists until oxygen is exhausted and cytochrome action ceases. We then get a further slow reduction of DPN that apparently depends upon the slow equilibration of the alcohol-aldehyde system anaerobically.

If now we repeat the same experiment shown in Fig. 24, *A* with glucose as a substrate, there is a large initial reduction of DPN that is reversed at about 10 seconds with a consequent nearly complete oxidation of DPNH in the steady-state. The DPNH-oxidizing activity completely reverses the initial reducing effect. However, the respiration rate is not much affected by the large change of DPN

---

[13] As far as we can tell, the absorption at 340 mμ is largely due to DPN and not TPN. We base this on the fact that we can obtain reduction of most of the pyridine nucleotide through the DPN-specific alcohol dehydrogenase and also on the fact that in IAA-inhibited yeast TPN reduction by *Zwischenferment* does not cause appreciable absorption of 340 mμ.

reduction because, as we have shown, DPN reduction of 15 per cent already gives half-maximal respiration rate. Upon exhaustion of the oxygen, cytochrome action ceases and we have the steady-state of anaerobic carbohydrate metabolism settling down to its final value.

Detailed kinetics of the initiation of respiration. In order to elucidate the relation of 'respiration rate and the DPN cycle caused by glucose, we record on a faster time scale, as shown in Fig. 25. The record shows that the respiration has reached its maximal rate before the extent of DPN reduction reaches a maximum. In addition, the subsequent oxidation of DPNH does not slow the respiration.

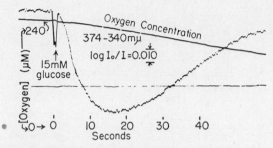

Fig. 25. A similar DPNH cycle to that shown in Figure 24, *B* but recorded on a faster time scale. $M/20$ PO$_4^{\equiv}$, pH 4.7, 26° C. (Expt. 177).

From this we conclude that the oxidation of the DPNH is not due to a lag in the diffusion of DPNH from the dehydrogenases to the cytochromes; if it were, the respiration rate would reach a maximum after the maximum DPNH level is reached. The process we are observing appears to be an equilibration of the DPN systems of carbohydrate metabolism.

The effect of iodoacetic acid. In order to identify in more detail the steps in the DPN cycle, iodoacetic acid has been used, and our results are shown in Fig. 26. The inset of Figure 26, *A* shows the effect of iodoacetic acid upon the triosephosphate-dehydrogenase–DPN compound already illustrated by the spectrum of Fig. 23. As would be expected, no effect is observed at 374-340 mμ except a deflection due to the absorption of IAA solution. After the decomposition of the DPN compound is complete, addition of glucose causes a negligible DPN cycle and scarcely any respiration. The fact that very little pyridine nucleotide is reduced shows that IAA-insensitive pathways are not activated by the substrate and that not much TPN is present in this yeast. Ethanol, however, initiates nearly

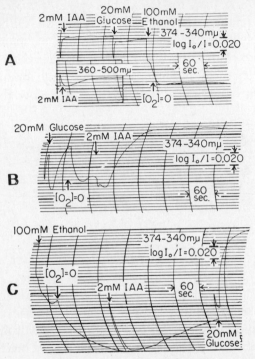

FIG. 26. The effect of iodoacetic acid upon the " cycles " of DPN in yeast with ethanol and glucose as substrates. The cessation of respiration (noted in the figure as $[O_2] = 0$) is confirmed by simultaneously recording oxygen uptake with a platinum microelectrode (trace not shown). The kinetic record of the inset in A corresponds to the spectrum of Fig. 23. pH 3.3, 0.1 M $PO_4^\equiv$ (Expt. 170c).

normal respiration. Thus we have been able to inhibit selectively the triosephosphate dehydrogenase and not the alcohol dehydrogenase in vivo.[14] And the absence of the DPN " cycle " shows that

[14] Dr. E. Racker (see discussion) notes that the DPN protection of ADH from IAA inhibition in vitro is greater than of glyceraldehyde-3-phosphate. Since a similar result is obtained in vivo we infer that ADH is bound to DPN in the aerobic, starved yeast cells.

the triosephosphate dehydrogenase is responsible for this phenomenon.

We must now determine whether the DPNH-oxidizing activity of the cycle is still present, and this is shown by Figs. 26, *B* and 26, *C*. In Fig. 26, *B* we have added IAA to the glucose-reduced DPN and, after a lag equal to the time required to decompose the triosephosphate-dehydrogenase–DPN complex (compare inset of Fig. 26,*A* and Fig. 23), a rapid oxidation of DPNH occurs. If IAA is added to ethanol-reduced DPN (Fig. 26, *C*), a slow oxidation of DPNH occurs that is tremendously accelerated by the addition of glucose. This definitive experiment shows that the DPN-reducing enzyme is inactive in the presence of IAA while the DPNH-oxidizing enzyme has even greater activity—sufficient activity to overcome completely the alcohol dehydrogenase system.

The enzymatic pathways involved in the DPN "cycle." On the basis of these experimental data we identify the DPN-reducing enzyme as the triosephosphate dehydrogenase. The DPNH-oxidizing enzyme on the basis of current knowledge would be the α-glycerolphosphate dehydrogenase (22); the former is shown to be specifically affected by IAA, and the latter is the only known DPN enzyme which has adequate activity towards dihydroxyacetone phosphate to overcome the full reductive capacity of the triosephosphate enzyme and oxidize DPNH so very rapidly.

The dynamics of the initiation of respiration in the starved yeast cell upon the sudden addition of glucose are believed to be as follows: From Fig. 25 the transport of glucose into the cell leads to the formation of triosephosphate in a few seconds. The DPNH produced at triosephosphate dehydrogenase is directly accessible to the respiratory enzymes, as evidenced by the rapid reduction of the rate-limiting "cytochrome b" and by the rapid onset of respiration as recorded by the platinum microelectrode.

There are several interacting factors in carbohydrate metabolism that can account for the further rapid reduction of DPN and its subsequent oxidation, the DPN "cycle." First we should consider that about 20 per cent of the intracellular DPN is already bound to the triosephosphate enzyme and that this DPN might well be rapidly reduced. The replenishment of the DPN would occur only after DPNH oxidation by other enzyme systems. It is reasonable to postulate that the DPNH must be dissociated from the triose-phosphate dehydrogenase, diffuse to the DPNH-oxidizing enzymes, and back to the triosephosphate dehydrogenase as DPN—a process that might require considerable time and thereby cause the decreased activity of the triosephosphate step when all the bound DPN is used up.

Second, the pile-up of 1, 3-diphosphoglyceric acid would put a limit to the extent of DPN reduction by the triosephosphate step, but it is difficult to see how the DPNH oxidation could be explained in this way. Also, rapid recordings of pH changes in the extracellular fluid do not show appreciable acid production by the cell until the DPN " cycle " is complete.

Third, the activation of other enzyme systems by DPNH and by the products of carbohydrate metabolism could readily cause the DPNH oxidative process to become dominant. We have already shown a DPNH oxidation system such as α-glycerolphosphate dehydrogenase to be very active in this yeast and its substrate, dihydroxy-acetone phosphate, becomes available from aldolase at the same time as the substrate for the triosephosphate dehydrogenase. Since the α-glycerolphosphate dehydrogenase must obtain its DPNH from the triosephosphate dehydrogenase, the initial rush in the reduction of triosephosphate-dehydrogenase-bound DPN could well be followed by a rapid oxidation of this DPNH by the active α-glycerolphosphate dehydrogenase. Other dehydrogenases further down the chain of carbohydrate break-down could also participate, especially alcohol dehydrogenase. But we doubt that these enzymes are as important as the α-glycerolphosphate dehydrogenase because our rapid recording of pH changes shows that the DPN " cycle " is complete before acid production begins, i. e., before much pyruvate is produced and split into CO_2 and acetaldehyde and before acetic acid is formed.

It is useful to consider the kinetic characteristics of a DPN-linked system represented by the triosephosphate dehydrogenase (E_1) and the α-glycerolphosphate dehydrogenase (E_2). We represent DPN by S_1, DPNH by S_2, glyceraldehyde-3-phosphate by A_1 and dihydroxy-acetone phosphate by A_2.

The reduction of DPN bound to the triosephosphate dehydrogenase will proceed

$$E_1S_1 + A_1 \xrightarrow{k_4} E_1 + S_2 + P_1 \qquad (27)$$

The DPNH (S_2) from triosephosphate dehydrogenase will diffuse to the α-glycerolphosphate dehydrogenase, where it is denoted S_2'

$$S_2 \underset{k_{-3}}{\overset{k_3}{\rightleftarrows}} S_2' \qquad (28)$$

The reaction of DPNH with α-glycerolphosphate dehydrogenase is represented in two steps:

$$E_2 + S_2' \xrightarrow{k_5} E_2S_2' \qquad (29)$$

$$E_2S_2' + A_2 \xrightarrow{k_7} E_2 + S_1' + P_2 \qquad (30)$$

The DPN now can diffuse back to the triosephosphate dehydrogenase

$$S_1' \underset{k_{-6}}{\overset{k_6}{\rightleftarrows}} S_1 \qquad (31)$$

The triosephosphate dehydrogenase-DPN complex can be reformed

$$E_1 + S_1 \underset{k_2}{\overset{k_1}{\rightleftarrows}} E_1S_1 \qquad (32)$$

and the cycle is complete.

An analysis of this reaction mechanism suggests that the minimum hypothesis for the cycle is that the reduction of the DPN bound to the triosephosphate dehydrogenase is rapid (Equation 27, k_4 large) and that the subsequent processes are slow. One process has already been shown to be surprisingly slow in vitro, namely, the combination of the yeast glyceraldehyde-3-phosphate dehydrogenase with DPN (17) (k_1 of Equation 32).

In summary, we find large fluctuations in the steady-state level of DPNH in the respiring cell that do not cause changes of the respiration rate. A "cycle" of reduction and reoxidation of the pyridine nucleotide that is initiated by the addition of glucose to the starved yeast cells is largely attributed to the initial rush in the reduction of DPN already bound to the triosephosphate dehydrogenase and to slower subsequent reactions in the DPN-linked system represented by this enzyme and α-glycerolphosphate dehydrogenase. Thus the steady-state of oxidation and reduction of the pyridine nucleotides in the respiring cell is dominated by the DPN-linked dehydrogenase reactions, and the part played by the respiratory enzymes appears to be relatively small for this particular type of yeast.

REFERENCES

1. Agner, K., *Acta Physiol. Scand.*, **2**, Supp. 8 (1941).
2. Ahmand, K., H. G. Schneider, and F. M. Strong, *Arch. Biochem.*, **28**, 281 (1950).
3. Altschul, A. M., R. Abrams, and T. R. Hogness, *J. Biol. Chem.*, **142**, 303 (1942).
4. Bach, S. J., M. Dixon, and L. G. Zerfas, *Biochem. J.*, **40**, 229 (1946).
5. Barron, E. S. G., and S. Levine, *Arch. Biochem. and Biophys.*, **41**, 175 (1952).
6. Bonnichsen, R., B. Chance, and H. Theorell, *Acta Chem. Scand.*, **1**, 685 (1947).
7. Bücher, T., *Advances in Enzymol.*, **14**, 1 (1953).
8. Chance, B., *Advances in Enzymol.*, **12**, 153 (1951).
9. Chance, B., in *Enzymes and Enzyme Systems* (J. T. Edsall, ed.), p. 95. Harvard University Press, Cambridge (1951).
9a. Chance, B., *J. Biol. Chem.*, **202**, 407 (1953).
10. Chance, B., *J. Biol. Chem.*, **197**, 557 (1952).
10a. Chance, B., *J. Biol. Chem.*, **197**, 567 (1952).
11. Chance, B., *Nature*, **169**, 215 (1952).
12. Chance, B., *Science*, **116**, 202 (1952).
13. Chance, B., unpub.
14. Chance, B., in *Warburg Festschrift, Biochim. et Biophys. Acta*, **12**, 289 (1953).
15. Chance, B., D. S. Greenstein, J. Higgins, and C. C. Yang, *Arch. Biochem. and Biophys.*, **37**, 322 (1952).
16. Chance, B., D. S. Greenstein, and F. J. W. Roughton, *Arch. Biochem. and Biophys.*, **37**, 301 (1952).
17. Chance, B., and J. Harting, *Federation Proc.*, **12**, 188 (1953).
18. Chance, B., and D. Herbert, *Biochem. J.*, **4**, 402 (1950).
19. Chance, B., and J. B. Neilands, *J. Biol. Chem.*, **199**, 383 (1952).
20. Clark, H. W., H. Neufeld, and E. Stotz, *Federation Proc.*, **10**, 172 (1951).
21. Davies, P. W., and F. Brink, *Rev. Sci. Instr.*, **13**, 523 (1942).
22. Fruton, J. S., and S. Simmonds, *General Biochemistry*, pp. 312, 449, John Wiley & Sons, New York (1953).
23. Harting, J., and B. Chance, *Federation Proc.*, **12**, in press (1953).
23a. Hayes, J., and S. Velick, in press.
24. Heppel, L. A., and V. T. Porterfield, *J. Biol. Chem.*, **178**, 549 (1949).
25. Herbert, D., and J. Pinsent, *Biochem. J.*, **43**, 193 (1948).

26. Kaplan, N., this volume.
27. Keilin, D., *Proc. Roy. Soc.* (London), B, **106**, 418 (1930).
28. Keilin, D., *Proc. Roy. Soc.* (London), B, **121**, 165 (1937).
29. Keilin, D., and E. F. Hartree, *Proc. Roy. Soc.* (London), B, **119**, 141 (1936).
30. Keilin, D., and E. F. Hartree, *Proc. Roy. Soc.* (London), B, **127**, 167 (1939).
31. Keilin, D., and T. Mann, *Proc. Roy. Soc.* (London), B, **122**, 119 (1937).
32. Krebs, E., *J. Biol. Chem.*, **200**, 471 (1953).
32a. Kun, E., *Proc. Soc. Exptl. Biol. Med.*, 77, 441 (1951).
33. Negelein, E., and H. J. Wulff, *Biochem. Z.*, **293**, 351 (1937).
33a. Neilands, J. B., pers. com.
34. Olson, J. A., and C. B. Anfinsen, *J. Biol. Chem.*, **202**, 841 (1953).
35. Pappenheimer, A. M., and E. D. Hendee, *J. Biol. Chem.*, **171**, 701 (1947).
36. Potter, V. R., and A. C. Rief, *Federation Proc.*, **10**, 234 (1951).
37. Racker, E., and I. Krimsky, *J. Biol. Chem.*, **198**, 731 (1952).
37a. Slater, E. C., *Ann. Rev. Biochem.*, **22**, 17 (1953).
38. Slater, E. C., *Biochem. J.*, **44**, 305 (1949).
39. Slater, E. C., *Biochem. J.*, **45**, 14 (1949).
40. Smith, L., pers. com.
41. Stoppani, A. O. M., A. S. Actis, J. O. Deferrari, and E. L. Gonzalez, *Biochem. J.*, **54**, 378 (1953).
41a. Strecker, H., pers. com.
41b. Strittmatter, C. F., and E. G. Ball, *Proc. Natl. Acad. Sci. U. S.*, **38**, 19 (1952).
42. Theorell, H., *Biochem. Z.*, **285**, 207 (1936).
43. Theorell, H., and A. Akesson, *Arkiv. Kemi Mineral. Geol.*, **17B**, no. 7 (1943).
44. Theorell, H., and R. Bonnichsen, *J. Biol. Chem.*, **5**, 1105 (1951).
45. Theorell, H., and B. Chance, *Acta. Chem. Scand.*, **5**, 1127 (1951).
46. Theorell, H., and A. Ehrenberg, *Arch. Biochem. and Biophys.*, **41**, 442 (1952).
47. Thurlow, S., *Biochem. J.*, **19**, 175 (1925).
48. Tsou, C. L., *Biochem. J.*, **47**, 493 (1952).
49. Velick, S., J. Hayes, and J. Harting, *J. Biol. Chem.*, **203**, 527 (1953).
49a. Velick, S., *J. Biol. Chem.*, **203**, 563 (1953).
49b. Velick, S., pers. com.
50. Vennesland, B., and F. H. Westheimer, this volume.
51. Warburg, O., *Biochem. Z.*, **177**, 471 (1926).
52. Wilson, T. G. G., and P. W. Wilson, pers. com.

DISCUSSION

DR. STOTZ: Dr. Chance's report again points out the confusion that exists concerning the role of cytochrome b and factors related to it in the electron transport scheme. This has been evident since the earlier reports on " S–C " factors and by Chance's belief that cytochrome b cannot be involved in the reduction of cytochrome c by succinate in heart muscle extracts. The report just given by Dr. Chance would appear to involve cytochrome b or a closely related component in the linking of DPNH with cytochrome c.

Since our laboratory has been engaged for some time in the chemical separation of the components of heart muscle, some recent findings with regard to cytochrome b and a new component apparently involved in cytochrome c reduction may be of interest. The availability of a succinic dehydrogenase preparation which in the presence of succinate was unable to cause the reduction of cytochrome c provided the tool for the isolation of a fraction capable of linking succinate with cytochrome c. Such a fraction was earlier labelled cytochrome b, but upon further purification of this fraction it is now clear that it contains not only cytochrome b but also another hemoprotein.

In the oxidized form this preparation shows a strong Soret band at approximately 413 mμ with no other very significant peaks. The peaks displayed in the spectrophotometer upon reduction of the preparation depends on the reducing agent employed. Thus upon the addition of hydrosulfite the principal band in the visible is at 562 mμ, belonging to cytochrome b, with a shoulder at approximately 553 mμ, indicating the presence of a second hemoprotein. Upon addition of succinate to the oxidized preparation (this preparation also contains an active succinic dehydrogenase) two distinct peaks are noted in the alpha band region namely at 562 mμ and at 553 mμ. In this case the cytochrome b band is lower than upon reduction with hydrosulfite indicating only incomplete reduction by succinate. Finally, upon addition of ascorbic acid the principal peak observed in the alpha band region is at 552 mμ with only a shoulder evident at 562 mμ. Ascorbic acid thus appears to cause a fairly selective reduction of the new hemoprotein without causing much reduction of cytochrome b. The new cytochrome component is also reduced by the leuco form of 2, 6-dichlorobenzenoneindo-3-chlorophenol indicating a rather high oxidation-reduction potential.

In spite of many similarities with cytochrome c the new cytochrome is readily distinguished from cytochrome c. The preparation containing this component is unable to function in conjunction with cytochrome oxidase in the oxidation of hydroquinone, and in a reconstructed system in which cytochrome c is limiting, this preparation cannot serve in place of cytochrome c. Finally a chromatographic analysis of the hemins in the preparation which contains the new cytochrome proves definitely the absence of cytochrome c.

The role of the new cytochrome in the reduction of cytochrome c by succinate must remain somewhat obscure until the new component is completely separated from cytochrome b, but several experiments already point to the probability that it functions in a chain according to the following scheme:

$$\text{succinate} \xrightarrow[\textit{dehydrogenase}]{\textit{succinic}} \text{cyto-b} \rightarrow \text{cyto-552} \rightarrow \text{cyto-c}$$

It has already been noted that addition of succinate causes the reduction of this component as well as of cytochrome b. A cytochrome b preparation which has been made using a higher than normal concentration of sodium cholate reveals a probable denaturation of the cytochrome b in that its reduced peak (hydrosulfite) has been shifted to 558 mμ. When succinate is added to this preparation, there is neither reduction of the cytochrome b nor of the new component. Nevertheless ascorbic acid can still reduce the new component which has its normal position at 552 mμ. That the new cytochrome is probably responsible for the reduction of cytochrome c is indicated by experiments with the SN-5949 inhibitor of Dr. Ball. While this inhibitor has no effect on the reduction of cytochrome b or of the new component, it completely blocks the reduction of cytochrome c by the preparation which contains cytochrome b and the new component. With regard to naming the new cytochrome component it is obvious that its proposed role might make it a candidate for the " BAL " or " Slater " factor. We hesitate to assign this name, however, since observations in other laboratories have indicated that the action of BAL is not specific and experiments in our own laboratory would indicate that cytochrome b rather than the new component is the one predominantly affected by incubation with BAL. The factor may also be identical with Keilin's " cytochrome e " but until we have completed experiments on the position of the reduced peak at liquid nitrogen temperature we prefer not to call the component cytochrome e. It would seem to be least confusing at this time to refer to it simply as " cytochrome 552."

DR. BALL: We have been studying in our laboratory for the past year, this same cytochrome component absorbing at 552 mμ that Dr. Stotz has talked about. There is no question about its being distinct from cytochrome c but what its role is I haven't any idea.

DR. RACKER: I would like to ask one question. I am a little unhappy about the direction in which Dr. Chance drew the arrows in his scheme for electron transport, and I wonder whether the evidence is really complete that the reaction can or cannot proceed in the reverse direction. Perhaps some of the data of Dr. Chance on the effect of peroxidase might be explained if one assumes that the peroxidase catalyses the reoxidation of some of the intermediates.

DR. CHANCE: Would you care to say which one?

DR. RACKER: Maybe all of them. What I mean is, do you have evidence for all the reactions that you studied that they are reversible and can proceed in either direction?

DR. CHANCE: The spectroscopic data of Fig. 3 show that addition of peroxide to anaerobic yeast cells causes the oxidation of the reduced forms of the pyridine nucleotides, flavoproteins, cytochrome c and cytochrome a. But antimycin-a inhibition shows that the oxidation of the reduced pyridine nucleotides and flavoproteins is not a direct reaction but must occur via Slater's factor. On the other hand, the oxidation of cytochrome a by the peroxidase complex II may be attributed to a direct reaction or to an indirect one proceeding via cytochrome c in the reverse of the usual direction of electron transport.

DR. BALL: Perhaps I ought to say for some of you who are not too familiar with these cytochrome enzymes which react in a chain, that following Dr. Eyring's colorful terminology not only are old shoes thrown in between the spaces of each of these protein molecules, but there are a lot of " old shoes " thrown into this whole complex of enzymes. I would remind you that it contains about 40 per cent lipid material in the purest state that we have been able to obtain it. One should take this into consideration, I think, in talking about the interactions of these enzymes and of agents which inhibit them.

DR. KAPLAN: I would just like to mention something which may be related to your peroxidase activity. Mr. Lenhoff in our laboratory has been working with a system from *Pseudomonas fluorescens.* The extracts from these cells contain a pigment which appears to be like cytochrome c. In the presence of reduced dyes or reduced DPN and hydrogen peroxide there is a peroxidase activity, and apparently this pigment is essential for the activity. This pigment, although it has an absorption spectrum which is characteristic of cytochrome c, doesn't seem to be exactly like the cytochrome c that you get from animal tissues. Added cytochrome c from animal tissues is not peroxidatively oxidized.

DR. CHANCE: This pigment is only a peroxidase itself and not a hydrogen peroxide producing oxidase as well?

DR. KAPLAN: Well, you have to add hydrogen peroxide to make the reaction go, so I believe it is a peroxidase. Whether the pigment itself is the peroxidase is at present not entirely clear. One interesting thing which is worth pointing out is that if you grow these cells under very good aerobic conditions you get very little pigment or peroxidase activity. On the other hand, when you grow the cells at low oxygen tension you get a very high concentration of the pigment and the peroxidase activity is also very high.

DR. CHANCE: Does this system oxidize DPNH?

DR. KAPLAN: Yes, but you have to have a dye as a carrier—that is, a diaphorase must be present to reduce the dye.

DR. CHANCE: The direct reaction of peroxidase complex II with DPNH isn't a very fast reaction; it is about 1/10,000 of the rate at which it oxidizes reduced cytochrome-c.

DR. STADTMAN: I was wondering if you have made any investigations of the peroxidase activity in obligate anaerobes. These organisms have a very active peroxidase, and to my knowledge the anaerobic bacteria—such as the clostridia—do not have cytochromes; and I was wondering whether it might not be possible that under anaerobic conditions (or even under aerobic conditions) you might not have, in addition to the peroxidases of the type that you have been studying, some additional peroxidases which may act on DPN without involving the cytochrome system.

DR. CHANCE: There may indeed be different types of peroxidases in anaerobic bacteria, but a direct reaction of DPNH and yeast peroxidase complex II proceeds too slowly to be of significance since antimycin-a blocks peroxide utilization by yeast; the oxidation of DPNH via cytochrome c is the much more rapid reaction.

DR. HUGHES: When you mentioned the concentration of hydrogen peroxide in the cell were you referring to free, bound, or total hydrogen peroxide?

DR. CHANCE: I was referring to the concentration of the free peroxide. The concentration of bound peroxide is appreciable.

DR. HUGHES: Then it's of the same order of magnitude as the free?

DR. CHANCE: No. It's even greater.

DR. MCELROY: I wanted to ask one question on part III. When you added the glucose you said you had rapid reoxidation of the DPN. Had the alcohol been depleted by the system before you added the glucose?

DR. CHANCE: No, it hadn't. This effect would depend upon the very, very high activity of the enzyme which reoxidizes reduced DPN, which we believe to be the alpha glycerophosphate dehydrogenase. This enzyme can completely overbalance the alcohol-aldehyde equilibrium.

DR. MCELROY: But doesn't the triose phosphate dehydrogenase tend to push the reaction the other way?

DR. CHANCE: Yes, triose phosphate dehydrogenase was not active here, since the cells were treated with iodoacetate.

DR. DEMOSS: Dr. Chance, you have spoken almost entirely in terms of DPN in this presentation. Should the possibility be excluded that TPN enzymes are operating here? In particular, in the last series of curves wouldn't one expect to get TPN reduction when iodoacetate is added to the system?

DR. CHANCE: Well, I think there is very good evidence on this point in the first slide; in the iodoacetate-inhibited system the addition of glucose did not cause any appreciable reduction of the pyridine nucleotides.

DR. DEMOSS: That's what I wondered. Why shouldn't one expect to get some TPN reduction?

DR. CHANCE: Apparently there isn't very much TPN in this type of yeast.

DR. STADTMAN: I wonder if you aren't assuming a little too much in saying that all of this absorption which you measure is due to triose phosphate dehydrogenase? Aren't there other substances present which might account for this absorption?

DR. CHANCE: We do not know of any other enzyme-coenzyme complex which has absorption at 360 mμ except that of the triose phosphate dehydrogenase-DPN complex.

DR. STADTMAN: There are a lot of other enzymes which might give similar complexes and similar bands.

DR. CHANCE: These complexes which are destroyed by IAA?

DR. STADTMAN: Yes.

DR. CHANCE: Which ones do you mean?

DR. STADTMAN: I mean ones that haven't been studied yet, and that's just the point: that many others may exist.

DR. CHANCE: Yes, but until they have been proved to exist, we will stick to the triose phosphate dehydrogenase-DPN complex, which is the only known one. It is perhaps significant to add that the time and IAA concentration required to cause the 360 mμ shift closely approximate the conditions for inhibition of DPN reduction by the triose phosphate dehydrogenase upon addition of glucose to the yeast cells.

DR. BALL: I believe your point is that the DPN might be reduced and then might migrate to combine with another enzyme.

DR. STADTMAN: My point is that maybe this 360 absorption which you observed on reduction might be given by any number of DPN complexes.

DR. CHANCE: Dr. Ball, this isn't a reduction; this absorption band is believed to be due to the linkage of sulphur with oxidized DPN in the triose phosphate dehydrogenase-DPN complex; this is believed to be a specific reaction.

DR. STADTMAN: But I wonder how specific it is. We know that DPN can react with other enzymes, and you might get the same band that you get with triose phosphate dehydrogenase.

DR. CHANCE: Well, we have been looking for similar absorption bands in other dehydrogenases, horse liver ADH, yeast ADH, lactic dehydrogenase, etc. but without success.

DR. KAPLAN: I was wondering, Dr. Chance, when you obtained your spectrum for the triose phosphate dehydrogenase-DPN complex in yeast did you actually add 40 micromols of DPN?

DR. CHANCE: No; much less. The units are in micromoles per liter.

DR. COLOWICK: There is another possible explanation, I believe, for at least part of this 360 mμ band. Dr. Klotz mentioned that when a metal goes onto an SH group it also gives a 360 band.

DR. KLOTZ: This is true only with copper.

DR. COLOWICK: In that case I suppose that this could not account for much of the band observed.

DR. BALL: Let me get this straight. Isn't this the reduced DPN-enzyme complex?

DR. CHANCE: No; the oxidized.

DR. KREBS: I was very much interested in Dr. Chance's estimation of the triose phosphate dehydrogenase content of yeast cells. By entirely different methods we found that yeast contains an unusually large amount of this enzyme and were actually able to extract an amount of the enzyme equal to 5 per cent of the dry weight of the yeast. The methods used for determining how much of the enzyme was extracted were of three types. The extract has an electrophoretic pattern with a number of small components and one large peak with the mobility of the crystalline enzyme making up 30 per cent of the total protein. Of course, this method is very crude because there are probably other proteins with the same mobility. From specific activity comparisons of yeast juice and crystalline enzyme it was determined that 14 per cent of the total protein of the yeast juice is triose phosphate dehydrogenase. The activity method as applied to the crude juice gives a lower limit of the total amount, because the activity test is interfered with by contaminating enzymes. The most accurate method applied for analysis of the crude extract was the quantitative precipitant test, using antiserum to crystalline triose phosphate dehydrogenase. By that method we found 20 per cent. There certainly is enough of this yeast protein to bind the DPN and give the spectrum of the complex Dr. Chance observed. I think he would be on fairly safe grounds in assuming that triose phosphate dehydrogenase was the protein being detected. I want to ask Dr. Velick, on the basis of experiments he has done on the dissociation constants of yeast triose phosphate dehydrogenase and alcohol dehydrogenase with DPN, which enzyme would have the DPN?

DR. VELICK: Triose phosphate dehydrogenase would have it.

DR. RACKER: May I make one brief comment on that? I don't think I quite agree with that. On the whole, I think that our ideas on the alcohol dehydrogenase equilibrium agree very well with those of Dr. Velick. There is one interesting experiment which has some bearing on the question of Dr. Krebs and on the reaction between DPN and the two enzymes and that is the following: Both enzymes are very sensitive to iodoacetate. If you mix crystalline alcohol dehydrogenase and triose phosphate dehydrogenase together and add DPN in the presence of IAA, the DPN nearly completely protects the alcohol dehydrogenase and does not at all protect the triose phosphate dehydrogenase.

DR. VELICK: I just wanted to comment on what Dr. Racker said. The dissociation constant of the triose phosphate dehydrogenase-DPN complex is much smaller than yeast alcohol dehydrogenase.

DR. RACKER: I think we agree on that, but these experiments I mentioned were carried out with an excess of DPN.

DR. VELICK: Yes, if it was done with enough DPN, then I would agree that what you observed might occur.

DR. BALL: As long as everyone agrees, that's fine.

Part V

THE FUNCTION OF ENZYMES IN GROUP TRANSFER

INTRODUCTION

Fritz Lipmann

Department of Biochemistry
Massachusetts General Hospital
Boston, Mass.

As an introduction to this session, let me briefly try to set off the biosynthetic mechanisms from the general type of enzyme catalysis referring mainly to hydrolytic reactions. I am much impressed by the wealth of recent observations which make us conscious of the fact that in most group transfer reactions, the enzyme molecule enters as a reactant. It appears more and more clearly that one of the important functions of the enzyme here is to preserve bond energy. The enzyme carries out this function by forming covalent links with groupings which are to be transferred. It is, I believe, really of relatively minor importance if such a binding occurs through a coenzyme or through some kind of a grouping in the enzyme molecule, which may or may not be bound covalently to the protein body. In some cases, such as, for example, triosephosphate dehydrogenase, which Dr. Racker will right away develop in more detail, the same enzyme has actually multiple functions. I feel, therefore, that we are dealing with enzymatic mechanisms, the understanding of which would profit much by some revision of our somewhat antiquated notions. The particular characteristics appear more clearly if one looks upon these catalysts as *enzyme reactors*. The enzymatic process is here quite comparable to common procedures in chemical processing, where a reactor is supplied with substances which, catalytically or otherwise, are brought into reaction in its body. After reaction has occurred, the products leave the reactor as finished or enter a second reactor, and so on until the finished product is ready. At the present moment, I favor stressing the differences between hydrolytic reactions and condensation processes rather than this similarity.

FORMATION OF ACYL AND CARBONYL COMPLEXES ASSOCIATED WITH ELECTRON–TRANSPORT AND GROUP–TRANSFER REACTIONS

E. RACKER

Department of Biochemistry, Yale University,
New Haven

THERE APPEARS to be a trend in modern biochemistry to abolish the boundaries that have been set up between the different dominions of cellular metabolism. The use of isotopes in the investigation of the metabolism of intact animals has particularly served to emphasize the incredibly rapid flow of intermediates in all directions. Although we may now begin to perceive some of the predominating currents, we have not yet been able to evaluate quantitatively the metabolic reactions within the cells. Isolated attempts have been made to solve this problem. The role of the neoformation of methyl groups as compared to methyl-group transfer, has been investigated with the aid of doubly labeled compounds (1). An approximate estimate of the relative roles of the shunt mechanism and the Meyerhof-Embden pathway in the utilization of glucose in *E. coli* cells has been made (2). Investigations into the fate of CO_2 labeled with C^{14} and rate measurements have been performed in the field of photosynthesis (3). But our tools and approaches in such studies are still few and limited, and the interpretation of data is subject to a good deal of disagreement.

What can we learn about the operation of an enzyme within the cell by studying its action in an isolated state? The most accurate determinations of specific activity, turnover number, and the amounts of enzyme present in cell extracts will at best give us a qualitative answer to its operation within the cell. On the other hand, it may be impossible to analyse the function of an enzyme unless it is isolated from the other enzymes; an example of this will be cited later.

In the approach to isolated enzymes a trend to a broader concept has also become apparent. Enzymes which for many years had been classified as hydrolytic have been discovered to catalyze transfer reactions. Probably these transfer reactions participate in both the degradation and the synthesis of cell constituents such as proteins, nucleic acids, and fats.

In energy metabolism, too, the fields seem to have converged. The process of phosphorylation has been found to be " coupled " to the electron-transport mechanism. A recent trend, away from the omnipotent ATP, has emphasized the importance of group-transfer reactions for synthetic processes. Thiolesters, acylimidazole, and sulfonium compounds have received special attention at the higher energy levels, while peptides, amides, esters, glycosides, and nucleosides have been shown to participate in transfer reactions at the lower energy level. Renewed attention has been given in recent years to a reaction that is concerned with the transfer of an aldehyde group to another aldehyde or to an alcohol. The enzymes that catalyze these reactions have been referred to as transketolase and transaldolase. These enzymes too, appear to participate both in synthetic and degradation reactions and are found to be widely distributed in cells of all forms of life.

Since many of these transfer reactions have been reviewed at this and at previous sessions of the Baltimore symposium, the present discussion will be restricted to the formation and utilization of acyl and carbonyl complexes.

The presentation will be divided into three parts: (I) the formation of carbonyl and acyl complexes in oxidative processes; (II) the degradation of acyl complexes; and (III) transfer reactions of acyl and carbonyl complexes.

I. FORMATION OF CARBONYL AND ACYL COMPLEXES IN OXIDATIVE PROCESSES

1. *Glyceraldehyde-3-phosphate dehydrogenase*

According to the hypothesis of Warburg and Christian (4), glyceraldehyde-3-phosphate and inorganic phosphate react chemically to yield 1, 3-diphosphoglyceraldehyde. The first indication that this hypothesis was incorrect came from the work of Meyerhof and his associates (5). From kinetic and equilibria data it was concluded that non-enzymatic formation of the hypothetical 1, 3-diphospho-glyceraldehyde does not take place, but the possibility that such a compound is formed by the enzyme was left open.

A study of the mechanism of the conversion of ketoaldehydes to the corresponding hydroxyacids by glyoxalase (6) has shown that the reaction proceeds in two major steps. The first step was found to involve an interaction between the aldehyde and the sulfhydryl group of glutathione, and results in the formation of a thiolester (III). In the second step the thiolester is hydrolysed to the acid, and the free SH compound is liberated.

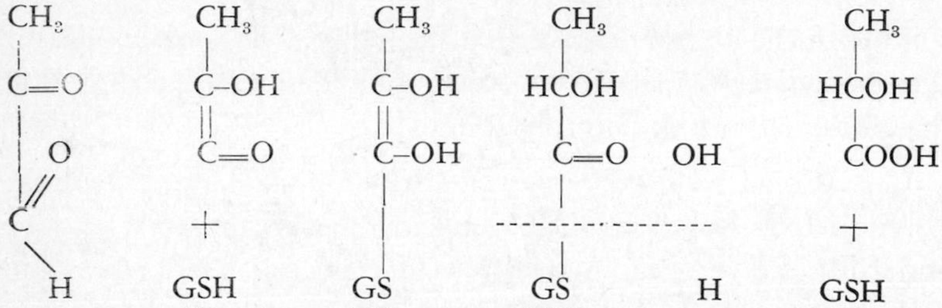

$$
\begin{array}{ccccc}
CH_2 & CH_3 & CH_3 & CH_3 & CH_3 \\
| & | & | & | & | \\
C{=}O & C{-}OH & C{-}OH & HCOH & HCOH \\
| & \| & \| & | & | \\
\ \ \ O & C{=}O & C{-}OH & C{=}O \quad OH & COOH \\
\diagdown\!\!/\!\!/ & & | & | & \\
C & + & | & -\!-\!-\!-\!-\!- & + \\
\diagdown & & | & | & \\
\quad H & GSH & GS & GS \quad H & GSH \\
(I) & (II) & (III) & & (IV)
\end{array}
$$

These findings suggested the possibility that a similar mechanism might operate in triose phosphate oxidation and the first variant of a scheme was suggested and is shown below:

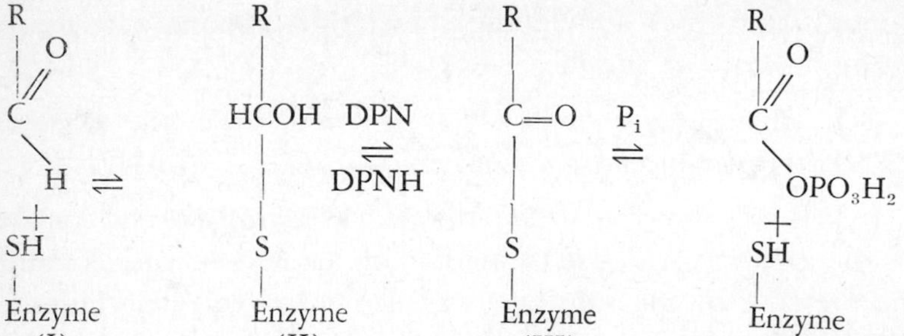

$$
\begin{array}{cccc}
R & R & R & R \\
| \quad O & | & | & | \quad O \\
\diagdown\!\!/\!\!/ & HCOH \ \ DPN & C{=}O \quad P_i & \diagdown\!\!/\!\!/ \\
C & | \qquad \rightleftharpoons & | \qquad \rightleftharpoons & C \\
\diagdown & | \quad DPNH & | & \diagdown \\
\quad H \ \rightleftharpoons & | & | & OPO_3H_2 \\
+ & | & | & + \\
SH & S & S & SH \\
| & | & | & | \\
Enzyme & Enzyme & Enzyme & Enzyme \\
(I) & (II) & (III) & (IV)
\end{array}
$$

By means of this scheme it was possible to explain the high sensitivity of triose phosphate dehydrogenase to iodoacetate (7) and to visualize a mechanism for the formation of the carboxyl phosphate by phosphorolysis of a thiolester. The identification of acetyl-CoA as a thiolester of coenzyme A (8) and its participation in the oxidation of pyruvate (9, 10) and aldehydes (11, 12) provided a complete analogy to the proposed mechanism. Moreover, the observation (13) that acetaldehyde and acetylphosphate are substrates for glyceraldehyde-3-phosphate dehydrogenase permitted analysis of the reaction with these readily available substrates. It was then demonstrated that several times recrystallized triose phosphate dehydrogenase catalyses a two-step reaction consisting of an oxidative and a phosphorolytic step. The evidence for this mechanism, obtained by the independent work in two laboratories (14, 15), can be summarized as follows:

(1) In the absence of a system to reduce DPN, arsenolysis of the acylphosphate was shown to occur, and P^{32} exchanged rapidly with the phosphate of the acylphosphate.

(2) When reduced glyceraldehyde-3-phosphate dehydrogenase (obtained by isolation of the enzyme in the presence of Versene, and fully active without addition of reducing agent) was blocked with an excess of IAA, the oxidation-reduction step, which was tested in both directions in the presence of glutathione, was obliterated. However, arsenolysis still took place if glutathione was added to the IAA-treated enzyme.

(3) The enzyme catalyzes a transfer from acetylphosphate to either glutathione or CoA. Accumulation of acetylglutathione was demonstrated when acetylphosphate and glutathione were incubated in the presence of enzyme.

(4) Thiolesters were slowly hydrolyzed, or in the presence of DPNH were reduced by the enzyme.

(5) It was shown that glutathione was a firmly bound component of the enzyme, and the formation of an acyl-enzyme complex in the presence of the substrate was demonstrated. The latter point will be discussed in greater detail.

The concept of an " acyl-enzyme complex " is not very new. It has been customary for enzymologists to retreat to the hilly surfaces of their enzymes when evidence for the existence of a postulated intermediate was not forthcoming. The availability of glyceraldehyde-3-phosphate dehydrogenase in gram quantities (16, 17) made it possible to approach this problem more directly. With acetylphosphate as substrate the formation of an acyl enzyme could be demonstrated by the following procedure (21):

The enzyme was incubated with an excess of acetylphosphate for a few minutes and then boiled for five minutes at pH 4.5. This procedure precipitated the enzyme and destroyed practically all the acetylphosphate present. The enzyme was centrifuged off and washed three times with water to remove all traces of residual substrate. When such a preparation was treated with hydroxylamine, a soluble hydroxamic acid was found in the supernatant solution and measured colorimetrically (18). Up to 1.8 equivalents of acyl groups per mole of enzyme were found to be formed by this procedure. When the acyl-enzyme complex was treated with proteolytic enzymes (trypsin was found to be most suitable for this purpose) the hydroxylamine-reactive component was solubilized. Fractionation of the mixture of amino acids and peptides thus formed proved to be difficult because of heavy loss of the thiolester. Small amounts of the thiolester (as determined by the alkaline nitroprusside test) were isolated on several occasions on paper chromatograms. However, final identification of this ester has not yet been achieved.

In the course of studies on the effect of SH-inhibitors on glyceraldehyde-3-phosphate dehydrogenase, it was observed that the enzyme exhibited an absorption at 340 mμ, which was decreased on addition of iodoacetate or p-chloromercuribenzoate (14). After treatment of the enzyme with charcoal, which removes DPN (19), the absorption at 340 mμ dropped and was restored to the original value by the addition of DPN. This reconstructed absorption band disappeared again on addition of IAA, as shown in Fig. 1. When the differences between the spectra with and without IAA were plotted, a rather broad absorption band with a peak at 360 mμ was obtained.

Because of the effect of compounds that react with SH groups, the data were interpreted in terms of a complex formed between DPN and the SH groups of the enzyme. To evaluate the participation of this complex in the reaction catalyzed by the enzyme, the effect of acylphosphate on the absorption was measured. It was

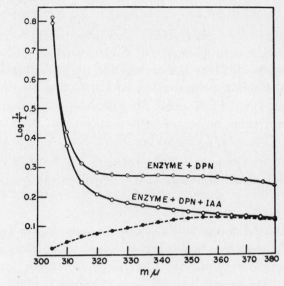

FIG. 1. Absorption spectra of enzyme-DPN complex.

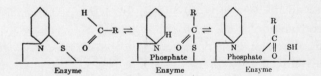

FIG. 2. Aldehydolysis of enzyme-DPN complex.

found that either 1, 3-diphosphoglyceric acid or acetylphosphate induced a drop in absorption at 360 mμ which was not further affected by addition of IAA. From these data a second variant of the mechanism of aldehyde oxidation was proposed, as shown in Fig. 2.

The two essential points of this theory are (a) a participation of the DPN-S-complex in the mechanism of electron transfer, and (b) a process of aldehydolysis by which that complex is cleaved.

In the above formulation the actual mechanism of electron transport was omitted from the scheme. Two alternatives could be suggested. According to the first, the addition of the SH group to DPN leads to a change of the quaternary to a tertiary nitrogen with the release of a proton, while in the aldehydolysis step the hydrogen of the aldehyde is donated to DPN. According to the second alternative, the hydrogen transfer occurs in the first step and is derived from the SH group, while aldehydolysis leads to the liberation of a proton. Recent data (20, 21) on the effect of pH on the equilibria of the two reactions (the formation of the DPN-enzyme complex and the aldehydolysis) favor the second alternative.

It should also be pointed out that in view of recent experiments on the entrance of hydrogen in the formation of reduced DPN (22), the sulfhydryl should add to carbon 4 of the pyridine nucleus.

2. *Pyruvic acid oxidase*

The solubilization of the enzyme system capable of pyruvate oxidation has permitted a most rapid advance in our understanding of its mechanism (10, 23, 24). One of the puzzling features of this reaction is the participation of several cofactors. Their functions have been greatly clarified by recent developments of our knowledge of CoA and lipoic acid. Cocarboxylase and Mg^{++} are most likely concerned in the first step, in which an active aldehyde is formed by decarboxylation of the ketoacid as shown in reaction below. This formulation is supported by the finding that CO_2 incorporation into pyruvic acid is dependent on cocarboxylase and is independent of CoA and DPN (25, 26). The observation of acetoin formation catalyzed by carboxylase (27) and other evidence (cf. 28) are in line with this conclusion.

$$
R-C{\overset{O}{\underset{COOH}{}}} \xrightarrow{\text{ThPP, } Mg^{++}} \left[R-C{\overset{O}{\underset{H}{}}} \right] + CO_2 \tag{1}
$$

Since free acetaldehyde is not liberated in this step, one must assume the formation of a carbonyl-enzyme complex which does not dissociate readily. An analogous situation will be discussed later in connection with the decarboxylation of hydroxypyruvate by transketolase.

In the next step, it has been visualized that the -SS- group of lipoic acid or lipothiamide is split by an aldehydolysis to yield an acetyllipoic compound, as shown in reaction (2).

$$
\begin{bmatrix} RC \overset{\displaystyle O}{\underset{\displaystyle H}{\diagup}} \end{bmatrix} + \underset{S}{\overset{S}{|}} R \rightleftharpoons \overset{\displaystyle R\text{-}C\text{-}S}{\underset{HS}{\diagdown}} R \qquad (2)
$$

The evidence for this step (29) lies in a demonstration of a stoichiometric relationship between the CO_2 liberated from pyruvate, the SH groups formed, and the appearance of a thiolester which is determined by the hydroxylamine reaction. In step (3), a transfer of the acyl group to CoA results in the formation of acetyl-CoA, which is measured with a pigeon-liver enzyme preparation (30) by transferring the acyl group to an acceptor arylamine.

In step (4) the lipoic acid, which has been reduced by the combined action of steps (2) and (3), now reduces DPN (29).

$$
\overset{\displaystyle O}{\underset{\displaystyle R}{R\text{-}C\text{-}S}} \diagdown_{HS} + CoA \rightleftharpoons \overset{HS}{\underset{HS}{\diagdown}} R + \text{acetyl-CoA} \qquad (3)
$$

$$
DPN^+ + \overset{HS}{\underset{HS}{\diagdown}} R \rightleftharpoons |\overset{S}{\underset{S}{\diagdown}} R + DPNH + H^+ \qquad (4)
$$

(1-4) sum: pyruvate $+ DPN^+ + CoA \xrightarrow[\text{lipoic}]{\text{ThPP, Mg}^{++}}$ acetyl-CoA

$+ CO_2 + DPNH + H^+$

It is apparent from the above formulation of the mechanism that an analogy between the enzymatic oxidation and the chemical oxidation of pyruvic acid in the presence of glutathione (31) can no longer be drawn, since the formulation of the chemical oxidation involving the formation of a thiohemiacetal as an intermediate has been challenged. Evidence has been presented that, in the presence of copper and glutathione, pyruvic acid is oxidized by hydrogen peroxide, which is formed by the metal-catalyzed oxidation of glutathione (32).

On the other hand, a closer analogy of this mechanism can be drawn to the aldehydolysis in triose phosphate oxidation. In the latter case a cleavage of an S-C bond, in pyruvic oxidation an alde-hydolysis of an S-S bond was postulated. A cleavage of an S-S bond was also proposed to occur during fatty acid oxidation (33).

Since Dr. Gunsalus will elaborate on the role of lipoic acid in pyruvic acid oxidation, no mention has been made in this report of the role of different enzyme fractions in the oxidation process, and no details of the experimental evidence concerning lipoic acid are quoted.

Attention should be drawn, however, to another type of approach which might prove useful in the elucidation of this problem. Acetate-requiring mutants of *Neurospora crassa* have been found which form acetylmethylcarbinol from pyruvic acid instead of oxidizing it (34). Since there appear to be at least three genetically different acetate-requiring mutants which accumulate acetoin, they may represent different lesions in the enzymatic process of pyruvate oxidation.

3. α-Ketoglutaric acid oxidase

In this field, too, rapid advances followed the solubilization of the enzyme system (35, 36). The purification and study of this enzyme have been carried out independently in two different laboratories and have led to the following concept of the reaction mechanism (37, 38, 26).

In the first step, as in the oxidation of pyruvate, the formation of an active carbonyl-enzyme complex is assumed. Although in this case the formation of free succinic semialdehyde could be demonstrated, the rate of its formation was not commensurate with the rate of the over-all oxidation of α-ketoglutaric acid. Therefore, in this reaction too, formation of " active succinic semialdehyde " must be assumed (Reaction 1):

$$
\underset{\substack{\| \\ R-C-COOH}}{O} \xrightarrow[Mg^{++}]{ThPP} \left[\underset{\substack{\| \\ R-C-H}}{O} \right] + CO_2, \text{ where } R = \left[\begin{array}{c} COOH \\ | \\ CH_2 \\ | \\ CH_2 \\ | \end{array} \right] \quad (1)
$$

$$
\left[\underset{\substack{\| \\ R-C-H}}{O} \right] + DPN^+ + CoA-SH \xrightarrow[\text{lipoic}]{Mg^{++}, ThPP}
$$

$$
\underset{\substack{\| \\ R-C-SCoA}}{O} + DPNH + H^+ \quad (2)
$$

With preparation from animal tissues the decarboxylating enzyme has not been separated from the dehydrogenase which catalyzes reaction (2), and the complete activity (reactions 1 and 2) has been ascribed to a single enzyme unit which contains cocarboxylase and lipoic acid (39). A separation of two enzymatic fractions in bacteria was reported (40). As in the case of the pyruvic oxidation system, a short-cut is accomplished by the addition of ferricyanide. The reaction then proceeds without the addition of any cofactors. The evaluation of these results is complicated by the fact that the preparation used for these experiments contains bound cocarboxylase and lipoic acid, is sedimentable at high speed, and has been stated to have a molecular weight of several millions. Moreover, α-ketoglutaric oxidase from *Acetobacter vinelandii* was recently reported to remain in the supernatant solution after centrifugation at $144,000 \times g$ (41). Although only a 10-fold purification from the crude extract was achieved, the bacterial enzyme had a higher activity than the pseudo-soluble animal enzyme; a dependency on cocarboxylase and DPN, with ferricyanide as electron acceptor, was reported for the bacterial system. The exact localization at which dyes and ferricyanide act as electron acceptors in enzyme-catalyzed systems is not known in many instances. Reexamination of the older data (42) using more highly purified enzyme preparations is desirable. The proposed analogy between the role of ferricyanide in α-ketoglutarate oxidation (37) and the participation of alloxan in the oxidation of alcohol by alcohol dehydrogenase in the absence of DPN (42) is not warranted, in the light of more recent observations. With crystalline alcohol dehydrogenase, aldehyde formation from alcohol was found to be completely dependent on DPN (43).

The next step in ketoglutarate oxidation is of special interest because of several unexplained features. The over-all reaction of this step, which results in the formation of ATP, is written as reaction (3).

$$\text{succinyl-CoA} + P_i + \text{ADP} \rightleftharpoons \text{succinate} + \text{CoA-SH} + \text{ATP} \qquad (3)$$

This reaction can be measured by the formation of hydroxamic acid, when succinate, ATP, reduced CoA and Mg^{++} are added to the enzyme in the presence of hydroxylamine. In the forward reaction ATP has been measured by means of glucose-6-phosphate formation in the presence of hexokinase. The succinylation of CoA in the presence of ATP appears analogous to the acetate activation in animal tissues and in yeast. However, it appears that a different mechanism is operating (38). The acetate reaction has been written as:

$$\text{acetate} + \text{ATP} + \text{CoA} \rightleftharpoons \text{acetyl-CoA} + \text{AMP} + \text{PP}$$

The formation of pyrophosphate in this reaction and its reversibility have been demonstrated (44). This formulation, however, does not hold for the succinate activation system in pig heart. Pyrophosphate is not formed nor is P^{32}-labeled pyrophosphate incorporated. ADP acts as acceptor, but AMP does not. Finally inorganic P^{32} is very readily incorporated into ATP (38). Further elucidation of the mechanism of these two different acid-activating systems should be very revealing.

4. *Bacterial aldehyde dehydrogenases*

Several types of aldehyde dehydrogenases have been described in recent years (11, 12, 45, 46, 47). Only the bacterial enzymes were actually demonstrated to catalyze the formation of an acyl compound. Aldehyde dehydrogenase from liver and two different dehydrogenases from yeast (45, 46, 47) were tested for acyl group formation, but the results were uniformly negative. Since these enzymes have been shown to catalyze the formation of the free acid from the aldehyde, it is clear that if an acyl group was formed in the course of this reaction it was hydrolyzed so rapidly that it escaped detection. A number of thiolesters that were tested for hydrolysis with partially purified liver dehydrogenases were attacked very slowly, or not at all (43). Nevertheless, the possibility of the formation of an acyl-enzyme complex has not yet been ruled out, and further investigations with larger amounts of enzyme and efficient acyl-acceptor systems appear to be indicated.

The bacterial dehydrogenases which require DPN or TPN and CoA as cofactors (11, 12) have been studied recently in greater detail (48). The data suggest a primary interaction between CoA and the aldehyde. The formation of acetyl-CoA by the bacterial dehydrogenase was demonstrated by linking the system to the citrate-forming condensing enzyme (cf. 28).

5. *Diacetyl oxidase*

This enzyme (alias: diacetyl mutase) had been shown to require ThPP (49). A reexamination of its mode of action revealed a number of similarities with the pyruvic oxidase system and the formation of an active aldehyde is suggested. More recently, it was shown (50) that lipoic acid is required for the oxidation of diacetyl with ferricyanide as electron acceptor, while it is not needed for the oxidation of free acetaldehyde. As in the case of the oxidation of pyruvate, the free aldehyde is not an intermediate in the reaction.

6. *Oxidation-reduction of glyoxals*

The formation of thiolesters from ketoaldehydes and glutathione was mentioned previously. Glyoxalase I obtained from yeast catalyzes this reaction with a number of ketoaldehydes (methylglyoxal, phenylgyloxal, glyoxal, and hydroxypyruvic aldehyde) with the formation of the corresponding thiolesters (lactyl-, mandelyl-, glycolyl-, and glycerylglutathione (51)). The reaction is readily followed by the hydroxylamine method (18). Of the thiolesters mentioned, only lactylglutathione has so far been prepared synthetically (52).

The detailed mechanism of the internal oxidation-reduction catalyzed by this enzyme is still obscure. Various aspects of this enzyme reaction have been reviewed elsewhere (53).

7. *Fatty Acid Oxidation*

The formation of acyl complexes during fatty acid oxidation was admirably reviewed at previous symposia by Barker (54) and by Kennedy and Lehninger (55), and more recently by Lynen (56) and Mahler (57). Rapid advances have been made in the field of fatty-acid metabolism, especially of animal tissues, again shortly after the solubilization of the enzyme systems (58, 59, 60, 61). The formation of an acyl complex between CoA and the fatty acid has been demonstrated in several instances with both short- and long-chain fatty acids (cf. 57, 58, 62). In all cases ATP is required for the reaction, except in certain exchange reactions in which acetyl-phosphate can be substituted (54, 55). The further oxidative degradation of the thiolesters formed will be discussed later.

II. Degradation of Acyl Complexes

1. *Glyceraldehyde-3-phosphate dehydrogenase and acetylphosphatases*

It has been observed (21) that the acyl enzyme formed from acetylphosphate in the presence of DPN is unstable. This phenomenon may be related to the observation that the oxidized enzyme (prepared in the absence of reducing agents) catalyzes the hydrolysis of acetylphosphate (63). This finding has been confirmed, and it was found in addition that acetylphosphate is also hydrolyzed in the presence of large amounts of reduced enzyme (21). This may account for the instability of the acyl-enzyme complex, since the reaction acetylphosphate $\rightleftharpoons$ acyl-enzyme complex is reversible.

The same argument applies to the instability of thiolesters formed by the action of other oxidative steps or by transfer reactions in the presence of acylphosphatase. Acetyl-CoA in the presence of phosphotransacetylase (64), acetylphosphatase (65), and inorganic phosphate is degraded as follows:

$$\text{Acetyl-CoA} + P_i \rightleftharpoons \text{Acetylphosphate} + \text{CoA} \tag{1}$$

$$\text{Acetylphosphate} + H_2O \rightarrow \text{acetate} + P_i \tag{2}$$

Sum: Acetyl CoA + H_2O → acetate + CoA

2. *Deacylases*

The direct hydrolysis of thiolesters to the acid and the SH-compound is catalyzed by a variety of enzymes which have often interfered in early investigations of acyl-complex formation. Later, after fractionation has been achieved, they become invaluable aids in the analysis of the reaction mechanism. Considerable specificity is encountered in the properties of some of these thiolesterases.

(a) *Thiolesters of glutathione.* An enzyme preparation from beef liver hydrolyzes glutathione thiolesters in which a hydroxyl group is adjacent to the ester group (R–CHOH–CO–S–R) (51). Acetylglutathione is hydrolyzed only very slowly by these preparations. An enzyme preparation which hydrolyzes acetylglutathione more rapidly than the thiolesters of hydroxy acids was found in rat liver (66). The beef-liver enzyme which has been referred to as glyoxalase II was shown to degrade synthetic DL-lactylglutathione (52) at about the same rate at which it degrades lactylglutathione formed by the action of glyoxalase I (53). Preparations of glyoxalase II are inactive toward acetyl thioglycolate or acetyl-CoA as substrates.

(b) *Thiolesters of CoA.* The hydrolysis of acetyl-CoA and succinyl-CoA is catalyzed by separate enzymes termed deacylases (67). These enzymes have been particularly useful in the investigation of reactions with unfavorable equilibria, since the hydrolysis of the thiolester permits the reaction to proceed to completion. Succinyl-CoA deacylase, which has been purified considerably (67), has been used for the quantitative assay of CoA (68). The formation of acetoacetate in liver extracts by a condensation of two molecules of acetyl-CoA (69, 70, 71, 72) is probably catalyzed by coupling of the reactions (1) and (2) involving the enzyme thiolase (72) and an acetoacetyl deacylase.

$$2 \text{ acetyl-CoA} \rightleftharpoons \text{acetoacetyl-CoA} + \text{CoA} \tag{1}$$

$$\text{acetoacetyl-CoA} + H_2O \rightarrow \text{acetoacetate} + \text{CoA} \tag{2}$$

3. *Oxidative degradation of thiolesters*

(a) *Glutathione thiolesters.* Enzymes have been obtained from yeast which catalyze the reduction and oxidation of thiolesters of

TABLE 1

CO_2 EVOLUTION IN THE PRESENCE OF FORMALDEHYDE AND GLYOXAL
IN YEAST EXTRACTS

Additions to yeast extracts *	Micromoles of CO_2 in 20 minutes
Formaldehyde (40 μ moles) + DPN (1 μ mole)	5.1
Formaldehyde	1.8
DPN	< 0.3
Formate + DPN	< 0.3
Formate + DPN + ATP (5 μ moles)	< 0.3
Glyoxal + DPN	12.5

* 1.5 ml. was used of a crude extract from dried yeast which contained only small amounts of DPN. The reaction was carried out in a final volume of 2 ml. in a Warburg vessel at 30° C. in an atmosphere of nitrogen.

glutathione. One enzyme fraction catalyzes the reduction of DPN in the presence of lactyl- or glycolyl-glutathione, while another fraction catalyzes the oxidation of reduced DPN in the presence of one of these two thiolesters. A dismutation of glycolyl-glutathione by crude yeast preparations is accompanied by a liberation of CO_2. These experiments have led us to postulate the degradation of the acyl group of the thiolester of a two-carbon acid to that of a one-carbon compound. To explore this possibility further, the action of these preparations on formaldehyde was tested. As can be seen from Table 1, addition of formaldehyde leads to CO_2 evolution, which is markedly stimulated by DPN (small amounts of DPN are present in the crude preparations). Formate is not decarboxylated even in the presence of ATP. Fluoride does not inhibit the CO_2 output, which makes it unlikely that the CO_2 is derived from the fermentation of contaminating polysaccharides. Addition of glyoxal, which is rapidly transformed to glycolylglutathione by these yeast preparations, also leads to the liberation of CO_2. It should be pointed out that the participation of glutathione in reactions involving formaldehyde, as outlined below, is still hypothetical.

$$HC\underset{H}{\overset{O}{\big\langle}} + GSH \rightarrow GS\text{--}CH_2OH \tag{1}$$

$$GS\text{--}CH_2OH + DPN^+ \rightarrow GS\text{--}CHO + DPNH + H^+ \tag{2}$$

$$GS\text{--}CHO + DPN^+ \rightarrow GS\text{--}COOH + DPNH + H^+ \tag{3}$$

$$GS\text{--}COOH \rightarrow GSH + CO_2 \tag{4}$$

The crude yeast preparations which were used for the above experiments contain considerable amounts of glutathione. Only slight stimulation by further addition of glutathione was occasionally observed. Dialysis of the preparation led to pronounced inactivation of the enzyme system, so that a dependency on glutathione could not be demonstrated. Attempts to demonstrate CO_2 fixation in this system have so far been unsuccessful.

(b) *CoA thiolesters.* Several enzymes have been described recently (72, 73, 74, 57) which catalyze the oxidation and reduction of thiolesters of CoA. A β-hydroxybutyryl-CoA dehydrogenase has been described, which catalyzes the reduction of acetoacetyl-CoA to β-hydroxybutyryl-CoA by reduced DPN. Starting with β-hydroxybutyrate and ATP, the oxidation was shown to be dependent on CoA and was found to be specific for D-β-hydroxybutyrate (74), while the dehydrogenase which acts on β-hydroxybutyrate in the absence of CoA is specific for L-β-hydroxybutyrate. From these and other studies the general formulation of the reaction sequence can be written as:

$$\text{CH}_3\text{CHOHCH}_2\text{COOH} + \text{CoA–SH} \xrightleftharpoons[]{\text{ATP}} \text{CH}_3\text{CHOHCH}_2\text{CO–S–CoA} \quad (1)$$

$$\text{CH}_3\text{CHOHCH}_2\text{CO–S–CoA} + \text{DPN}^+ \rightleftharpoons \text{CH}_3\text{COCH}_2\text{CO–S–CoA}$$
$$+ \text{DPNH} + \text{H}^+ \quad (2)$$

The formation of β-hydroxybutyryl-CoA from crotonyl-CoA by hydration has also been demonstrated (57, 73).

Thus it appears that as oxalacetate can act as a carrier of the acetyl group to permit the intramolecular rearrangements catalyzed by the tricarboxylic acid cycle, the two major SH-compounds in cells, glutathione and CoA, can fulfill a similar function. Though the requirements for such a carrier system is obvious in the case of two-carbon units, it is less obvious in the case of fatty acids such as butyrate, which could conceivably be oxidized directly to crotonate, β-hydroxybutyrate, and acetoacetate. In fact, enzymes which can catalyze some of these reactions have been described. However, it is likely that the main pathway of fatty acid metabolism proceeds through acyl compounds as intermediates, and this is most readily understood in terms of energy utilization in the degradation process and in terms of group transfer in synthetic reactions.

III. Transfer of Acyl and Carbonyl Complexes

1. *Chemical acyl-transfer reaction*

Of the early chemical work on the acyl-transfer reaction the use of thioacids for the acylation of aniline has been frequently cited. In a recent article (75) on this subject matter, later developments are discussed. Perhaps attention should be drawn to the work of Holmberg on the aminolysis of thiolesters (77) and particularly to that of Bergmann and his associates, on acyl-transfer reactions (78). The acetylation of amino acids by N, N'-diacetyl-2, 5-dioxyketo-piperazine (79) and the hippurylation of glycine by hippurylbenzoyl-L-histidine methyl ester are of particular interest in relation to the enzymatic transfer reactions to amines and imidazole to be discussed shortly. More recently aminolysis of acetylimidazole has been described (80).

2. *Enzymatic acyl-transfer reactions*

The discussion of these reactions will be divided into several parts: (a) transfer from a thiolester to inorganic P; (b) CoA transfer from thiolester to a free acid; (c) acyl transfer from one thiolester to another; (d) acyl transfer from a thiolester to choline, amino acids, amines, or imidazole and (e) transfer from a thiolester to oxaloacetate.

(a) The phosphorolysis of the acyl group of glyceraldehyde-3-phosphate dehydrogenase and the more complex interaction of phosphate and ADP with succinyl-CoA have been discussed above. In bacteria, an enzyme has been found which catalyzes the reversible transfer of acetylphosphate to acetyl-CoA. This enzyme, phosphotransacetylase, was studied in detail (64). From equilibrium measurements an approximate value of 10,000-12,000 calories per mole was assigned to the ΔF of hydrolysis of the thiolester linkage of CoA. With arsenate, a complete hydrolysis of acetylphosphate can be achieved. Since the reaction rate is proportional to CoA concentration over a wide range, this system has been most useful for the assay of CoA. Phosphotransacetylase appears to be absent from animal tissues, where another mechanism of acetate activation appears to operate. In several bacterial species the activation of acetate proceeds through reactions shown below, catalyzed by a bacterial kinase and phosphotransacetylase.

$$\text{Acetate} + \text{ATP} \rightleftharpoons \text{acetylphosphate} + \text{ADP}$$

$$\text{Acetylphosphate} + \text{CoA} \rightleftharpoons \text{acetyl-CoA} + \text{P}_i$$

Acetate activation in yeast and in animal tissues has been shown to be catalyzed by ATP and CoA and results in the formation of acetyl-CoA, pyrophosphate, and AMP. This reaction has been discussed previously.

(b) *Cl. kluyveri* contains an enzyme, referred to as CoA-transphorase (81). It catalyzes the reaction:

$$\text{Acetyl-CoA} + \text{propionate} \rightleftharpoons \text{propionyl-CoA} + \text{acetate}$$

This reaction may serve to activate an acid, for which no ATP-linked kinase is available. An enzyme from animal tissues catalyzes a similar CoA-transfer reaction (70, 71):

$$\text{Succinyl-CoA} + \text{acetoacetate} \rightleftharpoons \text{succinate} + \text{acetoacetyl-CoA}$$

The enzyme does not react with acetyl-CoA, but several other ketoacids (α-ketovalerate,-caproate,-hexanoate) can substitute for acetoacetate. Isolation of the acetoacetyl-CoA formed by this transfer reaction was also reported.

(c) The transfer of an acyl group to another thiolester with the liberation of a free SH group appears to be of particular importance in fatty acid metabolism. The reaction is readily reversible, and in the case of the reaction:

$$2 \text{ acetyl–CoA} \rightleftharpoons \text{acetoacetyl–CoA} + \text{CoA–SH}$$

an approximate estimate of the equilibrium constant has been made. It is found to favor greatly the thioclastic cleavage of acetoacetyl-CoA (72, 82). The enzyme was therefore named thiolase. The enzyme was found to be quite sensitive to SH-inhibitors, which suggested a participation of an acyl-enzyme complex of thiolase which reacts with the free thiolester of CoA. Thus a modified concept of a second active acetate has reappeared in the form of an acyl-enzyme complex. It readily explains the "oriented condensation" in the oxidation of carboxyl-labeled octanoate which results in an uneven distribution of label in acetoacetate (83, 84).

(d) The acyl transfer from acetyl-CoA to choline and amines has been reviewed elsewhere (85, 86). A convenient spectrophotometric assay method based on differences between spectra of free and acylated aromatic amines has been developed (87). The acetylation of amines by acetyl-CoA in the presence of the pigeon-liver enzyme preparation was used as the assay for the first isolation of acetyl-CoA from yeast (8). The transfer of the acyl group from acetylphosphate to amino acids has been studied further (88, 89). Several observations suggest the participation of phosphotransacetylase and acetyl-CoA in this reaction, which would permit the reaction to be included in this group of reactions. However, the activation of the reaction by a high concentration of cyanide remains unexplained, and further elucidation of the mechanism of this reaction should prove of interest.

Another acyl transfer in *Cl. kluyveri* has been discovered recently (90). It was demonstrated that imidazole can act as an acceptor for the acyl group of acetyl-CoA. From equilibrium data, the ΔF of hydrolysis of the acylimidazole linkage was estimated to be at least 12,000-15,000 cal. This is then another potential compound for energy-transfer reactions, and attention should be drawn to the chemical studies on acyl transfers with imidazoles (79, 80).

(e) The condensation of acetyl-CoA with oxalacetate is catalyzed by the condensing enzyme (91).

$$\text{Acetyl-CoA} + \text{oxaloacetate} + H_2O \rightleftharpoons \text{citrate} + \text{CoA}$$

The participation of water in this reaction and the release of a free carboxyl group separates this reaction from all the others. The mechanism of this methyl activation (85) is still unknown. Somewhat unexpected is the reversibility which can be readily demonstrated (92), since it must involve the interaction between a carboxyl group and the SH group of CoA. Attempts to show reversibility in other reactions of this type have not been successful (6). The availability of the condensing enzyme in crystalline form should facilitate further inquiries into the mechanism of its action, and the possibility of a citryl-CoA enzyme complex should be considered.

3. *Transfer of carbonyl groups*

(a) *Carboxylase.* The formation of acetoin (acetylmethylcarbinol) by yeast was interpreted over thirty years ago to be caused by a condensation between an " active aldehyde " and another aldehyde molecule (93, 94).

$$[CH_3CHO] + OHCCH_3 \rightarrow CH_3COCHOHCH_3$$

It was apparent that this was an " oriented condensation " because of the formation of optically active end products (cf. 95), as well as from later studies on isotope distributions in experiments performed with labeled acetaldehyde. Though some randomization did occur, free acetaldehyde preferentially contributed to the carbinol end of acetoin, while the active aldehyde became the carbonyl end (96).

Since the different types of acetoin formation were thoroughly discussed in a recent review (28), emphasis is placed here on some of the more recent developments in the field. Preparations of pyruvic oxidase from pigeon breast muscle were found to catalyze acyloin formation without addition of free aldehyde (23). Cocarboxylase is the only coenzyme required for this process. Addition of propionaldehyde increased the formation of acyloin with a proportionate inhibition of pyruvate oxidation, so that the net sum of pyruvate utilization remained essentially constant. Thus a direct competition for the active aldehyde by an electron acceptor (ferricyanide) and an acceptor aldehyde was demonstrated. Similar types of inhibitions had been observed also with " active acetate " (cf. 28). It is of interest that the purified pyruvic oxidase also decarboxylates hydroxypyruvate (23).

Studies on the mechanism of acetoin synthesis by α-carboxylase from wheat germ revealed that during a 2,700-fold purification the activities for decarboxylation and acetoin-formation ran parallel (27). This and several other similarities in behavior permitted the conclusion that a single enzyme catalyzes both reactions. α-Acetolactate is not an intermediate in this reaction, and free acetaldehyde alone lends to acetoin formation. Reversibility of the acetoin reaction could not be demonstrated. Since acetoin can be utilized for acetylation reactions when sodium acetate is inactive (97), it is very likely that acetoin must be oxidized to diacetyl before an active aldehyde or acetate can be produced.

It is clear from the above that an active carbonyl-enzyme complex is formed by the wheat germ carboxylase from either pyruvate or free acetaldehyde, and is condensed with another free aldehyde to an acyloin. It must be concluded therefore that in this case a separate carboligase enzyme is not operative, but that the concept of an " oriented condensation " of active and acceptor aldehyde by carboxy lase is strengthened by this recent work.

(b) *Transketolase.* A study of the degradation and biosynthesis of ribulose-5-phosphate revealed a mechanism quite similar to that of acetoin formation (98, 99). When ribulose-5-phosphate is incubated with a crystalline enzyme from yeast, triosephosphate formation is observed only when an acceptor aldehyde is added to the system (100). As acceptor aldehydes glycolaldehyde, glyceraldehyde, or ribose-5-phosphate serve about equally well. With ribose-5-phos· phate as acceptor, a heptulose phosphate is formed.

It has therefore been proposed that ribulose-5-phosphate is split by the enzyme to yield glyceraldehyde-3-phosphate and an active aldehyde-enzyme complex which does not dissociate readily (Reaction 1). In the presence of pentose isomerase (Reaction 2) ribose-5-phosphate is formed, which acts as an acceptor aldehyde and allows reaction (3) to proceed. It is clear therefore that for a detailed analysis of the reaction mechanism removal of pentose isomerase is essential.

$$CH_2OPO_3H_2CHOHCHOHCOCH_2OH \rightleftharpoons CH_2OPO_3H_2CHOHCHO$$
$$+ [CH_2OHCHO] \quad (1)$$

$$CH_2OPO_3H_2CHOHCHOHCOCH_2OH$$
$$\rightleftharpoons CH_2OPO_3H_2CHOHCHOHCHOHCHO \quad (2)$$

$$[CH_2OHCHO] + RCHO \rightleftharpoons RCHOHCOCH_2OH \quad (3)$$

Active aldehyde can be produced by this enzyme by decarboxylation of hydroxypyruvate, but pyruvate is inactive. Cocarboxylase and Mg^{++} was found to be required for the activity of the enzyme (98, 99). The role of these reactions in intermediary metabolism will be reviewed elsewhere (101). The similarity to the carboxylase system is obvious. There are a number of interesting differences, however. The carbonyl complex of the yeast and wheat carboxylase is dissociable, while the transketolase carbonyl-complex is not. In this respect it resembles the acetoin-forming muscle enzyme which does not exchange with free acetaldehyde (cf. 23). The latter enzyme can decarboxylate both hydroxypyruvate and pyruvate, while transketolase acts only on hydroxypyruvate. The specificity of transketolase in respect to acceptor aldehydes is also different. While in the case of the muscle enzyme acetaldehyde serves as an acceptor, it is inactive in the transketolase system. These points seem to emphasize that the condensation between the enzyme-carbonyl complex and the acceptor aldehyde is quite specific and it indicates an active participation of the enzyme catalyst in a " carboligase "-like reaction. The mechanism of cocarboxylase participation is still unknown. The ability of transketolase to form active aldehyde from either hydroxypyruvate or ribulose-5-phosphate demonstrates that a free carboxyl group does not necessarily participate in the interaction of the substrate with the enzyme-coenzyme complex.

(c) *Transaldolase.* It has been suggested that the formation of hexosemonophosphate from ribose-5-phosphate involves a transaldolase type of reaction (102). Partial purification of this enzyme from yeast has been obtained (103, 104). Isotope experiments are consistent with an aldol transfer from heptulose-7-phosphate to glyceraldehyde-3-phosphate, with the formation of fructose-6-phosphate and a tetrose phosphate (104). As a mechanism for this type of transfer reaction the formation of an " active alcohol " which can react with a free aldehyde might be postulated.

Concluding Remarks

The study of the formation of carbonyl- and acyl-complexes has brought to light a number of facts elucidating the mode of enzyme action. The participation of these complexes in transfer and in energy-yielding reactions emphasizes their importance in biosynthetic processes. Their role in the metabolism of carbohydrates and fats has been amply demonstrated. Recently Dr. R. B. Johnston at Yale has found that papain catalyzes a rapid hydrolysis of benzoylglycyl thiolesters (105). He has in progress experiments bearing on the possible role of these acyl compounds in peptide synthesis.

Perhaps a few words may be added in regard to some of the problems which still lie ahead of us in this field. There are several indications for the existence of an active one-carbon unit and for its transfer in important biological systems (106). The participation of vitamins in these reactions (107), and particularly the stimulating effect of homocysteine (cf. 106), point again to the participation of SH-compounds.

The history of the concept of "active acetates" has been most instructive. The identification of acetyl-CoA as an active acetate did not suffice to explain data obtained with isotopically labeled octanoate. An active acyl complex on the enzyme thiolase has now been suggested as the other "active acetate." Although "active aldehyde" had been postulated even before the "active acetates," the nature of the carbonyl complex is still unknown. Very likely cocarboxylase, which is a cofactor in the formation of active aldehydes from α-ketoacids and ketosugars, participates in the formation of these complexes. Perhaps one might add the "active alcohol" to the list of unknowns. The transaldolization reaction and the recent observation implicating alcohol dehydrogenase in the formation of esters (108) may well be interpreted in this sense.

These activated compounds bound to the enzymes are difficult to study directly. The availability of highly purified enzymes in large quantities will permit their investigations as stoichiometric reactants.

REFERENCES

1. Keller, E. B., J. R. Rachele, and V. du Vigneaud, *J. Biol. Chem.*, 177, 733 (1949).
2. Cohen, S. S., in *Phosphorus Metabolism*, Vol. 1 (W. D. McElroy & B. Glass, eds.), p. 148, Johns Hopkins Press, Baltimore (1951).
3. Buchanan, J. G., J. A. Bassham, A. A. Benson, D. F. Bradley, M. Calvin, L. L. Daus, M. Goodman, P. M. Hayes, V. H. Lynch, L. T. Norris, and A. T. Wilson, in *Phosphorus Metabolism*, Vol. 2 (W. D. McElroy & B. Glass, eds.), p. 440, Johns Hopkins Press, Baltimore (1952).
4. Warburg, O., and W. Christian, *Biochem. Z.*, 303, 40 (1939).
5. Meyerhof, O., and P. Oesper, *J. Biol. Chem.*, 170, 1 (1947).
6. Racker, E., *J. Biol. Chem.*, 190, 685 (1951).
7. Rapkine, L., *Biochem. J.*, 32, 1729 (1938).
8. Lynen, F., E. Reichert, and L. Rueff, *Liebig. Ann. Chem.*, 574, 1 (1951).
9. Chantrenne, H., and F. Lipmann, *J. Biol. Chem.*, 187, 757 (1950).

10. Korkes, S., A. del Campillo, I. C. Gunsalus, and S. Ochoa, *J. Biol. Chem.*, 193, 721 (1951).
11. Burton, R. M., *Federation Proc.*, 11, 193 (1952).
12. Pinchot, G. B., and E. Racker, in *Phosphorus Metabolism*, Vol. 1 (W. D. McElroy & B. Glass, eds.), p. 366, Johns Hopkins Press, Baltimore (1951).
13. Harting, J., *Federation Proc.*, 10, 195 (1951).
14. Racker, E., and I. Krimsky, *J. Biol. Chem.*, 198, 731 (1952).
15. Harting, J., and S. Velick, *Federation Proc.*, 11, 226 (1952).
16. Cori, G. T., M. W. Slein, and C. F. Cori, *J. Biol. Chem.*, 173, 605 (1948).
17. Krebs, E. G., G. W. Rafter, and J. McBroom Junge, *J. Biol. Chem.*, 200, 479 (1953).
18. Lipmann, F., and L. C. Tuttle, *J. Biol. Chem.*, 159, 21 (1945).
19. Taylor, J. F., S. F. Velick, G. T. Cori, C. F. Cori, and M. W. Slein, *J. Biol. Chem.*, 173, 619 (1948).
20. Velick, S. F., in *Mechanism of Enzyme Action* (W. D. McElroy and B. Glass, eds.), Johns Hopkins Press, Baltimore (1954).
21. Krimsky, I., and E. Racker, unpub. exper.
22. Pullman, M. E., *Federation Proc.*, 12, 255 (1953).
23. Schweet, R. S., M. Fuld, K. Cheslock, and M. H. Paul, in *Phosphorus Metabolism*, Vol. 1 (W. D. McElroy & B. Glass, eds.), p. 246, Johns Hopkins Press, Baltimore (1951).
24. Korkes, S., in *Phosphorus Metabolism*, Vol. 1 (W. D. McElroy & B. Glass, eds.), p. 259, Johns Hopkins Press, Baltimore (1951).
25. Korkes, S., pers. com.
26. Goldberg, M., and D. R. Sanadi, *J. Am. Chem. Soc.*, 74, 4972 (1952).
27. Singer, T. P., and J. Pensky, *Biochem. et Biophys. Acta*, 9, 316 (1952).
28. Ochoa, S., *Physiol. Rev.*, 31, 56 (1951).
29. Reed, L. J., and B. G. DeBusk, *J. Am. Chem. Soc.*, 75, 1261 (1953).
30. Chou, T. C., and F. Lipmann, *J. Biol. Chem.*, 196, 89 (1952).
31. Cavallini, D., *Biochem. J.*, 49, 1 (1951).
32. Slater, E. C., *Nature*, 170, 970 (1952).
33. Lardy, H. A., *Proceedings Natl. Acad. of Sciences*, 38, 1003 (1952).
34. Strauss, B. S., *J. Am. Chem. Soc.*, 75, 1012 (1953).
35. Kaufman, S. in *Phosphorus Metabolism*, Vol. 1 (W. D. McElroy and B. Glass, eds.), p. 370, Johns Hopkins Press, Baltimore (1951).
36. Sanadi, D. R., and J. Littlefield, *J. Biol. Chem.*, 193, 683 (1951).
37. Sanadi, D. R., and J. W. Littlefield, *J. Biol. Chem.*, 201, 103 (1953).
38. Kaufman, S., C. Gilvarg, O. Cori, and S. Ochoa, *J. Biol. Chem.*, 203, 869 (1953).
39. Sanadi, D. R., and J. W. Littlefield, and H. Bock, *J. Biol. Chem.*, 197, 851 (1952).
40. Hager, L. P., J. D. Fortney, and I. C. Gunsalus, *Federation Proc.*, 12, 213 (1953).
41. Lindstrom, E. S., *J. Bact.*, 65, 565 (1953).
42. Dixon, M., and L. G. Zerfas, *Biochem. J.*, 34, 371 (1940).
43. Racker, E., unpub. exper.
44. Lipmann, F., M. E. Jones, S. Black, and R. M. Flynn, *J. Am. Chem. Soc.*, 74, 2384 (1952).
45. Racker, E., *J. Biol. Chem.*, 177, 883 (1949).
46. Black, S., *Arch. Biochem. and Biophys.*, 34, 86 (1951).
47. Seegmiller, J. E., *J. Biol. Chem.*, 201, 629 (1953).
48. Burton, R. M., and E. R. Stadtman, *J. Biol. Chem.*, 202, 873 (1953).

49. Green, D. E., P. K. Stumpf, and K. Zarudnaya, *J. Biol. Chem.*, **167**, 811 (1947).
50. Dolin, M., *Federation Proceedings*, **12**, 198 (1953).
51. Racker, E., *Biochim. et Biophys. Acta*, **9**, 577 (1952).
52. Wieland, T., and H. Köppe, *Liebigs Ann. Chem.*, in press.
53. Racker, E., *Federation Proc.*, **12** (1953) in press.
54. Barker, H. A., in *Phosphorus Metabolism*, Vol. 1 (W. D. McElroy & B. Glass, eds.), p. 204, Johns Hopkins Press, Baltimore (1951).
55. Kennedy, E. P., and A. L. Lehninger, in *Phosphorus Metabolism*, Vol. 2 (W. D. McElroy and B. Glass, eds.), p. 253, Johns Hopkins Press, Baltimore (1952).
56. Lynen, F., *Federation Proc.*, **12** (1953) in press.
57. Mahler, H. R., *Federation Proc.*, **12** (1953) in press.
58. Drysdale, G. R., and H. A. Lardy, in *Phosphorus Metabolism*, Vol. 2 (W. D. McElroy & B. Glass, eds.), p. 281, Johns Hopkins Press, Baltimore (1952).
59. Mahler, H. R., in *Phosphorus Metabolism*, Vol. 2 (W. D. McElroy & B. Glass, eds.), p. 286, Johns Hopkins Press, Baltimore (1952).
60. Stadtman, E. R., and H. A. Barker, *J. Biol. Chem.*, **180**, 1085 (1949).
61. Brady, R. O., and S. Gurin, *J. Biol. Chem.*, **199**, 421 (1952).
62. Kornberg, A., in *Phosphorus Metabolism*, Vol. 2 (W. D. McElroy & B. Glass, eds.), p. 245, Johns Hopkins Press, Baltimore (1952).
63. Harting, J., pers. com.
64. Stadtman, E. R., *J. Biol. Chem.*, **196**, 527 (1952).
65. Lipmann, F., *Advances in Enzymol.*, **6**, 231 (1946).
66. Kielly, W., pers. com.
67. Gergely, J., P. Hele, and C. V. Ramakrishnan, *J. Biol. Chem.*, **198**, 323 (1952).
68. Von Korff, R. W., *J. Biol. Chem.*, **200**, 401 (1953).
69. Stadtman, E. R., M. Doudoroff, and F. Lipmann, *J. Biol. Chem.*, **191**, 377 (1951).
70. Stern, J. R., M. J. Coon, and A. del Campillo, *Nature*, **171**, 28 (1953)
71. Green, D. E., D. S. Goldman, S. Mil, and H. Beinert, *J. Biol. Chem.*, **202**, 137 (1953).
72. Lynen, F., L. Wessely, O. Wieland, and L. Rueff, *Angew. Chem.*, **64**, 687 (1952).
73. Stern, J. R., and A. del Campillo, *J. Am. Chem. Soc.*, **75**, 2277 (1953).
74. Lehninger, A. L., and G. D. Greville, *J. Am. Chem. Soc.*, **75**, 1515 (1953).
75. Pawlewski, B., *Ber. deut. chem. Ges.*, **31**, 661 (1898); **35**, 110 (1902).
76. Schwyzer, R., *Helv. Chim. Acta*, **36**, 414 (1953).
77. Holmberg, B., *Arkiv Kemi, Mineral., Geol.*, **17**, 1 (1944).
78. Bergmann, M., du Vigneaud, and L. Zervas, *Ber. deut. chem. Ges.*, **62**, 1902 (1929).
79. Bergmann, M., and L. Zervas, *Z. physiol. Chem.*, **175**, 145 (1928).
80. Wieland, T., G. Schneider, *Ann. Chem. Justus Liebigs*, **580**, 159 (1953).
81. Stadtman, E. R., *Federation Proc.*, **11**, 291 (1952).
82. Stern, J. R., M. J. Coon, and A. del Campillo, *J. Am. Chem. Soc.*, **75**, 1517 (1953).
83. Buchanan, J. M., W. Sakami, and S. Gurin, *J. Biol. Chem.*, **169**, 411 (1947).
84. Crandall, D. I., R. O. Brady, and S. Gurin, *J. Biol. Chem.*, **181**, 845 (1949).
85. Lipmann, F., *Harvey Lectures*, 1948-49, p. 99.
86. Nachmansohn, D., and I. B. Wilson, *Advances in Enzymol.*, **12**, 259 (1951).
87. Mehler, A. H., H. Tabor, and E. R. Stadtman, *Federation Proc.*, **12**, 245 (1953).
88. Katz, J., I. Lieberman, and H. A. Barker, *J. Biol. Chem.*, **200**, 417 (1953).
89. Katz, J., I. Lieberman, and H. A. Barker, *J. Biol. Chem.*, **200**, 431 (1953).

90. Stadtman, E. R., *J. Am. Chem. Soc.*, **75**, 2022 (1953).
91. Ochoa, S., J. R. Stern, and M. C. Schneider, *J. Biol. Chem.*, **193**, 703 (1951).
92. Stern, J. R., B. Shapiro, E. R. Stadtman, and S. Ochoa, *J. Biol. Chem.*, **193**, 703 (1951).
93. Neuberg, C., and J. Hirsch, *Biochem. Z.*, **115**, 282 (1921).
94. Neuberg, C., and E. Simon, *Ergeb. Enzymforsch.*, **2**, 118 (1933).
95. Neuberg, C., *Ann. Rev. Biochem.*, **15**, 435 (1946).
96. Gross, N. H., and C. H. Werkman, *Arch. Biochem.*, **15**, 125 (1947).
97. Doisy, E. A., Jr., and W. W. Westerfeld, *J. Biol. Chem.*, **149**, 229 (1943).
98. Horecker, B. L., and P. Z. Smyrniotis, *J. Am. Chem. Soc.*, **75**, 1009 (1953).
99. Racker, E., G. de la Haba, and I. G. Leder, *J. Am. Chem. Soc.*, **75**, 1010 (1953).
100. de la Haba, G., I. G. Leder, and E. Racker, *Federation Proc.*, **12**, 194 (1953).
101. Racker, E., *Advances in Enzymol.*, **15** (in press).
102. Dische, Z., in *Phosphorus Metabolism*, Vol. 1 (W. D. McElroy & B. Glass, eds.) p. 171, Johns Hopkins Press, Baltimore (1951).
103. de la Haba, G., and E. Racker, *Federation Proc.*, **11**, 201 (1952).
104. Horecker, B. L., P. Z. Smyrniotis, and H. Klenow, *Federation Proc.*, **12**, 219 (1953).
105. Johnston, R. B., unpub.
106. Cantoni, G. L., in *Phosphorus Metabolism*, Vol. 2 (W. D. McElroy & B. Glass, eds.), p. 129, Johns Hopkins Press, Baltimore (1951).
107. Welch, A. D., and C. A. Nichol, in *Ann. Rev. Biochem.*, **21**, 633 (1952).
108. Kendal, L. P., and A. N. Ramanathom, *Biochem. J.*, **52**, 430 (1952).

THE ALCOHOL AND GLYCERALDEHYDE-3-PHOSPHATE DEHYDROGENASES OF YEAST AND MAMMALS

SIDNEY F. VELICK

Department of Biological Chemistry,
Washington University, School of Medicine, St. Louis

THE REVERSIBLE oxidation equilibria catalysed by glyceraldehyde-3-phosphate dehydrogenase (GDH) and alcohol dehydrogenase (ADH) may be represented by the following equations

$$\overset{O}{\overset{\|}{R C H}} + DPN^- + HPO_4^= \longleftrightarrow R\overset{O}{\overset{\|}{C}}OPO_3^= + DPNH^= + H^+ \qquad (1)$$

$$\overset{O}{\overset{\|}{R C H}} + DPNH^= + H^+ \longleftrightarrow RCH_2OH + DPN^- \qquad (2)$$

Both enzymes activate the carbonyl group of the aldehyde and the pyridine ring of diphosphopyridine nucleotide (DPN), but the carbonyl group of the aldehyde is activated by GDH to act as a hydrogen donor and by ADH to act as a hydrogen acceptor. Both enzymes may be crystallized from yeast and from mammalian tissues in substantial amounts and in states of purity sufficient for qualitative and quantitative study of their separate interactions with substrate and coenzyme. The experiments discussed in this review deal with the properties and reactions of the two GDH enzymes and of the yeast and mammalian ADH.

The mammalian GDH, crystallized from rabbit skeletal muscle extracts by the method of Cori, Slein, and Cori (8), is a protein-DPN complex (31). The molecular weight of the complex has been found by Taylor from measurements of sedimentation velocity, diffusion, and partial specific volume, to be 120,000 (30). The bound DPN may be removed by adsorption on charcoal or by heat or acid denaturation of the protein but is not readily removed by

491

dialysis or recrystallization. From analyses of the spectrum in the 250 to 290 mμ region (Fig. 1) and from measurements at 340 mμ of the DPNH produced when excess substrate is added to the complex the composition of the recrystallized complex may be designated as GDH–(DPN)$_2$ (36). The yeast GDH crystallized by the method of Warburg and Christian (38) or by the totally

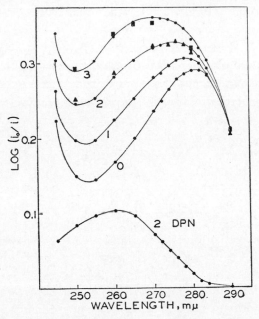

Fig. 1. Absorption spectra of glyceraldehyde-3-phosphate dehydrogenase, Curve O, charcoal-treated enzyme, no DPN. Curves 1, 2, and 3, the same concentration of charcoal-treated enzyme as in curve O but with 1, 2, and 3 equivalents of added DPN, respectively. The triangles, curve 2, are from the untreated enzyme-(DPN)$_2$ complex recrystallized four times. The squares, curve 3, are from the muscle extract. The lower curve is the contribution of two equivalents of DPN.

different method of Krebs, Rafter, and Junge (16) contains no significant amount of bound DPN but binds added DPN strongly (34). The molecular weight of this enzyme, according to measurements by Taylor, is 122,000.

Neither of the ADH enzymes is isolated as a DPN complex, but each has a strong and characteristic affinity for the reduced and oxidized forms of the coenzyme. The horse-liver ADH crystallized by the method of Bonnichsen and Wassen (4) has been reported to have a molecular weight of 73,000 (32). The yeast ADH, by different methods, has been crystallized by Negelein and Wulff (22) and by Racker (24). Its molecular weight, from sedimentation velocity and diffusion measurements, is 150,000 (13), or about twice that of mammalian ADH.

The two GDH proteins are of the same approximate size and have characteristically similar but not identical amino acid compositions (37). Although they appear to have many structural features in common they are immunologically distinguishable (15), and exhibit differences in substrate and coenzyme interactions and in physical properties. Although amino acid analyses of the ADH proteins from yeast and liver have not yet been reported, it is apparent from the differences in partial specific volume and in the molar extinction coefficients in the regions affected by the aromatic amino acids that the amino acid compositions are quite different (13). The difference in molecular weights therefore does not represent the dimerization of the same or closely related subunits. Other differences between these two enzymes indicate that they are less closely related than the GDH enzymes.

COENZYME BINDING

The stoichiometry and apparent dissociation constants of some of the complexes formed by the enzymes have been measured by an ultracentrifugal separation method. The proteins and their complexes sediment almost completely from solution under conditions which establish only small concentration gradients with the free substrates and coenzymes. One may therefore measure, with relatively small corrections, the amount of a coenzyme transported per mole of sedimented protein and so construct titration curves which yield binding capacities and dissociation constants. The experimental restrictions are (a) that the dissociation constant be small, and (b) that the protein be stable in solution during the 2 to 4 hours required for an experiment.

· *Mammalian GDH.* When the mammalian GDH–(DPN)$_2$ complex is sedimented in the ultracentrifuge in various buffers of pH 6.7 to 8.3 at 0° to 5° C. the small excess of free nucleotide over protein in the supernatant solution permits the calculation as an upper limit of a dissociation constant of the complex of about 2×10^{-7} moles per liter. See Table 1 (35). When the sedimentation is carried out in the presence of increments of added DPN the dissociation is suppressed, but no significant amount of extra DPN is bound.

TABLE 1

THE DPN-BINDING CAPACITY OF THE RECRYSTALLIZED MAMMALIAN GDH–(DPN)$_2$ COMPLEX; ULTRACENTRIFUGAL SEPARATION METHOD

Tube	Initial Concentrations		Supernatant solutions				Additional DPN bound
	GDH–(DPN)$_2$	Free DPN added	log $(io/_1)$ 260 mμ	280 mμ	GDH–(DPN)$_2$	Free DPN	per mole of enzyme
	(moles per liter) $\times 10^4$				(moles per liter) $\times 10^4$		
1a	0.318	1.94	3.55	0.846	0.005	1.80	
1b	0.000	1.94	3.57	0.80	0.000	1.82	0.06
			log $(io/_1)$ 340 mμ				
2a	0.512	4.05	2.38		0.006	3.78	
2b	0.000	4.05	2.44		0.000	3.88	0.02

In these experiments DPN was sedimented, alone in tubes 1b and 2b, and with GDH–(DPN)$_2$ complex in tubes 1a and 2a. The supernatant solutions in exp. 1 were analysed directly from optical measurements at 2 wave lengths; in exp. 2 they were analysed by enzymatic reduction and measurement of the DPNH at 340 mμ. The DPN established a small concentration gradient in the centrifugal field. Protein was almost completely sedimented. The DPN in the supernatant solutions in 1a and 2a was slightly less than that in the 1b and 2b.

Enzyme which during purification has become reversibly inactivated, in the absence of cysteine, still binds two equivalents of DPN strongly. The temperature coefficient of DPN-binding is small (34, 36).

Yeast GDH. When the yeast GDH which contains no bound DPN is sedimented with increments of added DPN, the DPN is strongly bound. The maximal binding capacity is two equivalents of DPN per mole of protein, (Table 2). The apparent dissociation constants decrease as saturation is approached (34). This suggests that the presence of one molecule of DPN on the protein increases the affinity of the protein for a second. The dissociation constants of the yeast GDH–(DPN) complexes are 5 to 10 times as large as those of the mammalian enzyme, but the stoichiometry is the same. Rate measurements at 26° C. show a decline in specific activity as a result of dilution of the complex and yield a dissociation constant close to that obtained at 0° C. by the ultracentrifugal separation method. The mammalian GDH–DPN complex on the other hand,

TABLE 2

THE BINDING OF DPN BY THE YEAST GDH;
ULTRACENTRIFUGAL SEPARATION METHOD

Tube	Initial Concentrations		DPN		moles DPN bound / moles GDH	K
	GDH	DPN	free	bound		(moles per
	(Moles per liter) $\times 10^4$					liter) $\times 10^5$
1	0.150	0.145	0.064	0.081	0.54	1.7
2	0.150	0.29	0.122	0.168	1.12	0.96
3	0.150	0.58	0.298	0.282	1.88	0.19
4	0.326	1.532	0.374	0.658	2.02	—
5	0.326	3.064	2.396	0.668	2.05	—

These experiments show the presence of two DPN-binding sites per molecule of yeast GDH. The drift in K is obtained irrespective of the method of analysis, i. e., by measurement of optical densities at 260 and 280 mμ or by enzymatic reduction of the DPN. K is calculated from the mass law relation

$$\frac{(2[GDH_{total}] - [DPN_{bound}])[DPN_{free}]}{[DPN_{bound}]}$$

in accord with its stronger DPN affinity, does not lose activity on dilution (9). Because of side-reactions that occur with DPNH at high concentrations of both the yeast and mammalian GDH (17, 36), satisfactory measurements of the binding of the reduced coenzyme, DPNH, have not been obtained by the ultracentrifugal separation method. The results with rather large and uncertain corrections indicate that both enzymes bind DPNH, with dissociation constants somewhat larger than for DPN.

Mammalian ADH. In contrast to GDH, both the yeast and mammalian ADH enzymes bind DPNH much more strongly than DPN.

The 340 mμ absorption band of DPNH is shifted to 325 mμ in the mammalian ADH–DPNH complex (32). This permitted Theorell and Chance (33) to measure DPNH-binding stoichiometry and the apparent dissociation constant of the complex by direct spectrophotometric methods. Two moles of DPNH are bound per mole of enzyme, with a dissociation constant of 10^{-7} M. The binding of DPN was not measured directly, but from the effect of enzyme concentration upon the over-all oxidation equilibrium it was con-

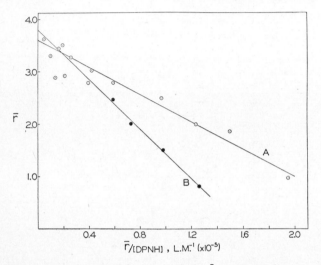

Fig. 2. The binding of DPNH by yeast ADH. $\bar{r}$ is the number of molecules of DPNH bound per molecule of protein. [C] is the free DPNH concentration. Curve A is for the binding of DPNH alone. Curve B is for the competitive binding of DPNH in the presence of 5.79×10^{-4} M DPN. Competition is shown by the extrapolation to the same maximal $\bar{r}$, and the steeper slope in the presence of DPN.

cluded that DPN was bound less "tightly" than DPNH, with a dissociation constant of the order of 10^{-5} M. The contributions of alcohol and aldehyde binding, if they occurred at all, were assumed to be negligible.

Yeast ADH. The 340 mμ absorption band of DPNH is not shifted appreciably in the complex with yeast ADH. It has been possible, however, to measure both DPN and DPNH binding by the ultracentrifugal separation method (13). In Fig. 2 and 3, $\bar{r}$, the number of molecules of coenzyme bound per mole of protein, is plotted against $\bar{r}/C$, where C is the coenzyme concentration. The relationship between the quantities plotted is

$$\bar{r} = n + K' \frac{\bar{r}}{C} \tag{3}$$

where n is the maximal binding capacity and K' is the apparent dissociation constant. This equation may be derived from the mass

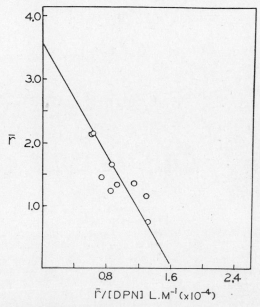

Fig. 3. The binding of DPN by yeast ADH. r is the number of molecules of DPN bound per molecule of protein. C is the concentration of free DPN.

law equilibrium (27). n is given by the intercept on the ordinate and K by the slope. The value for n is almost reached directly with DPNH, but because of the larger value of K', the corresponding n value for DPN requires extrapolation. In the experiments shown the value of n is the same with DPN and DPNH. Because of the limitation of the method with dissociation constants as large as that of the DPN complex, the points with DPN in different experiments show considerable scatter. That the extrapolated value of n is actually the same with both forms of the coenzyme is established by experiments to be described. The value of n obtained is 3.6. Under the conditions in which the experiments are carried out, up to 10 per cent of the enzyme becomes inactivated. This is sufficient to account for a 10 per cent error in n. The correct value of n is most probably 4. The dissociation constant, K', for yeast ADH–DPN is 2.6×10^{-4} and for ADH–DPNH, 1.3×10^{-5}. These are both much greater than the corresponding K's for liver ADH.

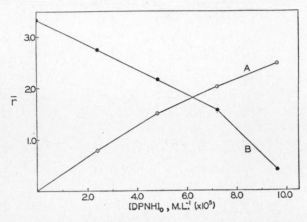

FIG. 4. Competition in the binding of DPN and DPNH by yeast ADH. Curve A is DPNH-binding in the presence of a constant total DPN concentration. Curve B is the DPN-binding when the total DPN is kept constant and the DPNH is varied. The DPN concentration in each tube was 5.79×10^{-4} M. The decrease in protein concentration in the top layers after sedimentation was 2.19×10^{-5} M.

When yeast ADH is sedimented with a constant high concentration of DPN and increments of DPNH, it is found that the bound DPN is displaced by DPNH (Fig. 4), while the total amount of bound coenzyme remains constant. The binding is thus competitive and is described by the relation

$$\bar{r}_1 = n - K \left(1 + \frac{[C_2]}{K_2}\right) \frac{\bar{r}_1}{[C_2]} = n - K^* \frac{\bar{r}_1}{[C_1]} \qquad (4)$$

where the subscripts $_1$ and $_2$ refer to DPNH and DPN, respectively. A similar equation may be solved for $\bar{r}_2$. A plot of $\bar{r}_1$ versus $\bar{r}_1/C_1$

in the competition experiments is a straight line (Fig. 2), which extrapolates to a value of n of 3.8. $K^* = 2.8 \times 10^{-5}$.

From the relation:

$$\frac{\bar{r}_1}{\bar{r}_2} = \frac{K_2[C_1]}{K_1[C_2]} \qquad (5)$$

it is found that $K_{DPN} = 3.3 \times 10^{-4}$ when $K_{DPNH} = 1.3 \times 10^{-5}$. This is in fair agreement with the results obtained under non-competitive conditions.

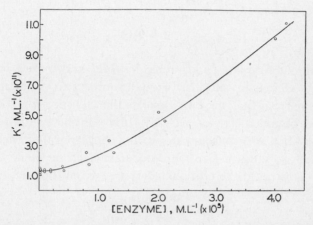

FIG. 5. The effect of yeast ADH concentration on the equilibrium $RCH_2OH + DPN \rightleftharpoons RCHO + DPNH + H^+$. The total coenzyme concentration in each tube was 3.85×10^{-5} M. The enzyme concentrations are indicated on the abcissa. Initial alcohol concentrations were varied from 0.1 M at low enzyme concentration to 5×10^{-4} M at high enzyme concentration. Equilibrium concentrations of DPNH and acetaldehyde varied from 2.8×10^{-5} to 0.71×10^{-5} M. The pH was measured after equilibrium was attained. The two sets of experiments were performed at 26° C., pH 7.5 to 7.9 with different enzyme preparations.

As with the liver ADH, the yeast enzyme at high concentration shifts the oxidation equilibrium. As shown in Fig. 5, a ten-fold increase in the apparent equilibrium constant is obtained at high enzyme concentration and the maximum has not been reached. Following the procedure of Alberty (1), the equilibrium may be formulated as

$$K'_{eq} = \frac{[DPNH][ALD]}{[DPN][ALC]} \; \frac{f_{DPNH}f_{ALD}}{f_{ALC}f_{DPN}} \qquad (6)$$

where the f's are those fractions of the total concentrations of the participants in the reaction which are not bound to the enzyme. The experimental conditions of Fig. 5 were such that in the region where the shift was pronounced the concentration of binding sites was well in excess of the total coenzyme concentration and greatly in excess of the total DPNH at equilibrium. DPNH therefore did not compete appreciably with DPN for binding sites. f_{DPN} could therefore be computed from the equations

$$\frac{(n[E] - [DPN_b])([DPN_t] - [DPN_b])}{[DPN_b]} = K_{DPN} \qquad (7)$$

$$f_{DPN} = ([DPN_t] - [DPN_b])/[DPN_t] \qquad (8)$$

where the subscripts t and b refer to *total* and *bound* forms, and $n = 4$. f_{DPNH} may be calculated from a similar pair of equations after subtracting from the total binding sites those occupied by DPN. The values so obtained do not account fully for the equilibrium shift. From the Michaelis constant for alcohol and from the concentrations employed, the value of f_{ALC} could not have been far from unity. The value of f_{ALD} could therefore be computed from the relation

$$f_{ALD} = \frac{K_{eq}}{K'_{eq}} \frac{f_{DPN}}{f_{DPNH}} \qquad (9)$$

These are shown in Table 3, together with the dissociation constants K_{ALD} computed from them. The corrected equilibrium constants, using the calculated coefficients for coenzyme and values of f_{ALD} calculated from an average ADH-acetaldehyde dissociation constant of 1.8×10^{-4} are shown in the last column of the table. Since the Michaelis constant for acetaldehyde is 1.1×10^{-4}, it may be inferred that the aldehyde binding, indicated by the equilibrium shift, represents the formation of an intermediary complex in the enzymatic reaction.

ESSENTIAL THIOL GROUPS

The inhibition of GDH in crude systems by reagents which oxidized thiol groups or formed derivatives with them was first observed by Rapkine and coworkers (26). Relations were also noted between the protein thiol groups and the coenzyme (19, 26). These functions were not considered by Warburg with the relatively stable crystalline yeast enzyme (38) but were quite apparent with the enzyme crystallized from rabbit muscle (8). Under conditions of recrystallization and testing in which the yeast enzyme may retain 90 per cent or more of maximal activity, the mammalian enzyme is spontaneously inactivated. Since activity is restored by cysteine or

TABLE 3

COENZYME AND ALDEHYDE BINDING BY YEAST ADH AND THE SHIFT
IN THE OXIDATION EQUILIBRIUM

ADH	$K'^{(1)}$	$f_{DPNH}^{(2)}$	$f_{DPN}^{(2)}$	$f_{ALD}^{(3)}$	$K_{ALD}^{(4)}$	$K^{(5)}$
(moles per liter) $\times 10^4$	$\times 10^{11}$				$\times 10^4$	$\times 10^{11}$
low	1.3 ± 0.1	1	1	1	—	1.3
11.9	3.39	0.38	0.81	0.82	2.0	1.25
19.8	5.24	0.26	0.73	0.70	1.8	1.31
39.7	10.2	0.14	0.53	0.48	1.4	1.6

[1] From experiments shown in Fig. 5.

[2] Calculated from eq. (7) and (8) with $K_{DPN} = 1.7 \times 10^{-4}$ and $K_{DPNH} = 2.3 \times 10^{-5}$.

[3] Calculated from $f_{ALD} = \dfrac{K}{K'} \dfrac{f_{DPN}}{f_{DPNH}}$; $K = 1.3 \times 10^{11}$.

[4] Calculated from $f_{ALD} = $ (free ALD)/(total ALD)

$K_{ALD} = $ [total ALD = bound ALD][4 AHD — bound ALD]/[bound ALD].

[5] From $K = K' \dfrac{f_{DPNH} f_{ALD}}{f_{DPN}}$, using the values of f_{DPN} and f_{DPNH} that are in the table and calculating f_{ALD} on the assumption $K_{ALD} = 1.8 \times 10^{-4}$.

reduced glutathione, the inactivation may result from oxidation of the essential thiol groups or mercaptide formation with traces of heavy metals. The enzyme is greatly stabilized and partly reactivated by metal complexing reagents.

Fig. 6 shows the complete inhibition of yeast GDH by two equivalents of *p*-chloromercuribenzoate (PCMB) and complete reactivation by cysteine. Similar results are obtained with the mammalian enzyme, except that slightly more than three equivalents of inhibitor are required. The yeast GDH–PCMB compound may be crystallized in the completely inactive form and completely reactivated by cysteine. The mammalian GDH-inhibitor compound retains potential activity sufficiently long enough to permit measurements of inhibition and full reactivation, but does not crystallize.

The yeast enzyme-inhibitor compound is incapable of binding

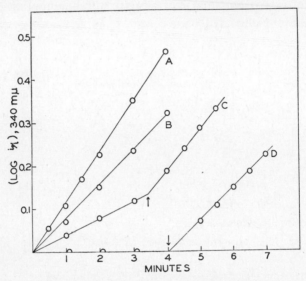

FIG. 6. The inhibition of glyceraldehyde-3-phosphate dehydrogenase (yeast) by *p*-chloromercuribenzoate. The reactions were carried out in 0.1 M sodium arsenate buffer, pH 7.6, and were followed by measuring the rate of increase in optical density at 340 mμ in the Beckman spectrophotometer in cuvettes of 1 cm. light path. The concentrations, in moles per liter $\times 10^3$, were for enzyme, 0.016; DPN, 0.286; DL-glyceraldehyde, 4.0. Reaction A was carried out in 0.003 M cysteine with no inhibitor. In reactions B, C, and D cysteine was omitted in the initial reaction mixtures. The inhibitor concentrations in these reactions were, respectively, 0.0000, 0.0128, and 0.0336 mole per liter $\times 10^3$. In reactions C and D cysteine at a final concentration of 0.003 M was added at the time indicated by the arrows.

DPN. The bound DPN on the mammalian enzyme is released when the complex with the inhibitor is formed (34). Fig. 7 shows the results of ultracentrifugal separations in which the binding of inhibitor and the release of DPN are measured. The DPN release is a direct function, and the enzyme activity is an inverse function, of the amount of inhibitor bound. At pH 7.6 the maximum number of equivalents of inhibitor bound was 3 per molecule of protein.

Boyer and Segal (5) by a direct spectrophotometric method at this pH find that 3 to 4 equivalents of inhibitor react. At a more acid pH which probably denatures the protein, amperometric titrations with *o*-iodosobenzoate indicate that the equivalent of 15 thiol groups react (private communication from Dr. Boyer).

Although some oxidation may have occurred beyond the disulfide stage, the above results indicate that most or all of the cystine sulfur

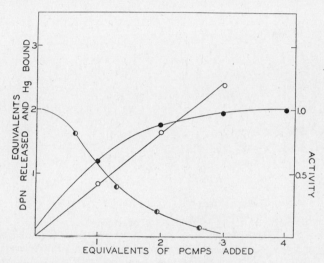

FIG. 7. The reaction of *p*-chloromercuriphenylsulfonate with the mammalian GDH. O, the number of moles of inhibitor bound per mole of enzyme: the number of moles of DPN released per mole of enzyme: ◑ the specific activity of the enzyme. These quantities are plotted against the number of moles of inhibitor added per mole of enzyme.

in the enzyme occurs in the reduced form. This would account in part for the instability of the mammalian enzyme, since there would be few or no stabilizing disulfide cross-linkages between peptide-chain segments.

The mammalian GDH in the fully activated state shows measurable absorption in the 315 to 400 mμ region. The absorption throughout most of this region decreases with the addition of increments of PCMB or of *p*-chloromercuribenzenesulfonate, and reaches a minimum of about 50 per cent of the starting values when 3 equivalents of the inhibitor have been added. The original spectrum is restored by the addition of cysteine. Slightly greater optical density decreases are obtained by treating the enzyme with charcoal to remove the bound DPN. The absorption may be titrated back by the addition of 3 equivalents [1] of DPN (Fig. 8). The absorption of the GDH–DPN complex was also observed by Racker and

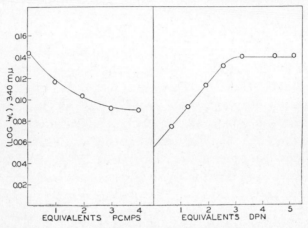

FIG. 8. In *A*, the curve shows the effects of increments of *p*-chloromercuriphenyl-sulfonate upon the optical density at 340 mμ of the GDH(DPN)$_2$ complex at an enzyme concentration of 0.031×10^{-6} moles per ml. The decrease in extinction coefficient per mole of DPN released is 0.06×10^7 cm^2 per mole. In *B*, the curve shows the increase in absorption at 340 mμ when increments of DPN are added to a solution of the charcoal-treated enzyme. On the basis of three equivalents of DPN bound to the enzyme in this experiment, the increase in extinction coefficient is 0.084 cm^2 per mole. The enzyme concentration in this experiment was 0.0317×10^{-6} moles per ml.

Krimsky (25). These workers have presented the difference spectrum between the complex and the charcoal treated enzyme and find a broad maximum at about 365 mμ which is in agreement with our results.

[1] The binding of 3 rather than 2 equivalents of DPN by the charcoal-treated mammalian GDH is also observed by the ultracentrifugal separation method (36). Charcoal treatment alters the protein in some way that makes available a binding site that is blocked or inoperative in the native recrystallized GDH–(DPN)$_2$ complex. The dissociation constant of the DPN complex with the charcoal-treated GDH is larger than for the untreated enzyme and, as with yeast GDH, decreases as saturation is approached.

The disappearance of the characteristic absorption band of the GDH–DPN complex with mercurial reagents is associated with the complete release of the bound DPN. However, enzyme which has become reversibly inactivated during purification and exhibits only 10 per cent of maximal activity in the absence of cysteine does not show the 365 mμ absorption band but still binds DPN strongly. Although this inactivation is assumed to involve the essential thiol groups, DPN-binding in this case is not affected. It is likely that the coenzyme release after mercaptide formation with phenyl mercuric chloride derivatives is an effect which depends upon the size and charge of the substituent group. The characteristic absorption band of the GDH–DPN complex requires the presence of the essential thiol groups in the free reduced state and may develop by an additional interaction after the DPN is already bound to the protein. Racker and Krimsky made the significant observation that the absorption band disappears in the presence of acetyl phosphate. This was assumed to result from acetyl-enzyme formation. We have confirmed the spectral effect and have tested it by the sedimentation method. Acetyl phosphate in concentrations which cause the disappearance of the 365 mμ band does not bring about the release of the bound DPN.

The 325 mμ absorption band of the liver ADH-DPNH complex reverts to 340 mμ in the presence of PCMB (32). The stoichiometry of this effect has not been reported and it is not known whether it is reversed by cysteine or whether it involves complete release of the coenzyme. Although some sort of thiol-coenzyme interaction is indicated with both proteins, a direct thiol-coenzyme bond is not a strict requirement, since the state of the thiol groups of the proteins can affect the coenzyme binding sites in several ways.

Intermediates and Mechanisms in the Action of GDH

The oxidative phosphorylation catalysed by GDH might occur in one of three types of reaction sequence. (1) In the mechanism suggested by Warburg and Christian the phosphorylation preceded the oxidation (38). The first step was supposed to consist in the addition of an orthophosphate ion to the carbonyl group of the aldehyde. The resulting compound was then assumed to be oxidized directly to an acyl phosphate. (2) The phosphorylation and oxidation might occur simultaneously by a displacement mechanism in which the phosphate ion attacked the carbonyl group at the same time that the hydrogen was transferred to DPN. (3) The third possibility was that the oxidation preceded the phosphorylation. In such a reaction the enzyme itself would be the primary acyl acceptor. Phosphorylation would then occur by acyl transfer from enzyme to phosphate. The action of an enzyme as an intermediary group acceptor was first postulated by Doudoroff, Hassid, and Barker (10), working with sucrose phosphorylase. They based their conclusions upon the observations that the enzyme catalysed a phosphate exchange between glucose-1-phosphate and inorganic phosphate in the absence of other glucose acceptors and also catalysed glucose-transfer reactions between glucosides and various carbohydrate acceptors.

Our attention was directed to mechanism (3) by the observation that the mammalian enzyme in high concentrations catalysed the oxidation of aldehyde in the absence of phosphate or arsenate. This was first observed when attempts were made to measure the simultaneous binding of glyceraldehyde-3-phosphate and DPN in pyrophosphate buffers, and it was confirmed with glyceraldehyde and acetaldehyde in other buffers. A convenient system for studying the mechanism of the catalysis was provided by the observation, during tests for specificity, that GDH catalysed the reversible oxidative phosphorylation of acetaldehyde to acetyl phosphate (11). By analogy with sucrose phosphorylase, it was found that the enzyme catalysed a phosphate exchange between acetyl phosphate and radioactive inorganic phosphate and also the arsenolysis of acetyl phosphate. Lynen and Reichert's observation that acetyl-coenzyme A was a thio-ester with the properties of a " high energy compound " led them to suggest that the function of the essential thiol groups in GDH is to form a thio-ester with an acyl intermediate (20). It was subsequently found that GDH catalysed the transfer of acetyl groups from acetyl phosphate to the thiol groups of glutathione and coenzyme A (12). The slowness of these reactions could be attributed to the nature of the substrates. The acyl-enzyme intermediate theory had been approached by Racker through consideration of the essential thiol groups (23). Using reactions of acetyl phosphate, Racker and Krimsky subsequently elaborated a detailed theory of the reaction mechanism (24).

The major experimental difficulty in establishing an acyl-enzyme mechanism was in the direct detection of an acyl-enzyme compound

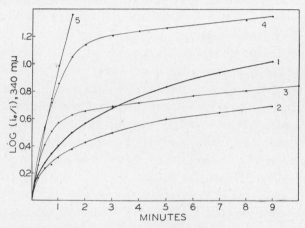

FIG. 9. The rate of reduction of DPN by glyceraldehyde as a function of phosphate concentration. The experiments were carried out in 0.05 M potassium bicarbonate and 0.05 M potassium chloride, pH 8.4. The concentrations in moles per liter $\times 10^3$ were as follows: enzyme, 0.017; total DPN, 0.281; DL-glyceraldehyde, 2.0. The initial concentrations of orthophosphate in moles per liter $\times 10^3$ for curves 1, 2, 3, 4, and 5, respectively, were 0.002, 0.04, 0.5, 1.0, and 5.0.

which had the properties required of an intermediate. By working at high enzyme concentration and omitting phosphate it should have been possible to stop the reaction at the acyl-enzyme stage, provided that the intermediate were stable. As shown in Fig. 9, with high enzyme and DPN concentrations and glyceraldehyde as substrate a series of equilibria were approached as a function of phosphate concentration, but at low phosphate concentration the DPN reduction exceeded the amount of phosphate present. In the absence of phosphate the reaction followed a different kinetic course. The reduction in the absence of phosphate was in excess of any reasonable number of acceptor groups on the enzyme. Since the initial rates were independent of phosphate concentration, the results could be accounted for by an acyl-enzyme intermediate provided that the intermediate was very unstable and hydrolysed in the absence of phosphate.

The results were different when the natural substrate, glyceraldehyde-3-phosphate, was tested (5, 35). The initial reduction of DPN was extremely rapid when the aldehyde was added to the system in the absence of phosphate, and was followed by a slow reduction

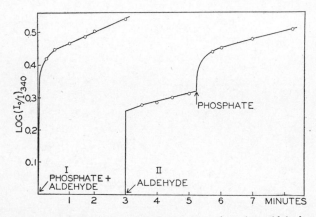

Fig. 10. Steps in the oxidative phosphorylation of D-glyceraldehyde-3-phosphate. Reactions I and II were carried out at 26° C. in 0.1 M trishydroxymethyl amino methane, hydrochloric acid buffer, pH 7.4, containing 0.001 M versene. The concentrations in moles per liter $\times 10^4$ were: aldehyde, 3.7; DPN, 1.76; and enzyme, 0.27. The initial orthophosphate concentration in reaction I was 0.0033 M and in reaction II 0.0000 M. Inorganic phosphate at a final concentration of 0.0033 M was added to reaction II at the time indicated by the arrow. Both reactions were initiated by the addition of aldehyde.

that was linear with time. The slow phase could be attributed to the slow breakdown of an acyl-enzyme compound, regenerating acceptor sites. With a large amount of DPN and aldehyde the maximal reduction in the initial rapid phase was two equivalents of DPN per mole of enzyme. An experiment with glyceraldehyde-3-phosphate analogous to that with glyceraldehyde is shown in Fig. 10. The final oxidative phosphorylation equilibrium was the same whether the reaction was carried out in one or two steps. An acyl-enzyme compound was therefore formed in the absence of phosphate which had the expected stoichiometry and served as an intermediate in the oxidative phosphorylation. It is to be observed that the oxidative step was more rapid than the phosphorylation.

The two steps may be formulated as:

$$\text{RCHO} + \text{DPN} + \text{ENZ–H} \rightleftharpoons \overset{\text{O}}{\overset{\|}{\text{RC}}}\text{–ENZ} + \text{DPNH} + \text{H}^+ \qquad (10)$$

$$\overset{\text{O}}{\overset{\|}{\text{RC}}}\text{–ENZ} + \text{HPO}^=_4 \rightleftharpoons \overset{\text{O}}{\overset{\|}{\text{RCOPO}}}{}^=_3 + \text{ENZ–H} \qquad (11)$$

TABLE 4

THE EQUILIBRIUM CONSTANT OF THE REACTION: GLYCERALDEHYDE-3-PHOSPHATE + DPN + ENZYME ⇌ 3-PHOSPHOGLYCEROYL-ENZYME + DPNH + H⁺

Tube	pH	Enzyme	DPN	DPNH	Aldehyde	$K \times 10^5$
		Moles per liter $\times\ 10^4$ at equilibrium				
A.	8.3	0.324	0.324	0.288	3.41	1.2
B.	8.0	0.37	0.37	0.182	3.52	0.7
C.	7.6	0.60	0.60	0.344	3.36	2.4
D.	7.4	0.20	12.9	0.416	3.28	0.8
E.	6.5	0.79	18.35	0.152	1.03	0.5
F.	6.5	0.86	18.42	0.080	0.39	0.3

The values given in the table are equilibrium concentrations calculated from the measured DPNH formation, determined spectrophotometrically, and the initial concentrations of the reactants. The enzyme in all cases was dissolved in 0.001 M versene. Enzyme concentrations are expressed as equivalent concentrations of catalytic or acceptor sites, two equivalents per mole. Reaction A was carried out in 0.1 M sodium bicarbonate, reaction B in 0.1 M trishydroxymethylaminomethane. No separate salt additions were made to reactions C and D. Reactions E and F were carried out in 0.05 M sodium pyrophosphate containing 0.002 M cysteine. The pH's were measured immediately after the completion of the reactions. No DPN other than that bound to the enzyme was added in reactions A — C.

The extent of the initial rapid reduction, equation (10), is a function of pH and the initial concentrations of aldehyde, enzyme, and DPN. Over a wide range of concentrations it satisfies the equilibrium:

$$K'_1 = \frac{[\text{DPNH}][\text{ACYL–ENZ}][\text{H}^+]}{[\text{DPN}][\text{ALD}][\text{ENZ}]} \qquad (12)$$

where the enzyme is treated as a stoichiometric participant (Table 4).

The phosphorylation equilibrium, established when phosphate is added, is:

$$K'_2 = \frac{[\text{ACYL–PHOS}][\text{ENZ}]}{[\text{ACYL–ENZ}][\text{PHOS}]} \tag{13}$$

and the equilibrium of the over-all oxidative phosphorylation is

$$K' = K'_1 K'_2 = \frac{[\text{DPNH}][\text{ACYL–PHOS}][\text{H}^+]}{[\text{DPN}][\text{ALD}][\text{PHOS}]} \tag{14}$$

where the equilibrium constant, K', is the product of the two intermediary equilibrium constants. Since K' is known to be 1×10^{-7} (9, 20), and K'_1 is now known, K'_2 may be computed from the relation $K'_2 = K'/K'_1$, and is found to be 10^{-2}. This is close to the value 1.6×10^{-2} obtained by Stadtman for the corresponding equilibrium constant in the acyl transfer between acetyl coenzyme A and inorganic phosphate (28).

The equilibrium, K'_1 may also be written as

$$K'_1 = K_1 \frac{f_{ALD} f_{DPN}}{f_{DPNH}} \tag{15}$$

where the f's have the same meaning as in equation (6).

The acyl enzyme is not considered dissociable in this system. It is to be noted from Table 4 that no significant trend of K_1 is obtained as a function of coenzyme concentration, when the aldehyde concentration is high enough to eliminate the effect of aldehyde-binding on the equilibrium. We had obtained similar results several years ago in the over-all oxidative phosphorylation·equilibrium (9). The scatter is too large in the present case to permit a significant evaluation of f_{DPN} and f_{DPNH} and of the corresponding dissociation constants, although it seems likely that in the complete system the K's for coenzyme are not grossly different. However, when the aldehyde concentration is lowered it is seen that the apparent equilibrium constant decreases. f_{ALD} thus becomes significantly less than unity. The dissociation constant of the GDH-aldehyde complex indicated by this shift is of the order of 10^{-5}. The Michaelis constant for glyceraldehyde-3-phosphate is 4×10^{-5} (8).

In a detailed treatment of the kinetics and mechanism of the reversible oxidative phosphorylation it is necessary to know which of the numerous possible combinations of enzyme with the five reactants occur as intermediates. It is clear that the GDH–DPN complex is formed independently. Glyceraldehyde-3-phosphate is also bound independently, in the absence of DPN and phosphate, by the charcoal-treated enzyme, with a dissociation constant of about 10^{-5} (35). That this also occurs in the complete system is shown by the equilibrium shift with aldehyde (Table 4). When an equilibrium mixture of glyceraldehyde-3-phosphate, acyl-enzyme, DPN, and DPNH is sedimented in the ultracentrifuge, the coenzyme is not released. The presence of aldehyde and acyl groups on the enzyme thus does not appreciably weaken the coenzyme binding. The ternary complexes, SEC_1 and $S'EC_2$, where S is aldehyde, E is enzyme, C_1 is DPN, C_2 is DPNH, and S' is acyl, may therefore be assumed to occur as intermediates, and they probably exist in equilibrium with $S'EC_1$ and the non-reactive complex SEC_2.

Phosphate ions are bound extensively by both yeast and mammalian GDH, as shown by the large shifts of the isoelectric points in the acid direction as the phosphate ion concentration is increased (Fig. 11). This has been confirmed with the mammalian enzyme by dialysis equilibrium measurements (35). However, most if not all of the phosphate-binding by the enzymes is relatively weak and non-specific and represents general anion affinities of the proteins. Attempts by the methods employed with the other substrates to detect an enzyme-phosphate complex with the properties of an intermediate have led to negative results (35). It is therefore possible that the phosphate ion reacts directly with the acyl-enzyme intermediate without independently forming a specific reactive complex with the protein. This is also in accord with the kinetics of glyceraldehyde oxidation as a function of phosphate concentration (Fig. 9).

The experiments that have been described permit the formulation of a complicated series of equilibria between enzyme and reactants to form both dissociable and non-dissociable compounds in the reversible oxidative phosphorylation of glyceraldehyde-3-phosphate.

However, the list of possible intermediates is not yet complete, and many details of the reaction require further investigation over a wide range of experimental conditions before a detailed treatment of the reaction mechanism will be very illuminating. It is suspected but not established, for example, that the 365 mμ absorption band

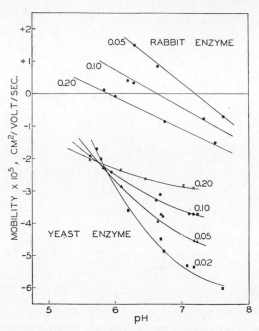

FIG. 11. The electrophoretic mobility vs. pH curves of the glyceraldehyde-3-phosphate dehydrogenases as a function of the ionic strength of the phosphate buffers. The ionic strength corresponding to each curve is indicated.

of the mammalian GDH–DPN complex represents the active form of the bound DPN. The conclusion that the orthophosphate ion does not form an intermediary complex with the enzyme in the oxidative phosphorylation has consequences which must be tested. Does the oxidative step involve a hydride ion or hydrogen atom transfer, or does the proton equilibrate with the medium? Little is known concerning the sequence of events in the reverse reaction leading to the formation of acyl enzyme from enzyme and acyl phosphate. Environmental conditions which greatly affect the physical properties of the enzyme also affect its catalytic activities (36). The Michaelis constant for one reactant is influenced by the concentrations of the others (6). Are these and related effects (7) to be explained purely in terms of the reaction mechanism, assuming a stable catalyst? or as postulated (36), does the enzyme itself possess internal degrees of freedom and undergo configurational and activity changes as a function of experimental conditions?

REACTIONS WITH ADH

Preliminary surveys of the kinetics of ADH reactions have been made by Negelein and Wulff (22) with the yeast enzyme and by Theorell and Chance with the mammalian enzyme (33). In connection with the binding studies with yeast ADH (13) we have repeated and extended some of the kinetic measurements of Negelein and Wulff. In particular, the Michaelis constants for alcohol and DPN have been found to be independent of each other over a wide range of concentrations. The Michaelis constant for DPN and the inhibitor constant for DPNH with ethanol as substrate are close to the respective dissociation constants determined by the direct-binding method. Whether or not they are actually identical cannot be determined until measurements of the temperature coefficients are completed. The constants which characterize the two ADH enzymes are summarized in Table 5.

The present results with yeast ADH indicate that a ternary complex, ethanol–ADH–DPN, occurs as a reactive intermediate, with no restrictions as to the sequence in which it is formed and with no effects of ethanol on DPN-binding or vice versa. Haldane has shown that a relationship exists between the equilibrium constant of a reversible "one substrate" reaction, the Michaelis constants, and the maximal velocities in the forward and reverse directions. Alberty has extended this relationship to a two-substrate reaction and has shown that the relation should depend upon the reaction mechanism (2). For a reaction of the type indicated for yeast ADH the relation should be:

$$K'_{eq} = \frac{V_f K_{DPNH} K_{ALD}}{V_r K_{DPN} K_{ALC}} \tag{16}$$

where K'_{eq} is the equilibrium constant divided by the hydrogen ion activity, V_f and V_r are maximal velocities respectively for alcohol oxidation and aldehyde reduction, and the other K's are Michaelis

TABLE 5

COMPARISON OF CONSTANTS FOR YEAST AND MAMMALIAN ADH

| | YEAST ADH | | MAMMALIAN ADH |
	Present work	ref. (22)	ref. (32)
Molecular weight	150,000		73,000
$S_{20, w}$ sec^{-1}	6.72×10^{-15}		4.88×10^{-15}
D cm^2 sec^{-1}	4.70×10^{-7}		6.5×10^{-7}
$\bar{V}$ cm^3 gm^{-1}	0.769		0.751
Binding sites per molecule	4		2
$E_{280} \dfrac{cm^2}{mole}$	1.89×10^5		0.332×10^5
	Michaelis Constants *		
	pH 7.9	pH 7.9	
DPN	1.7×10^{-4}	0.9×10^{-4}	1.3×10^{-5} pH 7
DPNH	2.3×10^{-5} +	3.0×10^{-5} +	1.2×10^{-5} pH 7
CH$_3$CH$_2$OH	1.8×10^{-2}	2.4×10^{-2}	5.4×10^{-4} pH 8.2
CH$_3$CHO		1.1×10^{-4}	1.2×10^{-4} pH 7
	Dissociation Constants		
DPNH	1.3×10^{-5} ++		1×10^{-7} *
DPN	2.6×10^{-4} ++		
CH$_3$CHO	1.8×10^{-4} ++		
	Maximal Velocities		
V_f moles min^{-1} binding site^{-1}	6700	(9350)	90
V_r moles min^{-1} binding site^{-1}		(15600)	1020

* Determined at 25° C.   ** Determined.
+ Inhibitor constants.   ++ Determined at 0 — 4° C.

constants. Using the constants in Table 5, K'_{eq} at pH 7.9 is calculated to be 0.9×10^{-3}, while the observed value is 0.74×10^{-3}.

The expressions corresponding to equation (16) for other reaction mechanisms vary in the power to which V_f and V_r is raised. Using the data of Theorell and coworkers (32, 33), Alberty finds that for the mammalian ADH the results at pH 8 fit best the relation:

$$K'_{eq} = \frac{V_f{}^2 K_{DPNH} K_{ALD}}{V_r{}^2 K_{DPN} K_{ALC}} \tag{17}$$

This relation is derived from a mechanism which, in this particular case, could involve a reaction in which the enzyme itself was alternately reduced by alcohol and oxidized by DPN, or oxidized by aldehyde and reduced by DPNH. The experiments of Kaplan and Ciotti seem to exclude this mechanism (14). V_f and V_r for the mammalian enzyme at pH 8 differ by a factor greater than 10, but those of the yeast ADH at this pH differ by a factor less than 2. Consequently when the data for the yeast enzyme are used in equation (17) the calculated K'_{eq} is found to be about 0.5×10^{-3}, which is still fairly close to the observed value. However, one may exclude an oxidation-reduction cycle of the yeast enzyme on the grounds that no rapid reaction can be observed spectrophotometrically between the recrystallized enzyme, at high concentrations, and DPN or DPNH. Actually, equations (16) and (17), although they provide a test for the consistency of the kinetic and equilibrium constants, are not necessarily a sensitive criterion of the reaction mechanism. In view of the great differences in the properties of yeast ADH and liver ADH, it is indeed possible that they catalyse the same over-all reaction by different mechanisms; but this remains to be established.

DISCUSSION

It is customary to study the catalytic properties of enzymes at enzyme concentrations of the order of micrograms per ml. In this concentration range many aspects of the kinetics, reaction mechanism, and specificity may be investigated, and inferences may be drawn concerning the affinities of the enzyme for substrates, coenzymes, and inhibitors and the formation of intermediary enzyme-substrate complexes. By increasing the enzyme concentration a thousand-fold or more, it is possible to measure complex-formation directly by separation methods and to test the conclusions so drawn by measuring equilibrium shifts of over-all enzymatic reactions as a function of enzyme concentration. It is possible under such conditions to study the enzyme as a stoichiometric reactant, and in cases such as GDH, to break the over-all reaction down into steps in which the enzyme is a stoichiometric participant. When some of the complexes have characteristic absorption bands, their formation and breakdown may be followed by direct spectrophotometry. The concentration ranges required in such cases depend upon the molar extinction coefficients and the instrumentation. Spectrophotometric methods, when applicable, are in principle rapid, flexible, and accurate, but frequently involve assumptions which need not be made by less accurate and more cumbersome chemical methods.

With the four dehydrogenases that have been discussed, these methods have supplemented and reinforced each other and have contributed to the beginnings of detailed pictures of the catalytic mechanisms. Thus, although the ultracentrifugal separation method leaves something to be desired in the way of accuracy and the range of conditions under which it may be used, it has provided a series of directly measured dissociation constants of intermediary complexes, uncomplicated by the conditions which prevail when the over-all reaction is occurring. With the yeast ADH it has provided for the first time direct quantitative evidence of the displacement of a substrate (DPN) by an inhibitor (DPNH) from an intermediary complex in the oxidation of ethanol, and has thus confirmed the conclusions drawn from the observation of competitive inhibition. In the cases of the GDH–DPN and of the mammalian ADH–DPNH complexes, direct binding measurements have shown that the Michaelis constants are strongly dependent upon steady-state conditions and are not direct measures of the dissociation constants. The Michaelis constants of some of the other complexes are essentially the same as the dissociation constants, although rigorous comparisons require further work, particularly with respect to temperature coefficients.

Since the binding of small molecules by enzymes need not necessarily occur at catalytic sites, the results of binding measurements must be submitted to kinetic tests before the complexes observed can be considered to be reaction intermediates. Of particular interest in this respect is the acetaldehyde-binding deduced from the equilibrium shift with high concentrations of yeast ADH. The dissociation constant of the aldehyde-enzyme complex derived by this indirect method is very close to the Michaelis constant for aldehyde.

The participation of inorganic phosphate in reactions catalysed by GDH may be a case in which a substrate does not form an intermediary complex directly with the enzyme. Although GDH-phosphate complexes can be detected and measured, they do not have the properties which seem to be required by the kinetics of the enzymatic reactions. The results suggest that the phosphate ion reacts directly on collision with the acyl-enzyme intermediate. The validity of this interpretation seems to rest upon the kinetic analysis which in its present state is still primitive.

The problem of the function of thiol groups in the catalytic activities of proteins is a frequently recurring one. In some cases, such as GDH, the formation of a thiol bond with substrate or coenzyme is a direct and simple hypothesis, but is not the only possible one. Many enzymes of diverse function have essential thiol groups, and the question is raised as to whether in all of these cases sulfur bonds are formed with substrates or intermediates. The alternative is that in some or all of these cases inhibition by substitution or oxidation of the thiol groups of the protein is a steric effect. The substituent itself might overlap a binding site, or a change in the state of the sulfur might affect the protein as a whole, and hence affect the catalytic activities, even though the thiol groups were some distance away from the catalytic centers. The possibility of the latter event would depend upon the rigidity of the protein structure. An enzyme with the stability properties of GDH might be considered less rigidly constructed in its native globular configuration than other proteins. It has few if any stabilizing disulfide cross-linkages. It is readily denatured by mild heating, dilute acids, and heavy metals. Its stability is decreased in the absence of salts and it is likely that the protection conferred by salts arises in part from the neutralization of internal electrostatic repulsions by reversibly bound anions (35). The stabilization of the protein by bound DPN, the decrease in apparent dissociation constants of the GDH–DPN complex as saturation is approached, and the requirement for bound coenzyme in acetyl-transfer reactions where oxidation-reduction is not occurring may be interpreted as resulting from mechanical stabilization of the protein by the bound coenzyme (36).

The information that is gained from the detailed study of an enzyme may be amplified when it is possible to compare it with an enzyme of the same function but isolated from another source. The two GDH enzymes show quantitative differences, but their structures and physical properties are in general quite similar. The two ADH enzymes, although they have several features in common, appear to be quite different in structure and physical properties. It is to be hoped that these differences will eventually be understood in terms of the catalytic mechanisms and the participation of the enzymes in their particular cellular environments.

REFERENCES

1. Alberty, R. A., *J. Am. Chem. Soc.*, 75, 1925 (1953).
2. Alberty, R. A., *J. Am. Chem. Soc.*, 75, 1928 (1953).
3. Barron, E. S. G., and S. Levine, *Arch. Biochem. and Biophys.*, 41, 175 (1952).
4. Bonnichsen, R. K., and A. M. Wassen, *Arch. Biochem.*, 18, 361 (1948).
5. Boyer, P. D., and H. L. Segal, *Federation Proc.*, 12, 181 (1953).
6. Bucher, T., and K. Garbade, *Biochim. et Biophys. Acta*, 8, 219 (1952).
7. Chance, B., and J. Harting, *Federation Proc.*, 12, 188 (1953).
8. Cori, G. T., M. W. Slein, and C. F. Cori, *J. Biol. Chem.*, 173, 605 (1948).
9. Cori, C. F., S. F. Velick, and G. T. Cori, *Biochim. et Biophys. Acta*, 4, 160 (1950).
10. Doudoroff, M., H. A. Barker, and Z. Hassid, *J. Biol. Chem.*, 168, 725 (1947).
11. Harting, J., *Federation Proc.*, 10, 195 (1951).
12. Harting, J., and S. F. Velick, *Federation Proc.*, 11, 226 (1952).
13. Hayes, J. E., Jr., and S. F. Velick, *J. Biol. Chem.*, in press.
14. Kaplan, N. O., and M. M. Ciotti, *J. Biol. Chem.*, 201, 785 (1953).
15. Krebs, E. G., and V. Najjar, *J. Exp. Med.*, 88, 569 (1948).
16. Krebs, E. G., G. W. Rafter, and J. M. Junge, *J. Biol. Chem.*, 200, 479 (1953).
17. Krebs, E. G., and G. W. Rafter, *Federation Proc.*, 11, 243 (1952).
18. Krimsky, I. M., and E. Racker, *J. Biol. Chem.*, 198, 721 (1952).
19. Labeyrie, F., *Bull. soc. chim. biol.*, 31, 1624 (1949).
20. Lynen, F., and E. Reichert, *Angew. Chem.*, 63, 47 (1951).
21. Meyerhof, O., and P. Oesper, *J. Biol. Chem.*, 170, 1 (1949).
22. Negelein, E., and H. J. Wulff, *Biochem. Z.*, 293, 351 (1937).
23. Racker, E., in *A Symposium on Phosphorus Metabolism*, Vol. I (W. D. McElroy and B. Glass, eds.), p. 145, Johns Hopkins Press, Baltimore (1951).

24. Racker, E., *J. Biol. Chem.*, **184**, 313 (1950).
25. Racker, E., and I. Krimsky, *J. Biol. Chem.*, **198**, 231 (1952).
26. Rapkine, L., S. M. Rapkine, and P. Trpinac, *Compt. rend.*, **209**, 253 (1939).
27. Scatchard, G., *Ann. N.Y. Acad. Sci.*, **51**, 660 (1949).
28. Stadtman, E. R., *J. Biol. Chem.*, **196**, 535 (1952).
29. Stadtman, E. R., and F. H. White, Jr., *J. Am. Chem. Soc.*, **75**, 2022 (1953).
30. Taylor, J. F., in *A Symposium on Phosphorus Metabolism*, Vol. I (W. D. McElroy and B. Glass, eds.), p. 104, Johns Hopkins Press, Baltimore (1951).
31. Taylor, J. F., S. F. Velick, C. F. Cori, G. T. Cori, and M. W. Slein, *J. Biol. Chem.*, **173**, 619 (1948).
32. Theorell, H., and R. Bonnichsen, *Acta Chem. Scand.*, **5**, 1105 (1951).
33. Theorell, H., and B. Chance, *Acta Chem. Scand.*, **5**, 1127 (1951).
34. Velick, S. F., *J. Biol. Chem.*, **203**, 563 (1953).
35. Velick, S. F., and J. E. Hayes, Jr., *J. Biol. Chem.*, **203**, 545 (1953).
36. Velick, S. F., J. E. Hayes, Jr., and J. Harting, *J. Biol. Chem.*, **203**, 527 (1953).
37. Velick, S. F., and S. Udenfriend, *J. Biol. Chem.*, **203**, 575 (1953).
38. Warburg, O., and W. Christian, *Biochem. Z.*, **303**, 40 (1939).

SULFHYDRYL GROUPS OF GLYCERALDEHYDE–3– PHOSPHATE DEHYDROGENASE AND ACYL– ENZYME FORMATION *

P. D. BOYER and H. L. SEGAL

Department of Agricultural Biochemistry,
University of Minnesota, St. Paul

FOLLOWING THE classical work of Warburg and Christian that showed formation of 1, 3-diphosphoglycerate by the action of the glyceraldehyde-3-phosphate dehydrogenase (25), there has been continuing interest and work on the mechanism of action of this important dehydrogenase. Particularly valuable contributions have been made by the St. Louis group on the preparation and characterization of crystalline muscle dehydrogenase (4, 20, 23, 5) and by Meyerhof and Oesper on careful measurements of equilibria under various conditions (10). More recently, evidence that acyl-enzyme intermediates might participate in the catalysis has been obtained by Harting and Velick (6) and by Racker and Krimsky (8, 13). These workers demonstrated a slow catalysis of transfer of acyl groups from acetyl phosphate to various acceptors, and the formation and utilization of thiol esters independent of the oxidation-reduction function of the enzyme. Convincing evidence that oxidation of the natural substrate, D-glyceraldehyde-3-phosphate, results in formation of an acyl-enzyme has been obtained in our laboratory (16) and confirmed by Velick (24) by demonstrations of the reduction of DPN⁺ independent of inorganic phosphate or other potential acceptors of the acyl group.

The necessity of sulfhydryl groups for the catalytic action of glyceraldehyde-3-phosphate dehydrogenase has been recognized for some time (14), and inhibition of the crystalline enzyme by p-mer-

* The experimental work reported was supported in part by a grant from the National Science Foundation. Contribution No. 3044, Scientific Series, Minnesota Agricultural Experiment Station.

curibenzoate was demonstrated by Barron and Dickman (1). Evidence for the importance of sulfhydryl groups in the interaction of the enzyme with glyceraldehyde-3-phosphate has been shown by the ability of this substrate specifically to protect the enzyme from iodoacetate inhibition (16, 7) ; quantitative studies of this protection give information as to the number of reactive sites and sulfhydryl groups participating in the catalysis (16).

The purpose of this paper is to discuss our experiments on acyl-enzyme formation together with the quantitative studies of the sulfhydryl groups in rabbit muscle D-glyceraldehyde-3-phosphate dehydrogenase and their mode of participation in the catalysis. Also included is a brief presentation of a spectrophotometric procedure for measuring the rate and extent of reaction of sulfhydryl groups with p-mercuribenzoate and application of this procedure to the dehydrogenase.

ACYL-ENZYME FORMATION IN THE OXIDATION OF GLYCERALDE-HYDE-3-PHOSPHATE DEHYDROGENASE

Strong evidence for acyl-enzyme formation accompanying oxidation of glyceraldehyde-3-phosphate was first obtained while using as substrate mixtures of D-glyceraldehyde-3-phosphate and dihydroxyacetone phosphate which contained inorganic phosphate (16). The greater reduction of DPN$^+$ obtained at equilibrium in the presence of high as compared to low enzyme concentrations could most readily be explained by participation of the enzyme in the equilibrium as an acyl acceptor. This was confirmed, and conclusive proof of the oxidation of the glyceraldehyde-3-phosphate independent of the participation of inorganic phosphate was obtained by use of synthetic D, L-glyceraldehyde-3-phosphate low in inorganic phosphate. Results of such experiments are shown in Fig. 1 (16). At the point indicated by E_1, experiment A, a catalytic concentration of enzyme was added to a reaction mixture containing excess D, L-glyceraldehyde-3-phosphate and DPN$^+$. The amount of enzyme was sufficient to catalyze rapid attainment of equilibrium, but little increase in optical density was noted. At the time indicated by E_2, 2.5×10^{-4} micromoles of dehydrogenase were added. The resultant optical density increase, which was immediate within limits of the experimental procedure, when corrected for the absorption of the enzyme per se at 340 millimicrons, gives a measure of the DPNH formed. Formation of DPNH must be accompanied by the bivalent oxidation of the aldehyde to the acyl derivative and the only acceptor for the acyl group is the enzyme itself. At the time indicated, the entire reaction mixture was analyzed for phosphate by a sensitive procedure. The amount of total inorganic and acyl phosphate found was equivalent

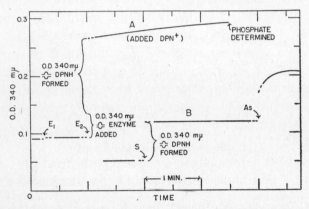

FIG. 1. Acyl-enzyme formation independent of the presence of inorganic phosphate.

to only $\frac{1}{4}$ the amount of DPNH formed; thus the phosphate could not have accepted acyl groups equivalent in amount to the DPNH formed. The continued slow increase in the optical density following addition of the high level of enzyme likely results from hydrolysis of the acyl enzyme. Added DPN⁺ is not essential for oxidation of the glyceraldehyde-3-phosphate, as shown in experiment B, Fig. 1. In this experiment D, L-glyceraldehyde-3-phosphate was added to 2.5×10^{-4} micromoles of enzyme at the time indicated by S. The enzyme-bound DPN⁺ was partly reduced, and further reduction occurred as anticipated when arsenate was added.

The data in Fig. 1 were obtained using a Beckman spectrophotometer adapted for recording changes of optical density with time, essentially as described by Bock and Alberty (2). In these and similar experiments, the addition of small amounts of reactants at a given time was considerably facilitated by the use of the simple adder-mixer shown in Fig. 2. Up to 0.2 ml. of reactants can be added to the chamber of the mixer; aqueous solutions do not wet the plastic and thus do not flow through the holes in the bottom. Addition and mixing in short time intervals is readily achieved by passing the mixer through the length of the cell and thus forcing the liquid through the holes or around the edges of the mixer. Complete mixing of additions with the contents of the square Beckman cell

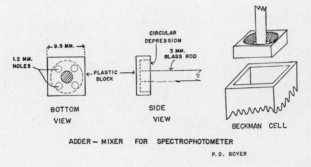

FIG. 2. A simple adder-mixer for the Beckman spectrophotometer.

is not conveniently obtained with use of an ordinary stirring rod. Tests with dyes have shown that with the mixer described in Fig. 2 mixing was nearly complete after 2 passages of the mixer through the liquid in the cell. Complete mixing was always obtained with 4 passages.

Probable Steps in the Over-all Reaction

Intermediate stages in the oxidation of the aldehyde and reduction of DPN^+ may be recognized by measurements of the amount of enzyme-bound DPN^+ reduced with the enzyme as the acyl acceptor at different pH and substrate concentrations. In Fig. 3 are shown optical density changes (corrected for dilution accompanying additions) produced when different additions were made to a 0.2×10^{-4} M dehydrogenase solution containing 3.3×10^{-4} M cysteine and

3.3 × 10⁻⁴ *M* ethylenediaminetetraacetate (EDTA) (3). In experiment 1, excess substrate and phosphate were added at pH 8.1 to give a measure of the total potential DPNH formation. The slow continued reduction following the addition of arsenate noted with this five-times recrystallized dehydrogenase has not been found with a later preparation. In experiment 2, substrate was added at pH 6.5 to give a final concentration of 4.9 × 10⁻³ *M*, followed by a second

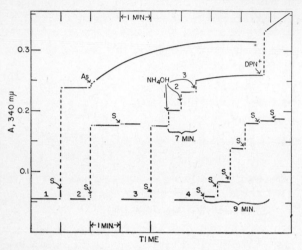

Fig. 3. Reduction of enzyme-bound DPN⁺ under different conditions.

addition of an equal quantity of substrate. The incomplete reduction of the enzyme-bound DPN⁺ obtained here and in experiment *B*, Fig. 1, shows that addition of the glyceraldehyde-3-phosphate alone is insufficient to drive the reduction to completion. In experiment 3 is shown the effect of the addition of increments of a ammonia-ammonium chloride buffer to a reaction mixture like that of experiment 2 so as to increase the pH in successive steps to 8.1. The shift in the equilibrium in favor of DPNH formation with increase in pH is evident. In experiment 4 are shown the results obtained when successive increments of substrate smaller in amount than those used for experiment 2 are added. These results show the dependency of the reaction on substrate concentration.

From the data obtained, the probable reaction sequence given in Fig. 4 is suggested for the catalysis. Reaction mechanisms are difficult to establish conclusively, and the recognition of four distinct possible steps from equilibrium measurements does not establish the steps as catalytically active intermediates, or give details as to the mechanism of the individual reactions. The existence of recognizable forms of the enzyme consistent with requisite chemical steps in the over-all reaction does justify consideration of the forms as probable steps in

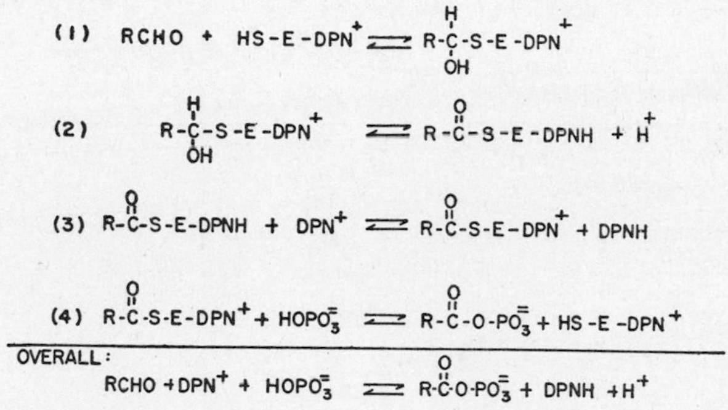

(1) $RCHO + HS-E-DPN^+ \rightleftharpoons R-\overset{H}{\underset{OH}{C}}-S-E-DPN^+$

(2) $R-\overset{H}{\underset{OH}{C}}-S-E-DPN^+ \rightleftharpoons R-\overset{O}{C}-S-E-DPNH + H^+$

(3) $R-\overset{O}{C}-S-E-DPNH + DPN^+ \rightleftharpoons R-\overset{O}{C}-S-E-DPN^+ + DPNH$

(4) $R-\overset{O}{C}-S-E-DPN^+ + HOPO_3^= \rightleftharpoons R-\overset{O}{C}-O-PO_3^= + HS-E-DPN^+$

OVERALL:

$RCHO + DPN^+ + HOPO_3^= \rightleftharpoons R-\overset{O}{C}-O-PO_3^= + DPNH + H^+$

FIG. 4. A possible reaction sequence for the glyceraldehyde-3-phosphate dehydrogenase catalysis.

the catalysis. Some evidence for the participation of the enzyme sulfhydryl in the reaction, as depicted, will be discussed later, although that the sulfhydryl group on the enzyme acts as an acyl acceptor is by no means established.

From experiments under different conditions the apparent equilibria of the various steps given in Fig. 4 may be calculated. The method of approach and the calculated results are given in Fig. 5. The symbols and equations in the upper left-hand corner correspond to the steps given in Fig. 4. The values are subject to some error, particularly because of uncertainty in a figure for the total potential acyl-enzyme concentration. Also, the results are based on use of the extinction coefficient of free DPNH for calculation of the molarities of the respective components. Nonetheless, the values for the equilibrium constants should represent reasonable approximations. From the value of K_4 (10) and the approximate free energy of hydrolysis of 1, 3-diphosphoglycerate of 15 kcals (11), the free energy of hydrolysis of the acyl-enzyme link may be estimated to be of the order of 10 kcals. This definitely identifies the acyl-enzyme bond as a " high-energy " bond.

$$S+E_1 \rightleftharpoons E_2 \qquad\qquad K_1 = 0.7 \times 10^4$$

$$E_2 \rightleftharpoons E_3 + H^+ \qquad\qquad K_2 = 8 \times 10^{-7}$$

$$E_3 + C_0 \rightleftharpoons E_4 + C_r \qquad\qquad K_3 = 0.13$$

$$E_4 + P_i \rightleftharpoons E_1 + P_e \qquad\qquad K_4 = 8 \times 10^{-5} \Leftrightarrow \Delta F \text{ of } 5.6 \pm 0.5 \text{ k cals.}$$

$$\overline{S + C_0 + P_i \rightleftharpoons P_e + C_r + H^+} \qquad K_0 = K_1 K_2 K_3 K_4 = 5.7 \times 10^{-8}$$

WITH EXCESS S, No C_0, MEASURE E_3 AND H^+

$$E_2 = E_T - E_3 \qquad K_2 = \frac{E_3 H^+}{E_2}$$

WITH VARIABLE S, No C_0, MEASURE E_3 AND H^+

$$E_2 = \frac{E_3 H^+}{K_2} \qquad E_1 = E_T - (E_2 + E_3) \qquad S = S_T - E_2 \qquad K_1 = \frac{E_2}{SE_1}$$

WITH EXCESS S AND VARIABLE C_0, MEASURE $(E_3 + C_r)$ AND H^+

$$E_4 = C_r \therefore (E_3 + C_r) = (E_3 + E_4)$$

$$E_2 = E_T - (E_3 + E_4)$$

$$E_3 = \frac{E_2 K_2}{H^+} \qquad\qquad K_3 = \frac{E_4 C_r}{E_3 C_0}$$

$$E_4 = E_T - (E_3 + E_2) \qquad\qquad K_4 = \frac{K_0}{K_1 K_2 K_3}$$

FIG. 5. Approximation of the equilibria for recognizable stages of the glyceraldehyde-3-phosphate dehydrogenase reaction.

QUANTITATIVE MEASUREMENTS OF THE PROTECTION OF ENZYME-SULFHYDRYL GROUPS FROM ALKYLATION BY IODOACETATE (IAA)

Additions of glyceraldehyde-3-phosphate will protect the dehydrogenase from inactivation by iodoacetate, while additions of phosphate and DPN$^+$ fail to protect the enzyme (16). The protection by glyceraldehyde-3-phosphate is obtained whether or not the bound DPN$^+$ is removed from the enzyme and in the absence or presence of arsenate to cleave any acyl-enzyme formed. Measurements of the number of enzyme -SH groups under different conditions, using an amperometric iodosobenzoate titration procedure, show that alkylation of approximately 5 groups per mole is required for complete inactivation of the enzyme (16). Of these, close to 2 groups per mole are specifically protected by glyceraldehyde-3-phosphate, and thus approximately 3 groups per mole may be alkylated without loss of activity.

The specific protection of the enzyme by glyceraldehyde-3-phosphate, the recognized reaction of aldehyde groups with thiols to form hemimercaptals (15), the probable functions of a carbonyl-thiol addition compound in the glyoxylase reaction (27, 12), and the knowledge of the important thio-ester linkage in acetyl coenzyme A (9), have suggested to various investigators that the initial step of the catalysis is as depicted in Fig. 4. This initial step gives a logical means for the formation of an acyl group attached to the sulfur of the enzyme. Such an acyl-S linkage is suggested by analogy with acetyl coenzyme A (9) and the high free energy of hydrolysis of acetyl coenzyme A (19, 17). However, other groups in the enzyme might be involved; for example, Stadtman (18) and Wieland and Schneider (26) have called attention to coupling of acetyl to a N of imidazole to form a " high-energy " linkage. Quantitative measurements of sulfhydryl groups in free and acylated enzyme may provide an answer regarding the location of the acyl group.

Racker and Krimsky have demonstrated an interesting spectral shift with the enzyme upon reaction with sulfhydryl reagents (13). This has led to the postulate that the substrate might add to the enzyme by " aldehydolysis " of a S-DPN$^+$ linkage on the enzyme. This cannot be the only mode of addition, inasmuch as glyceraldehyde-3-phosphate can protect the enzyme from alkylation by iodoacetate whether the DPN$^+$ is oxidized, reduced, or absent. The aldehyde can thus specifically protect a sulfhydryl group which is not involved in a S-DPN$^+$ linkage. Also if the only mode of addition of substrate were by an " aldehydolysis " mechanism, a reduction of one equivalent of DPN$^+$ would be required for each substrate molecule bound. The experimental results given previously show that only a portion of the DPN$^+$ may be reduced at neutral or slightly acidic pH in the presence of excess substrate. Elucidation of the details of the mechanism of the H transfer is likely to be a difficult task, and further speculation at this point appears unwarranted.

The finding that the substrate will protect approximately two -SH groups from alkylation by iodoacetate agrees well with the observations that the enzyme will accept two acyl groups per mole and that two DPN⁺ molecules are present in the native enzyme. These results are all in harmony with the existence of two active sites per enzyme molecule. Whether these are interacting sites is not known. An interesting problem is also posed by the finding of Velick that the enzyme after removal of the two DPN⁺ molecules accompanying the native protein requires binding of three DPN⁺'s per mole of enzyme for maximum activity (24).

SPECTROPHOTOMETRIC MEASUREMENT OF THE NUMBER AND REACTIVITY OF THE ENZYME SULFHYDRYL GROUPS

In conjunction with study of the enzyme sulfhydryl groups, a spectrophotometric procedure has been developed for measurement of the rate and extent of reaction of sulfhydryl groups with p-mercuribenzoate [1] (3). The procedure is based on the spectral shifts accompanying mercaptide formation, as illustrated by Fig. 6 for the reaction of p-mercuribenzoate with cysteine in acetate buffer at pH 4.6. At pH 4.6, measurement of the change in absorbancy at 255 mμ gives a sensitive measure of the extent of mercaptide formation; at pH 7 the curves are slightly different and the change at 250 mμ is used. The magnitude of the increase in absorbancy with different proteins varies slightly from that obtained with cysteine, so that each sulfhydryl compound should be used as its own standard for total absorbancy change possible with a given amount of p-mercuribenzoate. Once the total possible change has been noted, a single measurement suffices for determination of the amount of reactive -SH in a given protein or other -SH compound. Usefulness of the procedure for proteins in general is illustrated by the detection of a rapid reaction of 4 -SH groups per molecule of egg albumin at pH 4.6 and slow reaction of only 3 at pH 7. The reaction at pH 7 can be shown to be second order, and the velocity constant readily determined (3).

---

[1] This solution is preferred because p-chloromercuribenzoate when dissolved in neutral solution does not exist as the chloro derivative but more likely as the hydroxide or in combination with buffer anions that might be present.

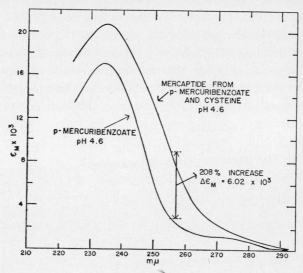

FIG. 6. Absorption of ultraviolet light by *p*-mercuribenzoate and its mercaptide with cysteine at pH 4.6.

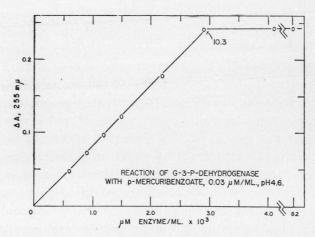

FIG. 7. Reaction of glyceraldehyde-3-phosphate dehydrogenase with *p*-mercuribenzoate at pH 4.6.

The application of the procedure to a glyceraldehyde-3-phosphate dehydrogenase preparation is illustrated in Figs. 7 and 8. The equivalence point at pH 4.6 corresponds to the presence in this five-times recrystallized preparation of 10.3 -SH groups per mole (118,000 grams) (21). At pH 7 the reaction of the -SH groups is much slower, as demonstrated by the results shown in Fig. 8, where the changes in absorbancy at different time intervals are given. The slower reaction rate when a smaller excess of *p*-mercuribenzoate

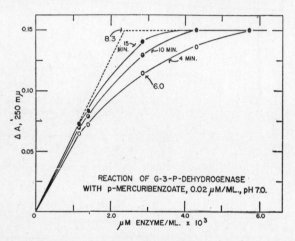

FIG. 8. Reaction of glyceraldehyde-3-phosphate dehydrogenase with *p*-mercuribenzoate at pH 7.0.

is present is readily apparent. With other preparations, the number of reactive sulfhydryl groups found at pH 4.6 has varied from 8 to 13.5. Higher values were obtained with a preparation recrystallized several times in the presence of cysteine and EDTA, followed by two recrystallizations in the presence of EDTA, or with preparations freshly prepared in the presence of EDTA. Amperometric iodosobenzoate titrations showed 14.7 reducing equivalents per mole for a freshly prepared five-times recrystallized preparation (16). These values do not agree with those reported by Barron and Dickman (1). The values for -SH groups may be compared to a value of 10.7 half-cystine residues per mole found by Velick and Ronzoni (22). From this comparison it is evident that all or most of the potential sulfhydryl groups exist as such in the preparations of crystalline muscle enzyme.

REACTION OF THE DEHYDROGENASE WITH ARSENATE AND L-GLYCERALDEHYDE-3-PHOSPHATE

The maximum turnover number of the enzyme obtainable in the presence of phosphate is higher than that obtainable with arsenate (3), as shown by the data in Fig. 9. In these measurements, made

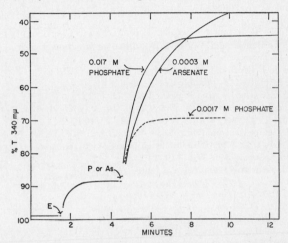

FIG. 9. Comparative reaction rates with phosphate and arsenate in the glyceraldehyde-3-phosphate dehydrogenase reaction.

with the recording spectrophotometer, enzyme was added to substrate and DPN$^+$ in pyrophosphate buffer, and a rapid equilibrium was obtained as noted. The addition of different levels of phosphate or arsenate to such a mixture gave the rates of reaction indicated. Higher levels of arsenate resulted in a decreased velocity. The estimated initial velocities with phosphate were 60 per cent greater than with arsenate, and correspond to turnover numbers of approximately 12,500 at 28° C. The rate of reaction with phosphate quickly falls off because of the rapid approach to equilibrium. These results suggest that arsenate either has an inhibitory effect on the steps leading to acyl-enzyme formation or that the cleavage reaction with arsenate is slower than with phosphate and is the rate-limiting step in the catalysis.

In trial assays of D, L-glyceraldehyde-3-phosphate preparations, a slow continued reduction of DPN⁺ was noted after DPNH formation equivalent to the oxidation of well over 50 per cent of the aldehyde had occurred. This result is most readily explained by a slow catalysis of the oxidation of the L-form of the substrate, the calculated turnover number being only 0.07 per minute at 28° C.

REFERENCES

1. Barron, E. S. G., and S. Dickman, *J. Gen. Physiol.*, 32, 595 (1949).
2. Bock, R. M., and R. A. Alberty, *J. Am. Chem. Soc.*, 75, 1921 (1953).
3. Boyer, P. D., unpub.
4. Cori, G. T., M. W. Slein, and C. F. Cori, *J. Biol. Chem.*, 173, 605 (1948).
5. Cori, C. F., S. F. Velick, and G. T. Cori, *Biochim. et Biophys. Acta*, 4, 160 (1950).
6. Harting, J., and S. F. Velick, *Federation Proc.*, 11, 226 (1952).
7. Holzer, H., and E. Holzer, *Z. physiol. Chem.*, 291, 67 (1952).
8. Krimsky, I., and E. Racker, *J. Biol. Chem.*, 198, 721 (1952).
9. Lynen, F., E. Reichert, and F. Ruoff, *Ann. Chem. Justus Liebigs*, 574, 1 (1951).
10. Meyerhof, O., and P. Oesper, *J. Biol. Chem.*, 170, 1 (1947).
11. Oesper, P., in A Symposium on *Phosphorus Metabolism*, Vol. I (W. D. McElroy and B. Glass, eds.), p. 523. The Johns Hopkins Press, Baltimore (1951).
12. Racker, E., *J. Biol. Chem.*, 190, 685 (1951).
13. Racker, E., and I. Krimsky, *J. Biol. Chem.*, 198, 731 (1952).
14. Rapkine, L., *Biochem. J.*, 32, 1729 (1938).
15. Schubert, M. P., *J. Biol. Chem.*, 114, 341 (1936).
16. Segal, H. L., and P. D. Boyer, *J. Biol. Chem.*, in press.
17. Stadtman, E. R., *J. Biol. Chem.*, 196, 535 (1952).
18. Stadtman, E. R., Paul-Lewis Award Address, 123rd meeting, Am. Chem. Soc., Los Angeles, 1953.
19. Stern, J. R., S. Ochoa, and F. Lynen, *J. Biol. Chem.*, 198, 313 (1952).
20. Taylor, J. F., S. F. Velick, G. T. Cori, C. F. Cori, and M. W. Slein, *J. Biol. Chem.*, 173, 619 (1948).
21. Taylor, J. F., *Federation Proc.*, 9, 237 (1950).
22. Velick, S. F., and E. Ronzoni, *J. Biol. Chem.*, 173, 627 (1948).
23. Velick, S. F., *J. Phys. & Coll. Chem.*, 53, 135 (1949).
24. Velick, S. F., pers. com.
25. Warburg, O., and W. Christian, *Biochem. Z.*, 303, 40 (1939).
26. Wieland, T., and O. Schneider, *Ann. Chem., Justus Liebigs*, 580, 159 (1953).
27. Yamazoye, S., *J. Biochem. (Japan)*, 23, 319 (1936).

DISCUSSION

DR. CHANCE: The reaction mechanism presented by Dr. Boyer does indeed suggest that more incisive data should be obtained from a kinetic study of the reaction of his "acyl enzyme" with hydrogen ions or with phosphate and I think that such experiments could readily be carried out with a suitable rapid flow apparatus. In fact, Dr. Harting and I have already measured the kinetics of the reaction of arsenate and the acyl enzyme obtained by reaction of the enzyme with acetyl phosphate. We feel that further kinetic studies are required to show whether the enzyme-DPN complex observed spectroscopically at 360 mμ is a "Michaelis-Menten" or rate-limiting enzyme-coenzyme compound or whether some other spectroscopically unseen site on the enzyme is responsible for the catalytic effect: our experiments on rapidly mixing the yeast enzyme with DPN and glyceraldehyde-3-phosphate often show an initial rapid reduction of DPN at a rate exceeding the rate at which DPN is observed to combine with the enzyme and to form the spectroscopically observed compound. (We take into account the small amount of nucleotide that may be initially bound to the enzyme.)

DR. LIPMANN: I wonder if we should not give up talking about enzyme-substrate complexes from now on and rather call them "enzyme-substrate" compounds.

DR. RACKER: Shall we change the title of my talk?

DR. LIPMANN: Well, I would not mind if you would.

DR. SMITH: Before you do, I wonder whether we are completely clear on the distinctions that have been made in the past. It seems to me that the distinction between a complex made between the enzyme and another substrate, which is essentially a co-substrate, doesn't reflect on the over-all problem of the nature of the catalytic effect of the enzyme. In the cases, for example, where an SH group is involved either as a loosely-bound compound with the protein or as a tightly-bound compound with the protein, in essence you are still forming a complex between the enyzme and two substrates, one of which may be called a co-substrate because you find it unchanged at the end of the reaction whereas the other substrate is changed in the course of the reaction. Nevertheless at a symposium like this on the mechanism of enzyme action, we still have to worry about the role of the protein, and it is the loose or tight binding of the protein with the substrate which makes the reaction go. Thinking only in terms of the over-all organic reaction, I think, tends to obscure a little bit the possible participation of the proteins in this process. Maybe the cocktail hour would be a good time to discuss this.

DR. LIPMANN: Yes, I think so. I think one should make a clear distinction between the enzyme-substrate complex and such compounds as are formed here, in which an energy-rich bond is formed between the enzyme and the substrate. The binding must be of a quite strong form in this type of reaction. I previously proposed to change the name from "enzyme" to "reactor" because the term "reactor" has a much better way of expressing what the enzyme in this kind of reaction actually does.

DR. RACKER: May we have a date at cocktails?

DR. LIPMANN: Yes.

DR. ASTRACHAN: I should like to mention some work we have been doing which bears on the mode of attachment of DPN to crystalline triosephosphate dehydrogenase. This problem was studied by comparison of free DPN, DPN attached to oxidized enzyme, and DPN attached to reduced enzyme, with respect to their rates of reaction with various DPN degradative enzymes and dehydrogenases. In addition, the triosephosphate dehydrogenase was isolated after reaction of its bound DPN in order to determine which fragments of DPN still possess ability to bind to the enzyme.

The three kinds of DPN were reacted with 1) *Neurospora* DPN-ase, which splits DPN to give nicotinamide and adenosine diphosphate ribose—, 2) snake venom pyrophosphatase—which yields adenylic acid and nicotinamide mononucleotide—, 3) takadiastase deaminase—which removes the adenine amino group of DPN—, 4) DPN kinase—which forms TPN from DPN— and 5) various DPN-linked dehydrogenases.

It was observed that DPN bound to oxidized enzymes reacted in all cases at 30-50 per cent the rate of free DPN.

When the triosephosphate dehydrogenase was reduced, the general result obtained was a marked further decrease in reactivity of the bound DPN. Two exceptions to the general result were seen. The reaction with pyrophosphatase proceeded equally well, whether the DPN was bound to reduced or oxidized enzyme. The reaction with DPN-ase, run on either side of the pH range 7-8 also proceeded equally well with DPN bound to reduced or oxidized enzyme. In the pH range 7-8, however, there was a marked decrease in the reactivity of the DPN bound to reduced enzyme. When triosephosphate dehydrogenase was reisolated after reduction of its bound DPN, the Cori group found that DPNH is bound to the enzyme. We have found that of all the split products obtained, only adenosine diphosphate ribose and desamino DPN retain the ability to bind to the enzyme.

We have interpreted these results to mean that DPN is bound to the oxidized enzyme through its pyrophosphate group. Favoring this postulate is the fact that the only split products bound are those that contain the pyrophosphate group. In addition, the fact that DPN attached to reduced or oxidized enzyme is attacked by pyrophosphatase at the same rate that DPN attached to oxidized triosephosphate dehydrogenase is attacked by all other enzymes, is consonant with the idea of a pyrophosphate binding.

The decrease in the reactivity of bound DPN when the sulfhydryl groups of the triosephosphate dehydrogenase are formed indicates the appearance of some new type of linkage between DPN and the enzyme, a linkage that is related directly or indirectly to the enzyme sulfhydryl group. The pH sensitive activity of DPN-ase on DPN bound to reduced enzyme indicates the formation of a new ionic linkage between DPN and the enzyme.

In summary, we believe that DPN is bound to oxidized triosephosphate dehydrogenase through the pyrophosphate group of DPN. When the enzyme is reduced, additional linkages appear to form between DPN and the enzyme.

DR. RACKER: As far as Dr. Boyer's discussion is concerned, there is one point I would like to make. We have carried out a simple experiment in an attempt to differentiate between the two alternative mechanisms which we have proposed, one in which a thiohemiacetal is formed as an intermediate and the other in which aldehydolysis of the DPN-enzyme complex takes place. We took triose phosphate dehydrogenase and varied the order of additions of DPN and acetaldehyde. If we added the DPN first and the aldehyde second, the rate was, as expected, that of the fully active enzyme. However, if we added the aldehyde first and then added DPN, the rate was very much slower—less than 1/10 as fast. This can be explained more readily by aldehydolysis than by formation of the thiohemiacetal as an intermediate.

DR. LIPMANN: I wasn't clear about the iodoacetate effect on the arsenolysis. Can you inactivate the SH and still get the arsenolysis?

DR. RACKER: Yes.

DR. LIPMANN: How can you explain that?

DR. RACKER: The reaction will not work in the absence of glutathione. I was afraid that somebody would ask that question. We really have no good answer for it, except that we assume that the glutathione reacts with the enzyme when it is added after iodoacetate treatment. There is some other evidence that this occurs which Dr. Harting may wish to discuss, and that is the inhibitory effect of the glutathione on the acetylphosphatase activity of triose phosphate dehydrogenase. These experiments also seem to indicate that there is secondary interaction between glutathione and the enzyme after treatment with iodoacetic acid.

DR. LIPMANN: It looks, then, as if another SH-group can take over in that reaction. Don't you think that the arsenolysis means that the acyl group is linked as a thioester to the enzyme and that the reaction takes place through transacylation?

DR. RACKER: Yes. I think that is why we have to add glutathione.

DR. HARTING: One thing that's very puzzling is that the acyl phosphatase reaction is inhibited by glutathione and must be carried out with the enzyme in the so-called oxidized state. If we use your terms and consider that the phosphatase reaction occurs at site II, then perhaps you can form an acetyl enzyme there without SH groups. With the transfer reactions the enzyme needs to be in the reduced state, and (as you point out) in the case of the iodoacetic acid-treated enzyme glutathione has to be added. Don't you think this raises the question as to the nature of the reaction at the second site?

DR. RACKER: I hope we made it clear in the papers we have published why we assume that the acyl phosphate goes onto the enzyme first and that from there it is transferred to the SH group. We have several indications for suggesting this, and I believe it fits in quite well with the observations on the acyl phosphatase reaction.

DR. HARTING: As I understand it, when you block site I with IAA and then carry out an arsenolysis of acetyl phosphate, you assume that the added glutathione may inhibit the acetyl phosphatase activity and thereby permit arsenolysis.

DR. RACKER: Yes. The mechanism of acetyl phosphatase activity of the enzyme and its inhibition by glutathione is certainly not clear. We don't have any explanation for it.

DR. HARTING: Perhaps, this question might be partially settled by a simple experiment. Let me just tabulate briefly the facts which we have observed about the phosphatase activity:

THE PHOSPHATASE ACTIVITY OF GLYCERALDEHYDE-3-PHOSPHATE DEHYDROGENASE

Glyceraldehyde-3-phosphate dehydrogenase	State of SH Groups of Enzymes *	Inhibitor Added	Acetyl Phosphate Disappearing μmoles
Enzyme-contained bound DPN	oxidized	None	4.1
Enzyme-contained bound DPN	reduced	2.0 μM Glutathione	0.6
Enzyme-contained bound DPN		2.0 μM Cyanide	0.3
Enzyme-recrystallized twice in presence of .001 M KCN, then once in absence of KCN	reduced	None	0.6
Enzyme-bound DPN removed by adsorption of charcoal	oxidized	None	0.5
Enzyme-DPN added to the charcoal treated enzyme	oxidized	None	4.1
None		None	0.3

* This notation is based on the assumption that the SH groups of an enzyme, which is recrystallized in the presence of cysteine, cyanide, or versene and has maximal oxidation activity, are in the reduced state.

Experimental Conditions: Veronal buffer, 40 μMoles, pH 8.2; acetyl phosphate, 5 μMoles; glyceraldehyde-3-phosphate which, unless otherwise indicated, was recrystallized from ammonium sulfate and contained two moles of bound DPN per mole of enzyme, .035 μMoles. Total vol., 2.0 ml. Incubation, 1 hour.

As shown above, the catalysis of the splitting of acetyl phosphate can be inhibited by the removal of the DPN bound to the enzyme, by glutathione, and by low cyanide concentrations. These concentrations of glutathione and cyanide do not inhibit the arsenolysis. One might, therefore, try an arsenolysis reaction with an IAA-treated enzyme in the presence of cyanide and the absence of glutathione. One could thereby determine whether the glutathione, which is required for arsenolysis in the presence of IAA, is functioning only as an inhibitor of the phosphatase activity or interacts with the enzyme in some other manner.

Dr. Lipmann: I wasn't aware of this phosphatase activity. Is that a very rapid reaction?

Dr. Racker: No; you need fairly large amounts of enzyme to get this.

Dr. Harting: However, it is faster than the transfer reactions such as the P^{32} exchange or the arsenolysis reaction. We have never tried the hydrolytic reaction with diphosphoglyceric acid, but from the rate of splitting of acetyl phosphate we would guess that this reaction would occur at a reasonably rapid rate.

Dr. Lipmann: If you boil the enzyme does it still have this acyl phosphatase activity?

Dr. Harting: We haven't tried boiling the enzyme.

Dr. Stadtman: I wonder if this is a specific or non-specific effect of the enzyme in catalyzing the hydrolysis of the acyl phosphates.

Dr. Harting: It looks pretty specific, because if you remove the DPN from the enzyme the phosphatase activity is not observed. Thus again there is a peculiar DPN requirement involved in this reaction.

Dr. Stadtman: It seems to me that there may well be certain problems involved in the use of enzymes at substrate concentrations which are ordinarily of little significance in studies with dilute enzyme solutions. For example, we have recently observed that at relatively high concentrations acyl phosphates and acyl mercaptans react with imidazole to form the N-acetyl derivative which undergoes spontaneous hydrolysis. It therefore appears possible that in those studies involving the use of enzymes in substrate amounts, the effective concentrations of imidazole groups may be sufficiently great to catalyze a nonspecific hydrolysis of energy-rich acyl compounds—a hydrolysis which under the usual conditions of enzyme studies would not be detectable.

Dr. Lipmann: There has been a good deal of interest in this reaction, and I wonder if we could take a few minutes to discuss it.

Dr. Racker: I agree with Dr. Stadtman as far as the experiments with large amounts of triose phosphate dehydrogenase are concerned. There are non-specific side reactions of that type possible, particularly hydrolytic ones. On the other hand, when we are dealing with oxidation-reductions I think we avoid that kind of difficulty since the reduction of a thiol ester for instance is a very specific process.

DR. BOYER: I think Dr. Stadtman's comment on this is very apt. This possible lack of specificity is one reason that Dr. Velick and I and Dr. Racker should feel compelled to check experiments on acyl-enzyme formation with low concentrations of the natural substrate. In comparison to the oxidation of glyceraldehyde-3-phosphate, the arsenolysis of acetyl phosphate and acetyl transfer reactions are very slow reactions which require relatively large concentrations of the enzyme preparations. Sulfhydryl or other groups on the enzyme could act non-specifically, and the possible action of other enzymes present as impurities needs consideration.

DR. LIPMANN: I think we might continue with the discussion. I wonder if Dr. Ochoa would like to make a few comments.

DR. OCHOA: I would just like to take a couple minutes to discuss enzymes which seem to transfer coenzyme-A from one acyl group to another. This type of enzymes was mentioned by Dr. Racker yesterday and was included in the group of acyl transfer reactions, but it would seem that one is dealing here with a thiol rather than with an acyl transfer reaction. Now, the enzyme with which we have been working transfers Co-A reversibly from succinyl Co-A to acetoacetic acid to form acetoacetyl Co-A. This is the same type of enzyme which was first found by Dr. Stadtman in extracts from *Clostridium kluyveri*. Dr. Stadtman found an enzyme which transfers Co-A from acetyl Co-A to several acids: propionic, butyric, lactic, and some others, I think. The enzyme which I am discussing was found in heart independently by Green and his co-workers, and by Stern, Coon and del Campillo in my laboratory. This enzyme has been purified to a rather high degree from this source. In this type of reaction we are probably dealing with a system in which enzyme compounds are formed, in this case probably enzyme-Co-A compounds. As shown by Gilvarg in our laboratory, this enzyme will rapidly catalyze the exchange of free succinate in with succinyl Co-A, that is, if you incubate C^{14} succinate with the enzyme and succinyl Co-A, there is a rapid exchange. Although perhaps several explanations to account for this are possible, one explanation is that a coenzyme-A-enzyme compound is formed as an intermediate. This would account for the exchange. It seems likely that we first have a succinyl Co-A-enzyme complex of the typical Michaelis-Menten type, but the true intermediate is probably the coenzyme-A-enzyme compound. It is interesting to speculate that the group on the enzyme which makes this possible may be a carboxyl group. In other words, you might be forming what I might call an enzymyl-Co-A compound. It would be very interesting to get evidence for this sort of thing. We have tried to get such a Co-A-enzyme compound by incubating the enzyme with succinyl Co-A, acetyl Co-A, or Co-A, and then dialyzing for long periods and seeing if the light absorption ratio between 280/260 mμ was changed. The purified enzyme has a ratio at these several links of about 1.7; but, when you incubate the enzyme with Co-A, Co-A is pretty firmly absorbed, and in all the experiments that we have done with the various compounds we have gotten a decrease in the ratio down to about 1.2. Something we plan to do is to incubate the enzyme with S^{35} labelled succinyl Co-A and then treat the reaction mixture more drastically and see if we have radioactivity in the isolated protein. If one has this type of reaction in which the enzyme is properly a substrate, then it becomes very important to get a large amount of the enzyme, so that one can deal with it the same way that one deals with substrates. Unfortunately, these enzymes cannot be obtained in very large amounts so far, and it will be a difficult job to get large amounts but I presume it will eventually be done.

DR. KOSHLAND: I would like to make a comment on this reaction as well as on other similar reactions which I have been worrying about for some time. From organic chemical considerations, some of which I will discuss later, I would make a guess that this exchange reaction is more complicated than it might appear on the surface. Most carboxyl activation reactions can be written as a simple mechanism. For example, if you have a carboxyl group reacting with ATP, then a simple displacement reaction in which the carboxyl oxygen-phosphorus bond is formed at the same time as the phosphorus-oxygen bond to ATP is breaking can account for the formation of the acyl phosphate, which

$$
\underset{\overset{\|}{RC-O^-}}{\overset{O}{}} + ATP \rightarrow \underset{\overset{\|}{RC-O}\ldots.\underset{\overset{|}{O^-}}{P}\ldots.OPO_3PO_3Ad}{\overset{O\quad O\quad O^-}{}} \rightarrow \underset{\overset{\|}{RC-OPO_3^=}}{\overset{O}{}} + ADP
$$

can then react with coenzyme A and other things. There is a good deal of evidence for this and one of the best bits is the O^{18} work of Dr. Mildred Cohn in the phosphoglycerate kinase reaction.

Now if you consider the reaction which Dr. Ochoa was discussing, then it seems to me you come up against some difficulties. In this case you are starting with an acyl coenzyme A compound and if this reacts with succinate, you must form a new carbon-sulfur bond and also break and form carbon-oxygen bonds. There is no simple way of writing this reaction because of the number of bonds that have to be formed and broken. There are several alternatives that one could consider. Perhaps other parts of Co-A are involved and perhaps and maybe more likely—the reaction doesn't go on one enzyme surface. When you can't write a simple organic mechanism, I think these possibilities should be considered.

DR. LIPMANN: Doesn't it help to bind these compounds on the surface of the enzyme?

DR. KOSHLAND: Since you have to form the carbon-sulfur bond of succinyl Co-A by breaking the carbon-oxygen bond of succinate the reaction will probably be complicated even on an enzyme surface.

DR. DOUDOROFF: May I ask if there is any hydrolysis of the acetyl Co-A or succinyl Co-A going on in this process?

DR. OCHOA: No, there is no hydrolysis going on.

DR. KAPLAN: I was wondering about the first step in the reaction of ATP plus Co-A plus acetate to give the pyrophosphate as one of the products. Now, what can that pyrophosphate do? If you add pyrophosphatase can you pull the reaction so that it will keep going? That is, if you have an equilibrium reaction where you have an adenylic-enzyme and free pyrophosphate formed, will adding inorganic pyrophosphatase pull the reaction? That is, it would be like an ATPase.

DR. LIPMANN: That is an interesting proposition.

DR. COLOWICK: But isn't the amount of enzyme the limiting factor here?

DR. KAPLAN: Maybe, but wouldn't there be hydrolysis of the adenylic enzyme complex? Wouldn't you expect that if the enzyme could act both with water and an acceptor.

DR. LIPMANN: I wouldn't expect it. Why should we? You would think, then, of some hydrolysis being part of the exchange reaction. We have no indications for hydrolysis. Our rather good balances speak much against it.

DR. OCHOA: Dr. Racker already mentioned yesterday the reaction of ATP plus Co-A plus succinate to give succinyl Co-A, ADP, and inorganic phosphate; and it seems interesting to compare this with the acetate reaction which Dr. Lipmann just mentioned and see what connections there may be between teleology and reaction mechanisms. Now, teleologically those two types of reactions seem to accomplish quite different functions and may be there for quite different purposes. One appears to have as its main function to activate not only acetate but a large number of fatty acids, forming fatty acid Co-A compounds, whereas the succinate reaction seems to be rather specific and seems to have as its main function the generation of phosphate bonds during alpha ketoglutarate oxidation—that is, the oxidation of alpha ketoglutarate leads to the formation of succinyl Co-A, which in the presence of ADP and inorganic phosphate can form ATP. Now, one would expect, however, that these two reactions should have a rather similar mechanism;

and yet our experience with this reaction, which Dr. Racker has already pointed out yesterday, is that inorganic phosphate is not incorporated significantly into ATP unless the other components of the system are present—in other words, we have to have also succinate and Co-A. There is another exchange catalyzed by this enzyme which we have investigated to some extent, which again is the incorporation of succinate into succinyl Co-A. This has been studied with C^{14} succinate. In this case, contrary to the transferase enzyme, which requires nothing but succinate and succinyl Co-A and enzyme, there is a requirement for orthophosphate. We are not sure, but we think maybe we also require adenine nucleotides, because the Co-A that we have used is contaminated with adenine nucleotides. It is possible that this enzyme is not a single enzyme. It has been purified very extensively, over 200 times—but that in itself doesn't mean anything; thus, it might be more than one enzyme. Apparently in Green's laboratory, where this enzyme has also been extensively studied, there is some indication of the separation. It may be that Co-A phosphate is formed as an intermediate. We have no evidence whatsoever for a separation or for the formation of an intermediate compound. One possibility we considered was that succinyl phosphate might be an enzyme-bound intermediate, and Dr. Kaufman in our laboratory synthesized succinyl phosphate—incidentally, he found that succinic anhydride would do this job very nicely. If the enzyme is incubated with succinyl phosphate, ATP, Co-A, and isotopic succinate there is no exchange between succinyl phosphate and succinate; so succinyl phosphate was eliminated as a possible intermediate. Therefore, I have been worrying considerably as to why these two reactions discussed should have apparently entirely different mechanisms.

DR. KOSHLAND: I would just like to mention some conclusions about exchange evidence that we have come to from our consideration of reactions in which stereochemical criteria apply. First of all, the evidence that an exchange is observed is not in itself conclusive for a stable enzyme-substrate intermediate unless you bring in specificity arguments. I think in the acetate activation reaction that Dr. Lipmann mentioned it is reasonable that only one site could accommodate the pyrophosphate and therefore the exchange evidence for an intermediate is good. When exchange is not observed as in the pyrophosphate ATP reaction in the pantothenate case, this does not mean you can exclude an AMP-enzyme intermediate or establish a pyrophosphate-enzyme intermediate. In the first place, the AMP-enzyme intermediate might be a transient one and, therefore, may not exist for a long enough time for exchange to occur. Secondly, the lack of exchange doesn't exclude a direct transfer reaction of the kind occurring with inversion of configuration as in the maltose phosphorylase reaction studied by Dr.

Doudoroff and in the beta amylase reaction. Therefore, the failure to observe exchange is a very slippery criterion to use as sole evidence for an intermediate.

DR. LIPMANN: I agree, but one has to start somewhere.

DR. MILDRED COHN: Most people put ATP in a reaction mixture and magnesium and then forget about it. Actually, there are several complexes which would tend to form when you mix ATP with magnesium, and I think there is enzymatic specificity for different complexes; and I think in the case where pyrophosphate is split off there may be a different type of magnesium pyrophosphate utilized as compared to the case where inorganic phosphate is split off. I think in a reaction like hexokinase it is quite clear that the substrate for the reaction is magnesium-ATP. Under these circumstances it must be a magnesium-phosphate complex formed with the two phosphates near the ribose residue of ATP which is the substrate for the reaction. On the other hand, in a reaction such as the one Dr. Lipmann has been discussing, where you split off pyrophosphate, then the active complex would presumably be with magnesium bound to the two terminal phosphates of ATP.

DR. KALCKAR: I would like to ask whether the mode of chelation (for example, of ATP with magnesium) can determine on which side of the oxygen fission will occur—that is, which bond is weaker and which is stronger. I also wonder if the question of whether you get phosphorylation or pyrophosphorylation by ATP may depend on whether you have one or the other chelate.

DR. LIPMANN: Here the possibility of forming the appropriate enzyme bond with phosphate or pyrophosphate might be the determining factor.

DR. MILDRED COHN: I don't think that the chelate determines which split you get. It determines only which phosphate comes off.

DR. KALCKAR: It doesn't determine which side of the oxygen is involved?

DR. MILDRED COHN: I don't think so. In all the phosphate transfer reactions that have been investigated, as well as in phosphatase reactions, the split always occurs between the phosphorus and the oxygen. This is also true of the myokinase reaction, where, for example, you can prove just by the fact that the ATP picks up no oxygen from the water that the splitting was between the P and the O. When the hexokinase reaction is run in H_2O^{18} if you isolate both the glucose-6-phosphate and the ADP which are formed, you find no O^{18} in either one of them, which means that no water is involved in the reaction, and that you don't have a di-ester intermediate. In the case of the myokinase, where the ATP molecule that you started with becomes ADP (as well as the AMP becoming ADP), if in either direction the split occurred anywhere except between the P and the O—that is, between the terminal P and the oxygen adjacent to it—you would be bound to get oxygen into the ATP from the water.

DR. KALCKAR: One of my colleagues in Copenhagen, Dr. Thomas Rosenberg, has proposed glucose metaphosphate is the first product of the hexokinase reaction and that glucose metaphosphate is formed primarily in the hexokinase reaction and that this then forms water. This should apply to all hexokinase reactions or perhaps primarily to those of mammalian tissues.

DR. MILDRED COHN: The O^{18} would show up in glucose-6-phosphate then, and it doesn't.

DR. LIPMANN: I think we are just warming up to it, and it's a shame to cut this discussion short; but I think we had better turn to the discussion of another part of Dr. Racker's reports and hear from Dr. Horecker now.

DR. HORECKER (and DR. SMYRNIOTIS): Recent studies on the mechanism of formation of glucose-6-phosphate from pentose phosphate have disclosed the participation of two types of group transfer reactions, involving ketol and aldol condensations.

Evidence has been obtained which indicates that sedoheptulose-7-phosphate is formed from pentose phosphate by the transfer of a C_2 group from ribulose-5-phosphate. This reaction is catalyzed by the enzyme transketolase which contains thiamine pyrophosphate as the active group (Horecker, B. L., and P. Z. Smyrniotis, *J. Am. Chem. Soc.*, 75, 1009 (1953), and Racker, E., G. de la Haba, and I. G. Leder, *J. Am. Chem. Soc.*, 75, 1010 (1933)). The transfer mechanism appears to involve a glycolaldehyde-ThPP enzyme complex, referred to as "active glycolaldehyde," and the reaction would thus be formulated as follows:

Ribulose-5-phosphate $\rightleftharpoons$ " active glycolaldehyde "

$+$ glyceraldehyde-3-phosphate

" Active glycolaldehyde " $+$ ribose-5-phosphate

$\rightleftharpoons$ sedoheptulose-7-phosphate

" Active glycolaldehyde " is formed either from ribulose-5-phosphate or from sedoheptulose-7-phosphate, since the transketolase reaction is reversible. It can also arise from L-erythrulose (Horecker, B. L., and P. Z. Smyrniotis, *J. A. Chem. Soc.*, 75, 1009 (1953)) or by the decarboxylation of hydroxypyruvate (Racker, E., G. de la Haba, and I. G. Leder, *J. Am. Chem. Soc.*, 75, 1010 (1953)). Other aldehyde acceptors will replace ribose-5-phosphate or D-glyceraldehyde-3-phosphate; among these are L-glyceraldehyde-3-phosphate or D-glyceraldehyde and glycolaldehyde (Horecker, B. L., and P. Z. Smyrniotis, *J. Am. Chem. Soc.*, 75, 1009 (1953); Racker, E., G. de la Haba, and I. G. Leder, *J. Am. Chem. Soc.*, 75, 1010 (1933)).

A second example of sugar interconversion by group transfer is the reaction catalyzed by transaldolase (Horecker, B. L., and P. Z. Smyrniotis, *J. Am. Chem. Soc.*, 75, 2021 (1953)). In this case the dihydroxyacetone group is transferred from sedoheptulose-7-phosphate to glyceraldehyde-3-phosphate and the products of the reaction are fructose-6-phosphate and a tetrose ester which is presumably erythrose-4-phosphate. The enzyme has been purified about 100-fold from yeast; no coenzyme requirement has yet been demonstrated.

Efforts to isolate the tetrose ester have thus far been unsuccessful, since in the presence of crystalline muscle aldolase and hexose diphosphate, used as a source of glyceraldehyde-3-phosphate, it is converted to a new heptulose ester. This ester, purified by ion exchange chromatography, has been found to contain two phosphate groups per mole of heptulose. These two groups show distinctly different rates of acid lability; one is hydrolyzed at the same rate as is sedoheptulose-1-phosphate, while the other is much more resistant to acid hydrolysis and is hydrolyzed at the same rate as is sedoheptulose-7-phosphate. With aldolase, the new ester yields one equivalent of dihydroxyacetone phosphate but no glyceraldehyde-3-phosphate. While the affinity of aldolase for this substrate is nearly as great as for fructose diphosphate, the rate of cleavage is only one-fourth as rapid. On the basis of these properties and the trans configuration expected in a condensation catalyzed by aldolase, the ester is presumed to be sedoheptulose-1, 7-diphosphate. The role of this ester in carbohydrate metabolism is as yet unknown.

GROUP TRANSFER AND ACYL–GENERATING FUNCTIONS OF LIPOIC ACID DERIVATIVES *

I. C. GUNSALUS

Laboratory of Bacteriology
University of Illinois
Urbana

RELATION OF LIPOIC ACID TO KETO ACID METABOLISM

THE STRESS of this conference on the mechanisms of enzyme action, with the attention of the present discussion to the transfer functions of lipoic acid, coincides with our recognition of the significance of the reaction types made possible by what Lipmann chooses to call the two-sulfur catalysts. As we shall see, the recognition of the reaction potentialities was the contribution of several groups of workers, but was made evident by the bulk of pertinent information already available when the disulfur nature of the catalytic agent was revealed by its isolation.

In terms of the mechanism of lipoic acid function and of keto acid decarboxylation and dehydrogenation, at this stage of development of the problem, one must be preoccupied with the reaction sequence, the electron rearrangements, and any substrate-cofactor, or substrate enzyme, compounds which occur, while awaiting more precise knowledge to inquire as to the roles of the enzymes in the mechanism of activation. The unraveling of the mechanism of oxidative decarboxylation of alpha-keto-acids, or more broadly the cleavage of dicarbonyl compounds with acyl generation, has progressed rapidly in the wake of the ideas, methods, and observations made available by the clarification of the reactions and the biological role of monothiols, especially thioesters, spearheaded by Lipmann and his coworkers.

* The original work from the author's laboratory has been supported by research grants from the office of Naval Research, the Atomic Energy Commission, and the Graduate College, University of Illinois.

545

As the site and mode of action of the two-sulfur catalyst, lipoic acid, clarifies and the separation and characterization of the enzymes in the keto acid systems progress, attention must again be turned in more detail to the identification of any cofactor-substrate compounds which occur and to the mechanism of the thiamine-catalyzed reaction in the initial keto acid, or dicarbonyl, cleavage; for example, toward finding whether a cocarboxylase-substrate compound is formed, if the first intermediates in the carboxylase, acetoin-forming and in the reverse acetoin condensations, are similar, and if they are the same intermediates presumed to occur in the keto acid dehydrogenase reaction. At the other end of the keto acid system, inquiry about the transformations of thioester bond energy, such as acyl-lipoic and acyl-CoA, to phosphate-bond energy already underway from other viewpoints, will be needed to complete the picture.

The studies of the pyruvate oxidation factor, which led to its isolation and synthesis (as alpha-lipoic acid), and to studies of its forms and mechanism of action, were focused on the oxidative decarboxylation of alpha-keto acids, particularly pyruvate, in *Streptococcus faecalis* (8, 41), subsequently in *Escherichia coli* (19, 30, 49), and later, based on an increased lipoic acid content (25, 58), on the keto acid dehydrogenases of tissue. As Green suggests (13), the occurrence of appreciable amounts of lipoic acid in the purified, high molecular weight, pyruvate (25) and ketoglutarate (58) oxidases from pig heart and pigeon breast muscle necessitates a reevaluation of the mechanisms previously suggested (35, 59). In our discussion, for economy of hypotheses, and because present evidence favors this as a generally correct view, a similarity of mechanism in all oxidative dicarbonyl cleavages will be assumed. In the developing knowledge of keto acid cleavage mechanisms, however, one must hasten to call attention to the accumulating evidence for alternate pathways of alpha-keto acid oxidation, especially in free aliphatic acid formation as contrasted to acyl formation (32, 60, 62). These pathways, possibly altered only in part, have received increased study as to mechanism, enzyme steps, and intermediate compounds formed (37, 60). Passing attention will be paid to some preliminary studies with *Proteus* which consider the free acid-forming steps in relation to the lipoic-acid-catalyzed acyl generation.

The present discussion, stressing the group transfer functions of lipoic acid, will center on the reactions in which this catalyst has been shown to function: acyl generation, acyl transfer, and hydrogen transfer. The reactions of lipoic acid with other cofactors and especially with the substrate, or portions of the substrate, will define its locus and mechanism of action, as well as its general importance to the formation and removal of biosynthetic intermediates. The individual steps in the alpha-keto acid decarboxylase-dehydrogenase systems, in so far as known, and the individual enzymes studied and separated will be considered in the light of the cofactor functions which they catalyze.

For clarity, passing attention to the forms and chemical properties of lipoic acid is needed. These remarks will be brief.

I appreciate the privilege of pointing out that the new data from our own laboratory reported here, as well as those reported previously at various meetings during the last three years as our laboratory at Illinois has developed, have been the result of the joint efforts of a number of workers, especially Mr. Hager and Mrs. Fortney, and more recently Mrs. Dougal, with continued contributions from Dr. Dolin, now of the Oak Ridge National Laboratory, and in increasing amount by Mr. Razzell, particularly with the " coli-type enzymes " recovered from *Proteus vulgaris*—the system under study by Moyed and O'Kane. Lipoic acid, in substrate quantities which permitted the studies of intermediate reactions in the keto acid systems, was initially made available by its synthesis by Dr. Hornberger and Mr. Heitmiller in our laboratory at Illinois, and by its final purification by Mr. Snackenberg of the Eli Lilly Research Laboratories, using the later steps in the method initially worked out for the isolation of lipoic acid from natural material.

Lipoic Acid: Forms and Chemical Properties

The isolation, determination of structure, and synthesis of lipoic acid are the subject of publications from a group effort of our laboratory at Illinois, Reed and coworkers at the University of Texas, and the Eli Lilly Research Laboratories of Indianapolis, on the one hand (24, 53, 55), and from the Lederle Research Laboratories on the other (23, 44). These studies will be reviewed in detail elsewhere; consequently only those aspects of the problem essential to a clear understanding of the biological functions of lipoic acid, principally its chemical properties, will be discussed here. Lipoic acid has been isolated in two forms: (1) as alpha-lipoic acid, a cyclic disulfide of 6, 8-dithiooctanoic acid (53), and (2) as a derivative of Protogen B, by Lederle workers (44), a sulfoxide form which corresponds to β-lipoic acid (54). The sulfoxide appears now to be a chemical oxidation product of the cyclic disulfide and not to function in the keto acid systems. A form equally as important biologically as alpha-lipoic acid is its reduction product 6, 8-dimercaptooctanoic acid. In these discussions the cyclic disulfide will be referred to interchangeably as alpha-lipoic acid, oxidized lipoic acid, lip_{ox}, $lipS_2$; and the 6, 8-dimercaptooctanoate as reduced lipoic acid, lip_{red} or $lip(SH)_2$. Evidence for the function of the dimercapto form in biological systems has been discussed in previous communications (15) documenting the arsenite sensitivity of the alpha-keto acid systems, and reversal of arsenite inhibition by 1, 2-dithiols (43), as contrasted to the lesser sensitivity of the monothiol systems (42). Lipoic acid as isolated in the disulfide form is optically active: $[\alpha]_D^{25}$ approximately $+ 97°$ in benzene (55)—as a result of the asymmetry of carbon 6 of the octanoate chain. The synthetic DL-alpha-lipoic acid used in these experiments (24) possesses on a weight basis half the biological activity of natural lipoic acid in the *Streptococcus faecalis* apopyruvate dehydrogenase assay system (16). As will be shown later in this discussion, only one of the isomers of synthetic DL-6, 8-dimercaptooctanoate is active with the isolated lipoic transacetylase enzyme, whereas both isomers are oxidized by the DPN-linked lipoic dehydrogenase enzyme.

If both the disulfide and dimercapto forms of lipoic acid function in keto acid metabolism, the free energy of the DPN-linked reaction, i. e., the oxidation-reduction potential of the pair,

$$\text{lipS}_2 \rightleftharpoons \text{lip(SH)}_2 \tag{1}$$

assumes considerable importance.

From calculations based on the lipoic content of *E. coli* Fraction A, and assuming all the lipoic acid present to be active as hydrogen donor to DPN, we have suggested that the potential of the lipoic acid system (eq. 1) lies near or below that of DPN—considerably more negative than values reported for linear disulfides of the glutathione type (5). Recent experiments with lipoic acid dehydrogenase indicate a potential somewhat more negative than DPN; i. e., below −.32 volts, pH 7.0. Reed and DeBusk (6) have stated at the last Federation Meetings that the potential of the pair lipothiamidepyrophosphate-reduced / lipothiamidepyrophosphate, which they have suggested as the coenzyme form of lipoic acid, approximates the hydrogen electrode (i. e., ca. −.42 volts, pH 7.0).

Acetyl lipoic acid, implicated in the reaction mechanism (20), and formed by transacetylase experiments (see Tables 2 and 3) has not yet been isolated and characterized. The biologically active form contains 1 acetyl group per mole of 6, 8-dimercaptooctanoic acid. Only one of the isomers, presumably the one corresponding to the dextro-rotatory alpha-lipoic acid, is acetylated by the transacetylase. Reed and DeBusk (48) have presented data for the formation of the acyl derivative of reduced LTPP (lipothiamidepyrophosphate) by the pyruvate dehydrogenase preparations of an *E. coli* mutant (see below). These workers too used DL-alpha-lipoic acid. Although they have not indicated whether one or both isomers were biologically active, the data in their communication show one-half of the added LTPP as stable hydroxamic acid. It was not stated whether or not the reaction had proceeded to completion (48).

Calvin and Baltrop (4) have suggested a cleavage of the lipoic acid disulfide bond by photo energy, mediated by chlorophyll, as the conversion step from photo to chemical energy. These authors' initial formulation postulates diradical formation, followed by a pickup of two hydrogen atoms by an undisclosed mechanism to form 6, 8-dimercaptooctanoic acid. The ultimate hydrogen donor function in photosynthesis is attributed to water, with consequent O_2 liberation.

A postulated reversal of the steps of the keto-acid dehydrogenase systems, i. e., acylation of reduced lipoic and transfer of the acyl group to diphosphothiamine (DPT), accompanied by reduction to the aldehyde oxidation level would regenerate oxidized lipoic acid, which could again be reduced, by the photo- and water-splitting steps, to reduced lipoic acid. By this formulation, reduction of lipoic acid would prevent keto acid breakdown by decarboxylation and acyl lipoic formation, since this reaction would occur only if oxidized lipoic acid were present. The formation of keto acids by this " reversal " mechanism would be concluded by carboxylation of the " aldehyde-DPT," or " carbanion-DPT," compound to release DPT^+. This reaction mechanism need not be confined to the reversal of the pyruvate, ketoglutarate, and related dehydrogenases, but could as well involve glycolaldehyde or phosphoglycolaldehyde, with the formation of glyceric or phosphoglyceric acid. One possible source of the " glycolaldehyde-DPT " compound would be the transketolase systems of pentose and heptulose metabolism (23, 45).

The important problem of the coenzyme form of lipoic acid has been approached directly only in one instance, viz., by the studies of Reed and DeBusk (50, 51). These workers have presented evidence for the formation, and activity, of a thiamine-lipoic compound, for which they suggest as the structure, the amide of lipoic acid with the 4-amino pyrimidyl group of thiamine (49, 50). The coenzyme is reported to be the pyrophosphate derivative: lipothiamide pyrophosphate (LTPP) (52).

Evidence for the coenzyme nature of LTPP is derived from its support of the growth, and activation of enzyme preparations, of a mutant of *E. coli* (51) prepared by the penicillin technique of Davis and Lederberg. Transfers of this mutant have shown slight instability and a need for reselection in the hands of Reed and DeBusk (6), and have given greater difficulty in the hands of other workers, who have found thiamine dependency of the resulting strains, presumably by back mutation (1). Evidence based on growth assay of bioautographs with the Reed-DeBusk mutant indicates the formation of several lipoic-thiamine compounds by incubation of cell suspensions of lactic acid bacteria and wild type *E. coli* with the two components (50). These workers further report the formation of an active substance by treating DPT with lipoyl chloride, and, using DPT-free samples of their LTPP, have reported the activation of the cell-free pyruvate dehydrogenase prepared from cells of their mutant essentially by the methods of Korkes et al. (30) and Hager et al. (19). Further data, and preferably confirmation of the Reed and DeBusk reports by other workers, can add much to the knowledge of the early steps of the alpha-keto acid dehydrogenase mechanism.

Several forms of lipoic acid, water-soluble but not soluble in organic solvents, have been reported to occur in extracts of keto acid enzymes (25, 58), of tissues (17), and of bacteria (10). These have not been identified, though several are active in the dried cell *Streptococcus faecalis* apopyruvate dehydrogenase assay (16). These preparations have not been used to activate cell-free pyruvate dehydrogenase systems. A sample of LTPP kindly furnished by Dr. Reed was not found, in our hands, to activate the apopyruvate dehydrogenase of *S. faecalis* nor the DPT-dependent purified *E. coli* Fractions A and B (unpublished data).

In summary: Lipoic acid occurs in disulfide, dimercapto, and mono-S-acyl mono-mercapto forms, all of which are active biologically. Synthetic DL-alpha-lipoic acid possesses half the biological activity of isolated alpha-lipoic acid, for the over-all pyruvate dehydrogenase and the lipoic transacetylase reactions (20, 24). Presumably only the dextro-rotatory isomer, which corresponds to the form isolated, is active. Both isomers of DL-6, 8-dimercaptooctanoic acid are oxidized by lipoic dehydrogenase. The potential of the O/R pair, disulfide-dimercapto lipoic acid, is as low as that of DPN^+–DPNH—may be as low as the potential of the hydrogen electrode. The experiments on the coenzyme form are not yet definitive. The exciting experiments of Reed and DeBusk, suggesting that LTPP is the coenzyme form of lipoic acid, should be confirmed and extended.

The properties of the naturally occurring acetyl lipoic acid have been explored, and its isolation and characterization have been undertaken along with experiments to obtain the analogous succinyl lipoate, presumably formed by the ketoglutarate dehydrogenase.

Lipoic Acid: Site and Mechanism of Action

The increased interest in, and multiple approaches to, the problems of acyl generation from alpha-keto acids have led to several assays for oxidative carboxylase activity (57, 58, 63) and for the over-all acyl-generating system (28, 30, 32, 35, 39, 59). The coenzyme and supplementary enzyme dependencies of the various assays and their relationship to the decarboxylative, acyl-generating, and transfer reactions have also been determined (19, 30, 37, 39, 59). A generalized scheme to account for all published assays, and for the straight (non-oxidative) carboxylase and acetoin-forming reactions, apparently similar in the first stage, was presented at the 2nd International Biochemical Congress in Paris and at the subsequent A. A. A. S. Conference on Vitamins and Metabolism last summer. It is as follows:

PYRUVATE   DEHYDROGENASE   MECHANISM

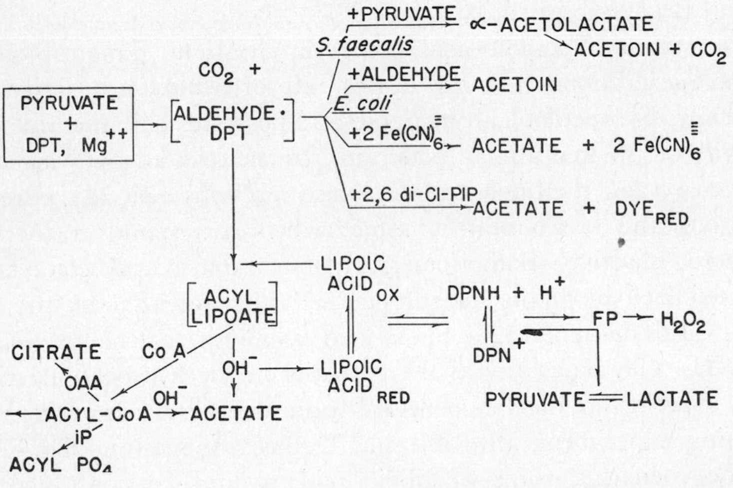

Fig. 1. Suggested reaction pathways in the pyruvate dehydrogenase mechanism.

In this scheme the locus of lipoic acid action was narrowed to the reactions between the proposed carbanion (aldehyde level of oxidation)-acceptor function of DPT and the acyl-transfer action of coenzyme A—that is, an acyl-generating step, and an acyl donor step to CoA. Since these two reactions leave the lipoic acid in the reduced state, a third reaction, a dehydrogenase linked to DPN to regenerate the oxidized lipoic acid, would complete the cycle. Thus lipoic acid follows diphosphothiamine and precedes both coenzyme A and DPN in the keto-acid dehydrogenase systems. In the three

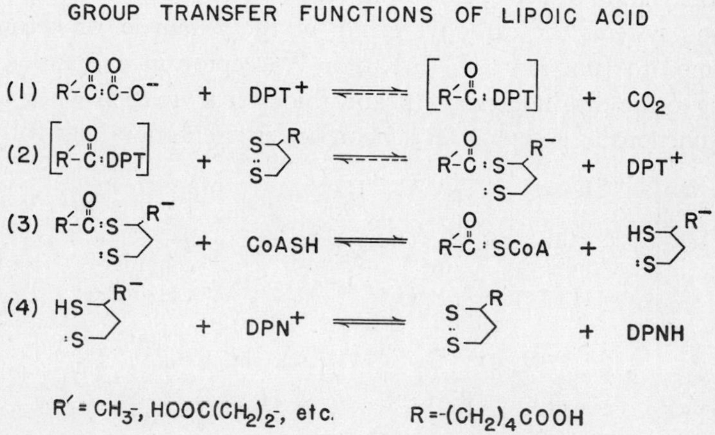

GROUP TRANSFER FUNCTIONS OF LIPOIC ACID

$$R' = CH_3, HOOC(CH_2)_2^-, \text{ etc.} \qquad R = -(CH_2)_4COOH$$

Fig. 2. Functions of thiamine and lipoic acid in acyl generation from α-keto-acids.

functions indicated, the lipoic acid reacts with each of the other cofactors in one of its functions, thus serving as the connecting cofactor. The multiple functions of internal oxidation-reduction, and of acyl and hydrogen transfer, are thus attributable to the unique characteristics of this disulfur catalyst.

The single-step reactions necessary to the oxidative decarboxylation and the acyl generation, as well as to return the cofactors to their initial state, as shown in Fig. 1, can be written in four separate reactions, as in Fig. 2. Of these reactions, reactions 3 and 4 have now been clarified, and the enzyme catalyzing reaction 4 has been completely separated from the others. The exact mechanism of reactions 1 and 2 remains to be clarified.

Reaction 1 of Fig. 2, visualized here as a heterolytic cleavage of the substrate to yield CO_2 and a carbanion coordinated with diphosphothiamine, has not been demonstrated directly, nor has the "DPT-carbanion" compound been isolated. Evidence for its occurrence can be adduced from the multiple reactions which the carbanion can undergo in biological systems and with "artificial" electron acceptors (15, 60).

As indicated in Fig. 1, lipoic acid is presumed to function only when acyl generation and transfer occur, and not in the "straight" decarboxylation or aceloin-forming reactions (9, 40). In the aceloin-forming systems the carbonyl group of the aldehyde, or ketone, is presumed to function as "carbanion" acceptor in a manner analogous to the disulfide cleavage and thioester formation when lipoic acid functions as acceptor. A schematic representation is as follows:

$$
\left[\begin{array}{c} O \\ \parallel \\ R_1-C: \end{array} \right]^{-}
+ \begin{array}{c} O \\ \parallel \\ C-R_2 \\ | \\ H \end{array}
\rightleftharpoons \begin{array}{c} O\ \ O^- \\ \parallel\ \ | \\ R_1-C:C-R_2 \\ | \\ H \end{array}
+ H^+ \rightleftharpoons \begin{array}{c} O\ \ OH \\ \parallel\ \ | \\ R_1-C-C-R_2 \\ | \\ H \end{array}
\tag{2}
$$

$$
\left[\begin{array}{c} O \\ \parallel \\ R_1-C: \end{array} \right]^{-}
+ \begin{array}{c} S \\ \cdot\cdot \\ S \\ | \\ R \end{array}\!\!\!>
\rightleftharpoons \begin{array}{c} O:\bar{S} \\ \parallel \\ R_1-C:S \\ | \\ R \end{array}\!\!\!>
+ H^+ \rightleftharpoons \begin{array}{c} O\ \ HS \\ \parallel \\ R_1-C-S \\ | \\ R \end{array}\!\!\!>
\tag{3}
$$

wherein equation (2) represents, in generalized form, an aceloin condensation and equation (3) an oxidative formation of thioester by disulfide bond cleavage of the lipoic acid type.

In the two types of acetoin-forming reactions (26, 27, 38): (1) pyruvate as "carbanion" acceptor leading to alpha-acetolactic acid formation, as occurs in S. faecalis (9) (see Fig. 1), and (2) aldehyde as acceptor leading directly to acetoin, as in E. coli (see Fig. 1), no acyl is generated and lipoic acid is not required (19). In the terminology of Ochoa, each of these reactions would presumably require a specific condensing-type enzyme. An analogous reaction for diacetyl cleavage with DPT as the acceptor for one-half of the molecule as carbanion, liberating the other half as acetate, has also been shown in *Streptococcus faecalis* extracts (7). Evidence for a role of DPT in the transketolase reactions (reverse aceloin condensation) possibly to form DPT-aldehyde, or enzyme-aldehyde, further extends these reactions (23, 45).

The reaction of ferricyanide or 2,6-dichlorophenolindophenol (2,6 diCl PIP) as electron, but not carbonion acceptor, apparently leads to the liberation of the carbon skeleton as a free acid (15, 60) (Fig. 1). A system occurring naturally in *Proteus vulgaris* appears also to connect at the DPT-aldehyde level of compound transporting the electrons, possibly via heme catalysts to oxygen, leaving the carbon skeleton as free acid (37, 62, for similar catalytic data on pigeon muscle enzyme, but no lipoic acid data, see 14, 60). As indicated above, the decarboxylations which lead to aceloins do not require lipoic acid, viz., reaction (1), Fig. 2 (9, 45). The particulate *Proteus* electron-transport system and the soluble *Proteus* decarboxylase of Moyed and O'Kane (37) presumably proceed without lipoic acid, as indicated by analyses which show these fractions to be essentially free of lipoic acid (36). Thus the *Proteus* carboxylase (.47 to .52 saturated ammonium sulfate precipitate) may be the enzyme which catalyzes reaction (1), Fig. 2. This carboxylase fraction is also reported to be DPT-dependent and to connect slowly to 2, 6-dichlorophenolindophenol and still more slowly to ferricyanide—in the absence of added lipoic acid (36). Reed and DeBusk have also reported the pyruvate dehydrogenase from their *E. coli* mutant to decarboxylate pyruvate with added DPT (48), using ferricyanide as electron acceptor. They further state that if LTPP is added in place of DPT, no ferricyanide reduction occurs—their interpretation being that the aldehyde from DPT is transferred to the lipoic acid so as to form an acyl instead of reacting with ferricyanide. In these studies no mention was made of the reaction rate as compared to the DPN reduction and dismutation rates.

The reaction rates so far reported for ferricyanide and 2,6-dichlorophenolindophenol are much slower, 0.1 to 0.001 as fast, as the reactions measured by oxygen uptake, dismutation, and DPN reduction (19)—the pig heart system does not react with ferricyanide (60). Furthermore, on purification of the enzymes, the reaction rate with ferricyanide as electron acceptor decreases for the E. *coli* system as compared to its dismutation and DPN reduction rates. In experiments with *Streptococcus faecalis* apopyruvate decarboxylase cells, ferricyanide acts as electron acceptor only if lipoic acid is added (22). The reaction rate, in this case, is the same as that obtained by the dismutation or oxygen uptake measurements. These data are most readily interpreted on the hypothesis that ferricyanide reacts at two, or possibly three, sites in the keto-acid system: namely (1) at the DPT-aldehyde compound level (DPT-carbanion), possibly with a mediating enzyme; (2) after the formation of reduced lipoic acid by the reoxidation to the disulfide form by purely chemical reaction; and (3) after reduction of DPN by its reoxidation via flavoprotein, as previously reported by Haas (18, 32). The second reaction has been shown to proceed by purely chemical means. The mechanism and rate of the first reaction, and the possibility of a mediating enzyme, require further clarification. In part, such evidence would appear to require the separation of the enzymes for the initial steps of the keto-acid system, especially for reactions (1) and (2), Fig. 2.

The exact mechanism of acyl generation, reaction (2), Fig. 2, is unknown. The mechanism suggested by the figure, carbanion cleavage of the disulfide bond to form thioester and free sulfhydryl, which Racker would term "aldehydolysis," would account for the observations, and also be compatible with the mechanism for reversing the carboxylation step postulated by Calvin et al. (4). The reversal of decarboxylation has been demonstrated using $C^{14}O_2$ for both the pyruvate and ketoglutarate systems (12; also see Korkes, 15), as indicated above. The hypotheses of reaction mechanism must remain tentative pending further information about the nature of possible "DPT-aldehyde" compounds and of the "carbanion" donor reaction. Although enzymes for reactions (1) and (2) Fig. 2, namely, the decarboxylation ("DPT-aldehyde" formation), and the acyl generation (acetyl lipoic acid formation), have not so far been separated, it seems clear that two distinct steps are involved. Reed and DeBusk (48) have suggested that the reactions indicated as (1) and (2), Fig. 2, occur at a single enzyme site and constitute a mandatory reaction sequence for alpha-keto-acid oxidation when LTPP is present. Their formulation is compatible with the outline indicated in Fig. 2 as to the site and order of DPT and lipoic acid action and of CO_2 and acyl formation.

The formulation of Reed and DeBusk (47) for the function of the B fraction as a conjugase for formation of LTPP from DPT and enzyme-bound lipoic acid is, however, difficult to rationalize with several pieces of available data:

(1) Partially purified *E. coli* A fraction can be freed of DPT, and of activity, by dialysis against alkaline pyrophosphate, or versene, and can be reactivated by adding DPT.

(2) Lipoic acid is not removed by the dialysis, but remains bound to the A fraction—the lipoic acid concentrates with Fraction A, not Fraction B.

(3) The dissociation constants for DPT in the assay reactions so far outlined approximate 10^{-6} molar, in the case of the ferricyanide reaction nearer 10^{-5} molar, whereas the dissociation data which are available for lipoic acid, i. e., those with *S. faecalis* apodecarboxylase, indicate a dissociation approximating 10^{-8} molar. Any error in this value, due to other limiting rates is likely to reduce rather than increase the K value.

(4) Dialysis against pyrophosphate or versene would not split most amide linkages, nor is there evidence for biological formation of an amide linkage in the absence of an added energy source.

(5) The B fraction which Reed and DeBusk used was an early fraction prepared by the methods of Korkes et al. (30). On further purification, the lipoic acid content of this fraction decreases. With more purified B fractions we were unable to confirm the Reed and DeBusk experiments (19).

In addition, the B fraction at several levels of purity has been shown to contain a DPN-linked lipoic dehydrogenase in proportion to the activation of the *E. coli* dismutation and DPN reduction systems (21). These data, shown in Table 1, will be discussed below.

The acetyl transfer, from lipoic acid to CoA, reaction (3), Fig. 2, will also be discussed in detail below.

In Summary: The site of lipoic acid function is between diphosphothiamine and coenzyme A, as an acyl-generating and -transfer catalyst, and as a hydrogen-transfer catalyst. These functions, outlined in Fig. 2, reactions (2), (3), and (4), assign a three-fold action to lipoic acid, and indicate three catalytically active forms of the sulfur portion of lipoic acid, namely: (1) a cyclic disulfide; (2) an S-acetyl derivative of the dimercapto form; and (3) a dimercapto form, which function in cyclic sequence.

The function of lipoic acid in the oxidative acyl-generating keto acid reaction appears to be preceded by a decarboxylase reaction to generate a " DPT-aldehyde," active as carbanion donor. The DPT step may be common to other keto acid decarboxylase reactions, which differ in the nature of the succeeding, donor, reactions of the DPT-bound aldehydes. Oxidative reactions appear also to occur at the " DPT-aldehyde " level, with both " natural " and " artificial " electron acceptors, to liberate free acids. Although this mechanism is not proved, it certainly is not precluded by available data (19, 60).

Each of the four reactions from alpha-keto acid, namely, (1) decarboxylation; (2) acyl generation; (3) acyl transfer, and (4) hydrogen transfer (see Fig. 2), constitutes a single-step reaction. Each may be catalyzed by a separate enzyme.

Alpha Keto Acid Dehydrogenation: Enzymatic Steps

Observations on the individual steps in oxidative decarboxylation of alpha-keto acids has centered mainly on bacterial systems because of their apparent stability, due largely, as we know now, to the presence of transacetylase which activates inorganic phosphate as acceptor for the acyl groups generated, and thus permits the reactions to proceed. Outlines of Lipmann's (33, 34) early experiments with *Lactobacillus delbrueckii* and the discovery of acetyl phosphate, the experiments of Still (61) with *Escherichia coli*, and of Stumpf (62) with *Proteus vulgaris* have been reviewed during the past year at the Oak Ridge Symposium on Microbial Metabolism (15). Later experiments undertaken in Ochoa's laboratory resulted, as most of you are aware, in fractionation of the *E. coli* system for acyl generation from pyruvate into separate protein fractions, clarified the cofactor requirements, and afforded insight into the complexity and general pattern of the keto acid decarboxylase-dehydrogenase systems. These experiments were discussed by Ochoa (38) as well as more recently by myself in the light of following experiments (15).

An analogous fractionation of enzymes from *Streptococcus faecalis*, the organism initially used to show the function of lipoic acid in pyruvate oxidation, extended the cofactor requirements for acyl generation to the pyruvate system of another organism and broadened the substrate list to include ketobutyrate with propionyl phosphate generation (8). Preliminary data of Dolin, using this organism, indicate that dimethyl pyruvate and ethyl methyl pyruvate (the alpha-keto acids corresponding to valine and isoleucine) also undergo the same reaction sequence. Ketobutyrate was first used to avoid the troublesome side reaction leading to acetoin which occurred with the *S. faecalis* extracts (8, 9). The acetoin reaction had previously been shown to be DPT-dependent but not lipoic-acid-dependent (9, 40)—thus the formulation in Figs. 1 and 2. A crossing of the protein fractions from *S. faecalis* and *E. coli* revealed a different distribution of enzyme components and indicated still a third enzyme before acyl-CoA formation and the reoxidation of DPN (Hager, Dolin, and Gunsalus, unpub.). The *E. coli* fraction A was shown to contain the carboxylase, and Fraction B was associated with the dehydrogenase for DPN reduction, presumably a lipoic dehydrogenase.

A ketoglutarate system with properties analogous to the pyruvate system has been obtained in extracts of *E. coli* cells grown aerobically in S_2 medium. The similarities extend to the cofactor requirements, a carboxylase (A′) fraction and an activation by the B fraction required for the pyruvate system. Keto acid systems for both pyruvate and alpha ketoglutarate have been solubilized from several animal tissues in Ochoa's laboratory, by Kaufman (28), and in Green's laboratory (25, 58). So far, these enzymes have resisted separation into fractions that catalyze the steps outlined in Figs. 1 and 2. Korkes and coworkers (31), however, were able to separate from pig heart a fraction replacing *E. coli*, B, in the dismutation reaction with *E. coli* fraction A, thus suggesting a similar reaction pattern in the animal keto acid enzymes. Data presented here, as well as earlier, associate the decarboxylase with Fraction A (see Korkes, 15) and would assign a dehydrogenase function to Fraction B (19); thus throwing into question Reed and DeBusk's (47) interpretation of the function of Fraction B as a conjugase for lipoic acid and DPT, and possibly rendering premature Sanadi and Littlefield's (59) conclusion that the pigeon breast muscle ketoglutarate oxidase is a single enzyme.

Of the reactions outlined in Fig. 1, until recently the carboxylase was best understood because a number of separate measurements were available for this step and a greater number of workers, including those interested in the animal tissue keto acid dehydrogenases were applying these measurments to the animal enzymes. More recently, with the availability of substrate quantities of lipoic acid, and particularly of reduced lipoic acid (6, 8-dimercaptooctanoic acid) studies of the nature of the lipoic transacetylase (Reaction 3) and the lipoic dehydrogenase (Reaction 4) have begun to clarify these steps and to return the main locus of study again to the initial reactions of carboxylation and acyl generation, Reactions (1) and (2), Fig. 2.

Enzyme and Cofactor Dependencies for (Pyruvate) Dismutation

As outlined by Korkes et al. (29, 30), acyl generation from pyruvate and its transfer to phosphate, forming acetyl phosphate, with hydrogen transport via DPN to pyruvate so as to form lactate, were shown to be catalyzed by four protein fractions, requiring at least three cofactors, plus a reducing agent and an acyl acceptor. These reactions were diagrammed as follows:

$$\text{pyruvate}^- + \text{DPT}^+ + \text{CoA} + \text{DPN}^+ \rightleftharpoons \text{acyl CoA}$$
$$+ \text{DPNH} + \text{CO}_2 + \text{DPT}^+ \qquad (4)$$

$$\text{DPNH} + \text{pyruvate} \underset{\textit{dehydrogenase}}{\overset{\textit{lactic}}{\rightleftharpoons}} \text{lactate} + \text{DPN}^+ \tag{5}$$

$$\text{CoA} + \text{P}_i \underset{\textit{acetylase}}{\overset{\textit{P-trans-}}{\rightleftharpoons}} \text{acetyl-PO}_4 + \text{CoA} \tag{6}$$

The system indicated in reaction (4), as expanded in Fig. 2, reactions (1) through (4), is catalyzed by the enzymes present in the two *E. coli* fractions, viz., (A + B) with added DPT, CoA, and DPN. The lipoic acid is bound to the A enzyme fraction. With catalytic amounts of DPN and CoA, and an excess of orthophosphate, reactions (5) and (6) occur to regenerate the oxidized DPN and free CoA, whereas with substrate amounts of DPN and CoA, the lactic dehydrogenase and phosphotransacetylase can be dispensed with and the reaction followed spectrophotometrically at 340 mμ. In this case the orthophosphate would also be dispensable. As indicated below, reaction (4) has been followed with the soluble pyruvate (35, 59) and ketoglutarate dehydrogenase from pigeon breast muscle and with *E. coli* fractions A and B free of lactic dehydrogenase and transacetylase (19).

Enzyme and Cofactor Requirements with CoA and DPN as Acceptors

In order to examine more closely the steps in the keto-acid dehydrogenase system, measurements for the individual steps with the separated enzymes are essential. Measurement of reaction (4) above [reactions 1 through 4, Fig. 2] is obviously only a small step in this direction. However, measurements of this type showing the cofactor requirements for DPN reduction with both pyruvate and alpha-ketoglutarate dehydrogenases are graphed in Figs. 3A and 3B. As one can note, the dependencies for each of the factors listed is absolute with the exception of glutathione, which in separate experiments was found to be dispensable when reduced CoA was used. An outline of the separation of the pyruvate and ketoglutarate systems from *E. coli* into three protein-containing fractions, one specific to pyruvate and one to ketoglutarate, plus a third fraction common to the two systems, is shown in Table 5. The dependency of each system for the "carboxylase"–containing enzyme fractions (A pyruvate and A' ketoglutarate) was also absolute. Since each of

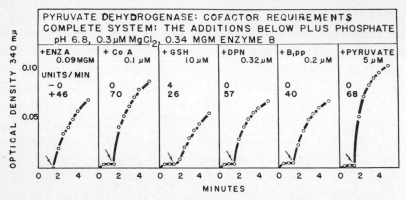

FIG. 3A. Pyruvate dehydrogenase measured by DPN reduction.

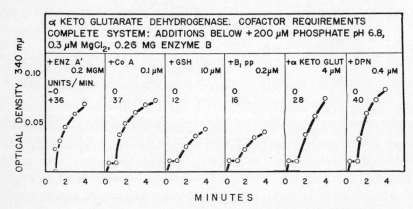

FIG. 3B. α-Ketoglutarate dehydrogenase measured by DPN reduction.

these fractions also contains lipoic acid, in increased amount, no evidence was obtained by this means for its participation.

The dependency of both the pyruvate and ketoglutarate dehydrogenases on the same Fraction B is shown in Fig. 4. As had been shown in Fig. 3, the B fraction (precipitable by 0.6-0.7 saturated ammonium sulfate) is without activity. Note that the A' enzyme is activated ten-fold by the presence of enzyme B, whereas at this stage of purity the A fraction of the pyruvate system is activated slightly more than four-fold. Further purification of the A fraction results in greater dependency upon B.

The difference between the pyruvate and ketoglutarate fractions, A and A', is exhibited in Fig. 5, in which it can be seen that in the presence of an excess of coenzyme A both reactions proceed essentially to the complete utilization of the CoA. The two enzymes

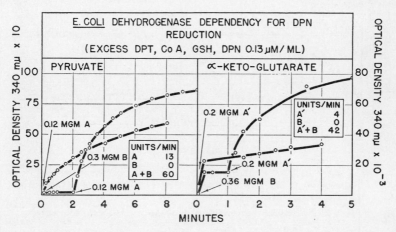

FIG. 4. Enzyme dependencies for DPN reduction by keto-acids.

differ, however, as shown by the replacement of the stoichiometric CoA requirement of the pyruvate system by the addition of trans-acetylase, whereas the ketoglutarate dehydrogenase, presumably forming succinyl CoA, is not activated by transacetylase. Presumably the stoichiometric CoA dependencies of the ketoglutarate system could be relieved by adding either the P enzyme of Kaufman et al. (39), or the deacylase of Gergely et al. (11). From these experiments it was concluded that the function of Fraction B, being common to the ketoglutarate and pyruvate systems, must be common to the keto acid systems in general. Based on the unlikelihood of a lack of specificity of the transacetylase, a dehydrogenase function was suggested for the common enzyme; i. e., Fraction B was considered to be lipoic dehydrogenase. The data presented in Figs. 3, 4, and 5 are in agreement with the reaction sequence suggested in Fig. 2. In addition they suggest that the lipoic dehydrogenase (Reaction 4) is subject to independent measurement.

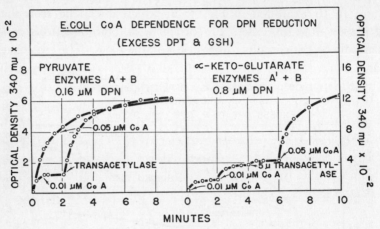

FIG. 5. Coenzyme A as acyl acceptor from pyruvate and ketoglutarate.

A DPN-LINKED DEHYDROGENASE—(ENZYME B)

The measurement of lipoic dehydrogenase by direct reduction of DPN^+ using reduced lipoic acid (6, 8-dimercaptooctanoic acid) as reductant, or reoxidation of DPNH with alpha-lipoic acid as oxidant, was shown to proceed in the presence of enzyme B fraction. The initial reaction rate with DPN^+ and reduced lipoic acid was rapid but proceeded only to the reduction of about 0.15 μM DPN/3 ml. regardless of the level of lip$(SH)_2$ or of enzyme added. The reverse reaction (DPNH + lipS$_2$) proceeded somewhat more slowly. So far equilibrium has not been attained, due apparently to the complexity of the lipoic-DPN reaction in the presence of high concentrations of DPN. Lipoic dehydrogenase activity was, however, found to be measurable by linking it with lactic dehydrogenase in the presence of pyruvate and catalytic amounts of DPN, according to the reactions:

Lipoic dehydrogenase (7)

$$Lip(SH)_2 + DPN^+ \rightleftharpoons LipS_2 + DPNH + H^+$$

Lactic dehydrogenase (8)

$$DPNH + H^+ + pyruvate \rightleftharpoons lactate + DPN^+$$

$$Lip(SH)_2 + pyruvate \rightleftharpoons lactate + LipS_2 \qquad (9)$$

The sum, Reaction (9), can be followed by measuring residual sulfhydryl groups with a quantitative nitroprusside, or ferricyanide, test. Data showing the enzyme and DPN dependencies of the coupled lactic dehydrogenase-lipoic dehydrogenase assay are recorded in Table 1. A complete dependency on lipoic dehydrogenase *E. coli* (Fraction B) and with only slight sulfhydryl disappearance in the absence of each of the other components is clearly shown. One unit of lipoic dehydrogenase has been defined as that amount of enzyme which will oxidize 1 μM of lipoic acid per hour in the protocol indicated in Table 1.

TABLE 1

Lipoic Acid Dehydrogenase

Additions	$Lip(SH)_2$ Oxidation
	$\mu M/30'$
1. Complete System [1]	7.7
2. " — DPN, 0.5 μM	0.4
3. " — Pyruvate, 20 μM	0.4
4. " — Lactic dehydrogenase, 2000 U	0.2
5. " — Fraction B, 140 γ (S.A. 200 [2] μM)	.0

[1] Additions 2 through 5, plus; 10 μM reduced lipoic acid ($Lip(SH)_2$), 100 μM phosphate buffer, pH 7.0.
[2] S.A. = μM lipoic acid oxidized/hr./mg. protein.

The response to increased amounts of enzyme is linear for 0.5 to 5 units. The specific activity of the dehydrogenase (units/mg. protein) of 200 compares to a specific activity of 4500 in the μl units of Korkes et al. (30), and represents about a 100-fold purification over the extracts of cells from S_2 medium.

From Table 1 it can be observed that more than half of the DL-6, 8-

dimercaptooctanoate added was oxidized (7.7 of 10 μM). Other experiments with an excess of enzyme show that 10 μM of lipoic acid can be oxidized completely, thus indicating the lack of specificity of this dehydrogenase for the D and L isomers of 6, 8-dimercaptooctanoic acid.

Demonstration of Lipoic Transacetylase and Its Assay

If the reaction sequence for pyruvate dehydrogenase outlined in Fig. 2 is correct, acetyl lipoic acid would be expected to transfer an acetyl group to coenzyme A (Reaction 3). In the presence of inorganic phosphate and phosphotransacetylase, the acyl group would accumulate as acetyl phosphate. An assay based on the reverse of these two reactions has been used to determine lipoic transacetylase in the absence of the over-all keto acid reaction, as follows:

Phosphotransacetylase (10)
$$AcPO_4 + CoASH \rightleftharpoons PO_4 + H^+ + AcSCoA$$

Lipoic Transacetylase (11)
$$AcSCoA + Lip(SH)_2 \rightleftharpoons CoASH + AcSLipSH$$

Sum: $AcPO_4 + Lip(SH)_2 \rightleftharpoons PO_4 + H^+ + AcSLipSH$ (12)

In the presence of a catalytic amount of CoA, reaction (12) can be followed by measuring the accumulation of heat-stable hydroxamic acid due to the acyl-lipoate formed, or by measuring the disappearance of sulfhydryl groups.

The data in Table 2 show the dependency of lipoic transacetylase upon the components indicated in reactions (10) and (11). Except for what appears to be a slight amount of lipoic transacetylase in the phosphotransacetylase preparation (obtained for *C. kluyveri* by the method of Stadtman), the dependencies are absolute. The units of lipoic transacetylase in this *E. coli* Fraction A are approximately half those necessary to account for the over-all dismutation rate, indicating that either this assay does not reproduce the conditions of the dismutation or that we are measuring a model reaction with a lower reaction rate than the true acyl-CoA-forming step of the keto-acid system.

In the presence of an excess of acetyl phosphate and the two transacetylases, only one mole of thioester is formed per 2 moles

TABLE 2

ACETYL LIPOIC FORMATION FROM ACETYL PHOSPHATE

Additions	Thio ester formed
	$\mu M/Hr$
1. Complete system [1]	3.2
2. " — Acetyl PO_4, 10 μM	.0
3. " — CoA, 0.1 μM	.0
4. " — Lipoic $(SH)_2$, 10 μM	.0
5. " — P transacetylase, 10 U [3]	0.3
6. " — Lipoic transacetylase, 3.2 U [2]	.0

[1] 100 μM Tris Buffer pH 7.5/1 ml.
[2] Coli A (.36-.48 Δ), 400 γ (S.A. 13 μM).
[3] We wish to thank Dr. Stadtman for the cells of *C. kluyveri* to prepare the phosphotransacetylase used in these experiments.

TABLE 3

ACYLATION OF DL-6, 8-DIMERCAPTOOCTANOATE; ACETYL PO_4-TRANSACETYLASE ASSAY

Additions		Formed			Used
Lipoic Transacetylase		DL-Lip$(SH)_2$	Thio Est.	*Acet*/Lip	–SH
ml.	min. 30°	μM	μM	$\mu M/\mu M$	μM
0.05	30	8.9	2.9		2.8
0.1	30	8.9	4.0		3.8
0.1	60	8.9	4.3	0.48	
0.2	60	8.9	4.6	0.51	
0.1	60	4.45	2.1	0.47	
0.2	60	4.45	2.2	0.5	

Fraction A (.42-.48 AmSO), 11.6 U/ml. lipoic transacetylase, S.A. 2.

of synthetic DL-6, 8-dimercaptooctanoate added and only one sulfhydryl group disappears per four added, thus indicating that only one of the isomers, presumably the dextrorotatory one, is acetylated and only one of the sulfhydryl groups of the molecule is acetylated.

These independent measurements for the lipoic transacetylase and lipoic dehydrogenase in the keto acid dehydrogenase preparations, afford evidence in accord with the formulation of reactions 3 and 4, Fig. 2. The presence of these enzymes in proportion to the over-all dehydrogenase rates are shown below for purified fractions A and B. The rates suggest, especially for the dehydrogenase, that uncombined lipoic acid may serve to mediate hydrogen transfer in the keto-acid systems. The optical specificity of the transacetylase indicates one of the sites responsible for the synthetic DL-alpha-lipoic acid possessing only half the activity of the isolated material.

FERRICYANIDE REDUCTION: CARBOXYLASE ASSAY

The coupling of pyruvate and ketoglutarate dehydrogenases to ferricyanide, measuring either the CO_2 evolved or the ferrocyanide formed, as for the purification of the animal enzyme systems by Green and coworkers (25, 58, 63), can also be applied to the *E. coli* enzyme fractions. In crude extracts ferricyanide will serve as electron acceptor, with a relatively high reaction rate, 10 per cent or more of the pyruvate dismutation rate. After separation of the "carboxylase"–containing fractions A and A' (see Table 5), ferricyanide can be used with either the pyruvate (A) or ketobutyrate (A') fraction showing only a DPT requirement. These data are in agreement with the data of Green et al. for the pig heart and pigeon breast muscle enzymes (60). The data in Table 4 show the equivalence of CO_2 released and ferrocyanide produced for a partially purified pyruvate fraction A. The DPT dependence, and lack of stimulation by the lipoic dehydrogenase fraction B is also indicated. Data indicating the reaction rate of ferricyanide, as compared to the DPN and dismutation systems, are shown in Table 6, and will be discussed below. In spite of the uncertainty as to the validity of the ferricyanide, and 2, 6-dichlorophenolindophenol assays for " carboxylase " activity, these are the only measurements available to date for an even partially simplified assay of the early steps of the oxidative keto-acid systems. The $C^{14}O_2$ exchange measurements, used to show reversibility (12), though somewhat cumbersome, and not as yet examined for enzymes and cofactor requirements beyond DPT (see Korkes, 15), might be adapted to this purpose should more straightforward methods prove slow to develop.

As indicated on p. 555, some evidence is accumulated to suggest an enzymatic step in ferricyanide reduction. More data on this point will also be presented in the section dealing with the aerobic, acetate-forming, pyruvate system of *Proteus vulgaris* (see Table 9).

TABLE 4

PYRUVATE CARBOXYLASE: FERRICYANIDE REDUCTION

		Formed	
Additions		$K_4Fe(CN)_6$	CO_2
		$\mu M/2$	μM
1. Complete System [1]		0.88	0.8
2. "	— DPT, 0.4 μM	.0	.0
3. "	— $K_3Fe(CN)_6$, 35 μM	—	.0
4. "	— Pyruvate, 50 μM	.0	.0
5. "	— Fraction A, 930 γ	.0	.0
6. "	+ Fraction B, 690 γ	0.85	0.8
7. "	— A + B	.0	.0

[1] Addns. 2 to 5 plus, 150 μM phosphate buffer pH 6
20 μM $MgCl_2$, 30° C, 30'.

ENZYME FRACTIONATION AND CORRELATION OF REACTION RATES

The initial pyruvate dehydrogenase fractionations of Korkes et al. (30) employed *E. coli* strain ATCC 4157, grown anaerobically under the conditions used by Umbreit and Gunsalus (64) to prepare glutamic carboxylase. When it became apparent that a large amount of cells would be needed to explore the pyruvate dehydrogenase system completely, Hager et al. (19) examined several aerobically grown strains of *E. coli* in order both to increase the yield of cells and to obtain more pyruvate dehydrogenase activity per cell. These experiments resulted in the selection of *E. coli*, Crooks strain, grown in S_2 medium at 30° C., aerated with 2 volumes of air per minute, the cells being harvested at the beginning of the stationary period. The change in culture, growth conditions, and method of preparation of extracts has resulted in minor alterations of the separation and purification procedure for the *E. coli* enzymes, but the essential features of separation and the properties of the fractions are not altered. The initial extracts of the S_2-grown Crooks strain contain 30 to 50 times the pyruvate dehydrogenase activity (measured by dismutation) of the anaerobically grown strain 4157 cells, and a higher concentration of enzyme B relative to the other enzymes. The essential steps used to obtain the pyruvate and ketoglutarate carboxylase fractions and the lipoic dehydrogenase are shown diagrammatically in Table 5.

TABLE 5

FRACTIONATION OF *E. coli* FOR:

PYRUVATE CARBOXYLASE — Fraction A
KETOGLUTARATE CARBOXYLASE — Fraction A'
LIPOIC DEHYDROGENASE — Fraction B

---

1. Sonicate: 10 G wet cells/50 ml., 20' 10 KC Raytheon
2. Cent. 60', 16,000 G (P 54, R .5, SA_{py} 50, kg.7)
3. Ammonium sulfate 0.25-0.75 saturation
4. Protamine sulfate; dialyze (phosphate-cysteine) (P 11, R 1.3, SA_{py} 242, kg9)
5. Ammonium sulfate — 2

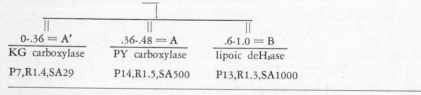

$0-.36 = A'$	$.36-.48 = A$	$.6-1.0 = B$
KG carboxylase	PY carboxylase	lipoic deH$_2$ase
P7,R1.4,SA29	P14,R1.5,SA500	P13,R1.3,SA1000

P = mg. protein/ml.; R = 280/260; SA = μlCO$_2$/hr./mg. P

It will be noted that the extracts contain 20 to 100 times as much pyruvate dehydrogenase as ketoglutarate dehydrogenase. This is due in part to the method of assay—pyruvate by dismutation and ketoglutarate by CO_2 release with ferricyanide as electron acceptor. The further purification of the ketoglutarate carboxylase (A' fraction) will not be dealt with here. The further purification of the pyruvate carboxylase-containing A fraction and of the lipoic dehydrogenase, B fraction, is outlined in Tables 6 and 7, respectively. The data for comparison of reaction rates, as measured by the various assays for steps in the alpha-keto-acid system, are included. For technical reasons not all assays were run under identical conditions. In each case comparisons have been made on representative enzyme fractions, at different levels of purity, in order to make valid comparisons of rates under the different conditions. For example, CO_2 release (dismutation) was usually measured manometrically at pH 6, whereas DPN reduction was measured at pH 7, where the reaction proceeded more nearly to completion and gave a linear response to the amount of enzyme over a greater range. Shift of DPN-reduction measurement, via lipoic acid, from pH 7 to 6 cuts the rate to 70 per cent.

The units have also been redefined to permit comparison of all activities. In the initial experiments of Korkes et al. (30), units were expressed in $\mu l CO_2$ released per hour (dismutation assay). The units have been redefined as $\mu M/hr.$; i. e., 1 μM unit $= 1$ μl unit/22.4. With micromole units the specific activities are also decreased by 1/22.4; i. e., $\mu M/hr./mg.$ protein. The data of Table 6 are in μl units, with a calculation in μM units in the last line for comparison. All data in Table 7 are in μM units except for the extract, which is shown in both units for comparison.

The data in Table 6 for the purification of the carboxylase-containing fraction A show a 150-fold purification over the extract with recovery of about 10 per cent of the initial activity. Two of the steps, heating to destroy the transacetylase and the final calcium phosphate gel, give poor recovery, but have been retained so far bcause of useful separations and increased specific activity.

It is to be noted that the DPN-reduction assay, usable only after removal of lactic dehydrogenase, gave approximately the same rates as the dismutation measurement. Corrected for pH difference, the DPN rate is about 80 per cent of the dismutation rate. Note that the ferricyanide reduction activity of Fraction A alone falls from

TABLE 6

FURTHER PURIFICATION: PYRUVATE CARBOXYLASE (A)
SONICATE 40 GM. CROOKS COLI, S_2 MEDIUM

Fraction	Dismutation = 1			Reduction			
				DPN [2]		$K_3Fe(CN)_6$	
	U [1]	S.A.	Rec.	U	R/1	U	R/1
	x 10³		%	x 10³		x 10³	
Extract	510	52	100				
.25-.75, Prot.	495	240	97				
AMSO-2 .36-.48	346 *	545	68			10	.03
" Δ	180 *	835	35				
AMSO-3 .35-.42	153 *	1500	30	162	1.1	3.0	.02
" Gel El	62 *	7600	12	77	1.2	0.6	.01
" (µM units) [3]	2.8	340	—	3.4	—	.02	—

[1] U = 1 µlCO₂/hr.
[2] DPN Redn. pH 7, others 6.
[3] µM units = µl units/22.4.
* With excess B.

TABLE 7

FURTHER PURIFICATION: LIPOIC DEHYDROGENASE (B)
SONICATE 40 G. CROOKS COLI, S_2 MEDIUM

Fraction	Pyruvate Dism. = 1			KG DPN [2]		Lip(SH)₂ Oxidn.	
	U [1]	S.A. [2]	Rec.	U	R/1	U	R/1
	x 10³		%	x 10³		x 10³	
Extract	(510	52	100)				
	(22.8	2.3	100)				
AMSO-2 .6-1	35	48	150	7.5	.22	59	1.7
"	15.4	33	68				
AMSO-3 .6-.7	22.7	105	100	5.1	.22	43	1.9
" Gel El	20	386	87	4.8	.23	34	1.7

[1] 1U = 1 µM/hr. (µ1U/22.4).
[2] SA = µMU/mg. P.
* KG pH 7, others 6.

3 to 1 per cent of the dismutation rate during the last 10 + -fold purification (see also p. 555).

Purification of the lipoic dehydrogenase, fraction B, shown in Table 7, is more straightforward, since this fraction shows no activity alone in the dismutation assay after the first separation (Table 5) and appears to contain a single activity for the keto-acid system. This fraction can be readily purified 200-fold over the extract without loss of total units. It is also noteworthy that the activity of this fraction for pyruvate dismutation, ketoglutarate dehydrogenase, and lipoic dehydrogenase remains parallel over the more than 10-fold purification achieved after its separation from Fraction A. The lipoic dehydrogenase rate is about twice the dismutation rate, and the ketoglutarate dehydrogenase, measured by DPN reduction, about 20 per cent of the pyruvate rate. The latter will bear more detailed analysis as the ketoglutarate A' fraction is purified.

NATURE OF PYRUVATE OXIDASE IN PROTEUS VULGARIS, X19

Stumpf (62) demonstrated in cell-free extracts of *Proteus vulgaris* the presence of a particle-bound oxidase which consumed one-half O_2 per mole of pyruvate and yielded acetate and CO_2. No dismutation occurred; methylene blue replaced oxygen, but at only about 1/10 the rate. A divalent metal and DPT were required. Inorganic phosphate was not required, nor was an acetyl phosphatase present. These observations led Stumpf to suggest a direct oxidation to acetate. [For similar data on the pigeon muscle pyruvation oxidase, see Schweet (60).] More recently Moyed and O'Kane (36, 37) have taken up the fractionation and study of the *Proteus* enzyme. Their experiments have led to the separation of two fractions, both of which are required for the reaction with oxygen. One of these fractions is soluble, the other particulate. The soluble fraction, precipitable at half saturated ammonium sulfate and by dialysis against distilled water, reacts with 2, 6-dichlorphenolindophenol in the presence of added DPT, and is therefore referred to as the "carboxylase fraction" (36). The particulate fraction, which is floculated by 0.3 saturated ammonium sulfate and by high speed centrifugation, appears to contain the link to oxygen; for our discussion the particulate fraction will be referred to as the hydrogen-transport fraction. Moyed and O'Kane (31) have purified these fractions, as outlined in Table 8. They have shown a DPT requirement associated with the soluble fraction, and have analyzed the two fractions and shown them to be essentially free of lipoic acid.

TABLE 8

PYRUVATE OXIDASE: PROTEUS VULGARIS, X19

CULTURE: 16 hr., 37° C., AC broth aerated
SONICATED: 20 min. 10 KC Raytheon (15 g. wet wt/50 ml.)
CENTRIFUGE: 1 hr., 2500 g.

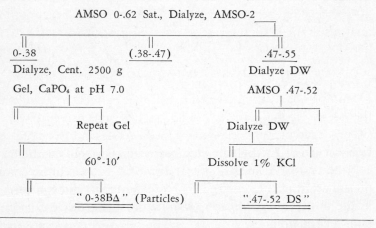

AMSO 0-.62 Sat., Dialyze, AMSO-2

0-.38	(.38-.47)	.47-.55
Dialyze, Cent. 2500 g		Dialyze DW
Gel, CaPO₄ at pH 7.0		AMSO .47-.52
	Repeat Gel	Dialyze DW
	60°-10′	Dissolve 1% KCl
	" 0-38BΔ " (Particles)	".47-.52 DS "

(Moyed, O'Kane, *J. B. C.*, 195, 375, 1952)

In agreement with Stumpf's data, this system forms acetate, not acetyl phosphate, and does not show an inorganic phosphate requirement. On first sight these findings would lead one to believe that the keto-acid oxidation system in *Proteus* is totally different from that found in *E. coli* and in animal tissue. However, O'Kane and Moyed have shown that with added CoA and without additional enzymes, their preparations acetylate sulfanilamide, thus indicating the presence of an acetyl-CoA–forming system as well as an acetylating enzyme. These preparations lack transacetylase and do not hydrolyze acetyl phosphate even with added transacetylase and CoA.

The O'Kane and Moyed *Proteus* fractions (Table 8) were subjected to the pyruvate oxidation (oxygen utilization) assay used by these workers and to the measurements employed with the *E. coli* fractions for dismutation, ferricyanide reduction (carboxylase), lipoic transacetylase, and lipoic dehydrogenase. The data shown in Table 9 indicate no oxygen uptake by either the particulate or soluble fractions, but good activity of the two combined. Each

TABLE 9

PYRUVATE METABOLISM, PROTEUS VULGARIS, X19

(Moyed & O'Kane, AC 16 Cells)

Measurement	" 0-38B "	" 48-52DS "	Both
	μM/hr.	μM/hr.	
Oxygen Uptake	0	0	400
Dismutation	10	8	18
Decarboxylase	10	5	105
Lipoic transacetylase	2	0	—
Lipoic dehydrogenase	5	0	—

fraction showed a slight ferricyanide reduction, but combined showed a 7- to 10-fold stimulation in rate. These data throw some doubt on the usefulness of ferricyanide as electron acceptor in the measurement of the carboxylase activity of keto-acid systems, viz., the A and A' fractions of *E. coli* and the purified enzymes for animal tissue (60). They may also indicate that there is an enzymatic step between the DPT-activated keto-acid carboxylases and ferricyanide acting as electron acceptor. Such a mechanism would account for the decreasing rate of reaction with ferricyanide, as compared to dismutation or DPN reduction, on purification of the *E. coli* enzyme —and the lack of activity of the pig heart enzyme (14, 60). As further shown in Table 9, neither fraction contained appreciable dismutation, lipoic transacetylase, or lipoic dehydrogenase activity, and no recombination of the two fractions is shown in the dismutation assay (experiments of Moyed and Razzell).

It is possible that the carboxylase in the soluble fraction is identical with the initial step of the *E. coli* and animal systems, but since lipoic acid is lacking from these fractions, only reaction 1, Fig. 2, could occur. Preliminary experiments (Razzell and Hager, unpub.) show that the *E. coli* fraction precipitable by 0.5-0.6 saturated ammonium sulfate will also combine with the *Proteus* particulate fraction to stimulate oxygen uptake, thus indicating that *E. coli* contains enzymes similar to those reported in *Proteus* by Moyed and O'Kane. Thus *Proteus* carboxylase may be helpful in reconstituting the *E. coli* and tissue systems. Clarification on this point would also furnish further evidence on the separate vs. combined functions of lipoic acid and DPT in the keto-acid dehydrogenases, thus helping to clarify the coenzyme activity of lipothiamide pyrophosphate suggested by Reed and DeBusk. The presence of a CoA-linked acetylating mechanism for sulfanilamide in Moyed and O'Kane's *Proteus* enzyme led us to apply the method of Korkes et al. (30) and of Hager, et al. (19) to *Proteus vulgaris*, X19. Since this organism shows growth factor requirements, yeast extract was added to the S2 medium, and the fractionation procedure for *E. coli* outlined in Table 5 was applied to the cells. The first ammonium sulfate separation, after protamine treatment to remove nucleic acid, gave fractions with A and B activity which recombined in the dismutation assay with a 2-fold stimulation. As shown in Table 10, the " carboxylase " and lipoic transacetylase were concentrated in the A fraction and the lipoic dehydrogenase in the B fraction. The A and B fractions both precipitated at slightly lower ammonium sulfate saturation than did the *E. coli* fractions, but possessed approximately the same specific activity as the *E. coli* fractions at this stage of purity. These *Proteus* fractions showed the same dependencies as the *E. coli* fractions for DPT, CoA, and DPN; the A fraction contains lipoic acid, and acetyl phosphate is formed. From these experiments it seems quite likely that more than one pathway for alpha-keto-acid oxidation exists in *Proteus vulgaris*. The analogous pathways—lipoic acid present but action not studied—may be presumed to occur in the pigeon breast muscle and pig heart systems (35, 59, 60).

Summary: The enzymes obtainable from *E. coli* for the various steps of the oxidative decarboxylation of keto acids have been further purified. The " B Fraction " has been shown to contain a lipoic dehydrogenase, thereby documenting reaction 4, Fig. 2. The fraction A of *E. coli*, so far only partially separated, contains both a lipoic transacetylase and a DPT-dependent step—as shown both by the CO_2 exchange and by a DPT requirement for the reactions with ferricyanide, 2, 6-dichlorophenolindophenol, and ace-

TABLE 10

PYRUVATE METABOLISM, PROTEUS VULGARIS, X19

(Coli-type Fractions, S_2 grown Cells)

Measurement	A	B	A + B
		μM/hr./mg. P	
Oxygen Uptake	0	0	0
Dismutation	45	3	100
Decarboxylase	7	1.6	8.6
Lipoic transacetylase	1.5	.5	
Lipoic dehydrogenase	5	20	

A = .3-.34, S.A. 2500
B = .5-.6, S.A. 1000 +

taldehyde. The transacetylase activity of fraction A is somewhat less than would be expected from the dismutation rate, which may indicate that the lipoic acid is reacting in model system. These experiments would not, however, indicate that the separation of the enzymes catalyzing the individual steps should not be possible. Partial separations have in fact already been made.

The *Proteus vulgaris* system, which bypasses acyl generation, connects enzymatically to both oxygen and ferricyanide. This organism in addition possesses an acyl-generating keto-acid system analogous to the enzymes already studied in *E. coli*, whereas the latter has been shown to possess a soluble carboxylase capable of linkage to the acyl bypass mechanism of *Proteus*. The steps and catalysts of this system require further exploration and to be considered in terms of the oxygen and "artificial" electron-linked acyl bypass systems of animal tissue.

REFERENCES

1. Barkulis, S. S. (Pers. com. and unpub. exp. by I. C. Gunsalus and W. E. Razzell). (1953).
2. Brockman, J. A., Jr., E. L. R. Stokstad, E. L. Patterson, J. V. Pierce, M. Macchi, and F. P. Day. Structure of Protogen-A. *J. Am. Chem. Soc.*, 74, 1868 (1952).
3. Bullock, M. W., J. A. Brockman, Jr., E. L. Patterson, J. V. Pierce, and E. L. R. Stokstad. Synthesis of DL-thioctic acid. *J. Am. Chem. Soc.*, 74, 1868-1869 (1952).
4. Calvin, M., and J. A. Barltrop. A possible primary quantum conversion act of photosynthesis. *J. Am. Chem. Soc.*, 74, 6153-6154 (1952).
5. Conn, Eric E., and Birgit Vennesland. Glutathione reductase of wheat germ. *J. Biol. Chem.*, 192, 17-28 (1951).
6. DeBusk, B. G., and L. J. Reed. Coenzymatic functions of thiamine pyrophosphate and lipothiamide pyrophosphate. *Federation Proc.*, 12, 193-194 (1953).
7. Dolin, M. Lipoic acid functions: alpha-dicarbonyl oxidation by *Streptococcus faecalis* 10 Cl. *Federation Proc.*, 12, 198 (1953).
8. Dolin, M. I., and 'I. C. Gunsalus. A soluble pyruvate-alpha-ketobutyrate dehydrogenase system from *Streptococcus faecalis*. *Federation Proc.*, 11, 203 (1952).
9. Dolin, M. I., and I. C. Gunsalus. Pyruvic acid metabolism. II. The acetoin-forming enzyme system in *Streptococcus faecalis*. *J. Bact.*, 62, 199-214 (1951).
10. Dolin, M. I., L. P. Hager, and I. C. Gunsalus. Enzyme systems for the heterolytic cleavage of dicarbonyl compounds. Abstract, Los Angeles Meeting, American Chemical Society, p. 27 C (1953).
11. Gergely, J., P. Hele, and C. V. Ramakrishnan. Succinyl and acteyl coenzyme A deacylases. *J. Biol. Chem.*, 198, 323-334 (1952).
12. Goldberg, M., and D. R. Sanadi. Incorporation of labeled carbon dioxide into pyruvate and alpha-ketoglutarate. *J. Am. Chem. Soc.*, 74, 4972-4973 (1952).
13. Green, D. E. Integrated enzyme activity in soluble extracts of heart muscle. *Science*, 115, 661-665 (1953).
14. Green, D. E., and H. Beinert. Oxidative phosphorylation in a non-mitochondrial system of pig heart. In *Phosphorus Metabolism*, Vol. I (W. D. McElroy and B. Glass, eds.), pp. 330-343. Johns Hopkins Press, Baltimore (1951).
15. Gunsalus, I. C. The Chemistry and function of the pyruvate oxidation factor (lipoic acid). *J. Cellular Comp. Physiol.*, 41, 113-136 (1953).
16. Gunsalus, I. C., M. I. Dolin, and L. Struglia. Pyruvic acid metabolism. III. A manometric assay for pyruvate oxidation factor. *J. Biol. Chem.*, 194, 849-857 (1952).
17. Gunsalus, I. C., L. Struglia, and D. J. O'Kane. Pyruvic acid metabolism. IV. Occurrence, properties, and partial purification of pyruvate oxidation factor. *J. Biol. Chem.*, 194, 859-870 (1952).
18. Haas, Erwin. Manometrische Mikrotitration mit Ferricyanide. In *Wasserstoff-übertragende Fermente*, by Otto Warburg, pp. 194-195. Werner Saenger, Berlin (1937).
19. Hager, L. P., J. D. Fortney, and I. C. Gunsalus. Mechanism of pyruvate and alpha-ketoglutarate dehydrogenase systems. *Federation Proc.*, 12, 213 (1953).
20. Hager, L. P., and I. C. Gunsalus (unpub.).
21. Hager, L. P., and I. C. Gunsalus. *J. Am. Chem. Soc.*, in press. (1953).

22. Hager, L. P., W. E. Razzell, and I. C. Gunsalus. *J. Bact.*, in press (1953).

23. Horecker, B. L., and P. Z. Smyrniotis. The coenzyme function of thiamine pyrophosphate in pentose phosphate metabolism. *J. Am. Chem. Soc.*, 75, 1009-1010 (1953).

24. Hornberger, Carl S., Jr., Richard F. Heitmiller, I. C. Gunsalus, G. H. F. Schnakenberg, and Lester J. Reed. Synthesis of DL-alpha-lipoic acid. *J. Am. Chem. Soc.*, 75, 1273-1277 (1953).

25. Jagannathan, Venkataraman, and Richard S. Schweet. Pyruvic oxidase of pigeon breast muscle. I. Purification and properties of the enzyme. *J. Biol. Chem.*, 196, 551-562 (1952).

26. Juni, E. Mechanisms of formation of acetoin by bacteria. *J. Biol. Chem.*, 195, 715-726 (1952).

27. Juni, E. Mechanisms of the formation of acetoin by yeast and mammalian tissue. *J. Biol. Chem.*, 195, 727-734 (1952).

28. Kaufman, S. Soluble alpha-ketoglutaric dehydrogenase from heart muscle and coupled phosphorylation. In *Phosphorus Metabolism*, Vol. I (W. D. McElroy and B. Glass, eds.), pp. 370-373 (1951). Johns Hopkins Press, Baltimore.

29. Korkes, S. Acetyl transfer in the enzymatic oxidation of pyruvic acid. In *Phosphorus Metabolism*, Vol. I (W. D. McElroy and B. Glass, eds.), pp. 259-264 (1951). Johns Hopkins Press, Baltimore.

30. Korkes, S., Alice del Campillo, I. C. Gunsalus, and Severo Ochoa. Enzymatic synthesis of citric acid. IV. Pyruvate as acetyl donor. *J. Biol. Chem.*, 193, 721-735 (1951).

31. Korkes, S., Alice del Campillo, and Severo Ochoa. Pyruvate oxidation system of heart muscle. *J. Biol. Chem.*, 195, 541-547 (1952).

32. Lindstrom, E. S. The alpha-ketoglutaric oxidase system of Azotobacter. *J. Bact.*, 65, 565-570 (1953).

33. Lipmann, F. An analysis of the pyruvate oxidation system. *Cold Spring Harbor Symposia Quant. Biol.*, 7, 248-259 (1939).

34. Lipmann, F. Enzymatic synthesis of acetyl phosphate. *J. Biol. Chem.*, 155, 55-70 (1944).

35. Littlefield, J. W., and D. R. Sanadi. Role of coenzyme A and diphosphopyridine nucleotide in the oxidation of pyruvate. *J. Biol. Chem.*, 199, 65-70 (1952).

36. Moyed, H. S., and D. J. O'Kane. The enzymes of the pyruvate oxidase system of *Proteus vulgaris*. *Arch. Biochem. Biophys.*, 39, 457-458 (1952).

37. Moyed, H. S., and D. J. O'Kane. Fractionation of the pyruvate oxidase of *Proteus vulgaris*. *J. Biol. Chem.*, 195, 375-381 (1952).

38. Ochoa, Severo. Biological mechanisms of carboxylation and decarboxylation. *Physiol. Rev.*, 31, 56-106 (1951).

39. Ochoa, S. Enzymatic synthesis of citric acid and other reactions of the tricarboxylic acid cycle. *Proc. 2nd International Congress of Biochemistry*, Paris. Symposium sur le cycle tricarboxylique. No. 3, p. 73-88 (1952).

40. O'Kane, D. J. Influence of the pyruvate oxidation factor on the oxidative metabolism of glucose by *Streptococcus faecalis*. *J. Bact.*, 60, 449-458.

41. O'Kane, D. J., and I. C. Gunsalus. Pyruvic acid metabolism: a factor required for oxidation by *Streptococcus faecalis*. *J. Bact.*, 56, 499-506.

42. Peters, R. A. The study of enzymes in relation to selective toxicity in animal tissues. *Symposia Soc. Exptl. Biol.*, 3, 36-59 (1949).

43. Peters, R. A., H. M. Sinclair, and R. H. S. Thompson. An analysis of the inhibition of pyruvate oxidation by arsenicals in relation to the enzyme theory of vesication. *Biochem. J.*, 40, 516-524 (1946).

44. Pierce, J. V., M. E. Macchi, C. E. Hoffman, C. T. O. Fong, E. L. R. Stokstad,

T. H. Jukes, E. L. Patterson, J. A. Brockman, and F. P. Day. Crystallization of a derivative of Protogen-B. *J. Am. Chem. Soc.*, 73, 5919-5920 (1951).

45. Racker, E., G. de la Haba, and I. G. Leder. Thiamine pyrophosphate, a coenzyme of transketolase. *J. Am. Chem. Soc.*, 75, 1010-1011 (1953).

46. Reed, L. J. Metabolic functions of thiamine and lipoic acid. *Federation Proc.*, 12, 558 (1953).

47. Reed, L. J., and Betty G. DeBusk. Lipoic acid conjugase. *J. Am. Chem. Soc.*, 74, 4727 (1952).

48. Reed, L. J., and B. DeBusk. Mechanism of enzymatic oxidative decarboxylation of pyruvate. *J. Am. Chem. Soc.*, 75, 1261-1262.

49. Reed, L. J., and Betty G. DeBusk. Lipothiamide and its relation to a thiamine coenzyme required for oxidative decarboxylation of alphaketo acids. *J. Am. Chem. Soc.*, 74, 3457 (1952).

50. Reed, L. J., and B. G. DeBusk. Chemical nature of an alpha-lipoic acid conjugate required for oxidation of pyruvate and alpha-ketoglutarate by an *Escherichia coli* mutant. *J. Biol. Chem.*, 199, 881-888 (1952).

51. Reed, L. J., and B. G. DeBusk. A conjugate of alpha-lipoic acid required for oxidation of pyruvate and alpha-ketoglutarate by an *Escherichia coli* mutant. *J. Biol. Chem.*, 199, 873-880 (1952).

52. Reed, L. J., and Betty G. DeBusk. Lipothiamide pyrophosphate: coenzyme for oxidative decarboxylation of alpha-keto acids. *J. Am. Chem. Soc.*, 74, 3964-3965 (1952).

53. Reed, L. J., B. G. DeBusk, I. C. Gunsalus, and C. S. Hornberger, Jr. Crystalline alpha-lipoic acid: a catalytic agent associated with pyruvate dehydrogenase. *Science*, 114, 93-94 (1951).

54. Reed, L. J., B. G. DeBusk, C. S. Hornberger, Jr., and I. C. Gunsalus. Interrelationships of lipoic acids. *J. Am. Chem. Soc.*, 75, 1271-1273 (1953).

55. Reed, L. J., I. C. Gunsalus, G. H. F. Schnakenberg, Q. F. Soper, H. E. Boaz, S. F. Kern, and T. V. Parke. Isolation, characterization and structure of alphalipoic acid. *J. Am. Chem. Soc.*, 75, 1267-1270 (1953).

56. Reed, L. J., Q. F. Soper, S. H. F. Schnakenberg, S. F. Kern, Harold Boaz, and I. C. Gunsalus. Identification of the carbon skeleton of alpha-lipoic acid. *J. Am. Chem. Soc.*, 74, 2383-2384 (1952).

57. Sanadi, D. R., and J. W. Littlefield. Studies on alpha-ketoglutaric oxidase. I. Formation of "active" succinate. *J. Biol. Chem.*, 193, 683-689 (1951).

58. Sanadi, D. R., J. W. Littlefield, and R. M. Bock. Studies on alpha-ketoglutarate oxidase. II. Purification and properties. *J. Biol. Chem.*, 197, 851-862 (1952).

59. Sanadi, D. R., and J. W. Littlefield. Studies on alpha-ketoglutaric oxidase. III. Role of coenzyme A and diphosphopyridine nucleotide. *J. Biol. Chem.*, 201, 103-116 (1953).

60. Schweet, Richard S., Maria Fuld, Katherine Cheslock, and M. H. Paul. Initial stages of pyruvate oxidation. In *Phosphorus Metabolism*, Vol. I (W. D. McElroy and B. Glass, eds.), 246-259 (1953). Johns Hopkins Press, Baltimore.

61. Still, J. L. Pyruvic acid dehydrogenase of *Escherichia coli*. *Biochem. J.*, 35, 380-389 (1941).

62. Stumpf, P. K. Pyruvic oxidase of *Proteus vulgaris*. *J. Biol. Chem.*, 159, 529-544 (1945).

63. Stumpf, P. K., K. Zarudnaya, and D. E. Green. Pyruvic and alpha-glutaric oxidase of animal tissue. *J. Biol. Chem.*, 167, 817-825 (1947).

64. Umbreit, W. W., and I. C. Gunsalus. The function of pyridoxine derivatives: arginine and glutamic acid decarboxylases. *J. Biol. Chem.*, 159, 333-341 (1945).

ON THE ENERGY–RICH NATURE OF ACETYL IMIDAZOLE, AN ENZYMATICALLY ACTIVE COMPOUND

E. R. STADTMAN

Laboratory of Cellular Physiology, National Heart Institute, National Institutes of Health, Public Health Service, Department of Health, Education and Welfare, Bethesda

IN A RECENT note (1) it was reported that extracts of *Clostridium kluyveri* catalyze the net synthesis of N-acetyl imidazole from acetyl phosphate and imidazole. This synthesis requires the presence of coenzyme A and involves the joint action of two enzymes, phosphotransacetylase and imidazole acetylase, which catalyze the following reactions: [1]

$$\text{Acetyl-P} + \text{CoA} \underset{\overleftarrow{\hspace{1cm}}}{\overset{PTA}{\rightleftharpoons}} \text{Acetyl-CoA} + \text{P}_i \tag{1}$$

$$\text{Acetyl-CoA} + \text{Imidazole} \overset{IA}{\rightleftharpoons} \text{Acetyl-Im} + \text{CoA} \tag{2}$$

$$\text{Sum: Acetyl-P} + \text{Imidazole} \rightleftharpoons \text{Acetyl-Im} + \text{P}_i \tag{3}$$

The energy-rich nature of acetyl-Im as an acetyl donor was inferred from the observation that it reacts nonenzymatically to acetylate mercaptans and orthophosphate [2] (1).

In view of the possibility that acylated imidazole may serve as an energy-rich acyl group carrier in biosynthetic reactions, it appeared worthwhile to investigate the enzymatic synthesis of this compound and in particular to obtain more definitive information regarding the energetics of this substance.

---

[1] The following abbreviations are used: acetyl phosphate, acetyl-P; phosphotransacetylase, PTA; imidazole acetylase, IA; acetyl-imidazole, acetyl-Im; coenzyme A, CoA; acetyl coenzyme A, acetyl-CoA; orthophosphate, P_i; glutathione, GSH; S-acetyl glutathione, acetyl-SG; diisopropylfluorophosphate, DFP.

[2] Acetyl-Im also reacts spontaneously with amines (1, 2) and alcohols (1) to form the corresponding amides and esters.

Absorption spectrum of acetyl-imidazole. The ultraviolet absorption spectrum of acetyl-Im (prepared by the method of Boyer, 3) is

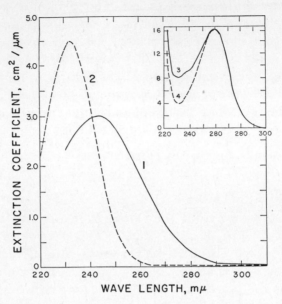

FIG. 1. Ultraviolet absorption spectra of acetyl-imidazole-CoA and acetyl-CoA. Curve 1 shows the spectrum of acetyl-Im at pH 7.0, 26° C. The spectrum was determined using a Cary ultraviolet recording spectrophotometer * set so that the entire spectrum was determined in 100 sec., thus obviating the necessity of correcting for the negligible decomposition of acetyl-Im that occurs in this short period of time. Curve 3 is the absorption spectrum of acetyl-CoA, which was prepared from Pabst CoA (C. 70% pure) by enzymatic acetylation (reaction 1). The acetyl-CoA was purified by paper chromatography (4) and was shown to have an acetyl/adenine ratio of 0.98. Curve 4 represents the spectrum of CoA produced by arsenolysis of the same acetyl-CoA sample in the presence of PTA. Curve 2 is a difference spectrum (curve 3 minus curve 4) representing the absorption of the thiol ester band of acetyl-CoA. The CoA spectra were determined in 0.03 M potassium arsenate buffer (pH 7.0) before (curve 3) and after (curve 4) the addition of PTA. A Beckman D. U. Spectrophotometer with a photomultiplier attachment was used. Temperature 26° C.

* The author is indebted to Mrs. Iris J. Siewers for making the measurements on the Cary Spectrophotometer.

given in Fig. 1. For comparison, the spectra of acetyl-CoA, CoA, and the thioester group of acetyl-CoA [3] are also presented. Acetyl-

[3] The absorption spectrum of the thioester group of acetyl-CoA is obtained by subtracting the spectrum of CoA from that for acetyl-CoA. The difference spectrum thus

Im and the thioester group of acetyl-CoA both show a strong absorption at 230–245 mμ; however, the absorption band of acetyl-Im is much broader and extends over into the region of 255–260 mμ, at which wave lengths the thioester has a negligible absorption. Free imidazole (not shown in the figure) has a relatively insignificant absorption in the range of 230–240 mμ (pH 5.0–8.0). In the present investigation, these characteristic light-absorption properties have been made the basis of spectrophotometric procedures for studying the acetylation reactions of orthophosphate and mercaptans by acetylimidazole.

I. ENZYME STUDIES

Preparation of imidazole acetylase. Crude extracts of *C. kluyveri* were treated with Dowex-1·HCl, as previously described (5), to remove most of the CoA. The Dowex-treated extract, pH 6.7, was then heated at 55° C. for 30 minutes. This destroys 98 per cent of the PTA (6) and about 45–50 per cent of the IA activity. The heated extract is fractionated at room temperature with ammonium sulfate, and the protein fraction precipitating between 48 and 68 per cent saturation (hereafter referred to as the IA preparation) was used in the present study. The specific activity expressed as units per mg. of protein is only about 2 times greater than that of the crude extract. However, this IA preparation is essentially free of CoA and contains only a trace of PTA.

Components of the enzymatic acetyl-P—imidazole reaction. Results of a spectrophotometric experiment showing the enzyme and coenzyme requirements for imidazole acetylation (reaction 3) are summarized in Fig. 2. The reaction was followed by measuring the increase in optical density at 245 mμ associated with the formation of acetyl-imidazole (cf. Fig. 1). This is possible since acetyl-P has a negligible absorption in the ultraviolet region. Fig. 2 shows that rapid acetylation of imidazole occurs in the complete system containing PTA, IA, CoA, imidazole, and acetyl-P. Little or no enzyma-

obtained is almost identical with that obtained by W. W. Kielley (pers. com.) for the thioester band of acetyl glutathione

tic acetylation [4] occurs in the absence of CoA or IA. The slight activity observed in the absence of added PTA indicates that the IA preparation is still contaminated with a small amount of the former

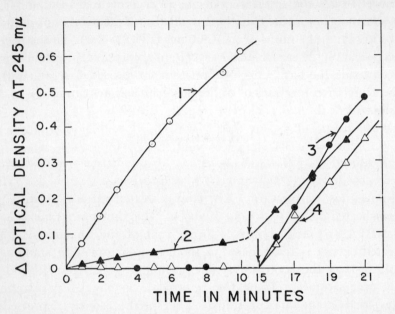

FIG. 2. The enzymatic acetylation of imidazole. All the reaction mixtures contained 300 μM of imidazole (pH 7.0), 100 μM of KCl; and 5.0 μM of acetyl-P. In addition, the complete system represented by curve 1 contained 16 units of PTA; 0.03 ml. of the IA preparation and 0.01 μM of acetyl-CoA. For conditions at zero time, Curve 2 represents the complete system minus PTA; Curve 3, the complete system minus IA; and Curve 4, the complete system without acetyl-CoA. The missing components were added at times indicated by the vertical arrows. Acetyl-CoA, which is added in only catalytic amounts, was used instead of free CoA so that no reducing agent would be necessary. The changes in optical density at 245 mμ are changes relative to a reference vessel containing all components except the enzymes and acetyl-CoA.

enzyme. When the missing components are added after 15 minutes, the rates of imidazole acetylation are essentially the same as that obtained when all components are present initially.

The need for PTA and CoA in addition to IA strongly suggests

[4] The rate of nonenzymatic acetylation of imidazole by acetyl-P is so slow under these experimental conditions (viz., low acetyl-P concentration) that it does not interfere in the present studies.

that the enzymatic acetylation of imidazole by acetyl-P occurs by reactions (1) and (2). If this be true, then one might expect to be able to demonstrate reaction (2) directly through the action of IA on acetyl-CoA and imidazole, in the absence of acetyl-P and PTA. As shown in Fig. 1, the extinction coefficient of the thioester group of acetyl-CoA at 232 mμ is about 1.8 times that of acetyl-Im; moreover, acetyl-Im absorbs strongly at 255–260 mμ, whereas the light-absorption of the thioester group is negligible at the latter wavelengths. Therefore, the acetylation of imidazole by acetyl-CoA should be associated with a decrease in optical density at 232 mμ and an increase in optical density at 255–260 mμ. Preliminary attempts to measure the direct acetylation of imidazole by acetyl-CoA, using the latter spectrophotometric criteria, were unsuccessful. It therefore appeared either (a) that the reaction mechanism is not adequately expressed by reaction (2), or (b) that the free-energy change of reaction (2) is so unfavorable that no appreciable synthesis of acetyl-Im from acetyl-CoA occurs under the conditions used (viz., 0.5 μM acetyl-CoA and 150 μM of imidazole per 3.0 ml.). The latter possibility seemed more likely, since preliminary experiments on the acetylation of orthophosphate by acetyl-Im in the absence of enzyme had indicated that the free energy of hydrolysis of acetyl-Im is greater than that of acetyl-P. Accordingly, the nonenzymatic reaction between acetyl-P and imidazole (reaction 3) was reinvestigated to obtain a more precise measure of the relative energies of acetyl-P and acetyl-Im.

II. Nonenzymatic Acetylation of Orthophosphate

As shown in Fig. 3, the hydrolysis of acetyl-Im is a unimolecular reaction which is greatly accelerated by H^+ and OH^-. In the presence of orthophosphate the decomposition of acetyl-Im is enhanced and acetyl-P is formed.[5] The influence of pH on the rates of hydrolysis

---

[5] Proof that acetyl-P is the end product has been obtained by showing that the accelerated decomposition of acetyl-Im in the presence of P_i is associated with the simultaneous disappearance of P_i and the appearance of acetyl-P, as determined by the selective precipitation of their calcium salts by the method of Lipmann & Tuttle (7). The acetyl-P was further identified on the basis of its heat instability and enzymatic reactivity in the PTA system (8).

and of acetyl-P formation is shown in Fig. 4. Maximum stability to hydrolysis is observed in the pH range of 6.0 to 7.5 but the rate increases rapidly at higher or lower pH values. Thus over the range of pH 6.0 to 7.5 the half-life is about 60 minutes, but at pH 5.0 and 8.8 it is only 2.5 minutes.

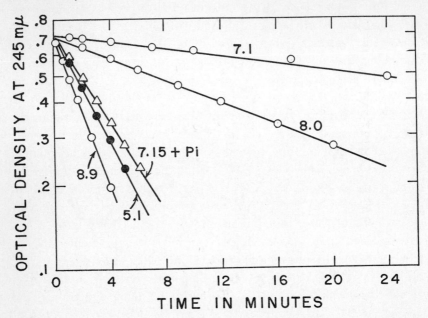

FIG. 3. Spectrophotometric measurement of acetyl-Im decomposition. All samples contained 0.7 μM of acetyl-Im per 3.0 ml. The numbers on the curve represent the pH, which was controlled by buffers, as indicated in the legend to Fig. 4. The Δ refer to a sample containing 750 μM of orthophosphate. On the ordinate the optical density at 245 mμ (due to acetyl-Im) is plotted on a logarithmic scale.

The acetylation of P_i (as judged by the enhancement in rate of acetyl-Im decomposition in the presence of P_i) is almost negligible at pH 8.5 and is increased very markedly by decreasing the pH over the range of 8.5 to 5.5. This suggests that the monobasic acid of orthophosphate ($H_2PO_4^-$) is preferentially acetylated, since the concentration of this ionic species increases with decreasing pH over the same range. Further support for this conclusion is presented in Fig. 5, showing that the rate of acetylation is directly proportional to the concentration of monobasic acid over a rather broad range. The rates of acetylation have been corrected for the rates of hydrolysis of acetyl-Im at the various hydrogen ion concentrations.

The sharp break in the $H_2PO_4^-$ rate curve at low concentrations

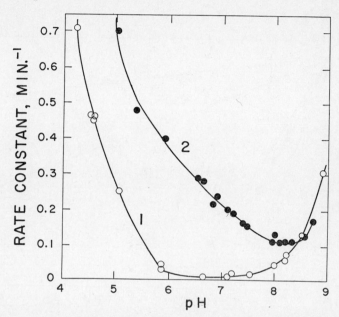

FIG. 4. The effect of pH on the hydrolysis of acetyl-imidazole and on the acetylation of orthophosphate by acetyl-imidazole. On the ordinate are plotted the first-order rate constants for the decomposition of acetyl-imidazole in the absence (Curve 1) and in the presence (Curve 2) of orthophosphate. All samples contained initially about 1 micromole of acetyl-Im. Curve 2 refers to samples in which 750 μM of orthophosphate were also present at the pH indicated. Acetate buffers (0.01 M) were used in the pH range of 4.0 to 5.0 and bicarbonate buffer (0.02 M) was used in the pH range of 8.0 to 9.0. For the data of Curve 1, imidazole buffer (0.02 M) was used in the pH range of 6.0 to 8.0, since free imidazole at this concentration has no detectable influence on the rate of hydrolysis. Acetate, imidazole, and bicarbonate buffers were all shown not to have any specific effects on the rates of acetyl-Im decomposition under the conditions tested. The final volume was 3.0 ml., temperature 26° C. The final pH was measured with a glass electrode.

of $H_2PO_4^-$ occurs at a pH of 7.5–8.0 and thus coincides with the point at which the rate of hydrolysis of acetyl-Im begins to increase rapidly with changing pH on the alkaline side (see Fig. 4). It is not yet clear whether any significance can be attached to this observation. The possibility that this change is due to a change in and dissociation of acetyl-Im appears unlikely, since no significant difference in the molecular extinction of acetyl-Im is observed over the pH range of 5.7 to 8.5.

Equilibrium between acetyl-P and acetyl-imidazole. Since the rate of acetylation of orthophosphate is significantly greater than the rate

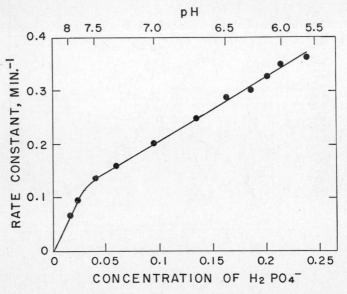

FIG. 5. The influence of $H_2PO_4^-$ concentration on the rate of acetyl-Im decomposition. See Fig. 4 for experimental details. The initial concentration of orthophosphate was 0.25 M in all instances. The concentrations of $H_2PO_4^-$ (plotted on the abscissa) were determined using the charts of Green (12) relating the dibasic and monobasic acid composition of orthophosphate buffers to pH and ionic strength. The corresponding pH values are shown on the upper abscissa.

of hydrolysis of acetyl-Im over the pH range of 6.0 to 7.5, it appeared possible to determine the equilibrium position of reaction (3) by following the reaction spectrophotometrically. The results of a typical experiment are shown in Fig. 6. In this experiment the equilibrium has been approached from both sides. Curve 1 shows the formation of acetyl-Im in a system containing initially a mixture of acetyl-P, imidazole, and P_i. Curve 2 contained initially 1.28 μM of acetyl-imidazole in addition to the latter compounds. It will be noted that after 85 minutes a steady state concentration of acetyl-imidazole is reached. However, since acetyl-Im is undergoing slow hydrolysis, the steady state concentration of acetyl-Im does not represent the

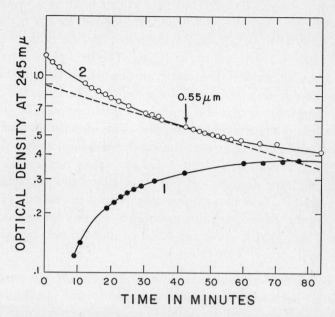

FIG. 6. The reversible acetylation of imidazole by acetyl-P. The reaction mixture represented by Curve 1 contained initially 100 μM of imidazole, 81 μM of acetyl-P; and 124 μM of orthophosphate. The total volume was 3.0 ml., pH 6.96, 26° C. The same conditions were used for Curve 2 except that 1.25 μM of acetyl-Im was also added initially. The dotted line represents the hydrolysis curve for acetyl-Im at pH 6.95, 26° C. and was deliberately drawn tangent to Curve 2. At this point (0.55 μM of acetyl-Im) the rate of disappearance of acetyl-Im is equal to its rate of hydrolysis, and the transfer reaction (acetylation of P_i) must therefore be at equilibrium. 0.55 μM thus represents the equilibrium concentration of acetyl-Im for reaction (3).

true equilibrium for reaction (3) but represents that concentration of acetyl-Im at which the rate of hydrolysis of acetyl-Im is exactly equal to the rate of its formation from acetyl-P. In order to arrive at a closer approximation to the true equilibrium concentration of acetyl-Im for reaction (3), the hydrolysis curve for acetyl-Im was drawn tangent to curve 2. The tangent point should represent the point at which the rate of decomposition of acetyl-Im is equal to the rate of hydrolysis of acetyl-Im; this point, therefore, represents the point at which the forward and backward reactions of reaction (3) are equal (i. e., the equilibrium point). In the experiment described, the acetyl-Im concentration at this point is 0.55 μM.

The concentration of acetyl-P was determined by the hydroxamic acid method (9) and P_i was determined by the Fiske-Subbarow method (10) and corrected for acetyl-P. The final pH was measured with a glass electrode. The concentration of $HPO_4^{=}$ [6] in the final reaction mixture was estimated, using the published charts of Green (12) relating the dibasic and monobasic salt composition of phosphate buffers to pH and ionic strength. The concentration of imidazole base was calculated from the final pH using a pKa value of 6.95 (13).[7] Presented in Table 1 are the data from several experiments of the type described in Fig. 6 in which the pH, orthophosphate, imidazole, and acetyl-P concentrations were varied. The last column in the table gives the calculated equilibrium constant for reaction (3). From the average value of .0084 it may be calculated that the ΔF_o is about 2800 calories.

The acetylation of glutathione by acetyl-imidazole. In view of the surprisingly high free-energy change found for the acetylation of P_i by acetyl-Im, it appeared worth-while to attempt to establish directly the changes in free energy associated with the acetylations of imidazole by a thioester. Although the reaction between acetyl-CoA and imidazole (reaction 2) is of immediate interest, the analogous reaction between acetyl-glutathione and imidazole (reaction 4)

$$\text{Acetyl-Im} + \text{GSH} \leftrightarrows \text{Acetyl-SG} + \text{Imidazole} \qquad (4)$$

[6] Although in the nonenzymatic acetylation of orthophosphate the monobasic acid ($H_2PO_4^-$) appears to be the reactive species (Fig. 6), the equilibrium constants for reaction (3) involving the dibasic acid ($HPO_4^=$) have been calculated so that the free-energy change of this reaction may be compared directly with other reactions previously studied (4, 11), in which $HPO_4^=$ was considered to be the reactive species.

[7] Since the activity coefficients of imidazole are not available, it was not possible to make accurate activity corrections for variations in ionic strength. However, from what is known about the effect of ionic strength or the pKa' of imidazole (14), it appears that such corrections are minor and will not affect significantly the calculated ΔF_o for the reaction.

TABLE 1

The Reaction Between Acetyl–Imidazole and Orthophosphate †

pH	Initial Concentrations μM per 3.0 ml.				Final Concentrations Moles per liter *				$K = \dfrac{(\text{Acetyl-Im})(\text{HPO}_4^=)}{(\text{Acetyl-P})(\text{Imidazole})}$
	Imidazole	P_1	Acetyl-P	Acetyl-Im	Imidazole (free base) ($\times 10^{-3}$)	$\text{HPO}_4^=$ ($\times 10^{-3}$)	Acetyl-Im ** ($\times 10^{-3}$)	Acetyl-P ($\times 10^{-3}$)	
6.45	200	74	73	1.5	16	7.4	0.32	24	.0062
6.45	100	74	73	1.1	8	6.9	0.23	24	.0083
6.45	100	124	73	1.1	8	12	0.12	24	.0075
7.2	100	74	82	1.2	21	17	0.33	27	.0099
6.95	100	124	81	1.2	17	28	0.18	27	.0110
6.15	100	124	81	1.5	4.6	7.5	0.10	27	.0060
7.30	500	200	40	1.2	115	51	0.27	13	.0092

Average = .0084

† Reactions carried out at 26° C. as described in Fig. 6.

* Concentration of $\text{HPO}_4^=$ and imidazole corrected for pH.

** Determined by the graphical method shown in Fig. 6.

has been selected for this investigation, since for technical reasons it is more suitable for study. High concentrations of thioester are required to obtain a detectable acetylation of imidazole; therefore it was necessary to use a thioester that could be used in high concentrations in spectrophotometric experiments. Since acetyl-SG exhibits relatively little light-absorption at 260 mμ, it is well suited for use

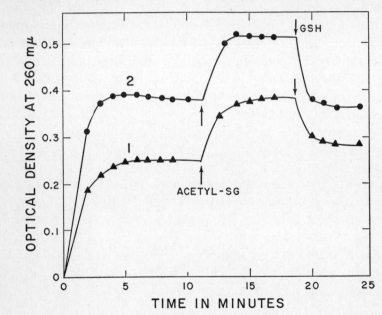

FIG. 7. The reversible acetylation of glutathione by acetyl-imidazole. The reaction mixture represented by Curve 1 contained initially 500 μM of imidazole (pH 7.0); 17.3 μM of acetyl-SG; 2.14 μM of GSH and 50 μM of versene (pH 7.0). The conditions for Curve 2 were the same except that 1000 μM of imidazole (total) were present initially. As indicated by the arrows at 11 minutes, 19 minutes, 17.3 μM of acetyl-SG and 1.8 μM of GSH were added respectively to both samples. The ordinate refers to the optical density at 260 mμ, which is a measure of the acetyl-Im concentration (see Fig. 1).

in the high concentrations required, whereas acetyl-CoA cannot be so used due to the strong adenine absorption at 260 mμ.

Results of a typical experiment showing the reaction between acetyl-SG and imidazole are shown in Fig. 7. The data of curves 1 and 2 are from an experiment in which 500 μM and 1000 μM respectively of imidazole were present initially (3 ml. volume). Both samples contained 17.3 μM of acetyl-SG and 2 μM of GSH also.

The increase in optical density at 260 mμ is a measure of acetyl-Im formation. The figure shows that a very rapid acetylation of imidazole occurs, with the establishment of an equilibrium after only 5 minutes. The addition of more acetyl-SG at 10 minutes resulted in a shift in the equilibrium toward the side of acetyl-Im formation, while the addition of GSH at 19 minutes caused a shift in the opposite direction. Table 2 gives the concentration of the various reactants at equilibrium obtained from these and other similar experiments. All data presented in the table are corrected for pH. The concentrations of GSH are also corrected for a complexing reaction between acetyl-SG and GSH.[8]

Discussion

The results presented in this paper indicate that the acetylation of imidazole by acetyl-P is an endergonic reaction with a ΔF_0 of $+2800$ calories. Assuming that the free energy of hydrolysis of acetyl-P is 12,000 to 15,000 calories (12), the free energy of hydrolysis of acetyl-Im is 15,000 to 18,000 calories. This places the acyl imidazoles in the class of energy-rich compounds along with the acyl phosphates, enolphosphates and phosphoamides.

[8] Recent studies by W. W. Kielley and the author have shown that there is a reaction between thioesters and free mercaptans which results in a loss in the thioester absorption band at 232 mμ. Although the nature of this reaction is not yet fully understood, under the experimental conditions used in the present study the reaction has been described as follows:

$$\text{Acetyl-SG} + \text{GSH} \rightleftharpoons \text{complex} \quad (5)$$

and the dissociation constant has been determined to be

$$K = \frac{\text{complex}}{(\text{Acetyl-SG})\,(\text{GSH})} = 7.5.$$

This constant has been used to correct the equilibrium concentration of GSH for the complexing reaction. It should be emphasized that the dissociation constant for reaction (5) varies with pH and to a certain extent with the concentration of reactants. The value of 7.5 used here does not generally apply, but is restricted to the approximate conditions used in the above experiments. It should also be pointed out that the applied correction is of secondary importance and changes the calculated equilibrium constants only 3 to 9%.

TABLE 2

The Reaction Between Acetyl-Imidazole and Glutathione †

Initial Concentrations μM per 3.0 ml.				Final Concentrations Moles per liter				$K = \dfrac{(\text{Acetyl-SG})\,(\text{Imidazole})}{(\text{Acetyl-Im})\,(\text{GSH})}$
Imidazole	Acetyl-SG	Acetyl-Im	GSH	Imidazole ** ($\times 10^{-3}$)	Acetyl-SG * ($\times 10^{-3}$)	Acetyl-Im ($\times 10^{-4}$)	GSH * ($\times 10^{-4}$)	
300	17.3	0.195	2.13	53	5.66	0.65	7.5	6160
280	31.8	0.369	2.13	50	10.6	1.23	7.5	6300
273	31.4	0.225	3.92	49	10.3	0.75	13	5200
500	17.3	0.339	2.13	89	5.62	1.13	7.8	5700
470	31.8	0.597	2.13	84	10.5	1.99	9.2	4800
455	31.4	0.393	3.92	81	10.3	1.31	13.7	4650
1000	17.3	0.612	2.13	178	5.46	2.04	8.9	5360
940	31.8	0.846	2.13	167	10.4	2.82	8.9	6900
910	31.4	0.582	3.92	162	10.2	1.94	15.0	5700
							Average	5640

† All measurements at pH 7.0, 26° C.

** Concentrations corrected for pH.

* Concentrations corrected for reaction (5) as described in Footnote 7.

From direct measurements of the equilibrium constant for the reaction between acetyl-P and CoA to form acetyl-CoA (reaction 1) it has been determined that this reaction is exergonic, proceeding with a ΔF_0 of —2600 calories.[9] Thus the calculated free-energy change associated with the acetylation of imidazole by acetyl-CoA (reaction 2) is

$$\Delta F_0 \text{ reaction } (2) = \Delta F_0 \text{ reaction } (3) - \Delta F_0 \text{ reaction } (1)$$
$$= 2800 - (-2600) = 5400 \text{ calories.}$$

As shown in Table 2, the average equilibrium constant for the reaction between acetyl-SG and imidazole (reaction 4) is 5640. The free-energy range is thus 5140 calories, which agrees comfortably with the calculated value of 5400 for reaction (2) and indicates that the free energy of hydrolysis of acetyl-SG and of acetyl-CoA are almost the same.

In view of the highly endergonic nature of reaction (2), it is no longer surprising that the attempts to measure this reaction directly were unsuccessful. In order to measure this reaction it will be necessary to use much higher concentrations of acetyl-CoA and imidazole than were employed in the previous studies.

Recently, Wieland and Schneider (2) have reported on the energy-rich nature of N-acyl imidazoles. Their studies, which were carried out concurrently with the present investigation, confirm, and in some respects extend the information on the properties of acetyl imidazole. Their conclusion that acetyl imidazole is an energy-rich compound, though correct, was predicated on the observations that this substance is unstable in aqueous solutions and readily undergoes acetylation reactions with ammonia and hydroxylamine. It should be pointed out that while there is a close correlation between such reactivity and energy-rich acetyl compounds, in the strict thermodynamic sense such observations cannot be taken as evidence for or against the high energy content of a compound, since these reactions

[9] The equilibrium constant for reaction (1) was formerly reported to be 60 ± 20. More recent studies in which a very sensitive spectrophotometric procedure has been used to follow the reaction (15) have shown that the equilibrium constant for reaction (1) is about 74, from which it can be calculated that the ΔF is — 2560 calories.

can occur at a relatively low (ordinary ester) energy level without an appreciable change in free energy.

In view of the fact that N-acetyl imidazole is an energy-rich substance, it is tempting to speculate on its role as an acyl group carrier in biosynthetic reactions. In particular the possibility that the imidazole moiety of the histidine residues in proteins may serve as a prosthetic group functioning as an acyl group carrier in enzyme reactions is an appealing consideration. Such a role of the imidazole nucleus in enzyme reactions is already suggested by the experiments of Wilson and Bergmann (16), which indicate that the imidazole groups of cholinesterase may be active centers for this enzyme. In view of the fact that diisopropylfluorophosphate (DFP) is a potent inhibitor of cholinesterase, the recent studies of Wagner-Jauregg and Hackley (17) showing a catalytic role of histidine and imidazole on the hydrolysis of DFP and the preparation by them of an unstable DFP derivative of imidazole give further support to the idea that imidazole may be an active center in cholinesterase.

Doherty and Vaslow (18) have suggested the possibility that the formation of a chymotrypsin-substrate complex may involve a binding to the imidazole groups of this enzyme. This view is strengthened by the experiments of Weil and Buchert (19) showing that complete inactivation of chymotrypsin is effected by mild photooxidation in which one of the two histidine residues and 2.6 of the 6 tryptophan residues of chymotrypsin are destroyed. Schaffer et al. (20) have recently isolated serine phosphoric acid from acid hydrolysates of DFP-treated chymotrypsin. Although this might be interpreted to indicate that DFP reacts directly with the hydroxyl group of serine, the possibility is not excluded that the DFP reacts with an imidazole group on the protein before it becomes bound to the serine. The finding that there is a rapid non-enzymatic transfer of the acetyl group of acetyl-Im to alcohols (1) indicates that the latter is a reasonable possibility. Indeed, the fact that only one out of a total of 27 serine residues in the chymotrypsin molecule is esterified by DFP (20) indicates that some specific mechanism must be available for activating a particular serine residue. Such a specific activation might be possible if the serine residue is adjacent to a histidine residue, in which case a preliminary esterification of the histidine moiety might be followed by a $N \rightarrow O$ shift, as postulated by Wagner-Jauregg and Hackley (17).

Although it is demonstrated in this paper that the acetylation of imidazole is enzyme-catalyzed (reaction 2), it should be kept in mind that a relatively rapid reversible acetylation of imidazole by acetyl-P and thioesters also occurs non-enzymatically, provided the concentration of reactants is fairly high. In particular, the latter fact should be kept in mind in those studies involving the use of enzymes in substrate amounts, in which case the effective concentrations of imidazole groups may be sufficient to undergo a detectable, non-specific interaction with energy-rich compounds. Thus, in recent studies on the mechanism of action of the enzyme glyceraldehyde-3-phosphate dehydrogenase, in which this enzyme is used in substrate quantities, it appears possible that some of the curious observations (viz., the arsenolysis of acetyl-P by completely oxidized pyridine nucleotide—free enzyme) may be due to the interaction of acetyl-P with imidazole, followed by arsenolysis of the acetyl imidazole derivatives.

Thus far, attempts to extend the enzymatic acetylation of imidazole (reactions 1 and 2) to substances of a more genuine biochemical interest (viz., histidine, carnosine, and various other imidazole derivatives and related nitrogen compounds) have been unsuccessful. To date only urocanic acid has been found to substitute for imidazole in the enzyme-catalyzed reactions. Work on the further purification of this enzyme, its distribution and specificity is in progress.

REFERENCES

1. Stadtman, E. R., and F. H. White, Jr., *J. Am. Chem. Soc.*, 75, 2022 (1953).
2. Wieland, T., and G. Schneider, *Ann. Chem., Justus Liebigs*, 580, 159 (1953).
3. Boyer, J. H., *J. Am. Chem. Soc.*, 74, 6274 (1952).
4. Stadtman, E. R., *J. Biol. Chem.*, 196, 535 (1952).
5. Stadtman, E. R., G. D. Novelli, and F. Lipmann, *J. Biol. Chem.*, 191, 365 (1951).
6. Stadtman, E. R., *J. Biol. Chem.* (in press).
7. Lipmann, F., and L. C. Tuttle, *J. Biol. Chem.*, 153, 571 (1944).
8. Stadtman, E. R., *J. Biol. Chem.*, 196, 527 (1952).

9. Lipmann, F., and L. C. Tuttle, *J. Biol. Chem.*, **158**, 505 (1945).
10. Fiske, C. H., and Y. Subbarow, *J. Biol. Chem.*, **66**, 375 (1925).
11. Lipmann, F., *J. Biol. Chem.*, **155**, 55 (1944).
12. Green, A. A., *J. Am. Chem. Soc.*, **55**, 2331 (1933).
13. Kirby, A. H. M., and A. Neuberger, *Biochem. J.*, **32**, 1146 (1938).
14. Cowgill, R. W., and W. M. Clark, *J. Biol. Chem.*, **198**, 33 (1952).
15. Stadtman, E. R., *J. Comp. Cell. Physiol.*, **41**, 89 (1953).
16. Wilson, I. B., and F. Bergmann, *J. Biol. Chem.*, **186**, 683 (1950).
17. Wagner-Jauregg, T., and B. E. Hackley, Jr., *J. Am. Chem. Soc.*, **75**, 2125 (1953).
18. Doherty, D. G., and F. Vaslow, *J. Am. Chem. Soc.*, **74**, 931 (1952).
19. Weil, L., and A. R. Buchert, *Federation Proceedings*, **11**, 307 (1952).
20. Schaffer, N. K., S. C. May, Jr., and W. H. Summerson, *J. Biol. Chem.*, **202**, 67 (1953).

ON THE MECHANISM OF SOME ATP–LINKED REACTIONS AND CERTAIN ASPECTS OF PROTEIN SYNTHESIS

FRITZ LIPMANN

Biochemical Research Laboratory, Massachusetts General Hospital and the Department of Biological Chemistry, Harvard Medical School, Boston

ATP-CoA-acetate reaction. Through the recent presence of Feodor Lynen in my laboratory, a burst of activity was catalyzed, using isotope exchange reactions in the analysis of intermediary pathways. Primary consideration was given to the mechanism of the ATP-CoA-acetate reaction in which both our laboratories had been interested for a long time (1, 2), and which more recently had been found to involve a pyrophosphate split of ATP with an over-all equilibrium as follows:

$$Ad \cdot P \sim PP + CoASH + acetate \rightleftharpoons Ad \cdot P + CoAS \sim Ac + PP \qquad (1)$$

Lynen visualized the possibilities of the use of P^{32}-pyrophosphate and C^{14}-acetate for an analysis of the mechanism of this reaction. The results of such experiments have been reported briefly (5) and will be summarized here.

Pyrophosphate was found to equilibrate very rapidly through our yeast enzyme (3, 4) with ATP. This equilibration, independent of the presence of other reaction partners, invited as an explanation to postulate an interchangeability of AMP $\sim$ *enzyme* and AMP $\sim$ *pyrophosphate*, in other words, an intermediate energy-rich attachment of AMP (Ad $\cdot$ P) to enzyme. Addition of CoA inhibits the exchange between ATP (Ad $\cdot$ P $\sim$ PP) and PP, indicating CoA to compete with AMP for attachment to the enzyme. The formulation of the first two steps in the reaction cycle is proposed:

$$Enzyme + Ad \cdot P \sim PP \rightleftharpoons Enzyme \sim P \cdot Ad + PP \qquad (2)$$

$$Enzyme \sim P \cdot Ad + CoASH \rightleftharpoons Enzyme \sim S \cdot CoA + Ad \cdot P \qquad (3)$$

Furthermore, it was found that acetyl-CoA and acetate interchange readily, although less rapidly than ATP and pyrophosphate. This indicates, as the cycle's end-result, an exchange of acetate for enzyme, yielding acetyl-CoA and releasing free enzyme for a new start of the cycle,

$$\text{Enzyme} \sim \text{SCoA} + \text{acetate} \rightleftharpoons \text{Enzyme} + \text{acetyl} \sim \text{SCoA} \qquad (4)$$

During this study, the observation was made that magnesium is a component only of the $\text{Ad} \cdot \text{P} \sim \text{PP} \rightleftharpoons \text{PP}$ equilibrium. Magnesium appears not to participate in the $\text{acetyl} \sim \text{S} \cdot \text{CoA} \rightleftharpoons \text{acetate}$ exchange, which is if anything slightly inhibited by its addition.

Pantothenic acid synthesis. The rather successful use of isotope exchange for the analysis of a mechanism has prompted us to use this tool with a similar reaction, the synthesis of pantothenic acid, discovered some time ago by Werner Maas, as catalyzed by extracts of *E. coli* (6). Dr. Maas spent the last year in Boston and studied the finer mechanisms of this interesting reaction, which represents a model peptide synthesis (7). It appeared that he was dealing here again with a pyrophosphate split of ATP, initiating, in this case, a peptidic condensation of pantoic acid and β-alanine to pantothenic acid:

$$\text{Ad} \cdot \text{P} \sim \text{PP} + \text{CH}_2\text{OH} \cdot \text{C(CH}_3)_2\text{CHOH} \cdot \text{COOH}$$
$$+ \text{NH}_2 \cdot \text{CH}_2\text{CH}_2\text{COOH} \rightarrow$$
$$\text{Ad} \cdot \text{P} + \text{CH}_2\text{OH} \cdot \text{C(CH}_3)_2\text{CHOH} \cdot \text{CONH} \cdot \text{(CH}_2)_2\text{COOH} + \text{PP} \qquad (5)$$

Using again radioactive pyrophosphate as a tool, the pyrophosphate in this case did *not* equilibrate *independently* with ATP, but equilibrated only when the *second* reactant, *pantoic acid*, was added. Significantly, the addition of the other partner, β-alanine, did not promote an equilibration between ATP and pyrophosphate.

We find here in some manner the reverse situation to that encountered in the ATP-CoA-acetate reaction; ATP and pyrophosphate do not equilibrate except on the addition of pantoate. The first step here, therefore, should be a transfer of the pyrophosphoryl end of ATP to the enzyme with liberation of AMP. This course of reaction is further confirmed by experiments with radioactive adenylic acid, which exchanges with ATP without the pantoate.

In the second stage, the covalently enzyme-bound pyrophosphoryl exchanges for pantoate, thus yielding a reactive pantoyl ~ enzyme. In this manner, the initial lack of exchange between inorganic pyrophosphate and ATP is explained: pantoate is needed to release the enzyme-bound pyrophosphate and thus catalyze a two-step exchange with ATP: (Fig. 1).

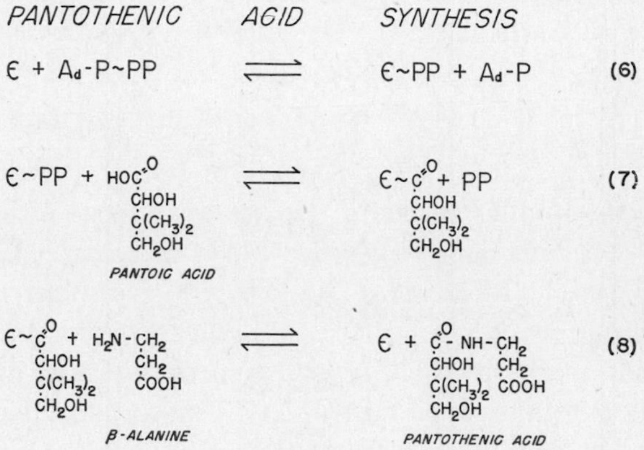

PANTOTHENIC   ACID   SYNTHESIS

$$\epsilon + A_d\text{-}P\text{~}PP \rightleftharpoons \epsilon\text{~}PP + A_d\text{-}P \qquad (6)$$

$$\epsilon\text{~}PP + HOC\overset{O}{\underset{\substack{CHOH \\ C(CH_3)_2 \\ CH_2OH}}{}} \rightleftharpoons \epsilon\text{~}C\overset{O}{\underset{\substack{CHOH \\ C(CH_3)_2 \\ CH_2OH}}{}} + PP \qquad (7)$$

PANTOIC ACID

$$\epsilon\text{~}C\overset{O}{\underset{\substack{CHOH \\ C(CH_3)_2 \\ CH_2OH}}{}} + \underset{\substack{CH_2 \\ COOH}}{H_2N\text{-}CH_2} \rightleftharpoons \epsilon + \underset{\substack{CHOH \quad CH_2 \\ C(CH_3)_2 \; COOH \\ CH_2OH}}{C\overset{O}{}\text{-}NH\text{-}CH_2} \qquad (8)$$

β-ALANINE   *PANTOTHENIC ACID*

FIG. 1.

The cycle closes eventually with reaction 8, the linking of the activated pantoyl-carboxyl to the amino group of β-alanine.

The isotope result in this case then indicates a primary activation of the enzyme by pyrophosphorylation, in contrast to the adenylation step encountered in the ATP-CoA-acetate reaction. CoA, by the way, is in no manner involved in the pantothenic acid synthesis (6, 7). The catalysis of pyrophosphate exchange by pantoate, but not by β-alanine, shows that carboxyl activation (8) initiates peptide bond formation. The final condensation, reaction 8, appears to be irreversible, judging from preliminary tests with radioactive β-alanine. Furthermore, the rate of exchange between ATP and PP by way of pantoate, i. e., backwards $(7)\rightarrow(6)$, is about 10 times slower than the over-all synthesis $(6)\rightarrow(7)\rightarrow(8)$. This may mean that the replacement of the pyrophosphoryl group by pantoate is a downhill reaction.

A Model for Polypeptide Synthesis. It is attempted here to translate this mechanism of synthesis of a peptidic bond into a system for
polypeptide synthesis. This proposition leans, in part, on the observation of Britton Chance (9) that in the electron transmission from
cytochrome to cytochrome, the specific sequence of electron transfers
is realized through a structural fixation of the individual cytochromes. The rate of electron transfer, according to Chance, is too

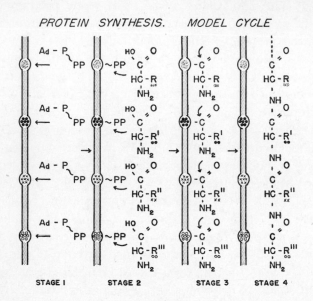

FIG. 2.

fast for a random meeting of the cytochrome molecules and could
be realized only by a sequential arrangement of the cytochromes to
allow a directed transfer of electrons along the line.

Similarly, it is assumed that amino-acid-specific activation spots are
lined up on a structure in a demanded sequence. To take an example, lysine $(= R)$, glutamic acid $(= R')$, aspartic acids $(= R'')$,
and glycine $(= R''')$ are to be linked in this order. To achieve this,
activation centers strictly specific for R, R', or R'' and R''' would be
set up in this sequence on our structure, as pictured in Fig. 2. The
centers would be activated by a transfer of phosphoryl groups from

ATP to enzyme, seen in stage 1. The second stage of the cycle would be the exchange of the pyrophosphoryl (or phosphoryl) for the carboxyl of the particular amino acid. After the amino acids are lined up through the carboxyl links in the required sequence, the activated carboxyls react in stage 3 with amino groups of the neighboring amino acids. This condensation forms the polypeptide chain of a pattern laid down through the specific attraction of the active centers for particular amino acids. The ready polypeptide leaves the enzyme structure, which can perform a new cycle and thus reduplicate this protein structure indefinitely.

It is well understood that the synthesis of the peptide bond, assuming standard conditions, requires much less energy than is available in energy-rich phosphate bonds. Linderstrøm-Lang (10), however, introduced the important consideration that such " excess " energy is needed for a concentration lift of the amino acid. In order to accommodate for such a utilization of phosphate-bond energy, part of the energy may be made available by exchange of energy-rich phosphoryl links for a less energy-rich carboxyl link. If, for example, the carboxyls were attached to the enzyme structure by a bond, the hydrolysis of which would yield only 5–7 kilocalories against the 12 kilocalories of the pyrophosphoryl bond, the exchange of the pyrophosphoryl for the carboxyl would then leave available 5–7 kilocalories to be used for capturing the carboxyl of the amino acid at high dilution. To indicate such a possibility, the *wave* symbol (= 12–15 kilocalories) is used only with the pyrophosphoryl group, while for attachment of the carboxyl to the structure, a *dash* symbol has been used, leaving it open as to what bond energy may be residing in this link. Recently, in a private discussion, Dr. Leo Szilard pointed out the probable importance of the concentration effect, suspecting it to appear with a rather large contribution in the energy balance of protein synthesis.

A structural arrangement specifically directing amino acid activation and therewith amino acid sequence was mainly constructed to help with a rationalization of reduplication mechanisms in general, and more specifically, of such concepts as the presently much discussed gene-enzyme relationship. A protein synthesis from individual amino acids, as is assumed in this model, is indicated strongly by the studies on adaptive enzyme formation of Monod and his group (11) and of Spiegelman and coworkers (12).

There is some value in the utilization of well-founded simpler schemes for constructing more complex synthetic reactions. It appears that in this manner one can devise a mechanism of genetic determination and reduplication of a specific protein, primary consideration being given to a fixed amino-acid sequence as the background of specificity. A reasonably well integrated, possible mechanism is thus presented which, however, does not claim to reflect the real one, except in a very general sense.

REFERENCES

1. Chou, T. C., and F. Lipmann, *J. Biol. Chem.*, 196, 89 (1952).
2. Lynen, F., E. Reichert, and L. Rueff, *Ann. Chem. Justus Liebigs*, 574, 1 (1951).
3. Lipmann, F., M. E. Jones, S. Black, and R. M. Flynn, *J. Am. Chem. Soc.*, 74, 2384 (1952).
4. Lipmann, F., M. E. Jones, S. Black, and R. M. Flynn, *J. Cell. Comp. Physiol.*, 41, Suppl. 1, 109 (1953).
5. Jones, M. E., F. Lipmann, H. Hilz, and F. Lynen, *J. Am. Chem. Soc.*, 75, 3285 (1953).
6. Maas, W. K., *J. Biol. Chem.*, 198, 23 (1952).
7. Maas, W. K., and G. D. Novelli, *Arch. Biochem. and Biophys.*, 43, 236 (1953).
8. Lipmann, F., *Federation Proc.*, 8, 597 (1949).
9. Chance, B., *Nature*, 169, 215 (1952).
10. Linderstrøm-Lang, K. U., *Lane Medical Lectures*, VI, p. 93, Stanford Univ. Press, Stanford, Cal. (1952).
11. Monod, J., A. M. Pappenheimer, Jr., and G. Cohen-Bazire, *Biochim. et Biophys. Acta*, 9, 648 (1952).
12. Halvorson, H. O., and S. Spiegelman, *J. Bacteriology*, 65, 496; 601 (1953).

DISCUSSION

DR. LIPMANN: Dr. Calvin, would you like to say a few words? And I suppose we all wait for you to start things off.

DR. CALVIN: I didn't come prepared to talk about this, but this question of whether or not the thiamine and lipoic are one seems to me to be very important, to which we still haven't had the answer. There is one piece of data, if I can remember it, which might bear on this. Relying entirely upon an unprepared memory (so this is really uncertain), as I recall the data this was work done by George Milhaud from the Pasteur Institute, who is now in our laboratory. He did some work on acetoin synthesis in extracts from aerogenes while he was in Paris; and when he came to our laboratory, in which everyone in some way or another was concerned with this sulphur business, he felt that he ought to do something, too; so he tried to see whether the acetoin synthesis in aerogenes had anything to do with this lipoic acid. The first thing he did was to prepare some labelled pyruvate (carbonyl-labelled pyruvate, it was) and incubated it with extracts of aerogenes. These extracts were very successful in making acetoin out of pyruvate. After incubation most of the pyruvate is converted to acetoin. He then made an 80 per cent alcohol extract of the reaction mixture and made a chromatogram of that. He did two-dimensional chromatography, using phenol and butyl alcohol as the two solvents. He found two spots on the paper—that is, two unknown major radioactive areas: one in the phosphate area, and one in the lipid area. In addition to radioactive assays of these chromatograms, he was able to make bioassays for the lipoic acid activity, with *Streptococcus faecalis*. This is a quantitative assay procedure and is very specific — you would have to ask a bacteriologist about how specific it is — they have convinced me that it is. Both of these spots have lipoic acid activity. The spot in the lipid area was eluted from the paper and rechromatographed. The radioactivity and the lipoic response are still found in the lipid area. This evidence, of course, might indicate that a lipoic complex is involved in acetoin synthesis — it does not prove it, but it is suggestive. This seems to require that there is some very weak combination between the two-carbon fragment from pyruvate and the lipoic acid. This is not the kind of thing one would expect if it were a lipothiamide compound, as Reed has suggested. As a matter of fact, we have made that one—or, at least, put it together—according to Reed's directions. This kind of amide would not go to pieces with the ease that the compound that we observed does. We haven't made anywhere near the progress that Dr. Gunsalus has with respect to finding out just what this loose compound is, but it does seem to suggest that there is a combination between all three of these things which is not the kind of amide that Reed suggests. Our labile "conjugate" spot very readily yields what appears to be free monoacetyl-6, 8-dithiol octanoic acid. I should have mentioned that the lipid area can be co-chromatographed and demonstrated to be acetyl lipoic acid. This lipoic acid spot appears not only in aerogenes extracts, but also in muscle — and of course in the whole algae, as you might expect. There is one other piece of information, before this is all taken apart by Dr. Racker: there are many different forms of lipoic acid in the algae—and in other things, too, I suppose. We can extract a certain fraction with 80 per cent alcohol, extract another fraction with strong acid, and extract still another fraction that is not extractable by the other two methods by using other treatments; so I would think that one would find this stuff in a whole variety of combinations—perhaps each with a different function—at least, I like to think so.

DR. RACKER: I would just like to say that we should keep the issues clear here. In the ketol condensation, such as in acetoin synthesis, I think there is good evidence that lipoic acid is not required. Carboxylase will form acetoin in the absence of lipoic acid. Dr. Gunsalus was kind enough to assay transketolase for lipoic acid, and there is no lipoic acid there, either. Since the extracts you are dealing with are very crude, there may be many side reactions going on, and your results do not show that lipoic acid is involved in acetoin synthesis.

DR. CALVIN: You mean as far as aerogenes is concerned.

DR. RACKER: Yes.

DR. CALVIN: Yes, that's quite right.

DR. OCHOA: I would just like to say that *Aerobacter aerogenes*, in addition to having a very strong acetoin system, also has the pyruvate oxidation system. Dr. Strecker last year in our laboratory found fractions in aerogenes similar to the *E. coli* fractions. The typical fractions A and B were found which carry out the formation of acetyl Co-A from pyruvic acid. Similar fractions can be obtained from *Staphylococcus aureus*. It would, therefore, appear that the organism used by Dr. Calvin, as well as many others, not only converts pyruvate to acetoin, but also has the typical pyruvate oxidation system, which we know to require lipoic acid.

DR. GUNSALUS: That would be my interpretation also. In the *A. aerogenes* cells, side reactions occur other than the acetoin formation which require thiamine and lipoic acid or a complex of the two. Thiamine is required for the acetoin reaction, whereas lipoic acid is not. Dolin and O'Kane have both shown that *Streptococcus faecalis* cells grown in a synthetic medium free of lipoic acid form acetoin rapidly but do not carry out the dismutation or pyruvate oxidation reactions. Acetoin synthesis can also be shown to occur in bacterial preparations such as *Proteus vulgaris* by the addition of aldehyde and pyruvate as substrates in the absence of lipoic acid. Lipoic acid is then required for the oxidative or acyl forming systems, but not for the straight decarboxylases.

DR. CALVIN: Well, let's leave out the question of whether this complex is involved in acetoin synthesis. The only point I wanted to raise is that there is something in the lipoic acid function which involves all three fragments. The acetyl (or whatever you want to call it) seems to be tied to the lipoic and does not seem to be an amide-type compound. This is the only point that I wanted to make.

DR. RACKER: I wonder whether Dr. Gunsalus would care to comment on the binding of thiamine and lipoic acid to enzyme preparations he is working with?

DR. GUNSALUS: There are several viewpoints on the thiamine lipoic acid combination; for example, the A fraction which has lipoic acid bound to it, can be purified and the lipoic acid content does not decrease, but rather increases. If one dialyzes a purified A fraction against alkaline pyrophosphate, one can show a cocarboxylase requirement but not a lipoic requirement; presumably the two are separated and can be added back together after dialysis. It is difficult to visualize splitting an amide linkage by dialysis and bringing about its reformation without an added energy source. Reed's initial experiments on the biological formation of lipothiamidepyrophosphate were performed with partially purified B fractions to which he added cocarboxylase and incubated and then heated the preparation. He reported the activation of coli A fractions with these hot water extracts and assigned it to the B fraction "conjugase" activity. We were quite sure that conjugase action could not be the only function of the B fraction and now feel quite certain, as shown this morning, that it does contain other functions; for example, a lipoic dehydrogenase. The lipoic acid appears to be strongly bound to the enzyme and may exist as a complex with thiamine on the enzyme though possibly not as an amide linkage. The reason we have reserved judgment on the correctness of Reed's interpretation and not concentrated too great a portion of our effort on this part of the problem arises from a sort of philosophical matter on how one does research. We have felt that by following our own experimental leads and hypothesis as outlined today, as well as previously, we would be led to the answer more quickly and that in any event further separations of the enzymes and cofactors were needed and were more likely to be obtained by this means. Lipothiamidepyrophosphate has not been generally available nor have we had a keto acid system which appeared to require this cofactor. I believe we can expect further information from Reed on this point shortly.

DR. NASON: This is sort of a question for the physical chemists; but what kind of physical explanation might explain the fact that lipoic acid is so much more electronegative than other more simple sulfhydryl-containing compounds?

DR. VENNESLAND: With respect to the question that Dr. Nason raised, I should say that we have been told by the chemists that it is not surprising that in a compound like lipoic acid one might expect the reduced form to be a better reducing agent than, say, cysteine. This is due to an entropy effect. In reduced lipoic acid, the –SH groups are in the same molecule, whereas in cysteine they are not.

GROUP TRANSFER AS AN ENZYMATIC SUBSTITUTION MECHANISM*

DANIEL E. KOSHLAND, JR.

*Biology Department, Brookhaven National Laboratory,
Upton, L.I., N.Y.*

THE STOICHIOMETRY of the group-transfer reactions can be summarized by the formulation of equation (1) in which $B–X$ is the "donor" molecule, B is the group being transferred and Y is the "acceptor" molecule. It is clear, however, that equation (1) fits a much wider range of reactions than those commonly included in the "group-transfer" category. Thus, in the case that Y is a water molecule, equation (1) represents the stoichiometry of a hydrolytic reaction. If we should like to discuss all these reactions together,

$$B–X + Y \rightarrow B–Y + X \tag{1}$$

we can either broaden the definition of group transfer, so that hydrolytic reactions can be considered as transfer reactions in which the acceptor is water, or we can use a different term to describe the entirety of those enzymatic reactions covered by equation (1). The latter seems preferable, since it will not upset the existing nomenclature and because the chemical reactions summarized by equation (1) are already called "substitution reactions." It is logical, therefore, to refer to their biological analogs as "enzymatic substitution reactions" and to consider the traditional group-transfer reactions— the transacylases, the transphosphorylases, etc.—as individual examples of this larger class.

The term "enzymatic substitution mechanisms" is chosen not primarily to simplify nomenclature, but to emphasize the interrelations of this group of reactions with each other and with their chemical counterparts. Extensive studies have shown that a few basic

* Research carried out at Brookhaven National Laboratory under the auspices of the U.S. Atomic Energy Commission.

mechanisms can explain the wide variety of chemical reactions described by equation (1). If the number of basic mechanisms is likewise found to be small in the enzyme-catalyzed reactions, then evidence obtained from hydrolytic enzymes, for example, will be pertinent to the group-transfer enzymes, and vice versa. It is too early to say whether this hypothesis is true, but in this paper I shall at least attempt to show that a few basic mechanisms can explain the existing enzymatic facts in terms that are consistent with the evidence from physical organic chemistry.

MECHANISMS OF NON-ENZYMATIC SUBSTITUTION REACTIONS

Before discussing the enzymatic reactions, I should like to summarize very briefly the pertinent information available from studies of organic mechanisms (4, 32).

In the first place, it may be well to point out that equation (1) focuses attention on the replacement of X by Y and deemphasizes the rapid proton shifts which frequently accompany substitution reactions. Thus, in the hydrolysis of an acetate ester, BY would be $CH_3-C(OH)_2^+$. At pH 7 this " product " would immediately lose two protons to the solvent or buffer to form the acetate ion. In the formation of a polysaccharide from a sugar phosphate, the inorganic phosphate produced frequently adds a proton from the solvent or buffer. These rapid transfers of hydrogen ion are tacitly assumed and are omitted only to emphasize the slow rate-determining steps of the substitution reaction, i. e., the substitution of a C–OH bond or a C–OR bond for a C–OP bond. That this is justified can be seen, for example, from the many similarities in the reactions of tertiary amines and primary amines in spite of the difference in proton shifts with these two reagents.

A large amount of stereochemical and kinetic evidence indicates that the replacement of a group X by a group Y at a primary or secondary saturated carbon atom takes place by the mechanism illustrated in equation (2). The reagent Y^- with its unshared pair of

$$Y^- : + \overset{\overset{r}{|}}{\underset{\underset{H}{|}}{S—C—X}} + A^+ \rightarrow Y^- : \ldots . \overset{\overset{r \quad S}{\diagdown \diagup}}{\underset{\underset{H}{|}}{C^+}} \ldots . : X : A$$

$$\rightarrow Y—\overset{\overset{r}{|}}{\underset{\underset{H}{|}}{C—S}} + AX \qquad (2)$$

electrons is said to make a *nucleophilic attack* on the carbon atom and the reagent, A is said to make an *electrophilic attack* on the departing group X. In effect, the group A attracts the electrons of X, weakening the C–X bond, while the group Y shares its electrons with the carbon atom and thus helps to push out the X group. (The A and Y groups are not necessarily charged, but clearly a positive charge on A and a negative charge on Y will increase the effectiveness of the action of these agents.) If the Y group is a very powerful nucleophilic reagent, i. e., if it has a great tendency to share its electrons, the reaction may occur with very little aid from A. Thus, in the alkaline hydrolysis of methyl bromide the hydroxide ion is such a strong base that the reaction goes readily in aqueous solution with water, which is a weak electrophilic reagent, acting as the group "pulling" on the bromine (equation 3). Conversely, a reagent A

$$HO^- + CH_3Br + H_2O \rightarrow HO^- \ldots . \overset{\overset{H \quad H}{\diagdown \diagup}}{\underset{\underset{H}{|}}{C}} \ldots . Br : HOH$$

$$\rightarrow HOCH_3 + Br^- + H_2O \qquad (3)$$

which exerts a very strong attraction for electrons may furnish such a strong pull on the departing X group that only a weakly nucleophilic reagent is needed as Y. Thus, in the silver-ion–catalyzed hydrolysis of isopropyl bromide the weakly basic water is sufficient as the electron-sharing reagent (equation 4).

$$H_2O + Me_2CH–Br + Ag^+ \rightarrow H_2O \ldots . \overset{\overset{Me \quad H}{\diagdown \diagup}}{\underset{\underset{Me}{|}}{C^+}} \ldots . Br : Ag$$

$$\rightarrow Me_2CHOH + H^+ + AgBr \qquad (4)$$

It is clear from the foregoing mechanism that the strength of the C–X bond and the susceptibility of the carbon to attack will also affect the strength of reagents A and Y needed to cause reaction. A substituent X which forms a weak C–X bond to a tertiary carbon atom may, for example, dissociate with little or no aid from the nucleophilic reagent Y. In the cases of the primary and alkyl-substituted secondary carbon atoms, however, the mechanism illustrated in equation (1) is apparently obeyed in all known cases for the X substituents under discussion here.

A consequence of this mechanism is that the replacement occurs with inversion of configuration if the carbon atom involved is asymmetric. The evidence that all such non-enzymatic replacements on primary or alkyl-substituted secondary carbon atoms occur with inversion is overwhelming, and those cases which appear to proceed

$$\underset{\underset{Me}{|}}{\overset{\overset{H}{|}}{\phi\text{-C}}}\text{-OH} + \text{SOCl}_2 \longrightarrow \underset{\underset{Me}{|}}{\overset{\overset{H}{|}}{\phi\text{-C}}}\text{-O-SOCl} \longrightarrow \underset{\underset{Me}{|}}{\overset{\overset{H}{|}}{\phi\text{-C}}}\overset{O}{\underset{Cl}{\diagdown}}S=O \longrightarrow \underset{\underset{Me}{|}}{\overset{\overset{H}{|}}{\phi\text{-C}}}\text{-Cl} + \text{SO}_2$$

$$(5)$$

with retention of configuration have been shown to be the result of two successive steps, each involving an inversion. In the case of tertiary carbon atoms or aryl-substituted secondary carbon atoms, a replacement involving a cyclic intermediate has been shown to proceed in some cases with retention of configuration without involving an inverted intermediate. This occurs only under special conditions and with special reagents. An example is the reaction of an aryl-substituted alcohol with thionyl chloride which can react via a cyclic intermediate, as shown in equation (5). Here, presumably the favorable geometry of the cyclic intermediate plus the stabilizing effect on the carbonium ion of the aryl ring combine to allow this rather unusual mechanism.

The extensive and self-consistent literature on carbon compounds lends great assurance to the basic features of the mechanisms proposed for displacements at a carbon atom. The correlation of theoretical with kinetic and stereochemical material also allows extrapolation to elements other than carbon with reasonable confidence, even though the data on the latter compounds are far less numerous. Recently, however, Dostrovsky and Hallman (20) have made fairly detailed studies of the displacement of halogen atoms from phosphorus compounds, studies which show a good correlation with the analogous displacements of halogen from carbon. It is, therefore, highly probable that displacements on phosphorus atoms have the same fundamental characteristics as the displacements on carbon, a fact which we shall see is of particular pertinence to the "phosphate-transfer" reactions.

MECHANISMS OF ENZYMATIC SUBSTITUTION REACTIONS

In surveying the enzymatic reactions whose stoichiometries are expressed by equation (1), the available chemical and biological

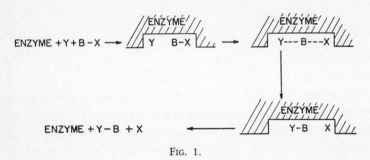

FIG. 1.

evidence seemed to be consistent with a few basic mechanisms. Before applying the mechanisms to the enzymatic reactions, I shall briefly describe the fundamentals of each mechanism.

The first mechanism involves the direct reaction of the two substrates Y and BX on the surface of the enzyme, as illustrated in Fig. 1. The role of acidic and basic groups on the enzyme surface is omitted to emphasize the main features of the displacement, but it would be anticipated that basic groups would enhance the electron-sharing tendency of the substrate Y and acidic groups would decrease the strength of the $B-X$ bond. Important features of the mechanism are that the $Y-B$ bond has started to form simultaneously with or before the $B-X$ bond has started to break and that the attacking group Y approaches from the " backside," i. e., the $Y-B-X$ angle is ca. $180°$. The role of the enzyme in this mechanism, in addition to the juxtaposition of the substrates, is to polarize the electrons in the substrate molecules so as to increase their tendency to react. Because this mechanism involves only one displacement on the group B, it has been called a single displacement mechanism (44).

The second mechanism involves a preliminary attack on the substrate $B-X$ by a nucleophilic group on the enzyme surface, with cleavage of the $B-X$ bond (cf. equation 6). This is then followed

$$En : + B-X \rightarrow En-B + : X \tag{6}$$

by a nucleophilic attack on the enzyme-substrate intermediate, $B-En$, by the second substrate Y to give the final product $Y-B$ (cf. equation 7). In this case, as in the previous one, acidic groups would aid the

$$En-B + : Y \rightarrow En : +B-Y \tag{7}$$

cleavage of the $B-X$ bond, and basic groups would increase the electron-sharing tendency of the substrate Y. The mechanism is illustrated by two discrete equations to illustrate the two displacements which take place but should not be construed to indicate that the X group has dissociated from the enzyme surface before the Y group is absorbed or that a full covalent bond is formed between B and En. This may be the case, but it is not so of necessity, as we shall see in the subsequent discussion. The essential features are (1) that two successive displacements occur, (2) that the enzyme itself acts as an electron-sharing reagent approaching the backside of B, and (3) that the $B-X$ bond is broken before the $B-Y$ bond is formed. Because two displacements on B occur, this mechanism is called a double displacement mechanism (44).

The designations single and double refer to the displacements on B only and are not meant to indicate the number of steps involved in the over-all enzymatic reaction. Thus, the absorption of substrates, activators, and coenzymes and the desorption of the products, etc., may well occur in orders which may be designated as discrete steps without in any way impairing the validity of characterizing a reaction as occurring by a single displacement mechanism.

A third mechanism can be patterned on that postulated for the reaction of phenylmethylcarbinol with thionyl chloride (equation 5). In this mechanism the enzyme's affinity for the X, B, and Y groups would be assumed to create a favorable geometric arrangement equivalent to that obtained with the cyclic intermediate. The displacement by Y, therefore, occurs from the front side, i. e., the Y–B–X angle is acute, instead of from the rear; and this mode of action can be called for convenience a "front-side displacement mechanism." In the double displacement mechanism the displace-

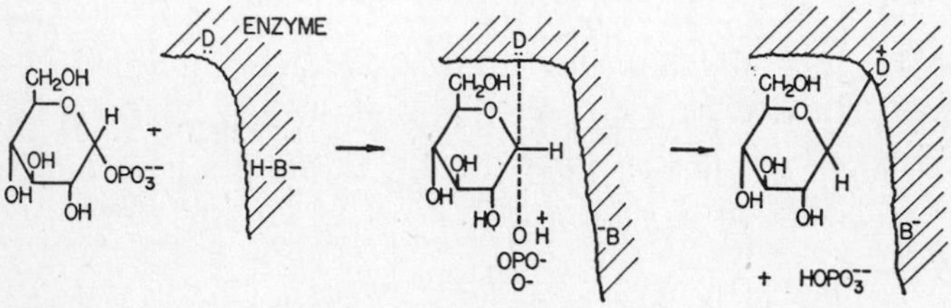

Fig. 2.

ment by Y also occurs from the front-side but only *after* a back-side attack by an electron-sharing site *on the enzyme surface*. For reasons which will be discussed later, the front-side displacement mechanism is considered less likely to occur as a general mechanism than the other two mentioned above, but its applicability in at least some cases must be considered a possibility.

To give an example of one of the mechanisms in a specific case, the double displacement mechanism for the reaction of alpha glucose-1-phosphate with fructose catalyzed by sucrose phosphorylase is shown in Figs. 2 and 3. In Fig. 2, as the bond between the carbon atom and the oxygen of the phosphate starts to break, the electron donor site, D, on the enzyme surface starts to share its electrons with the "back-side" of the C-1 atom of the glucose. The departure of the phosphate is aided by some electrophilic group, here designated as a proton, which attaches to the phosphate oxygen and thereby weakens the carbon-oxygen bond. The intermediate formed may not have a perfect tetrahedral arrangement of the bonds around the C-1 atom, but the relative arrangements of the enzyme, H, O, and C groups is opposite to that of the phosphate, H, O, and C groups in the substrate. In the second stage of the reaction (Fig. 3), a fructose molecule makes an electron-sharing attack on the carbon, displaces the enzyme and forms the product sucrose with the alpha configuration. In this second step a basic group B' on the enzyme

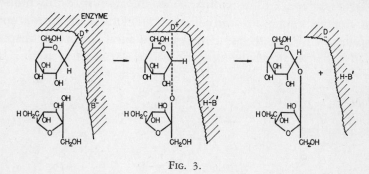

FIG. 3.

surface is shown abstracting a proton to increase the electron-sharing tendency of the fructose oxygen.

It is seen that these mechanisms constitute a combination of some commonly accepted features of enzyme action with some commonly accepted non-enzymatic reaction theory. The justification for this lies in the hope that it will lead to more precise descriptions of the role of the enzyme in enzyme-substrate intermediates, the development of new criteria for distinguishing enzyme mechanisms, and a reappraisal of old criteria for these mechanisms.

STEREOCHEMICAL CRITERIA OF REACTION MECHANISMS

Having defined the mechanisms it remains to distinguish between them experimentally. One criterion can be readily derived from the chemical analogies. If X is bonded to an asymmetric carbon atom, the single displacement mechanism should lead to a product of inverted configuration, whereas the double displacement and front-side displacement mechanisms should lead to a product of retained configuration. The stereochemistry of the enzymatic reaction will, therefore, distinguish between the mechanisms, provided the reaction proceeds by a displacement with cleavage of the $B–X$ bond (44).

Four enzymatic reactions are known which result in a product of inverted configuration. Of these, two, the hydrolysis of amylose catalyzed by beta amylase (equation 8) (25) and the phosphorolysis of maltose (equation 9) (24), involve the replacement with inversion of a group X by a group Y at the asymmetric carbon, and undoubtedly proceed by a single displacement mechanism. In the remaining two reactions an inversion occurs but the products contain the same structural groups attached to the asymmetric atom. Thus,

$$\text{(8)}$$

$$\text{(9)}$$

in the conversion of glucose to galactose, the only apparent change is the interchange of the H and OH groups in space. Similarly, in the racemization catalyzed by alanine racemase the only change is that of the relative positions of the hydrogen and amino groups.

In the alanine racemase reaction the coenzyme is pyridoxal phosphate (79), which has been shown to catalyze the racemization in the absence of enzyme (57). These facts support the postulated formation of a Schiff's base intermediate (57), and it is, therefore, unlikely that the alanine racemase reaction involves a displacement mechanism.

In the conversion of glucose to galactose it has been demonstrated that inversion occurs in the transformation of uridine diphosphoglucose into uridine diphosphogalactose (47), that galactose-1-C^{14} forms glucose-1-C^{14} (65), and that glycogen, when synthesized from galactose in D_2O, contains no more deuterium than when synthesized from glucose (64). These facts are inconsistent with a transformation via an inositol type of compound (23), or by a dehydrogenation mechanism (47). They are consistent with a single displacement mechanism (equation 10) or possibly with an aldol type of cleavage (equation 11). Several arguments can be adduced

$$\text{(10)}$$

$$\text{(11)}$$

against the aldol type of cleavage—the cis-trans stereochemistry, the lack of extra deuterium exchange, the lack of an alpha carbonyl group—although these facts are indicative rather than conclusive. O^{18} data could be (and are being) used to establish the result conclusively, but in the interim it can be said that the single displacement mechanism probably obtains for this reaction.

Fitting and Doudoroff have examined the specificity requirements of maltose phosphorylase and have shown that arsenate can be substituted for phosphate and xylose for the glucose acceptor, but that the specificity requirements are otherwise quite severe (24). Fructose, galactose, mannose, ribose, and inorganic phosphate, for example, cannot act as acceptors in the reaction with glucose-1-phosphate, and alpha methyl glucoside, trehalose, cellobiose, and isomaltose, for example, cannot act as donors in place of maltose. These data indicate clearly that in the maltose phosphorylase reaction the phosphate (X) and glucose (Y) are absorbed on different portions of the enzyme surface which are quite specific for their particular components.

A number of reactions which proceed with retention of configuration are listed in Table 1. Retention of configuration can be explained, in some enzymatic reactions, e. g., alkaline phosphatase (12) (62) and invertase (45), by the fact that no bond to the

TABLE 1

ENZYMATIC SUBSTITUTION REACTIONS PROCEEDING WITH RETENTION OF CONFIGURATION

Enzyme	Substrate B—X	Substrate Y	Evidence for Configuration of Substrate B—X	Evidence for Configuration of Product B—Y
Sucrose phosphorylase	α Glucosyl—phosphate	Fructose	Optical rotation (15), (77)	Cleaved by maltase (67)
Muscle phosphorylase	α Glucosyl—phosphate	Glycogen	Optical rotation (15), (77)	Degradation to maltose (32b), (47a), (49a), (59a)
Alpha amylase	α Maltosyl—polysaccharide	Water	Degradation to maltose (28), (29), (34); optical rotation (27), (51) attacked by α-glucosidase (49)	Mutarotation downwards (46)
Alpha glucosidase	α Glucosyl—methyl	Water	Optical rotation (5), (36); analogy to benzyl compound (2)	Mutarotates downwards (1)
Beta glucosidase	β Glucosyl—methyl	Water	Optical rotation (5), (36); analogy to benzyl compound (2)	Mutarotates upwards (1)
Trans N-glycosidase	β Ribosyl—hypoxanthine	Adenine	Deamination of adenosine (40)	Synthesis; Metaperiodate degradation (17), (18)
Amylosucrase	α Glucosyl—fructose	Polysaccharide	Cleaved by maltase (67)	Enzyme specificity (34a), (34c); degraded to maltose (34b)
Transglucosidase of A. oryzae	α Glucosyl—glucose	Maltose	Optical rotation; enzyme specificity (58)	Degradation to maltose and isomaltose (26)
Dextransucrase	α Glucosyl—fructose	Dextran	Cleaved by maltase (67)	Optical rotation (22a), (57a), (32a), (16a)
Dextrandextrinase	α Glucosyl—polysaccharide	Dextran	Degraded to maltose (32b), (47a), (49a), (59a)	Optical rotation (22a), (57a), (32a), (16a)
Q. Enzyme	α Glucosyl—polysaccharide	Polysaccharide	Degraded to maltose derivatives (28), (29), (34); optical rotation (27), (51)	Degradation to α-1, 6-disaccharide (53), (55), (56)

asymmetric carbon atom is broken, but in the reactions shown in Table 1 there is either direct isotopic evidence or indirect theoretical evidence (vide infra) for cleavage at the bond indicated in the second column. Thus, in these reactions the bond to the asymmetric carbon in the *B* groups is broken, and yet the configuration of this carbon atom is the same in the product as in the initial substrate.

The retention of configuration can be explained by either the front-side or the double-displacement mechanisms. Against the front-side mechanism is the fact that the compounds usually undergoing this reaction are not the same as those involved in the enzymatic reactions shown here. All the reactions listed in Table 1 concern the anomeric carbon atom, and it has been shown in the Koenigs-Knorr reactions that replacement at this atom is accompanied by a back-side attack (58). Acetals give incipient carbonium ions fairly readily, however, and under the influence of the enzyme this mechanism might occur. As I shall discuss below, the front-side mechanism is not compatible with the data on sucrose phosphorylase unless some rather unusual assumptions are made to explain the specificity, but it is compatible with the muscle phosphorylase data. The double-displacement reaction mechanism is consistent with all the reactions listed in Table 1 and is in better accord with the non-enzymatic chemistry of these compounds. It is, moreover, in far better accord with the observations in other group-transfer and hydrolytic reactions which do not involve an asymmetric carbon atom. For these reasons the double displacement mechanism is to be preferred although the validity of the " front-side displacement " mechanism for at least some of the enzymes listed in Table 1 must be considered a possibility.

EXCHANGE CRITERIA OF REACTION MECHANISMS

The observation of Doudoroff, Barker, and Hassid (21) that sucrose phosphorylase catalyzed the exchange of inorganic phosphate with glucose-1-phosphate without addition of any fructose (equation 12) opened the way to much of our present knowledge of enzyme-

$$\text{Glucose--1--PO}_4^= + \text{HP}^{32}\text{O}_4^= \rightarrow \text{Glucose--1--P}^{32}\text{O}_4^= + \text{HPO}_4^= \qquad (12)$$

substrate intermediates. Subsequently, Cohn and Cori (14) demonstrated that no such exchange is catalyzed by muscle phosphorylase;
and now Fitting and Doudoroff (24) have established that no
exchange is apparent for maltose phosphorylase. Thus, the stereochemical evidence indicates that the sucrose and muscle phosphorylase reactions are fundamentally similar, whereas the exchange evidence would indicate a similarity between maltose phosphorylase
and muscle phosphorylase. It is imperative, therefore, to examine
precisely what is indicated by the positive or negative findings in an
exchange experiment.

For an exchange reaction of the type shown in equation (13) to

$$B–Z + Z^* \rightarrow B–Z^* + Z \tag{13}$$

occur by a single displacement mechanism, it is necessary that the
group Z be able to occupy both the site normally occupied by the
"acceptor," Y, and that occupied by the displaced part of the
"donor" molecule, X. For example, if the exchange catalyzed by
alkaline phosphatase (62) (equation 14) occurs by a single displace-

$$H_2O^{18} + HOPO_3^= \rightarrow HO^{18}PO_3^= + H_2O \tag{14}$$

ment mechanism, this merely indicates that the position normally
occupied by the OR of the phosphate ester can be occupied by the
OH of inorganic phosphate. In view of the latitude of structures
permissible as substrates for this enzyme, the substitution of OH
for OR is a perfectly reasonable extrapolation, and the observation
of an exchange cannot, therefore, be used to exclude a single displacement mechanism. The same arguments would hold for many
other exchanges, of which notable examples are those catalyzed by
chymotrypsin (19, 61) (equation 15) and papain (38) (equation
16).

$$
\begin{array}{c}
\overset{\displaystyle O}{\overset{\|}{}} \\
CH_3C–NH–CHR^1–COOH + H_2O^{18}
\end{array}
$$

$$
\overset{\displaystyle O}{\overset{\|}{}}
$$
$$\rightarrow CH_3C–NH–CHR^1–COO^{18}H + H_2O \tag{15}$$

$$\Phi CONHCH_2CONH_2 + N^{15}H_3 \rightarrow \Phi CONHCH_2CON^{15}H_2 + NH_3 \tag{16}$$

If the specificity requirements do not allow Z to occupy both positions, then no exchange can occur by a single displacement mechanism. In the maltose phosphorylase reaction, the inversion indicates that the reaction proceeds by a single displacement mechanism. The fact that the enzyme would accept only xylose and glucose as substrates from the many sugars structurally similar to glucose is consistent with the failure to observe any exchange of phosphate with glucose-1-phosphate, since that exchange would require phosphate to occupy the position specific for glucose and xylose (24). Conversely, the failure to observe exchange of glucose with maltose (24) can be used as evidence for the specificity of the phosphate site on the enzyme surface.

Since each exchange event occurring by a single displacement mechanism at an asymmetric carbon atom is accompanied by an inversion, any extensive exchange by this mechanism would lead to extensive racemization. The fact that the exchange catalyzed by sucrose phosphorylase occurs *with retention of configuration* is, therefore, evidence that the enzyme action does not involve a single displacement mechanism. It does not distinguish, however, between the double displacement and the front-side displacement mechanisms. To distinguish between these two we must in addition invoke specificity arguments. Sucrose phosphorylase catalyzes the exchange of inorganic phosphate with glucose-1-phosphate (21) and of fructose with sucrose (78). To explain these facts by a front-side displacement would require that phosphate could act at the site normally occupied by fructose and that fructose could act at the site normally occupied by phosphate. This is extremely difficult to reconcile with the failure to react (33) of compounds such as D-xylose, D-arabinose, D-glucose, L-xyloketose, etc., which are structurally much more similar to fructose than is phosphate. A more reasonable explanation is that the phosphate (or arsenate) can act at one site and the sugar can act at the other, but that the glucose-enzyme intermediate is relatively stable kinetically. If the rates of reaction of the X and Y groups with the inverted glucose-enzyme intermediate are slow compared to the rates of absorption and desorption of these components from their respectives sites on the enzyme surface, the observed exchanges are explained. Thus the assumption of a glucose-enzyme intermediate requires stereochemical and specificity considerations in addition to the exchange data.

It remains to determine whether the double-displacement mechanism can explain the failure to observe any exchange between inorganic phosphate and glucose-1-phosphate in the presence of muscle phosphorylase. One explanation is basically a kinetic one. Perhaps in contradistinction to the sucrose phosphorylase reaction, the relative rate of reaction of the X and Y groups with the glucose-enzyme intermediate are very rapid compared to the rates of desorption of these groups from the enzyme surface. This essentially says that the glucose-enzyme intermediate is a transient one, the enzyme providing the electrons to preserve the stereochemistry but not to form a stable intermediate. There is ample chemical analogy to this. Studies on the role of neighboring groups in chemical reactions by Winstein and coworkers (72, 73, 74) have shown that a group adjacent to the site at which a substitution is occurring can participate in such a way as to preserve the stereochemistry of the original compound. This neighboring group which approaches from the back-side, and is subsequently displaced itself, has thus a close resemblance to the postulated role of the enzyme. It is found that the inverted intermediate formed may vary from a full covalent bond, as in the formation of an epoxide (equation 17), to only a very transient and loose sharing of electrons, as in the participation by adjacent chlorine in the solvolysis of a tosylate (equation 18).

$$(17)$$

$$(18)$$

We might expect, therefore, that the analogous enzyme-substrate intermediate might vary greatly in stability, and the different results of exchange experiments between sucrose and muscle phosphorylase may reflect a difference in this stability rather than a fundamentally different role for the enzyme in the two cases. A second explanation for the non-exchange might be that a suitable geometric arrangement for reaction does not occur unless both the $B–X$ and Y groups are on the enzyme surface. There is evidence that groups not directly involved in the enzyme action can exert an influence on the enzyme activity, and it is not unreasonable to expect that the acceptor molecule which might occupy a position at the active site may be required to activate the reaction. The double-displacement mechanism is, therefore, consistent with the muscle phosphorylase data.

If evidence can be obtained that Z and Z^* both occupy the same site on the enzyme surface, then a positive exchange experiment is evidence for a stable B-enzyme intermediate. This criterion has, of course, the difficulty that it is not easy to determine whether one or more positions are involved, but some indications, if not rigorous conclusions, can frequently be obtained. For example, the chymotrypsin-catalyzed exchange of glycinamide with benzoyltyrosylglycinamide indicates either (a) that glycinamide can occupy the position normally occupied by H_2O, (b) that a second site, normally unused, but specific for amines is available for the exchange reaction, or (c) that a relatively stable enzyme-substrate intermediate is formed. Of these alternatives, the latter seems most reasonable, particularly in view of the fact that diisopropylfluorophosphate (37) inhibits the chymotrypsin (vide infra).

It might be worthwhile to mention that the exchange symbolized by equation (13) may be indicated without actually performing the radioactive experiment. Thus, the fact that alkaline phosphatase catalyzes the hydrolysis and transphosphorylation of many phosphate esters makes it almost a foregone conclusion that it would catalyze an exchange between labeled glycerol and glycerophosphate.

The failure to observe exchange between $B–X$ and X^* is evidence against a stable B-enzyme intermediate which does not require activation by the "acceptor," Y. It is not evidence against any kind of enzyme-substrate intermediate, since a transient intermediate or one which requires activation by the Y group would also give negative results. Thus, if one assumes that nicotinamide mononucleotide is not required for activation of the DPN-synthesizing enzyme of Kornberg and Pricer (42), the lack of exchange between ATP and labeled pyrophosphate can be taken to indicate the absence of a stable enzyme-adenylic acid intermediate.

OTHER CRITERIA OF DISPLACEMENT MECHANISMS

In their studies on the mechanism of hydrolysis of acetylcholine catalyzed by acetylcholinesterase, Nachmansohn and Wilson (56) have used inhibitor experiments and pH data in support of a mechanism involving an acyl-enzyme intermediate. From activity-pH curves it can be shown that a basic group is present at the active site and that the substrate competes with the hydrogen ion for this position on the enzyme surface. Diisopropylfluorophosphate (DFP) also reacts with a site on the enzyme surface to cause inactivation of the enzyme, and the substrate acetylcholine is capable of protecting the enzyme against this inactivation (56). In view of the known formation of a compound between the fluorophosphate and other esterases (3) and the slow reactivation of the enzyme by nucleophilic reagents (44), it is concluded that a basic site on the enzyme surface forms a compound with the DFP by displacement of fluoride and that the protection by the substrate indicates that this basic site is located at that portion of the enzyme surface which attracts and reacts with the acetylcholine. Moreover, the pH dependence of the inactivation of enzyme by tetraethyl pyrophosphate (56), the inhibition by prostigmine (70), and the enzymatic hydrolysis of acetylcholine (71) are all similar. These facts are most readily explained by the theory that the basic group makes a nucleophilic attack on either the carbon of the acetylcholine or the phosphorus of the inhibitor, thus forming an unstable acyl-enzyme intermediate which hydrolyzes readily, or a phosphoryl-enzyme intermediate which hydrolyzes slowly (56). The argument, although not rigorous, is a strong one. A basic group would be expected at the site occupied by water to increase its nucleophilic tendencies, but it would, if anything, decrease the electrophilic tendencies of the carboxyl group and hence decrease the catalytic action in a single displacement mechanism. The protection afforded by the substrate indicates that the nucleophilic group is located at the acetylcholine site, and hence its contribution to the catalytic action of the enzyme would seem to be either that it is the group which reacts to form the acyl-enzyme intermediate or that it is the " anionic group " responsible for attracting the positively charged quaternary nitrogen. The latter seems less probable but it would be interesting to determine whether or not simple quaternary bases such as Me_4N^+ protect against DFP inhibition.

Another approach to the nature of the enzyme-substrate inter-actions has been suggested (44, 62, 63) for application to hydrolytic reactions of compounds that contain doubly bonded oxygen such as phosphate esters and carboxylic esters. It had been shown that in the non-enzymatic hydrolysis of benzoate esters, an exchange between the water of the medium and the unhydrolyzed ester occurred (6). This was interpreted as indicating the presence of an addition inter-mediate which could decompose either to form the free acid or to reform the unhydrolyzed ester (equation 19). Applying this to the

$$
\underset{\substack{\| \\ RC-OR}}{O} + H_2O^{18} \rightleftharpoons \underset{\substack{| \\ O^{18}H}}{\overset{OH}{\underset{|}{R-C-OR}}} \rightarrow RCOO^{18}H + ROH
$$

$$
\underset{\substack{\| \\ R-C-OR}}{O^{18}} + H_2O \tag{19}
$$

enzymatic reactions, it can be seen that the presence of O^{18} in the unhydrolyzed ester would indicate a displacement on the carbonyl carbon by a water molecule *before* cleavage of the C–OR bond. This would exclude the double-displacement mechanism and would unequivocally establish the direct primary reaction of the two sub-strates. (A necessary control for this criterion is to exclude the over-all reversal of the reaction which is readily accomplished with radioactive tracers, e. g., by adding C^{14}-labeled RCOOH in the reaction shown in equation 19.) The absence of O^{18} in the unhydrolyzed ester is informative, but is not in itself unequivocal evidence for a single-displacement mechanism. Thus, in the case of acetylcholinesterase (63), the absence of O^{18} in the unhydrolyzed acetylcholine is compatible with the acyl-enzyme intermediate of Nachmansohn and Wilson but is also consistent with a single-displacement mechanism in which the affinity of the enzyme for the carboxyl oxygen prevents a randomization of the labeled and unlabeled oxygen atoms. This approach, therefore, like the stereochemical one, can lead to unequivocal results in some cases and must in others be assessed in conjunction with other data.

Cleavage Point of the Substitution Enzymes

The hydrolytic and transfer enzymes catalyze a number of reactions in which cleavage occurs at an oxygen bridge and in which the "acceptor" is an oxygen compound. These enzymes, which obey the general formulation of equation (20), may be hydrolytic enzymes

$$ROQ + HOR' \rightarrow ROR' + QOH \tag{20}$$

$(R' = H)$, transglycosidases $(R,Q,R' = \text{sugar residues})$, transphos-

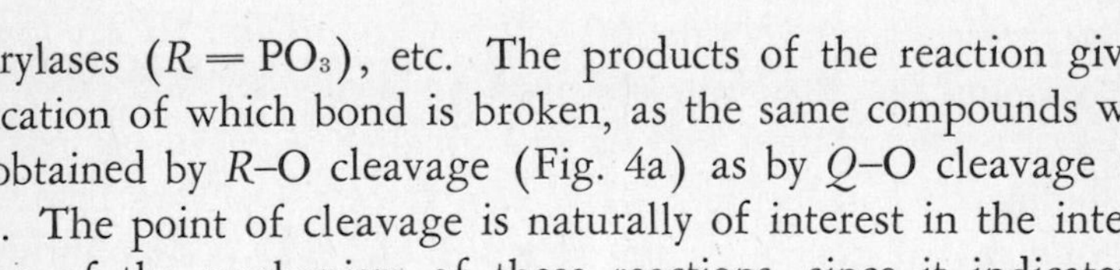

$$
\begin{array}{ll}
R-\{-O-Q & R-O-\{-Q \\
R'-O-\{-H \quad \text{(a)} & R'-\{-OH \quad \text{(b)}
\end{array}
$$

Fig. 4.

phorylases $(R = PO_3)$, etc. The products of the reaction give no indication of which bond is broken, as the same compounds would be obtained by R–O cleavage (Fig. 4a) as by Q–O cleavage (Fig. 4b). The point of cleavage is naturally of interest in the interpretation of the mechanism of these reactions, since it indicates the point at which the displacement occurs and the type of enzyme-substrate intermediates which might be formed.

There are several methods of determining the point of cleavage in these reactions. The most direct is to label the oxygen (as O^{18}) in either the acceptor ($R'OH$) molecule or in the donor (ROQ) and then determine the presence or absence of the label in one of the products. An inversion at an asymmetric carbon atom indicates that a bond to that atom has been broken and hence that cleavage occurs on that side of the oxygen bridge. The replacement of the

TABLE 2

CLEAVAGE POINT OF ENZYMES CATALYZING THE REACTION
$$ROQ + R'OH \rightarrow ROR' + HOQ$$

Enzyme	Bond Undergoing Cleavage in ROQ	ROH	Evidence
Muscle Phosphorylase	Glucosyl—OPO_3	Glycogen	O^{18} (12)
Sucrose Phosphorylase	Glucosyl—OPO_3	Fructose	O^{18} (12)
Maltose Phosphorylase	Glucosyl—OPO_3	Glucose	Inversion (24)
Alkaline Phosphatase	O_3P—O (Glucosyl)	H_2O	O^{18} (12)
Acid Phosphatase	O_3P—O (Glucosyl)	H_2O	O^{18} (12)
Adenosinetriphosphatase	O_3P—OPO_3PO_3Ad	H_2O	O^{18} (11)
Acetylcholinesterase	$CH_3\overset{\displaystyle O}{\overset{\|}{C}}$—$OCH_2CH_2NMe^+_3$	H_2O	Sulfur analog (56), O^{18} (63)
Invertase	Fructosyl—O (Glucosyl)	H_2O	O^{18} (45)
Beta amylase	Maltosyl—O (Glucose)$_n$	H_2O	Inversion (25)
Acetylphosphatase	O_3P—O–$\overset{\displaystyle O}{\overset{\|}{C}}$ CH_3	H_2O	O^{18} (7)

oxygen compound by an analog such as a sulfur compound was used in the case of acetylcholinesterase (56) to predict an acyl-oxygen cleavage, and this has been confirmed by oxygen-18 data (63). The results of applying these criteria to a number of enzymatic reactions are summarized in Table 2. The substrates, ROQ, are listed with the bond drawn in at the point at which cleavage occurs during the enzymatic reaction. The group at the left of the bond is, therefore, the B group of equation 1.

Cohn has demonstrated by O^{18} studies that a given compound does not necessarily always split in the same way in all of these enzymatic reactions, even when the acceptor group has rather similar nucleo-philic properties. Glucose-1-phosphate was found to give glucose-oxygen cleavage in the reactions of sucrose and muscle phosphory-lases but gives phosphorus-oxygen cleavage in the reactions of the phosphatases (12). Moreover, if the correlation of specificity with cleavage point advanced by Koshland and Stein (45) is correct, it is clear that the same two reactants (sucrose and water) can react to give the same products (glucose and fructose) in the presence of different enzymes, and can do so by fructose-oxygen cleavage in the presence of one enzyme (invertase) and by glucose-oxygen cleavage in the presence of the other (maltase). This emphasizes that an enzyme by the proper location of catalytic groups at the active site can influence the course of the reaction.

Since the number of reactions listed in Table 2 is small, it may be desirable to determine whether any generalizations may be derived which would allow us to predict the cleavage point in other enzymatic reactions, in particular those catalyzed by the group-transfer enzymes. This appears to be possible and two general rules can be stated: (1) if chemical reactions have demonstrated that cleavage of the R–O bond occurs much more easily than cleavage of the Q–O bond, then cleavage in the enzymatic reaction occurs between R and O; (2) if the enzyme exhibits severe specificity requirements for one group, e. g., R, and wide tolerance for structural changes in the other group, Q, then R–O cleavage will be observed.

The first rule can be illustrated by applying it to the hydrolysis of acetylcholinesterase. Here the choice is between cleavage of

$$\overset{\text{O}}{\underset{\|}{}}$$

an acyl-oxygen bond ($-\overset{\text{O}}{\underset{\|}{\text{C}}}-\text{O}-$) and a methylene-oxygen bond ($-CH_2-O$). Chemical studies have shown that the acyl-oxygen linkage is readily split in aqueous solution under mild conditions, whereas the methylene-oxygen bond is split only slowly even under vigorous forcing conditions. Acyl-oxygen splitting would, therefore, be expected and is observed (56) (63). This rule should only be applied when the indicated differences are very marked, i. e., when the choice is between relatively easily split groups such as acetal-oxygen and acyl-oxygen on the one hand and groups relatively difficult to split, such as aryl-oxygen and methylene-oxygen on the other. The phosphoryl-oxygen bond is much easier to rupture than the aryl-oxygen bond, and the fact that phenyl phosphate is a substrate for alkaline phosphatase, is, therefore, compatible with the observed P–O splitting by this enzyme (62).

These considerations predict, for example, that the esterases catalyze cleavage of the acyl-oxygen bond, and the transglycosidases catalyze cleavage between the oxygen of the bridge and the carbon of the group being transferred.

The second rule is applied in those cases such as invertase, in which the enzyme will allow only minor structural changes in one group, the beta fructofuranoside ring, but will tolerate wide variations, viz., benzyl to methyl to glycosyl, in the other. In these cases cleavage occurs on the side of high specificity (45). As in the case of the previous rule, this should be applied only when the differences are marked and no subjective evaluation of specificity data is required. Thus the predicted cleavage points of beta glucuronidase, maltase, and beta glucosidase can be deduced unequivocally. It would be fruitless, however, to predict the cleavage of acetylcholinesterase by assigning more weight to the tolerated changes in the acyl portion as compared to the tolerated changes in the choline portion.

Some of the enzymes whose cleavage point is indicated by specificity data can also be treated by the chemical considerations of the first rule, and in all these cases both lead to the same prediction. It is of particular interest that the enzyme requires the group at which the displacement occurs to obey more rigid structural requirements than the group being ejected, in those cases in which a marked difference is observed.

With these rules in mind, the cleavage points of many of the enzymes not directly tested can be assigned and this was the basis for the listing in Table 1 of those enzymes which have not been tested experimentally. It is of interest that the point of cleavage of trans-glucosidases indicated by the chemical considerations is further reinforced by the analogies to sucrose phosphorylase, which has transglycosidic properties (33) and which has been shown to cause glucose-oxygen cleavage (12). The analogous prediction of fructose-oxygen cleavage in transfructosidase is also supported by the observed fructose-oxygen cleavage in invertase (45), which appears to have some transfructosidase properties (68).

MECHANISM OF THE KINASE REACTIONS

The most important phosphate-transfer reactions are those catalyzed by the kinases. We can make some progress in the detailed mechanism of these reactions by applying the type of reasoning described above. In the "phosphokinase reactions," the terminal phosphate of ATP is transferred to a hydroxylic compound. This could occur in either of two ways, as illustrated in equation (21).

$$
\begin{array}{c}
\text{(a)} \quad \text{Ad-OPO}_3\,\text{PO}_3 \xrightarrow{} \text{PO}_3 \\
\text{H} \xrightarrow{} \text{OR} \\
\text{ATP + ROH} \qquad\qquad\qquad\qquad \text{ADP + ROPO}_3 \\
\text{(b)} \quad \text{Ad-OPO}_3\,\text{PO}_2 \xrightarrow{} \text{OPO}_3 \\
\text{HO} \xrightarrow{} \text{R}
\end{array}
$$

We do not yet know what type of displacement mechanism occurs, but we shall illustrate with a single displacement, since arguments presented here would be equally valid for any of the displacement mechanisms and the single is the more easily visualized. If the reaction of (21a) occurs by a single-displacement mechanism the activated complex can be visualized as in equation (22), where the

$$
\underset{\text{H}}{RO} : \ldots \ldots \overset{\overset{\displaystyle O}{\displaystyle \diagdown} \overset{\displaystyle O^-}{\displaystyle \diagup}}{\underset{\displaystyle \underset{O_-}{|}}{P}} \ldots \ldots : OPO_3PO_3Ad \qquad (22)
$$

dotted lines indicate the bonds being formed and broken. It is noted that only one P–O bond is being formed and one P–O bond is being broken in direct analogy to the displacements observed in the chemical reactions of phosphate. If the reaction proceeds by (21b), the bonds which would have to be formed and broken can be illustrated as in equation (23), although all these reactions would undoubtedly

$$
\begin{array}{c}
\text{O} \quad \text{O}^{-} \\
\diagdown \diagup \quad \text{O} \\
\text{AdOPO}_3 \text{ P} \ldots \text{OPO} \\
\cdot \qquad \text{O} \\
\cdot \qquad \cdot \\
\cdot \qquad \cdot \\
\text{HO} \ldots R
\end{array}
\qquad (23)
$$

not proceed simultaneously. This mechanism requires the cleavage of a P–O bond and the formation of a P–O bond as before, but it also requires the cleavage of a C–O bond and the formation of a C–O bond. Since the carbon atom in the hexokinase reaction is a methylene carbon whose bond to oxygen is very difficult to break, this alternative is not only more complicated but much more demanding energetically. While it might be said that alternative (21a) also involves the cleavage of OH bonds, it is known that these are broken extremely rapidly in aqueous solution, in strong contrast to the CH_2–O bonds. The analogy to the non-enzymatic substitution mechanism and the relative ease of the bond cleavages, therefore, favor alternative 21a.

This is further supported by three closely similar enzymatic processes. One is the kinase reaction with creatine (48), where the formation of a nitrogen-phosphorus bond is unequivocal evidence for a nucleophilic displacement on the terminal phosphorus atom of ATP. The second is the hydrolysis of ATP catalyzed by lobster muscle where, as in the hexokinase reaction, the terminal phosphate is transferred to a hydroxylic compound. In this case, O^{18} data again demonstrate (11) that attack occurs on the terminal phosphorus atom. The third is the phosphoglycerate kinase reaction, in which the transfer of oxygen from the carboxyl group of the glycerate to the phosphate has been demonstrated (13), and which must, therefore, involve a nucleophilic attack by the carboxylate oxygen on the phosphorus atom. In view of the chemical and enzymatic analogies, it is almost certain that the hexokinase reaction involves an attack on the terminal phosphorus atom of the ATP. If this occurs by a single displacement mechanism the transition state will be as shown in equation (22); if it occurs by a double-displacement mechanism the initial attack will be by a nucleophilic group on the enzyme surface. These arguments indicate that the fructokinase (16), galactokinase (66), phosphofructokinase (59) reactions etc., involve attack on the terminal phosphate of ATP.

By analogy the myokinase reaction also involves a displacement on the terminal phosphate of ATP. The oxygen on the phosphate of AMP would be the displacing agent in this reaction, as shown in equation (24).

$$AMP + ATP \longrightarrow AdOPO \overset{O}{\underset{O}{\cdots}} \overset{O}{\underset{\underset{O^-}{|}}{\overset{\backslash\!\backslash}{P}}} \overset{O^-}{\diagup} \cdots OPO_3 PO_3Ad \longrightarrow 2\,ADP \tag{24}$$

The analogy can also be extended to the reaction of ATP with nicotinamide mononucleotide (NMN) studied by Kornberg and coworkers (41). In this case the displacement would occur on the innermost phosphorus atom, and the displacing agent would be the oxygen atom on the phosphate of the nicotinamide mononucleotide (equation 25).

$$NMN + ATP \longrightarrow Nic\text{-}ribose\text{-}OPO \overset{O}{\underset{O}{\cdots}} \overset{O}{\underset{\underset{O^-}{|}}{\overset{\backslash\!\backslash}{P}}} \overset{O\,Ad}{\diagup} \cdots OPO_3 PO_3 \longrightarrow DPN + P_2O_7^{-4} \tag{25}$$

Mechanism of the Transphosphorylases

The transphosphorylases catalyze reactions in which the phosphate donor is a compound other than ATP, but the reasoning applied in the previous section will hold even more unequivocally in this latter category. The transphosphorylases, in which we include the phosphomutases, therefore probably catalyze a displacement on the phosphorus atom by either the ultimate acceptor Y, as shown in equation (26), or by the enzyme and then the Y acceptor (equations 27 and 28). Fortunately, in this group of enzymes we have addi-

$$Y^- + ROPO_3^= \rightarrow Y \dots \overset{\displaystyle O \quad O^-}{\underset{\displaystyle \underset{|}{O_-}}{\diagdown\!\!\diagup}} \dots OR \rightarrow YPO_3^= + {}^-OR \qquad (26)$$

$$En^- + ROPO_3^= \rightarrow En \dots \overset{\displaystyle O \quad O^-}{\underset{\displaystyle \underset{|}{O_-}}{\diagdown\!\!\diagup}} \dots OR \rightarrow EnPO_3^= + {}^-OR \qquad (27)$$

$$Y^- + EnPO_3 \rightarrow YPO_3 + En^- \qquad (28)$$

tional evidence that the proposed mechanism is correct. Alkaline phosphatase has been shown to have transphosphorylase activity (52) and also to cause P–O cleavage during the enzyme action (12, 62). In addition, the enzyme catalyzes the exchange of oxygen between water and inorganic phosphate (62). The hydrolysis and exchange reactions must, therefore, involve a displacement on phosphorus. Since the enzyme undoubtedly catalyzes transphosphorylation and synthesis by a similar mechanism, we can say that the mechanism applies in all cases and that Y can be H_2O or an alcohol and R can be hydrogen or an organic group. Whether the reaction is exchange, hydrolysis, synthesis, or transphosphorylation depends only on the particular combination of Y and OR.

Thus the phosphokinases, transphosphorylases, and alkaline and acid phosphatases, are basically similar, in that they all catalyze the transfer of a PO_3 group which would be the B group of equation (1). The different reactions observed on going from one enzyme to another or by varying the substrates to a particular enzyme represent only the range of specificities of the enzyme involved for the acceptor, Y, and the displaced group, X. The phosphorylases, on the other hand, act by a displacement on carbon, so that the B group is a glycoside and the displaced group is PO_4.

Methyl Transfer and Methylene Transfer Reactions

The methyl transfer, like most of the other group-transfer reactions, would also seem to involve displacement mechanisms. The well-known chemical properties of the sulfhydryl group as a nucleophilic group and as a readily displaced group have already been cited as being closely analogous to the acyl transferase activities of acetyl-coenzyme A (43). It is, therefore, of particular interest that Cantoni (10) has identified the active methionine as a sulfonium compound, since the non-enzymatic mechanism of reaction of these sulfur compounds has also been studied in some detail. In the absence of enzyme, primary sulfonium compounds readily undergo nucleophilic attack to form the sulfide (equation 29). (In ethyl and higher

$$HO^- + RCH_2S^+R_2 \rightarrow HO^- \ldots \overset{\overset{\displaystyle H \quad H}{\diagdown \diagup}}{\underset{\underset{\displaystyle R}{|}}{C^+}} \ldots SR_2 \rightarrow HOCH_2R + SR_2 \quad (29)$$

homologs, an elimination reaction frequently competes with the direct displacement reaction, but this will not be of concern in this discussion.) It is noted that the uncharged sulfide is ejected with its pair of unshared electrons and, as might be expected, the reaction rate is enhanced by the positive charge which attracts the incoming electron-sharing reagent. A similar and strictly analogous reaction also occurs between nucleophilic reagent and quaternary ammonium compounds, with the resulting liberation of a tertiary amine.

There is a direct analogy between these reactions and the enzymatic methyl transfers in which the S-adenosyl-methionine transfers its methyl group to nicotinamide or to guanidoacetic acid (9). One cannot say conclusively whether a single or double displacement mechanism is involved but a front-side displacement would seem very unlikely in view of the reluctance of methyl groups to form free carbonium ions. Using a single displacement for illustration, the methyl transfer to nicotinamide would appear as shown in equation (30). It is of interest that the other known methyl-transfer

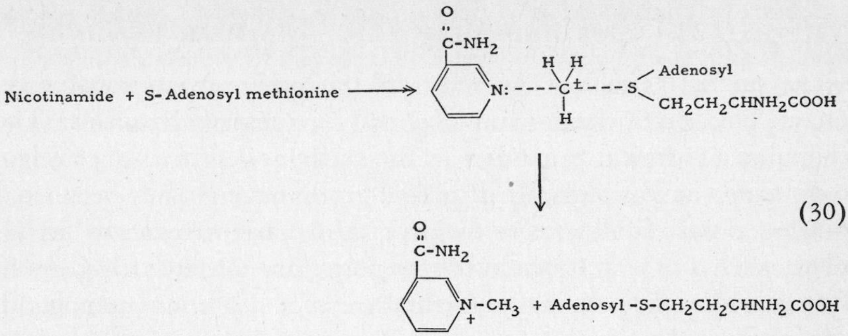

$$\text{Nicotinamide + S-Adenosyl methionine} \longrightarrow$$

(30)

reactions also appear to involve onium salts, as in the cases of the methyl donors, betaine and the methyl-substituted thetins (22).

A closely similar reaction, which might be termed a substituted methyl- or methylene-transfer reaction has been discovered in the case of thiaminase (31, 60, 80). In this case the quaternary ammonium ion is involved, and it has been shown that any of a rather large number of bases will react to displace the thiazole portion of the amine. This seems readily compatible with the known ease of displacement reactions with onium salts, and the mechanism for the reaction of thiamine with meta nitroaniline can be pictured (for the single displacement) as in equation (31).

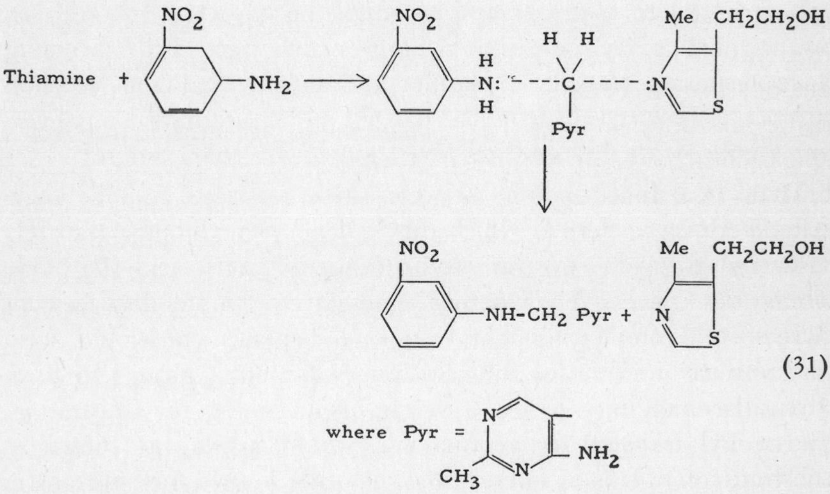

(31)

This explanation of the methyl-transfer reactions which stresses their essential similarity to the other group transfer reactions is in some contrast to that of Woolley (81), who emphasizes the rather unique position of the onium compounds and the oxidation-reduction character of the thiaminase reaction. While it is true that onium compounds have a higher energy content than some of their reaction products, the stability varies widely, e. g., from the acetyl pyridinium ions to the tetramethylammonium ion, and the decrease in free energy accompanying the methyl-transfer reactions varies within the range of the other group-transfer reactions which do not involve a positive charge. Moreover, although the sharing of electrons may vary somewhat during a reaction of this type, the formation of an onium ion from its free base, e. g., NH_4^+ from NH_3, is not normally described as an oxidation-reduction reaction. It would seem preferable, therefore, to consider these enzymatic reactions in the same way as their chemical analogs—as substitution reactions.

SUMMARY

The enzymatic reactions which catalyze the substitution of a group Y for a group X in the molecule BX have been considered as a single category because of their similarity to each other and to their chemical analogs. Examples of enzymes in this category are the hydrolases, the phosphorylases, and the group-transfer enzymes. By analogy to the chemical mechanisms it is postulated that the enzymatic substitutions proceed by displacement mechanisms in which a single covalent bond is formed as another single covalent bond is broken. By delineating these mechanisms in physical chemical terms, criteria for characterizing the nature of the enzyme-substrate intermediates can be evaluated. From these it can be seen that the similarities between different subgroups may be greater than between different enzymes in the same subgroup. Thus, the shift from a phosphatase to a transphosphorylase or from a glycosidase to a transglycosidase may involve merely a change in specificity, whereas two phosphorylases may react through entirely different kinds of enzyme-substrate intermediates. It is further suggested that, as in the case of their chemical analogs, a few simple mechanisms may suffice to explain the mode of action of those enzymes which catalyze the wide variety of substitution reactions.

REFERENCES

1. Armstrong, E. F. 1903. Study on enzyme action. I. The correlation of the stereoisomeric and glucosides with the corresponding glucoses. *J. Chem. Soc.*, 83, 1305.
2. Ballou, C. E., S. Roseman, and K. P. Link. 1951. Reductive cleavage of benzyl glycosides for relating anomeric configurations. *J. Am. Chem. Soc.*, 73, 1140.
3. Balls, A. K., and E. F. Jansen. 1952. Stoichiometric inhibition of chymotrypsin. *Advances in Enzymol.*, 13, 321-343.
4. Bartlett, P. D. The study of reaction mechanism. In *Organic Chemistry* (H. Gilman, ed.), 3, 1-121. John Wiley & Sons, New York.
5. Bates, C. J. 1942. "Polarimetry, saccharimetry and the sugars," Circular C-440 of the National Bureau of Standards, p. 411.
6. Bender, M. L. 1951. Oxygen exchange as evidence for the existence of an intermediate in ester hydrolyses. *J. Am. Chem. Soc.*, 73, 1626-1629.
7. Bentley, R. 1949. The mechanism of hydrolysis of acetyl dihydrogen phosphate. *J. Am. Chem. Soc.*, 71, 2765-2767.
8. Boyer, P. D. Pers. comm., cited in no. 13.
9. Cantoni, G. L. 1951. Activation of methionine for transmethylation. *J. Biol. Chem.*, 189, 745-754.
10. Cantoni, G. L. 1952. The nature of the active methyl donor formed enzymatically from L-methionine and adenosinetriphosphate. *J. Am. Chem. Soc.*, 74, 2942-2943.
11. Clarke, E., and D. E. Koshland, Jr. 1953. Mechanism of hydrolysis of adenosine triphosphate catalyzed by lobster muscle. *Nature*, 171, 1223-24.
12. Cohn, M. 1949. Mechanisms of cleavage of glucose-1-phosphate. *J. Biol. Chem.*, 180, 771-781.
13. Cohn, M. 1953. A study of oxidative phosphorylation with O^{18}-labeled inorganic phosphate. *J. Biol. Chem.*, 201, 735-750.
14. Cohn, M., and G. T. Cori. 1948. On the mechanism of action of muscle and potato phosphorylase. *J. Biol. Chem.*, 175, 89-93.
15. Cori, C. F., S. P. Colowick, and G. T. Cori. 1937. The isolation and synthesis of glucose-1-phosphoric acid. *J. Biol. Chem.*, 121, 470.
16. Cori, G. T., and M. W. Slein. 1947. Gluco- and fructokinase in mammalian tissues. *Federation Proc.*, 6, 245-246.
16a. Daker, W. D., and M. Stacey. 1939. The polysaccharide produced from sucrose by *Betabacterium vermiforme* (Ward-Meyer). *J. Chem. Soc.*, 585.
17. Davoll, J., B. Lythogoe, and A. R. Todd. 1946. The configuration at the glycosidic centre in natural and synthetic pyrimidine and purine nucleosides. *J. Chem. Soc.*, 833.
18. Davoll, J., B. Lythogoe, and A. R. Todd. 1948. A synthesis of adenosine. *J. Chem. Soc.*, 967.
19. Doherty, D. G., and F. Vaslow. 1952. Thermodynamic study of an enzyme-substrate complex of chymotrypsin. I. *J. Am. Chem. Soc.*, 74, 931-6.

20. Dostrovsky, I., and M. Hallman. 1953. Kinetic studies in the phosphinyl chloride and phosphorochloridate series. Pt. IV. *J. Chem. Soc.*, 516-519.
21. Doudoroff, M., H. A. Barker, and W. Z. Hassid. 1947. Studies with bacterial sucrose phosphorylase. I. The mechanism of action of sucrose phosphorylase as a glucose-transferring enzyme (transglucosidase). *J. Biol. Chem.*, 168, 725-732.
22. Dubnoff, J. W., and H. Borsook. 1948. Dimethylthetin and dimethyl-β-propiothetin in methionine synthesis. *J. Biol. Chem.*, 176, 789-796.
22a. Fairhead, E. C., M. Hunter, and H. Hibbert. 1938. The structure of dextran synthesized by *Leuconostoc dextranicus*. *Can. J. Research* B, 16, 151.
23. Fischer, H. O. L. 1944-1945. Chemical and biological relationships between hexoses and inositols. *Harvey Lectures*, 40, 156-178.
24. Fitting, C., and M. Doudoroff. 1952. Phosphorolysis of maltose by enzyme preparations from *Neisseria meningitidis*. *J. Biol. Chem.*, 199, 153-163.
25. Freeman, G. G., and R. H. Hopkins. 1936. LXXII. The mechanism of degradation of starch by amylases. III. Mutarotation of fission products. *Biochem J.*, 30, 451-456.
26. French, D. 1951. Structure of Pan's crystalline trisaccharide. *Science*, 113, 352.
27. Freudenberg, K., G. Blomquist, L. Ewald, and K. Soff. 1936. Hydrolyse und Acetolyse der Stärke und der Schardingerdextrine. *Ber. deut. chem. Ges.*, 69, 1258.
28. Freudenberg, K., and K. Soff. 1926. Uber den Abbau der Stärke mit Acetylbromid. *Ber. deut. chem. Ges.*, 69, 1252.
29. Freudenberg, K., and K. Friedrich. 1930. Methylierte Tri-, und Tetrasaccharide Cellulose und Stärke. *Naturwissenschaften*, 18, 1114.
30. Frush, H. L., and H. S. Isbell. 1941. Sugar acetates, acetylglycosyl halides and orthoacetates in relation to the Walden inversion. *J. Research Nat. Bur. Standards*, 27, 413-428.
31. Fujita, A., Y. Nose, S. Kozuka, T. Tashiro, K. Ueda, and S. Sakamoto. 1952. Studies on thiaminase. I. Activation of thiamine breakdown by organic bases. *J. Biol. Chem.*, 196, 289-295.
32. Hammett, L. F. 1940. *Physical Organic Chemistry*, p. 96. McGraw-Hill Book Co., New York.
32a. Hassid, W. Z., and H. A. Barker. 1940. The structure of dextran synthesized from sucrose by *Betacoccus arabinosaceus, Orla jensen*. *J. Biol. Chem.*, 136, 163.
32b. Hassid, W. Z., G. T. Cori, and R. M. McReady. 1943. Constitution of the polysaccharide synthesized by action of crystalline muscle phosphorylase. *J. Biol. Chem.*, 148, 89.
33. Hassid, W. Z., M. Doudoroff, and H. A. Barker. 1951. Phosphorylases-phosphorolysis and synthesis of saccharides. In *The Enzymes*. (J. B. Sumner K. Myrbäck, eds.), 1, pt. 2, 1014-1039. Academic Press, New York.
34. Haworth, W. N., and E. G. Percival. 1931. Evidence of continuous chains of α gluco-pyranose units in starch and glycogen. *J. Chem. Soc.*, 1342.
34a. Hehre, E. J., and D. M. Hamilton. 1946. Bacterial synthesis of an amylopectinlike polysaccharide from sucrose. *J. Biol. Chem.*, 166, 777.
34b. Hehre, E. J., D. M. Hamilton, and A. S. Carlson. 1949. Synthesis of a polysaccharide of the starch-glycogen class from sucrose by a cell-free bacterial enzyme system. *J. Biol. Chem.*, 177, 267.
34c. Hestrin, S. 1949. Action pattern of crystalline muscle phosphorylase. *J. Biol. Chem.*, 179, 943.

35. Hudson, C. S. 1909. The inversion of cane sug.ir by invertase III. *J. Am. Chem. Soc.*, 31, 655.

36. Hudson, C. S. 1909. The significance of certain numerical relations in the sugar group. *J. Am. Chem. Soc.*, 31, 66.

37. Jansen, E. F., M.-D. F. Nutting, and A. K. Balls. 1948. The reversible inhibition of acetylesterase by diisopropyl fluorophosphate and tetraethyl pyrophosphate. *J. Biol. Chem.*, 175, 975-987.

38. Johnston, R. B., M. J. Mycek, and J. S. Fruton. 1950. Catalysis of transamidation reactions by proteolytic enzymes. *J. Biol. Chem.*, 185, 629-641.

39. Johnston, R. B., M. J. Mycek, and J. S. Fruton. 1950. Catalysis of transpeptidation reactions by chymotrypsin. *J. Biol. Chem.*, 187, 205-211.

40. Kalckar, H. M. 1947. Studies of the enzymes of purine metabolism. *J. Biol. Chem.*, 167, 461.

41. Kornberg, A. 1950. Reversible enzymatic synthesis of diphosphopyridine nucleotide and inorganic pyrophosphate. *J. Biol. Chem.*, 182, 779-793.

42. Kornberg, A., and W. E. Pricer, Jr. 1951. Enzymatic cleavage of diphosphopyridine nucleotide with radioactive pyrophosphate. *J. Biol. Chem.*, 191, 535-541.

43. Koshland, D. E., Jr. 1952. Effect of catalysts on the hydrolysis of acetyl phosphate. Nucleophilic displacement mechanisms in enzymatic reactions. *J. Am. Chem. Soc.*, 74, 2286-2292.

44. Koshland, D. E., Jr. 1953. Stereochemistry and the mechanism of enzymatic reactions. *Biol. Rev.* (in press).

45. Koshland, D. E., Jr., and S. S. Stein. 1953. Enzyme specificity and enzyme mechanism. *Federation Proc.*, 12, 233-234.

46. Kuhn R. 1925. Der Wirkungsmechanismus der Amylasen: ein Beitrag zum Konfigurationsproblem der Stärke. *Ann. Chem. Justus Liebigs*, 443, 1.

47. Leloir, L. F. 1951. The metabolism of hexosephosphates. In *A Symposium on Phosphorus Metabolism* (W. D. McElroy and B. Glass, eds.), I, 77. Johns Hopkins Press, Baltimore.

47a. Ling, A. R., and D. R. Nanji. 1925. The constitution of polymerized amylose, amylopectin and their derivatives. *J. Chem. Soc.*, 127, 629.

48. Lohmann, K. 1934. Über die Enzymatische Aufspaltung der Kreatinphosphorsäure: zugleich ein Beitrag zum Mechanismus der Muskelkontraktion. *Biochem. Z.*, 271, 264-277.

49. Meyer, K. H. 1942. Recent developments in starch chemistry. *Advances in Colloid Sci.*, 1, 143.

49a. Meyer, K. H., W. Brentano, and P. Bernfeld. 1940. Recherches sur l'amidon (II). Sur la nonhomogeneite de l'amidon. *Helv. Chim. Acta*, 23, 845.

50. Meyer, K. H., P. Gurtler, and P. Bernfeld. 1947. Structure of amylopectin, *Nature*, 160, 900.

51. Meyer, K. H., H. Hopff, and H. Mark. 1929. Ein Beitrag zur Konstitution der Stärke. *Ber. deut. chem. Ges.*, 72, 1103.

52. Meyerhof, O., and H. Green. 1949. Synthetic action of phosphatase. I. Equilibria of biological esters. *J. Biol. Chem.*, 178, 655-667.

53. Montgomery, E. M., F. B. Weakley, and G. E. Hilbert. 1947. Isolation of 6-(α-D-glucopyranosyl)-D-glucose (isomaltose) from enzymic hydrolyzates of starch. *J. Am. Chem. Soc.*, 71, 1682.

54. Myrbäck, K., and K. Ahlborg. 1940. Über Grenzdextrine und Stärke. VIII Mitteilung: Die Konstitution eines Stärkegrenzdextrins. Nachweis α-glykosidischer 1, 6-Bindungen in Dextrin und Stärke. *Biochem. Z.*, 307, 69.

55. Myrbäck, K., and K. Ahlborg. 1940. Über Grenzdextrine und Stärke. XXII Mitteilung: Spezifität der Amylasen und Produkte ihrer Wirkung. *Biochem. Z.*, 311, 213.

56. Nachmansohn, D., and I. B. Wilson. 1951. The enzymic hydrolysis and synthesis of acetylcholine. In *Advances in Enzymol.*, 12, 259-339.

57. Olivard, J., D. E. Metzler, and E. E. Snell. 1952. Catalytic racemization of amino acids by pyridoxal and metal salts. *J. Biol. Chem.*, 199, 669-674.

57a. Peat, S., E. Schlucterer, and M. Stacey. 1939. Constitution of the dextran produced from sucrose by *Leuconostoc dextranium* (*Betacoccus arabinosaceous haemolyticus*). *J. Chem. Soc.*, 581

58. Pigman, W. W., and R. M. Goepp, Jr. 1948. *Chemistry of the Carbohydrates*, p. 444. Academic Press, New York.

59. Racker, E. 1947. Spectrophotometric measurement of hexokinase and phosphohexokinase activity. *J. Biol. Chem.*, 167, 843-854.

59a. Samec, M. 1935. Über die Wirkung von β-Amylase auf einige Stärkesubstanzen. *Z. physiol. Chem.*, 236, 103.

60. Sealock, R. R., and N. C. Davis. 1949. The activating effect of m-nitroaniline on thiamine destruction by the Chastek paralysis enzyme. *J. Biol. Chem.*, 177, 987-988.

61. Sprinson, D. B., and D. Rittenberg. 1951. Nature of the activation process in enzymatic reactions. *Nature*, 167, 484.

62. Stein, S. S., and D. E. Ksohland, Jr. 1952. Mechanism of action of alkaline phosphatase. *Arch. Biochem.*, 39, 229-230.

63. Stein, S. S., and D. E. Koshland, Jr. 1953. Mechanism of hydrolysis of acetylcholine catalyzed by acetylcholinesterase and by hydroxide ion. *Arch. Biochem. and Biophys.*, 45, 467.

64. Stetten, D., Jr., and B. V. Klein. 1946. Studies in carbohydrate metabolism. VIII. The origin of the stable hydrogen in glycogen formed from various precursors. *J. Biol. Chem.*, 165, 157-162.

65. Topper, Y. J., and D. Stetten, Jr. 1951. The biological transformation of galactose into glucose. *J. Biol. Chem.*, 193, 149-155.

66. Trucco, R. E., R. Caputto, L. F. Leloir, and N. Mittelman. 1948. Galactokinase. *Arch. Biochem.*, 18, 137-146.

67. Weidenhagen, R. 1928. Zur Frage der Enzymatischen Rohrsuckerspaltung. *Naturwissenschaften*, 16, 654.

68. White, L. M., and G. E. Secor. 1952. The oligosaccharides formed during the sucrose-invertase reaction. *Arch. Biochem.*, 36, 490-491.

69. Wilson, I. B. 1951. Acetylcholinesterase. XI. Reversibility of tetraethyl pyrophosphate inhibition. *J. Biol. Chem.*, 190, 111-117.

70. Wilson, I. B., and F. Bergmann. 1950. Studies on cholinesterase. VII. The active surface of acetylcholine esterase derived from effects of pH on inhibitors. *J. Biol. Chem.*, 185, 479-489.

71. Wilson, I. B., and F. Bergmann. 1950. Acetylcholinesterase. VIII. Dissociation constants of the active groups. *J. Biol. Chem.*, 186, 683-692.

72. Winstein, S., and E. Grunwald. 1948. The role of neighboring groups in replacement reactions. XIII. General theory of neighboring groups and reactivity. *J. Am. Chem. Soc.*, 70, 828-837.

73. Winstein, S., E. Grunwald, R. E. Buckles, and C. Hanson. 1948. The role of neighboring groups in replacement reactions. XI. Some reactivities involving neighboring groups. *J. Am. Chem. Soc.*, 70, 816-821.

74. Winstein, S., E. Grunwald, and L. L. Ingraham. 1948. The role of neighboring

groups in replacement reactions. XII. Rates of acetolysis of 2-substituted cyclohexyl benzene sulfonates. *J. Am. Chem. Soc.*, 70, 821-8.

75. Winstein, S., and R. B. Henderson. 1950. Ethylene and trimethylene oxides. In *Heterocyclic Compounds* (R. C. Elderfield, ed.), I: 1-60. John Wiley & Sons, New York.

76. Wolfrom, M. L., A. Thompson, and T. T. Calkowski. 1951. 4-α-Isomaltopyranosyl-D-glucose. *J. Am. Chem. Soc.*, 73, 4093.

77. Wolfrom, M. L., C. S. Smith, D. E. Pletcher, and A. E. Brown. 1942. The beta form of the Cori ester (D-glucopyranose-1-phosphate). *J. Am. Chem. Soc.*, 64, 23.

78. Wolochow, H., E. W. Putman, M. Doudoroff, W. Z. Hassid, and H. A. Barker. 1949. Preparation of sucrose labeled with C^{14} in the glucose or fructose component. *J. Biol. Chem.*, 180, 1237-1242.

79. Wood, W. A., and I. C. Gunsalus. 1951. D-Alanine formation: a racemase in *Streptococcus faecalis*. *J. Biol. Chem.*, 190, 403-416.

80. Woolley, D. W. 1951. Enzymatic synthesis of folic acid by the action of carp thiaminase. *J. Am. Chem. Soc.*, 73, 1898.

81. Woolley, D. W. 1953. Biosynthesis and energy transport by enzymic reduction of onium salts. *Nature*, 171, 323-328.

THE MECHANISM OF ENZYME HYDROLYSIS STUDIED WITH ACETYLCHOLINESTERASE *

IRWIN B. WILSON

*Department of Neurology, College of Physicians and Surgeons,
Columbia University, New York.*

THE CATALYTIC proficiency of enzymes is certainly among the most remarkable of chemical phenomena. Enzymes have attracted the attention of many biochemists with regard to the elucidation of intermediary metabolism and the explanation of physiological function. Few, however, have considered the catalysis itself, so that even today it remains a major problem of theoretical biochemistry.

In this paper I shall present studies on a particular enzyme—acetylcholinesterase—but it will be apparent that while part of the theory will apply to this esterase alone, much will be of greater generality. We are not here to review the large body of information which has accumulated concerning the distribution, purification, and distinction from other enzymes, which questions have been thoroughly reviewed (1, 2); but rather to present a theory of enzyme catalysis and to consider only those experimental facts which are pertinent to this purpose.

The first major advance in understanding enzymes in general was made by Henri and by Michaelis and Menten in introducing the concept of a dissociable enzyme substrate complex, leading to the formulation:

$$E + S \underset{k_2}{\overset{k_1}{\rightleftharpoons}} ES \overset{k_3}{\longrightarrow} E + \text{Products}$$

* This discussion is based on investigations supported (in part) by the Medical Research and Development Board, Office of the Surgeon General, Department of the Army, Contract No. DA-49-007-MD-37, and in part by the Division of Research Grants and Fellowships of the National Institutes of Health, Grant No. RG-1463, United States Public Health Service.

The reaction velocity is then given by:

$$v = \frac{V_{max} \cdot S}{\dfrac{k_2 + k_3}{k_1} + S}$$

We shall first describe the enzyme-substrate complex in terms of the forces of interaction which contribute to its stability, and then the hydrolytic process whereby this complex is transformed to the final products, with the concurrent regeneration of the enzyme. We shall also discuss the question of specificity and the role of the protein molecule in the process.

The stoichiometric equation for the hydrolysis of the acetylcholine ion,

$$(CH_3)_3N^+C_2H_4OCOCH_3 + 2H_2O \rightleftharpoons (CH_3)_3N^+C_2H_4OH$$
$$+ CH_3COO^- + H_3O^+$$

does not, of course, describe the mechanism of the reaction. These details depend upon the conditions under which the reaction occurs, and part of our problem is to supply this information for the enzyme-catalyzed reaction.

A. Intermolecular Forces Between Enzyme and Substrate; the Enzyme-substrate Complex

The positive electrical charge of the normal substrate suggests that the enzyme might contain a suitably located negatively charged region which augments the enzymic activity by contributing to the attraction, orientation, and fixation of the substrate upon the enzyme surface.

This possibility was investigated with the aid of competitive inhibitors (3). Fig. 1 compares the inhibition of prostigmine and eserine as a function of pH. These compounds are similarly constituted and both are powerful inhibitors, but prostigmine is a quaternary ammonium salt, whereas eserine is a tertiary amine ($pK_a = 8.1$). The structure of prostigmine is consequently independent of pH, whereas eserine exists predominantly as the cationic conjugate acid below pH 8, and as the uncharged base at higher pH. Since prostigmine inhibition does not change in this pH range, the difference observed with eserine can be ascribed to a marked prefer- ence in the binding of the cationic form, by a factor of 16.

Dimethylaminoethanol ammonium ion is a 30-fold better competi- tive inhibitor of the esterase than the structurally similar but uncharged isoamyl alcohol (4). Similarly nicotinamide, which exists

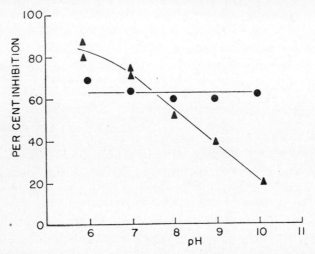

FIG. 1. Inhibition of acetylcholinesterase by prostigmine (●) and eserine (▲) as a function of pH.

as the uncharged base at neutral pH, is an 8-fold poorer inhibitor than the positively charged N-methyl nicotinamide (5).

Further evidence that coulombic forces are involved in the binding is found in the marked salt effect that decreases the inhibition caused by positively charged inhibitors (6).

The effect of charge can be analyzed, approximately, in terms of electrostatic theory. The electrical contribution to the free energy of binding ΔF_e is given by:

$$\Delta F_e = - RT\ln \frac{K_{\text{(neutral)}}}{K_{\text{(charged)}}} = \sum_i \frac{Z_i \epsilon^2}{D_i r_i}$$

where the K's are the dissociation constants of the inhibitor-enzyme complexes, Z_i is the ith charge in the protein at a distance r_i from the positive substrate charge in the complex, and D_i is the corresponding effective dielectric constant and is a function of r_i and can be estimated from work of Schwartzenbach.

These data are summarized in Table 1. The value of r calculated from equation (1), assuming a single negative charge as responsible for the coulombic effects, is indicated in column 3. Column 4 indicates calculated values of r when a term for the ionic strength of the

TABLE 1

THE EFFECT OF POSITIVE ELECTRICAL CHARGE ON THE POTENCY OF INHIBITORS

	K^0/K^+	$-\Delta F_e \left(\dfrac{Kcal}{mol}\right)$	r	r correct for salt
N-methyl nicotinamide-nicotinamide	8	1.2	7.7	5.8
eserine cation-eserine	16	1.7	6.7	5.4
dimethylethanolammonium ion isoamyl alcohol	30	2.0	6.3	5.0

medium is introduced using an approximate Debye Huckel form intended for small spherical molecules and low ionic strength and assuming that the distance of closest approach for the salt ions is the same as r.

The calculated values agree well with what might be expected for a close fit of enzyme and inhibitor as judged from atomic radii. A methylated quaternary structure has a radius of about 3.5 Å, and the smallest distance of the negative charge from the protein surface is one unbonded atomic radius, or about 1.5 Å. The closest approach would thus be about 5.0 Å. These data show a closer approach, the more nearly the structure resembles the ammonium portion of acetylcholine. There are other experiments not yet reported, however, which indicated that the anionic site is probably effectuated by a more diffuse distribution of charge at larger distances, the summation of all the charge effects being equivalent in its binding to a single charge 1.5 Å within the protein.

The effect of electrical charge is also demonstrable with substrates.

Dimethyl aminoethyl acetate ($pK = 8.3$) at pH below 8.3 exists predominantly in the cationic form and in neutral form at higher pH. The hydrolytic rate relative to acetylcholine (in arbitrary units) as a function of pH (Fig. 2) reflects the change in electrical charge of the substrate, decreasing rapidly between pH 8 and 9, yet remaining constant at other pH (3).

Similarly, isoamyl alcohol has a Michaelis-Menten constant 10-fold higher than that of the dimethylaminoethyl acetate cation (4).

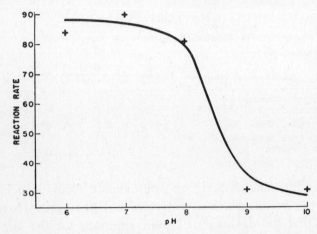

FIG. 2. Rate of hydrolysis of dimethylaminoethyl acetate relative to acetylcholine (arbitrary units) as a function of pH.

Similar conclusions have been derived by comparing 3, 3-dimethyl butyl acetate with acetylcholine (7).

Experiments with competitive inhibitors are preferable for this type of work because of uncertainty in the interpretation of the Michaelis-Menten constants of substrates.

The importance of alkyl groups on the cationic portion of the molecule is illustrated by methylated competitive inhibitors of the ammonia and ethanolamine series (Table 2) (4). All of these inhibitors are cationic at pH 7. Except for the methyl group which corresponds to the fourth alkyl group in the ethanolamine series, each methyl group has binding properties amounting to about 1.2 kcal./mols and on the average increasing the potency of an inhibitor

6.7-fold. If we make the plausible assumption that the change in hydration characteristics attending binding does not differ very greatly for all members of the series nor do the entropies of binding, we may conclude that the additional binding associated with each methyl group arises from van der Waals attraction (London dispersion forces) between the methyl group and a hydrocarbon moiety of the protein. The latent energy of evaporation of methane is about 2.0 kilocalories per mol, so that we have in this force energies of suitable

TABLE 2

INHIBITORY POTENCY OF METHYLATED AMMONIUM IONS

No. of methyl groups	$-\overset{\mid}{\underset{\mid}{N}}-$	$-\overset{\mid}{\underset{\mid}{N}}-C_2H_4OH$
4 — 3	.018	.005
3 — 2	.015	.005
2 — 1	.12	.07
1 — 0	.70	.28

The concentration necessary to produce 50 per cent inhibition when the acetylcholine concentration is 4×10^{-4} M. In the ethanol-ammonium series the member containing n methyl groups ($n + 1$ alkyl) corresponds to the member of the simple ammonium series containing $n + 1$ methyl groups.

magnitude for explaining the observed binding property of a methyl group. In accordance with expectation, larger alkyl or aryl groups improve the binding properties of ammonium ions.

It is of interest to consider why the trialkyl and tetraalkyl members are bound equally well. The explanation lies in the tetrahedral structure of the ammonium group that renders the protein unable to come into the requisite close contact simultaneously with all four alkyl groups, lest the protein fold itself about the ion so as to engulf it. Apparently such a reorientation of the protein either does not occur, or if it does the attending increase in free energy which such a process would imply, just offsets the decrease in energy due to extra binding, so that there is no apparent difference in the binding of these quaternary and tertiary inhibitors.

Besides an anionic site there must also be an enzyme region which interacts with the ester group—an esteratic site. The carbonyl group has a marked polar character; the positive carbon and negative oxygen contribute about 50 per cent of the bond strength. Since this electrophilic carbon is a site of attack for basic reagents, it is of interest to compare the inhibitory properties of a series of compounds in which there is a large difference in the electrophilic character of a carbonyl carbon. The importance of an electrophilic carbon is well illustrated by a series of nicotinic acid derivatives (Fig. 3). The order of increasing electrophilic character

$$\underset{\parallel}{\overset{O}{-C}}-O^- < \underset{\parallel}{\overset{O}{-C}}-NH_2 < \underset{\parallel}{\overset{O}{-C}}-N(C_2H_5)_2 = \underset{\parallel}{\overset{O}{-C}}-CH_3 < \underset{\parallel}{\overset{O}{-C}}-O-C_2H_5$$

parallels the observed order of inhibition and suggests that a covalent

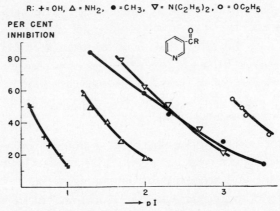

FIG. 3. Effect of substitution of the carboxyl group of nicotinic acid upon the inhibitory strength.

bond is formed between the carbon and some basic group in the enzyme (5).

Similar effects are observed with substrates, e. g., the Michaelis-Menten constant decreases rapidly in the order ethyl acetate, ethyl chloroacetate, acetic anhydride, although the maximum velocity remains about the same. Hydrogen-bonding does not seem to be of importance in the enzyme-substrate complex, since choline and tri-methylamino propane inhibit equally (4).

Valuable information has been obtained from the pH dependence of the enzyme-catalyzed hydrolysis (8). The structure of acetylcholine does not vary with pH, so that changes in activity must be attributed to changes in protein structure. The activity is at a maximum between pH 8 and pH 9 and declines in more acidic or alkaline media. These changes may be interpreted in terms of the dissociation of acidic and basic groups and represented schematically as follows:

$$EH_2^+ \underset{}{\overset{H^+}{\rightleftharpoons}} EH \underset{}{\overset{OH^-}{\rightleftharpoons}} E^- + H_2O$$
$$\text{inactive} \qquad \text{active} \qquad \text{inactive}$$

where EH the active enzyme is arbitrarily assigned a relative charge of zero. The forms EH_2^+ and E^- either cannot form complexes at all, or such complexes are inactive, but while the form of the deductions is the same, whichever may be the case, the calculated constants will be different. It is less cumbersome to anticipate the presentation and simply state that while the forms represented by EH_2^+ can form complexes only with much higher dissociation constants than EH and may therefore be neglected, the complexes of E^- are of equal stability but are inactive. These concepts suggest the following equilibria and dissociation constants:

$$EH_2^+ \rightleftharpoons EH + H^+ \quad K_{EH_2^+}$$
$$EH \rightleftharpoons E^- + H^+ \quad K_{EH}$$
$$EHS \rightleftharpoons ES^- + H^+ \quad K_{EHS}$$
$$EHS + S \rightleftharpoons EHS_2 \quad K_2$$

and the rate equation

$$EH + S \underset{k_2}{\overset{k_1}{\rightleftharpoons}} EHS \overset{k_3}{\longrightarrow} EH + \text{Products}$$

where S is the substrate and EHS_2 is an inactive super-complex which accounts for substrate inhibition observed at concentrations greater than 4×10^{-3} M.

Analysis of these relations leads to the equation for the velocity, v:

$$\frac{v^0}{v} = 1 + \frac{K_1}{K_{EH_2}^+(K_1 + (S) + \frac{(S)^2}{K_2})}(H^+) + \frac{K_1 K_{EH} + (S) K_{EHS}}{(K_1 + (S) + \frac{(S)^2}{K_2})(H^+)}\frac{1}{}$$

where v^0 is the reaction velocity at optimum pH and K_1 is the apparent dissociation constant $\frac{k_2 + k_3}{k_1}$.

The prediction that v^0/v will vary linearly with H^+ on the acid side of the pH optimum and linearly with OH^- on the basic side has been borne out experimentally (Fig. 4) (8).

These experimental observations are thus in agreement with the concept that certain basic and acidic groups are essential for enzyme activity and are consonant with the previous conclusion that the interaction of a basic group in the enzyme with the carbonyl carbon atom of substrates and inhibitors contributes to the binding of these compounds. The decline of enzyme activity in acid media can be attributed in part to poorer binding caused by the conversion of the basic group of the esteratic site to the conjugate acid, and in part by a similar conversion of the negatively charged groups of the anionic site. The binding of inhibitors containing a carbonyl group as well as a methylated ammonium structure declines much more rapidly than those containing the ammonium structure alone (9).

The decline in alkaline media is not, however, caused by poorer binding. This is indicated by the fact that non-competitive inhibition by prostigmine, while declining in acid media at precisely the same rate as acetylcholine hydrolysis, remains constant in alkaline media even to pH 11 where acetylcholine hydrolysis has fallen to 30 per cent (10). That the binding is just as good in alkaline media indicates that the acid group is not involved in binding and suggests that the decline in enzyme activity is due to the requirement of the acid group in the hydrolytic process.

The enzyme-substrate complex (Fig. 5) is stabilized by coulombic attraction by the anionic site, by van der Waals-London dispersion forces and by covalent-bond formation between the carbonyl carbon and the basic group of the esteratic site. The esteratic site is here

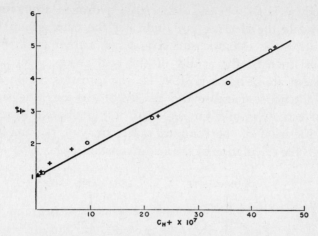

FIG. 4 A. v^0/v as a function of hydrogen ions.

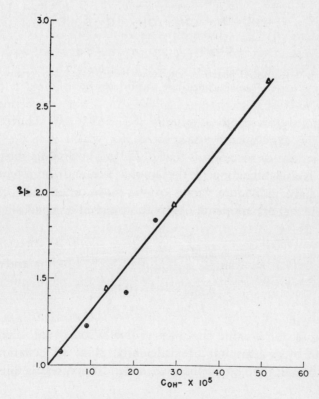

FIG. 4 B. v^0/v as a function of hydroxyl ions.

symbolized by H–G where a dissociable hydrogen atom represents the acid while the electron pair indicates the basic group. In this representation the esteratic site acquires a formal positive charge which must increase the acidity of the acid group. Moreover, the cationic substrate brings a positive charge into this region and this too would tend to increase the acidity of the esteratic site. The decline of activity in alkaline region is best attributed, therefore, to acidic dissociation of the complex rather than of the free enzyme. This affects the calculation of the acidic constant (since $S \gg K_i$). We

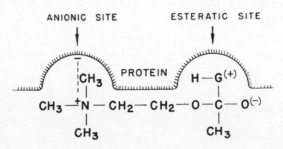

FIG. 5. Hypothetical picture of interaction between the active groups of acetylcholinesterase and its substrate.

had previously presented a value of $K_{EH} = 5 \times 10^{-10}$, but this was prior to the experiments just referred to, which indicate that the more important dissociation is that of EHS. The dissociation constant for EH_2^+ is a combination of the anionic site and the esteratic site, but both have individual values of the same order. The constants calculated from experimental observations based on equation (2) are

$$K_1 = 2.6 \times 10^{-4}$$

$$K_{EH_2} \genfrac{}{}{0pt}{}{\text{anionic site}}{\text{esteratic site}} \sim 5 \times 10^{-7}$$

$$K_{EHS} = 4 \times 10^{-11}$$

$$K_2 = 3 \times 10^{-2}$$

As discussed, the value of K_{EH} is probably somewhat smaller than K_{EHS}. Since the constants are calculated from an equation based upon a scheme, the values obtained depend upon the details of the scheme and their validity upon the closeness with which it represents the enzyme reactions. However, the scheme appears well justified, modifications will not alter the order of magnitude of the constants, and they may be safely used as clues to the chemical nature of the active sites (8).

B. THE HYDROLYTIC PROCESS

The discussions so far have described the nature of the enzyme-substrate complex. We now turn to the mechanism of the hydrolytic process and fix our attention upon the esteratic site. It will be convenient first to present the mechanism of hydrolysis which has been proposed (11) and then to show how this theory conforms to the observations

$$
G-H + R-\overset{O}{\overset{\|}{C}}-OR' \rightleftharpoons
\begin{array}{c} H-G^{(+)} \\ | \\ R-\overset{}{\underset{}{O}}-C-O^{(-)} \\ | \\ R \end{array}
\rightleftharpoons
\begin{array}{c} G^{(+)} \\ \| \\ C-O^{(-)} \\ | \\ R \end{array} + R'OH
$$

$$\text{(A)} \qquad\qquad \text{(B)}$$

$$
\begin{array}{c} H \\ | \\ H-O: \end{array} +
\begin{array}{c} G^{(+)} \\ \| \\ C-O^{(-)} \end{array}
\rightleftharpoons
\begin{array}{c} H-G^{(+)} \\ | \\ H-O-C-O^{(-)} \\ | \\ R \end{array}
\rightleftharpoons H-G + R-\overset{O}{\overset{\|}{C}}-OH
$$

$$\text{(C)}$$

The structure symbolized by G is assumed to have electron-transmitting properties, as shown for example by a conjugate double-bond system. The mechanism is a two-step process involving the simultaneous acylation of the enzyme and the internal elimination of a small molecule followed by the deacylation of the enzyme.

(A) is the ester-enzyme Michaelis-Menten complex, (B) is a resonance form of the acylated enzyme, and (C) is an acid-enzyme complex similar to the ester-enzyme complex.

The mechanism follows readily from the structure of the enzyme-substrate complex and assigns a positive role to the enzyme in launching a combined acid-base attack. The critical complex is a ring involving a kind of hydrogen bond which helps to stabilize the complex so that a low energy of activation is possible and explains the function of the acid group.

The acyl enzyme reacts with nucleophilic reagents such as water, hydroxylamine, alcohol, and choline. The rate-controlling step is the formation of the acyl enzyme. We may start with acids or esters, but only the undissociated acid molecules have the electrophilic carbon atom necessary for the enzyme-substrate complex. Consequently any reaction which the enzyme will catalyze involving carboxylic acids as substrates should occur much more rapidly with the corresponding esters. This was found to be the case in the comparison of the enzyme-catalyzed formation of hydroxamic acids and choline esters from simple esters and the corresponding acids where reaction with the esters is about 100 times faster (11).

This mechanism predicts that the enzyme should catalyze oxygen exchange between acids and water. This prediction has been confirmed directly (12) and in an indirect manner using thioacetic acid (13). In the latter case H_2S is evolved and acetic acid formed. This reaction can be inhibited completely by prostigmine. It is of especial interest that the small cationic inhibitor trimethyl ammonium ion, although it inhibits ethylacetate hydrolysis completely, can inhibit the H_2S liberation (even in enormous concentration) only by 30 per cent. Evidently the bonding of this small molecule at the anionic site does not seriously interfere with reaction by the relatively small thiolacetate acid molecule at the neighboring esteratic site. This illustrates the spatial and functional independence of the anionic and esteratic sites. On the basis of this mechanism the irreversible inhibition caused by certain phosphate esters, such as dialkyl fluorophosphonates, tetraalkyl pyrophosphates, and dialkylnitrophenyl phosphates has been explained (3, 14). While phosphate esters in general tend to react (hydrolyze, for example) by a mechanism which involves the dissolution of a carbon-oxygen bond and thus preserves the phosphate moiety, these inhibitors tend to react in such a manner that a phosphorus bond is broken and a phosphonium moiety is transferred to the attacking reagent, i. e., the reactions of these compounds tend to involve a nucleophilic attack at the electrophilic phosphorus atom. We would expect, therefore, that the enzyme would attack these substances in the same way as substrates and that a phosphorylated intermediate would be formed, but that the reaction of this intermediate with water would be very slow in contrast to the rapid reaction of the analogous acylated enzyme. The phosphorylation is itself an enzyme process. It is the slowness of the water reaction which makes these compounds inhibitors rather than substrates. This would explain the apparently irreversible inhibition. It is highly significant that the pH dependence of tetraethylpyrophosphate inhibition is similar to the pH dependence of acetylcholinesterase activity. The inhibitor is most potent in just that pH range where the enzyme is most active. Moreover, if the compound contains an unesterified acid group, so that in aqueous solution the molecule is negatively charged and the electrophilic property of the phosphorus atom is largely lost, the compound does not inhibit. On the basis of this theory we should expect that the enzyme would be regenerated by prolonged standing in solution, due to slow reaction with water, and this was found to be the case (14). Nucleophilic reagents, according to the theory, should be good reactivators, and in fact compounds containing amino, pyridyl, guanidine, amidino, hydroxyl, or mercaptyl groups were found to be effective reactivators (15). Choline and hydroxylamine are especially good. The reactivation itself is an enzymic process similar to the water reaction and showing saturation when the reactivator contains a binding group as well as a nucleophilic center (e. g., choline). As with the normal enzymic hydrolytic activity, the reactivation process can be inhibited by methylated ammonium ions.

The approximate values of the dissociation constants of the acidic and basic groups are a valuable aid in considering the chemical nature of the esteratic site. In this connection it is interesting to note that imidazole derivatives have about the right constants, have the electron fluidity assumed for G and would form a favorable 5- to 6-membered ring in the critical complex. However, the planar structure of the imidazole ring introduces geometrical difficulties in the proposed critical complex.

C. Specificity

Specificity of an enzyme toward substrates may be involved in either the formation of the enzyme-substrate complex or the ensuing hydrolytic process. The former shows up at low substrate concentrations and the latter at the maximum velocity. In the case of acetylcholinesterase, the Michaelis-Menten constant reflects the binding; while there is no relationship between this constant and the maximum velocity, just those structural features which the inhibition experiments have shown to produce greater binding decrease the constant (4). The Michaelis-Menten constant of a simple ester such as ethyl acetate is larger than that of acetylcholine by a factor of 10^3, but the maximum velocity is only 0.1 as great. The greater binding of acetylcholine has already been explained. There remains to be explained the greater maximum velocity. As yet there are no experimental measurements available, but some thoughts on the matter may be pertinent. The free energy of activation contains an energy and an entropy term. It would appear that when the bonds to be hydrolyzed are intrinsically the same, say all esters, the energies of activation would be about the same, but that when bonds intrinsically more difficult to transform, say amides, are compared to esters, then the energies of activation would be higher and the rates correspondingly lower. It would appear that the major differences in a series of esters would be in the entropy term. The critical complex would be expected to be a structure in which there is very little freedom in the orientation of the substrate relative to the enzyme surface. A substrate such as acetylcholine, which is bound at several points, forms a highly defined enzyme-substrate complex compared to ethyl acetate, which has greater freedom in its orientation relative to the enzyme. The change from the enzyme susbtrate complex to the critical complex involves, therefore, a lower entropy of activation for ethyl acetate than acetylcholine. This theory can be summed up as saying that a substrate bound at many points will have a higher entropy of activation and a correspondingly greater maximum velocity than a similar substrate bound at fewer points. This proposal can readily be subjected to experimental test.

Specificities of a negative type—where the addition of a group spoils the substrate rather than improves it, can usually be explained in terms of repulsion either with regard to the formation of the enzyme-substrate complex or of the critical complex. Thus while butyryl choline and benzoyl choline are well bound by cholinesterase, they are exceedingly poor substrates. The bulkiness of the acid moiety probably hinders these compounds in forming quite the right complex.

What is the role of the protein? First the protein forms a matrix for the multipolar attraction of substrates and orients the substrate in a manner which is easily distorted into the critical complex. If there is any validity in the preceding theory, this in itself has catalytic properties. Since intermediates are apt to involve such unfavorable features as separations of charge, the protein may facilitate the reaction by introducing many possible resonance forms which would provide the necessary stabilization.

REFERENCES

1. Nachmansohn, D. and I. B. Wilson, *Advances in Enzymol.*, **12**, 259 (1951).
2. Augustinsson, K. B., in *The Enzymes*, (J. B. Sumner and K. Myrbäck, eds.), Vol. I, Part I, p. 443. Academic Press, New York (1950).
3. Wilson, I. B., and F. Bergmann, *J. Biol. Chem.*, **185**, 479 (1950).
4. Wilson, I. B., *J. Biol. Chem.*, **197**, 215 (1952).
5. Bergmann, F., I. B. Wilson, and D. Nachmansohn, *J. Biol. Chem.*, **186**, 693 (1950).
6. Myers, D. K., *Arch. Biochem.*, **27**, 341 (1950).
7. Adams, D. H., and V. P. Whitaker, *Biochim. et Biophys. Acta*, **4**, 543 (1950).
8. Wilson, I. B., and F. Bergmann, *J. Biol. Chem.*, **186**, 683 (1950).
9. Bergmann, F., *Biochim. et Biophys. Acta.*
10. Wilson, I. B., *Biochim. et Biophys. Acta*, **7**, 466 (1951).
11. Wilson, I. B., F. Bergmann, and D. Nachmansohn, *J. Biol. Chem.*, **186**, 781 (1950).
12. Sprinson, D. B., and D. Rittenberg, *Nature*, **167**, 484 (1951).
13. Wilson, I. B., *Biochim. et Biophys. Acta*, **7**, 520 (1951).
14. Wilson, I. B., *J. Biol. Chem.*, **190**, 111 (1951).
15. Wilson, I. B., *J. Biol. Chem.*, **199**, 113 (1952).

ON THE MECHANISM OF ENZYMIC TRANSFER
OF PHOSPHATE AND OTHER GROUPS *

P. D. BOYER and W. H. HARRISON

Department of Agricultural Biochemistry
University of Minnesota
St. Paul

A NUMBER OF enzymes catalyzing the transfer of phosphate in glyco-lytic reactions have been purified and studied in some detail (16), but little information has been available regarding the mechanism of the transfer reactions. The possibility that hydrolysis to and esteri-fication of inorganic phosphate might accompany the transfer reac-tion is unlikely on energetic considerations and has been definitely ruled out by studies with P^{32}-labeled phosphate. For example, Meyerhof et al. (29), in early studies with P^{32} phosphate, showed that enzymic interconversion of the glucose monophosphates was not accompanied by exchange of the ester phosphate with radioactive inorganic phosphate.

Two hypothetical mechanisms of phosphate transfer which may be checked experimentally are given in Fig. 1. The suggestion that phosphate transfer might involve, as one step, the formation of an enzyme-phosphate intermediate is in harmony with the postulate of Langenbeck (27) that enzymes may act by forming intermediates with one moiety of the substrate. Formation of an enzyme-glucose intermediate has been suggested for the sucrose phosphorylase reac-tion (19). This enzyme has a transglucosidase action, and will catalyze an exchange between glucose-1-phosphate and inorganic phosphate in the absence of any acceptor for the glucose moiety other than the enzyme. Similar exchange reactions have been ob-tained for a bacterial enzyme catalyzing transfer of the desoxyribose

* The experimental work reported was supported in part by grants from the National Institutes of Health, U. S. Public Health Service and the Nutrition Foundation, Inc. Contribution No. 3055, Scientific Series, Minnesota Agricultural Experiment Station.

group of nucleosides (28), and for spleen diphosphopyridine nucleotidase (36). The group-transferring activity of various hydrolytic enzymes noted in recent years has been suggested as evidence that the action of these enzymes involves formation of intermediate complexes of the enzyme with the group transferred (36). The possibility that phosphate transfer might involve formation of enzyme-phosphate intermediates also receives some support from the brief mention by Stadtman (33) of exchange of the acetyl moiety of acetyl phosphate with radioactive acetate in the presence of an extract

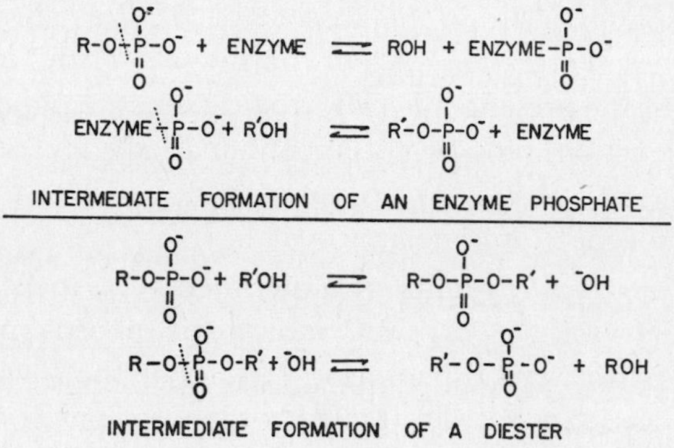

$$R-O\overset{O^-}{\underset{O}{\overset{|}{P}}}-O^- + ENZYME \ \rightleftharpoons \ ROH + ENZYME-\overset{O^-}{\underset{O}{\overset{|}{P}}}-O^-$$

$$ENZYME-\overset{O^-}{\underset{O}{\overset{|}{P}}}-O^- + R'OH \ \rightleftharpoons \ R'-O-\overset{O^-}{\underset{O}{\overset{|}{P}}}-O^- + ENZYME$$

INTERMEDIATE FORMATION OF AN ENZYME PHOSPHATE

$$R-O-\overset{O^-}{\underset{O}{\overset{|}{P}}}-O^- + R'OH \ \rightleftharpoons \ R-O-\overset{O^-}{\underset{O}{\overset{|}{P}}}-O-R' + {}^-OH$$

$$R-O\overset{O^-}{\underset{O}{\overset{|}{P}}}-O-R' + {}^-OH \ \rightleftharpoons \ R'-O-\overset{O^-}{\underset{O}{\overset{|}{P}}}-O^- + ROH$$

INTERMEDIATE FORMATION OF A DIESTER

FIG. 1. Two hypothetical mechanisms of enzymic phosphate transfer.

of *C. kluyveri* containing an active phosphoferase for this reaction. That group transfer does not necessarily involve formation of such complexes is shown by the lack of exchange reactions of glucose-1-phosphate in the presence of phosphorylase but in the absence of an acceptor for the glucose moiety (12).

The possibility of diester formation, involving the splitting out and addition of water (or of hydroxyl ions as shown in Fig. 1), has been suggested for the creatine phosphoferase reaction (5). Such a possibility may be checked by measurement of exchange reactions with O^{18}, and has recently been reported by Cohn (14) to be unlikely for the phosphoglycerate phosphoferase reaction.

In this paper experimental studies will be presented which give strong evidence against the applicability of either of the mechanisms of Fig. 1 for the pyruvate phosphoferase reaction. A mechanism consistent with the experimental data for this and other phosphate-transfer reactions will be presented, together with a brief discussion of the role of magnesium ions in phosphate transfer, a hypothesis for the action of other group-transferring enzymes, and the nomenclature of phosphate-transferring enzymes.

Exchange studies with pyruvate-ADP phosphoferase and pyruvate-2-C^{14}. The possibility that this phosphate transfer might proceed by formation of an enzyme-phosphate intermediate as depicted in Fig. 1 may be checked by measurement of possible exchange reactions of phosphopyruvate in the absence of ADP as an acceptor for the phosphate. Formation of an enzyme-phosphate intermediate independent of the presence of ADP would necessitate the occurrence of exchange reactions; however, as mentioned later, the occurrence of such exchange reactions is by no means proof of the formation of an enzyme-phosphate intermediate.

In Fig. 2 are shown results of experiments on the exchange of pyruvate-2-C^{14} with the pyruvate moiety of phosphopyruvate, as catalyzed by pyruvate phosphoferase (9). For the lower curve all components necessary for the transfer of phosphate from phosphopyruvate to ADP except ADP (formed from the ATP added) were incubated with a high concentration of enzyme. No exchange was observed within the experimental error. With ADP present under equilibrium conditions (upper curve), a slow but definite exchange was observed. These results clearly rule out the formation of an enzyme-phosphate intermediate with release of pyruvate independent of the presence of ADP as a possible step in the catalysis. It is possible that an enzyme-phosphate intermediate will for some reasons form only when ADP is present, but a simple and more logical mechanism is offered later.

From the data of Fig. 2, together with measurements of the fraction of phosphopyruvate separated from the incubation mixture in the sample used for counting and the amount and radioactivity of the pyruvate in the incubation mixture, the rate of the phosphate-transfer reaction at equilibrium may be estimated. This rate may be compared to the initial velocity of the phosphate transfer from phosphopyruvate to ADP under similar conditions but with much shorter time periods. Such a comparison showed that the velocity at equilibrium was only roughly 1/4,000 of the initial velocity of the phosphate transfer from phosphopyruvate. This result is not necessarily in disagreement with the data reported briefly by Meyerhof and Oesper from measurements of the rate of this reaction at equilibrium

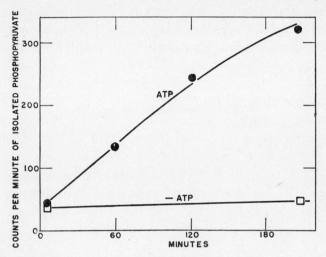

Fig. 2. Acceleration of the incorporation of pyruvate-2-C¹⁴ into phosphopyruvate by ATP. The reaction mixtures contained in a 2.5 ml. total volume 0.16 M sodium phosphate buffer pH 7.4, 0.0032 M phosphopyruvate, 0.12 M KCl, 0.032 M NaF, 0.008 M MgSO₄, 0.008 M sodium pyruvate, 0.1 ml. stock pyruvate-2-C¹⁴ in 0.1 N HCl, 0.1 ml. of 0.1 N NaOH, and 0.1 ml. of a rabbit muscle pyruvate phosphoferase preparation. The mixtures were incubated at 37° C in the presence and absence of 0.008 M ATP. Aliquots were removed at intervals for determination of the radioactivity in the phosphopyruvate. Phosphopyruvate was separated from the pyruvate through a fractionation procedure involving conversion of the pyruvate together with excess added non-labeled pyruvate, to the dinitrophenylhydrazine derivatives, followed by isolation and counting of the phosphopyruvate as the barium salt.

(30). Their reaction conditions are not given and the ratio of initial velocities to velocity at equilibrium would be definitely dependent upon the reaction conditions. Only when the concentrations of reactants are sufficiently low so that the initial and equilibrium velocities are, within experimental error, first order with respect to all reactants would the equilibrium velocity be the same as the respective initial velocities.

Exchange studies with phosphoferases using O^{18}. The pioneering studies of Cohn (13, 14) demonstrate well the feasibility of studying the participation of phosphate in enzymic reactions with O^{18}. Evidence against a diester type of mechanism, as shown in Fig. 1, was obtained by measurement of the possible incorporation of O^{18} of water into the phosphate group when it was transferred to ADP in the pyruvate phosphoferase reaction. Results of such measurements are given in Table 1, and show clearly that no incorporation of O^{18} into the phosphate occurred. It is possible that the reaction

TABLE 1

LACK OF EXCHANGE OF PHOSPHATE OXYGEN WITH O^{18} OF WATER IN THE PYRUVATE PHOSPHOFERASE REACTION

Source of water	Atom % excess O^{18} in the water
Non-labeled phosphate	0
Phosphate from labile groups of ATP	0.002*
O^{18}–labeled phosphate	0.427

* Calculated value for exchange of one O atom = 0.076

might have occurred in such a manner that O^{18} was introduced into the pyruvate if the C–O bond of the ester link of the phosphopyruvate were split. However, in the action of phosphatases and of all phosphate-transferring enzymes that have been studied (14, 9, 34), the P–O bond is split, and it appears highly likely that the same cleavage occurs with phosphopyruvate. Direct experimental check of this possibility is difficult because of the lack of adequate procedures for determination of the O^{18}-content of the carbonyl group of pyruvate and the possibility of exchange of any O^{18} in such a group with water.

As mentioned earlier, Cohn has recently presented evidence that the phosphoglycerate phosphoferase reaction proceeds without exchange of the O atoms of the phosphate with those of water (14). In addition, she has demonstrated that in the hexokinase reaction carried out in H_2O^{18} no excess O^{18} is found in the phosphate of either the glucose-6-phosphate or adenosine diphosphate (15). In our laboratory we have found that the oxygen of labeled inorganic phosphate appears in the carboxyl group of 3-phosphoglycerate produced by the glyceraldehyde-3-phosphate dehydrogenase and the 3-phosphoglycerate phosphoferase reactions (9).

The phosphate-transfer reactions of the pyruvate and the 3-phosphoglycerate phosphoferase and of the hexokinase reactions are thus all similar, in that there is no exchange of the phosphate oxygen with oxygen of water during the transfer. These results rule out any direct participation of water or hydroxyl ions in the transfer. In these and probably in other similar enzymatic transfers of phosphate the oxygen atoms not combined in ester linkage in the original ester must remain as such in the subsequent transfers. The attachment of the phosphate to the acceptor molecule involves the oxygen

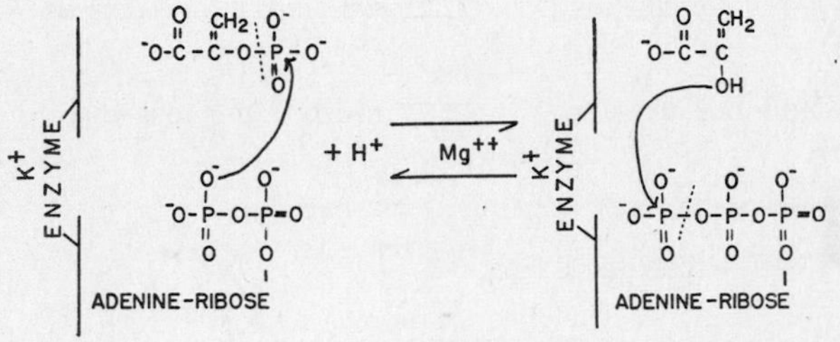

Fig. 3. Diagrammatic scheme for the pyruvate phosphoferase reaction.

(or the nitrogen in case of phosphocreatine) of the acceptor molecule. The results of exchange studies with O^{18} and pyruvate-2-C^{14} lead logically to either of two closely related mechanisms. In Fig. 3 an oxygen atom of the acceptor molecule is visualized as attacking and forming a bond with the positively charged P in the donor molecule, resulting in cleavage of the O–P bond in the C–O–P linkage of the donor. Alternatively the ester linkage of the donor could conceivably ionize transitorily to the forms RO^- and $^+\overset{\displaystyle O}{\underset{\displaystyle OH}{\overset{\|}{P}}}\text{–OH}$, with reaction of the positive ion and the oxygen from the acceptor.

A similar reaction mechanism for the phosphoglycerate phosphoferase reaction and associated enzymic reactions is depicted in Fig. 4.

Evidence for the formation of a " high-energy " acyl-enzyme in the glyceraldehyde-3-phosphate dehydrogenase reaction is discussed elsewhere in this volume (8). In the cleavage of the acyl derivative of glyceraldehyde-3-phosphate dehydrogenase, an oxygen of the inorganic phosphate molecule reacts with the carbonyl carbon on the acyl group to give the acyl phosphate; the oxygen of the anhydride bond is thus contributed by the phosphate.

With regard to the phosphoglyceric mutase and phosphoglucomutase reactions, the excellent studies of Cardini (11), and of Suther-

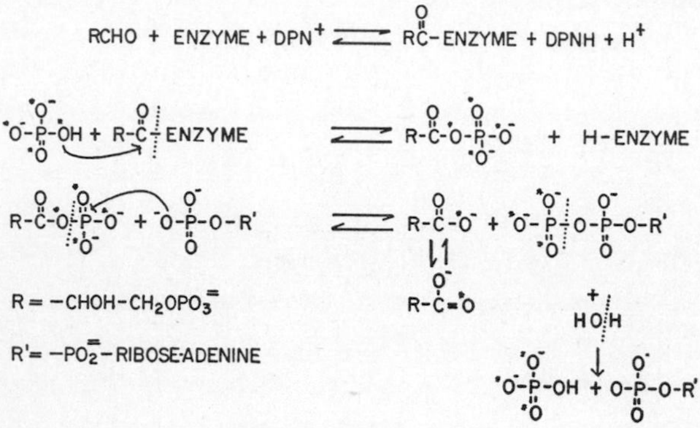

FIG. 4. Cleavage and reaction mechanisms for glyceraldehyde-3-phosphate dehydrogenase, phosphoglycerate phosphoferase, and adenosine triphosphatase reactions. The asterisks indicate labeled oxygen atoms.

land (35) and their associates have given strong evidence that the transfer is not intramolecular, but actually involves transfer of phosphate from glucose-1, 6-diphosphate (or 2, 3-diphosphoglycerate) to one of the corresponding monophosphates. The considerations given above for the phosphoferase reactions would also likely apply to mutase reactions.

There is little experimental information as to the specific spatial relationships of the substrates on the enzyme during phosphate transfer. Bucher has presented data which suggest that the binding of ADP and ATP by phosphoglycerate phosphoferase may be essentially independent of each other (10). He suggests that the phosphate to be transferred remains attracted to the same position on the enzyme whether combined to ADP or 3–phosphoglycerate. Nothing in Bücher's interesting findings is in conflict with the cleavage mechanisms presented above. Extension of kinetic studies of the interaction of various substrates with phosphoferases should give interesting additional information about the catalysis mechanism.

In accordance with the preceding reaction mechanisms, conditions which favor an increased positive charge on the phosphorus atom would favor phosphate transfer. Acid but not alkaline conditions will catalyze phosphate migration in glycerol monophosphates (4); this is in harmony with the expectation that in highly acid solutions

$$\text{R--O--}\overset{\displaystyle \text{OH}}{\underset{\displaystyle \text{OH}}{\text{P}^+}}\text{--OH}$$

forms of the phosphate such as R–O–P⁺–OH would be favored. The proximity of the adjacent hydroxyl group, the oxygen of which attacks the positively charged phosphorus, probably accounts for the migration in preference to the hydrolysis of the phosphate.

The importance of the positive charge on the phosphate in various enzymic reactions of phosphate is also indicated by the observations of lack of reactivity of glucose-6-phosphite, monoalkyl phosphites, and inorganic phosphite in enzyme reactions (9). Phosphite esters have a C–O–P linkage and two negatively charged oxygen atoms at slightly alkaline pH, as do phosphate esters. Phosphites would, however, be expected to have a considerably reduced residual positive charge on the phosphorus atom.

The mechanism of phosphate transfer is also somewhat analogous to that suggested for acyl migrations of glycerol monoester, in which increased positive charge in the carbonyl carbon is regarded as favoring migration (18).

Function of metal ions in phosphate transfer. The importance of magnesium in various phosphate-transfer reactions has been well discussed recently by Lardy (26) and by Colowick (16). Increasing evidence has become available that adenosine triphosphate probably participates in reactions in combination with magnesium (24, 20), and that metal activations may frequently involve formation of reactive metallosubstrates (31). That the action of pyrophosphatase involves reaction with magnesium pyrophosphate was suggested in 1937 by Bauer (6), and is supported by recent work in our laboratory (9). The combination of magnesium with phosphate derivatives, like highly acid conditions, would favor increase in the residual positive charge on the phosphorus atom. This would logically lead to increased ease of attack by nucleophilic reactants. The small size and high charge density of magnesium may contribute considerably to its effectiveness in catalysis. Recognition of the importance that combination of magnesium with substrates may have in catalysis does not rule out the additional possibilities that combination of the magnesium with the enzyme may be necessary for the active configuration of the enzyme or that the binding of magnesium to the substrate may be aided by enzyme. However, suggestions along these lines are at present quite tenuous.

The potassium activation of the phosphate transfer by pyruvate phosphoferase most likely involves combination of the potassium with the enzyme independent of combination with phosphopyruvate (23). This result, together with the lack of a potassium requirement for many phosphate-transfer reactions and the potassium activation of various types of enzymes (7) suggests that the activation of the pyruvate phosphoferase reaction by potassium, unlike the magnesium activation, has no specific relation to the phosphate transfer.

Phosphate transfer by phosphatases. Cohn has shown that in the enzymic cleavage of phosphate esters the bond between oxygen and phosphorus is cleaved (13), and Stein and Koshland have demonstrated that alkaline phosphatase will catalyze the exchange of inorganic phosphate with O^{18} in water (34). These results agree well with hydrolysis mechanisms involving reaction of the positively charged phosphorus with oxygen of water. The enzyme may function by increasing the positive charge on the phosphorus atom and thus favoring such cleavage. The labilized enzyme-bound substrate could react with water or with the hydroxyl group of another acceptor for the phosphate, such as an organic alcohol. In the latter instance transfer of the phosphate group would result without involving formation of an intermediate of the enzyme and group transferred.

Action of other group-transferring enzymes. In analogy with the mechanisms proposed for transfer of phosphate by phosphoferases and phosphatases, the simplest explanation of the transfer of other groups does not necessitate the postulation of intermediates of the enzyme and group transferred. Labilization of the substrate for direct reaction with water or other acceptor groups would logically explain group transfer by hydrolytic enzymes, such as the catalysis by chymotrypsin of exchange of the glycineamide moiety of benzoyl-L-tyrosyl glycineamide with N^{15} glycineamide (22) and exchange of the carboxyl oxygen of carbobenzoxyphenylalanine with O^{18} of water (32), the formation of various mixed saccharides in the enzymic hydrolysis of sucrose (3, 2) or lactose (1), and the incorporation of nicotinamide into DPN in the presence of spleen DPN-ase (36). Pertinent in this regard is the observation that the acid-catalyzed hydrolysis of lactose will also lead to the formation of various mixed saccharides (1). Clearly, in the acid catalysis the group transfer must result from labilization of the substrate to attack by a suitable acceptor molecule.

The feasibility of enzymic group transfer through direct attack upon the labilized substrate by the acceptor molecule should by no means be interpreted as a postulate that no group-transfer reactions involve the formation of intermediates of group with enzyme or with a coenzyme. One need only consider the role of coenzyme A in acetyl transfer and of ADP in phosphate transfer to recognize the fallacy of such a postulate. With glyceraldehyde-3-phosphate dehydrogenase, as discussed elsewhere in this volume (8), there is good evidence for the formation of an acyl-enzyme intermediate as an essential step in the catalysis.

However, in the absence of supporting evidence the inclusion of enzyme-group intermediates in reaction schemes introduces an unnecessary extra reaction step. One could suggest, for example, that transfers of acyl groups to coenzyme A involved intermediate formation of an acyl-enzyme rather than direct reaction of the coenzyme A with the acyl donor. With sucrose phosphorylase, the appearance of α-glucose-1-phosphate from the α-glucosidic bond of sucrose can, as pointed out by Koshland (25), be logically explained by the formation of an enzyme-β-glucose intermediate. Formation of such an intermediate is, however, by no means essential for the retention of a configuration. Steric relationships near the C_1 of the glucose may be of prime importance. The proximity of groups of the enzyme could readily affect the configuration of the product of the catalysis. With muscle and potato phosphorylase, exchange reactions analogous to those found with sucrose phosphorylase have been carefully sought but not found (12), yet these phosphorylases cleave an alpha linkage in the polysaccharide to give α-D-glucose-1-phosphate. A tenable explanation would be that exchange reactions would be observed with enzymes where there is low specificity towards the acceptor molecule. Thus with sucrose phosphorylase the positively charged carbon at C_1 of enzyme-bound glucose-1-phosphate could be subject to nucleophilic attack by another phosphate as well as various sugar-hydroxyl groups. Present information is insufficient to allow a choice among alternate mechanisms.

An addendum on the nomenclature of phosphate-transferring enzymes. The recognition of the confusion arising from various terminologies used in the literature for phosphate-transferring enzymes has led to suggestions for clarifying the terminology (17, 21, 23). Some justification for the use of the phosphoferase terminology given here may be warranted. The complete description for phosphoferase enzymes would include names of both reactants which accept the phosphate. Thus for the enzyme catalyzing a transfer of phosphate from phosphopyruvate to ADP the name would be pyruvate-ADP phosphoferase. For this and analogous enzymes that catalyze the interchange of phosphate with ADP the designation may be shortened to pyruvate phosphoferase, 3-phosphoglycerate phosphoferase, etc.

The term phosphorylase can be most logically and usefully applied to enzymes which catalyze the reversible cleavage of substrates through addition of inorganic phosphate; the use of transphosphorylase for enzymes catalyzing a transfer of ester phosphate falls outside of the thus-defined use of the term phosphorylase. Likewise the term phosphatase is best retained for enzymes whose principal reaction is the hydrolysis of phosphate esters, and the use of the name transphosphatase incorrectly suggests a transferring hydrolysis. Use of a name such as pyruvate kinase is not descriptive of the action of the enzyme referred to; the term implies, contrary to experimental findings, that pyruvate is readily phosphorylated by ATP. Also pyruvate activation is probably not the principal basis for the catalysis by the enzyme. The use of the suffix kinase for the enzymes catalyzing an essentially irreversible transfer of phosphate from ATP to various sugar derivatives is rather firmly established and understood, and thus any change does not seem advisable, even though the terminology is in some ways unfortunate. Among other things, it does not lead to a convenient group designation for enzymes of this type; the term kinase alone is not a satisfactory designation for a group of phosphate-transferring enzymes. Extension of the use of the term kinase to describe other types of phosphate-transferring enzymes appears unwarranted and not essential.

REFERENCES

1. Aronson, M., *Arch. Biochem. and Biophys.*, 39, 370 (1952).
2. Bacon, J. S. D., *Biochem. J.*, 50, xviii (1952).
3. Bacon, J. S. D., and J. Edelman, *Arch. Biochem.*, 28, 467 (1950).
4. Baer, E., and M. Kates, *J. Biol. Chem.*, 175, 79 (1948).
5. Baldwin, E., *Dynamic Aspects of Biochemistry*, p. 156, Cambridge University Press, Cambridge (1947).
6. Bauer, E., *Z. physiol. Chem.*, 248, 213 (1937).
7. Boyer, P. D., *J. Lancet*, 73, 195 (1953).
8. Boyer, P. D., H. L. Segal, and M. P. Stulberg, *The Mechanism of Enzyme Action*, Baltimore (1953).
9. Boyer, P. D., W. H. Harrison, H. E. Robertson, and E. R. Robbins, unpub.
10. Bucher, T., *Biochim. et Biophys. Acta*, 1, 292 (1947).
11. Cardini, C. E., A. C. Paladini, R. Caputto, L. F. Leloir, and R. E. Trucco, *Arch. Biochem.*, 22, 87 (1949).
12. Cohn, M., and G. T. Cori, *J. Biol. Chem.*, 175, 89 (1948).
13. Cohn, M., *J. Biol. Chem.*, 180, 771 (1949).
14. Cohn, M., *J. Biol. Chem.*, 201, 735 (1953).
15. Cohn, M., pers. com.

16. Colowick, S. P., in *The Enzymes* (J. B. Sumner and K. Myrbäck, eds.), 2, 114, New York (1951).
17. Dixon, M., *Multi-enzyme Systems*, p. 38, Cambridge University Press, Cambridge (1949).
18. Doerschuk, A. P., *J. Am. Chem. Soc.*, 74, 4202 (1952).
19. Doudoroff, M., H. A. Barker, and W. Z. Hassid, *J. Biol. Chem.*, 168, 725 (1947).
20. Hers, H. G., *Biochim. et Biophys. Acta*, 8, 424 (1952).
21. Hoffman-Ostenhof, O., *Enzymologia*, 14, 72 (1950-51).
22. Johnston, R. B., M. J. Mycek, and J. S. Fruton, *J. Biol. Chem.*, 187, 205 (1950).
23. Kachmar, J. F., and P. D. Boyer, *J. Biol. Chem.*, 200, 669 (1953).
24. Kielley, W. W., and R. K. Kielley, *J. Biol. Chem.*, 200, 213 (1953).
25. Koshland, D. E., Jr., *Federation Proc.*, 11, 242 (1952).
26. Lardy, H. A., in *A Symposium on Phosphorus Metabolism* (W. D. McElroy, and B. Glass, eds.), Vol. 1, p. 477, Johns Hopkins Press, Baltimore (1951).
27. Langenbeck, W., *Ergeb. Enzymforsch.*, 2, 314 (1933).
28. MacNutt, W. S., *Biochem. J.*, 50, 384 (1952).
29. Meyerhof, O., P. Ohlmeyer, W. Gentner, and H. Maier-Leibnitz, *Biochem. Z.*, 298, 296 (1938).
30. Meyerhof, O., and P. Oesper, *J. Biol. Chem.*, 179, 1371 (1949).
31. Najjar, V. A., in *A Symposium on Phosphorus Metabolism* (W. D. McElroy and B. Glass, eds.), Vol. I, p. 500, Johns Hopkins Press, Baltimore (1951).
32. Sprinson, D. B., and D. Rittenberg, *Nature*, 167, 484 (1950).
33. Stadtman, E. R., M. Doudoroff, and F. Lipmann, *J. Biol. Chem.*, 191, 377 (1951).
34. Stein, S. S., and D. E. Koshland, Jr., *Arch. Biochem. and Biophys.*, 39, 229 (1952).
35. Sutherland, E. W., M. Cohn, T. Posternak, and C. F. Cori, *J. Biol. Chem.*, 180, 1285 (1949).
36. Zatman, L. J., N. O. Kaplan, and S. P. Colowick, *J. Biol. Chem.*, 200, 197 (1953).

DISCUSSION

DR. DOUDOROFF: This is all over my head, but I would like to say a few words about the sucrose phosphorylase which we have purified to some extent from *Leuconostoc*. This enzyme does act as a hydrolase also—that is, it can act with OH as an acceptor to catalyze the hydrolysis of both glucose-1-phosphate and sucrose. We have looked for stable intermediates by putting in radio-active substrates and then boiling up the enzyme and chromatographing the mixtures in Dr. Calvin's laboratory. We have not found anything. There were a few phosphate spots other than the substrate, but I think these were probably due to some impurity in the enzyme. There was certainly nothing like a stable glycoside formed, which you might expect to find there. There was no evidence of UDPG, nor did the enzyme exchange glucose with alpha glucose-1-phosphate. There is another very peculiar behavior of the enzyme. I'll tell you about it, but I won't take any responsibility for the interpretation. When you use very concentrated enzyme solution and add substrate to it, whether it be glucose-1-phosphate or sucrose, there seems to be a burst of hydrolytic activity—for instance, you can detect a burst of phosphate production in the first few minutes, after which you get a steady, slow rate of hydrolysis. At first we thought this might be due to the formation of a glucose enzyme complex. The burst is roughly proportional to the amount of enzyme, rather than to the amount of substrate. Over a large range of substrate concentrations you get almost the same amount of hydrolysis, which occurs very quickly; but you can vary the amount by varying the enzyme concentration. I think it is true hydrolysis—I am not absolutely certain—but, for one thing, free reducing sugar, which appears to be glucose, is produced at exactly the same rate at which phosphate is liberated from glucose-1-phosphate during this period. Of course, in making the measurements we have to boil the enzyme in order to determine reducing sugar, so that if it's a very weak complex with the enzyme we might be breaking it up in the process of boiling. However, there are two other reasons for believing that we have not seen any active glucose on the enzyme. One is that too much of this occurs in comparison with the amount of protein added. The amount of glucose produced appears to be of the same order by weight as the amount of protein present. The second reason is based on rather devious and indirect kind of evidence. We allowed this burst to proceed with a small amount of radioactive glucose-1-phosphate and we assumed that, if this apparent glucose production which accompanies the phosphate production were actually the formation of some sort of "active glucose"; then there should be a measurable amount of labelled glucose which would be glucose phosphate. Similarly, if "active glucose" were formed in the initial attack on labelled sucrose, the addition of phosphate should result in the formation of more labelled glucose-1-phosphate than the remaining amount of sucrose. We tried the experiment by taking the enzyme and letting it go through this short burst with labelled substrate. In one aliquot, the reaction was stopped by boiling. In another aliquot, an exchange with inactive material was permitted. In the case of sucrose, inorganic phosphate was added and the resultant glucose-1-phosphate was tested for radioactivity. There was no evidence of any greater amount of radioactive exchangeable glucose in the unboiled preparation than in the boiled ones. In other words, it does look as though it's simply a hydrolytic reaction. Now, this is a very peculiar business, because it means that when we first take the enzyme and put it with the substrate it looks as though it acts as a hydrolase, but in a few minutes it becomes accustomed to being a phosphorylase — that is, it changes in its activity simply by acting on the substrate. This might be, of course, due to something like a glucose moiety from the substrate becoming a coenzyme necessary for phosphorylase activity. However, there is no evidence of any glycosides from the experiments that I mentioned using chromatography. It might be that the enzyme is reversibly inactivated in some way and that the substrate re-forms the enzyme, so that now it can hang on to the glycosyl moiety. As I say, this has just recently been done and needs a lot of confirmation.

DR. HARTING: Since the phosphatase activity of glyceraldehyde-3-phosphate dehydrogenase can be inhibited by phosphate under certain conditions, I would like to ask Dr. Doudoroff if phosphate also inhibits this hydrolytic activity.

DR. DOUDOROFF: No. You can add glucose or phosphate to it, and you still get the same burst. Once the burst has occurred, you can add more substrate and there is no further burst.

DR. KAPLAN: Do you get the exchange reaction when you add labelled phosphate to glucose-1-phosphate?

DR. DOUDOROFF: Oh, yes. The enzyme, I might say, is almost identical with that from saccharophila, but it's easier to purify, and that's why we are using it. There are two differences—one is the different solubility. It comes out in a much higher ammonium sulphate fraction, so that it is easier to separate it from other things. The other thing is that it is much less poisoned by glucose. We have now examined three sucrose phosphorylases: these two, and a third one from *Pseudomonas putrefaciens*. All three seem to act in exactly the same way. They have remarkably similar specificities, with the exception that the putrefaciens enzyme is a little more selective. It won't react with sorbose. In most ways the three enzymes are very, very close.

DR. LEVINTOW: Dr. Koshland has shown how clues to the mechanism of enzyme action may be obtained by the use of stereochemical considerations. Similarly, in studying the enzymatic synthesis of D and L glutamine from the respective isomers of glutamic acid, we have obtained evidence which appears to have implications in terms of the mechanism of this reaction (Levintow, L. and Meister, A.; 1953, *J. A. C. S.* 75, 3039).

In the course of our studies, using a purified enzyme from peas (Elliott, W. H., 1953, *J. Biol. Chem.* 201, 661), we found that the reaction:

$$ATP + Glutamate + NH_3 \rightleftharpoons ADP + Glutamine + P$$

does not proceed to completion. When the three products were incubated with enzyme, appearance of ATP, glutamate, and ammonia was observed, as well as disappearance of inorganic phosphate. The back reaction requires magnesium ions; AMP will not replace ADP. The magnitude of the reversal is on the order of 5 per cent at pH 7.

DR. LIPMANN: I would like to add that Elliott had demonstrated rather clearly that the same enzyme is responsible for the exchange reaction as for the synthesis. Also, you may remember that Stumpf found ADP and inorganic phosphate to be necessary for the exchange reaction, and there was a suspicion that this requirement of inorganic phosphate and ADP for the exchange reaction may indicate that the reaction may go all the way back. Now, Dr. Levintow has verified this very amazing reverse reaction. I wonder if Dr. Koshland would like to comment about the energetics in this case?

DR. LEVINTOW: It seems strange at first blush that a relatively low energy bond, such as that in glutamine, could be involved in a reversible reaction in which a high energy bond of ATP is synthesized; but I think that when the free energy change of all the reactants is taken into consideration, reversibility of the reaction becomes reasonable.

DR. KOSHLAND: I would just like to say something about an exchange reaction. Thermodynamics will never stop an exchange reaction. All that thermodynamics says is that if you have a ratio of two rates, k_1 and k_2 being the forward and reverse reaction velocity constants, this ratio k_1 and k_2 will be fixed. Therefore, if it happens that these are both enormous quantities, then it is quite possible that you can observe a measurable change even though the equilibrium is far to the right.

DR. LEVINTOW: Well, this is not merely an exchange. This is a net reaction.

DR. LIPMANN: This is a real synthesis, but the exchange reaction also requires ADP and phosphate.

DR. BOYER: Doesn't your evidence show that free ammonia is the active component of this reaction?

DR. LEVINTOW: We have no evidence on this point, although we have been seriously considering the possibility.

DR. BOYER: It would seem that if ammonia were formed at pH 7 it would go over entirely to the ammonium ion. This would account for the supply of energy necessary to push the reaction toward ATP synthesis.

DR. LEVINTOW: That is exactly what I meant when I said that a consideration of all the components of the reaction would bring the experimental data in line with theoretical predictions.

DR. LIPMAN: This seems essentially to be the formation of ATP by the use of the energy of a peptide bond. This is quite remarkable and makes us believe still more that we need energy to form peptide bonds.

DR. DEMOSS: I think that another enzyme system which might be very amenable to test with your O^{18} technique as far as racemization is concerned was reported some time ago by Stevenson in the Clostridium species and involves lactic acid racemization. I am not sure of the experimental details, and it may be that pyruvate is involved as an intermediate, but if that can be disproven then this might be a system worthy of study.

DR. GUNSALUS: There is a mandelic acid racemase in pseudomonases that would also be interesting to study. This should also be relatively easy since the D and L isomers can be differentiated enzymatically and have a specific notation of about 150.

DR. E. SMITH: I would like to say—if one can make a generalization—that what we used to call hydrolytic enzymes are really enzymes for synthesis, transfer, exchange, and hydrolysis. What we are dealing with is largely a thermodynamic question of where the equilibrium is. I think that we should be aware that in reactions such as Fruton has studied, with papain, chymo-trypsin and some of the cathepsins, exchanges were demonstrated in spite of the fact that the equilibrium was way over in the direction of hydrolysis, so that with respect to specificity of the enzyme it can't tell what it's going to do. As far as the exchange mechanism is concerned, we are forming an enzyme-substrate complex in any case, and the final equilibrium is simply determined by the over-all thermodynamics of the system. I would like to stick my neck out and perhaps get a few more scars. If people take the trouble, they are going to find exchange reactions and synthesis in all the so-called classical hydrolytic systems if the situation can be made favorable. Now, with the peptidases we are dealing with an extremely unfavorable situation because of the enormous difference in the pK values of the amino groups of the pep-tides as compared with the free amino acids. Such pH considerations have been shown by Fruton and coworkers to play an extremely important role in demonstrating exchange and synthesis. Whereas at one pH there is very little exchange and very little synthesis, at another pH there is a very large amount of exchange and synthesis.

DR. LIPMANN: I would like to say that thermodynamics could not play a role in deciding between whether hydrolysis or transfer would occur, but rather it is the structure of the enzyme which is the important factor. With an exchange you don't need to form a bond—the bond is already there. The enzyme can now decide whether it wants to split it or transfer the bond intact. Generally transferases do not hydrolyze their substrates. The nico-tinamide transferase also hydrolyzes but that probably is a special case and I still think that the hydrolytic enzymes in general have the function of hydrolyzing, and transferases, on the contrary, have the function of rather keeping the water away.

DR. E. SMITH: That's a matter of the relative affinity of water for the complex.

DR. LIPMANN: That's right.

THE MECHANISM OF TRANSGLYCOSIDATION

HERMAN M. KALCKAR

University Institute of Cytophysiology,
University of Copenhagen,
Denmark

INTRODUCTION

A DISCUSSION of group transfer of glycosyl groups and the mechanism of transglycosidic reactions should comprise an evaluation not only of studies on transglycosidases but also of work on phosphorylases. This may best be illustrated by the fact that phosphoglycosyl compounds (ribose-1-phosphate, desoxyribose-1-phosphate, glucose-1-phosphate) when participating in the enzymatic formation of glycosyl compounds (nucleosides, polysaccharides, disaccharides) undergo fission between the carbon and the oxygen of the esterified phosphate and not between the phosphorus and the oxygen, as shown in the following structural formula:

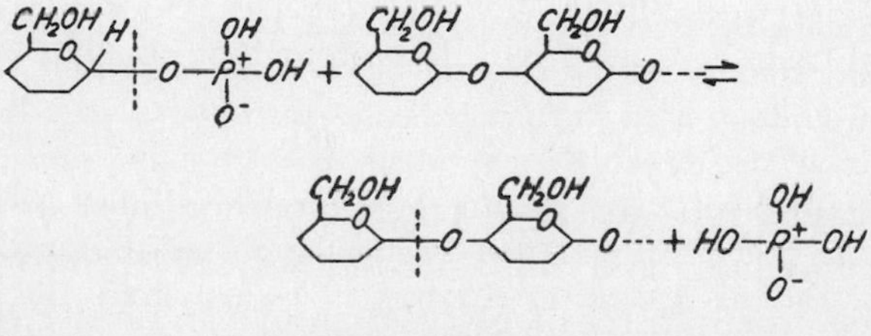

FORMULA 1. Phosphorolytic fission of glucose-1-phosphate.
(After M. Cohn, 14)

This fact became evident when it was demonstrated that ribose-1-phosphate and deoxyribose-1-phosphate in the presence of the proper enzyme could react with the imidazole nitrogen of hypoxanthine and form a direct C–N linkage to make a typical nucleoside (56, 32). This is illustrated in formula 2:

675

FORMULA 2. Phosphorolytic fission of inosine (hypoxanthine-β-furanoriboside).

It has also been demonstrated (14) by means of the ^{18}O isotope that α-glucose-1-phosphate (Cori ester) undergoes a fission of the corresponding bond in the enzymic formation of polysaccharide.* We are therefore confronted with an enzymatic transfer of glycosyl groups whenever we are dealing with phosphorylases or with transglycosidases. The glycosyl acceptors are the hydroxyls of free orthophosphate (or perhaps also phosphate compounds) or the hydroxyls of bound or free sugars (the OH groups in the 4 or 6 positions) or in special cases a 2 carbonyl. The other type of glycosyl acceptor

$$\overset{\diagdown}{\underset{|}{N}}\diagup$$

is the ring-bound nitrogen H of purines, pyrimidines, and pyridines. Both phosphorylases and transglycosidases are therefore enzymes which catalyze the transfer of glycosyl groups and hence the decision to put the phosphorylases in the same category as transglycosidases in this discussion.

Inasmuch as this symposium is devoted to a discussion of mechanisms of enzyme reactions and speculation about them, and since we are fortunate enough to have some recent exhaustive surveys of the transglycosidases and phosphorylases of hexoses (40, 83), I shall not here make an attempt to give a full survey of this field but

* See note, p. 739.

rather play up themes which might encourage speculation regarding mechanisms of action.

In the present review I shall first discuss problems dealing with substrate specificity, including steric specificity; then thermodynamical considerations; and finally the more or less speculative aspects of the mechanism of enzymic transglycosidations.

ENZYMIC TRANSGLYCOSIDIC REACTIONS

One might get an impression of the vastness of this field from Table 1, in which an attempt has been made to list all the enzymic reactions in which the glycosyl group can be transferred without significant loss of bond energy from one acceptor to another.

Enzymic phosphorolysis of glycosidic linkages in starch and glycogen was discovered by the Coris in 1937 (16). A transglycosidic reaction which is completely independent of phosphate was first clearly described by Hehre and Sugg in 1943 (43), when they isolated the enzyme which forms dextran from sucrose. The fact that hydrolases can catalyze glycosyl-transfer reactions was recognized as early as 1935 by Rabaté in his studies on β-glucosidase (88). He found that a considerable amount of phenolic bound glycosyl ("glucose naissant," as Rabaté called it) reacts with primary alcohols to form the corresponding glycosyl compound.

Polysaccharide phosphorylase. The action of this enzyme can be illustrated by a reaction between α-D-glucose-1-phosphate and the terminal glucose units of a priming polysaccharide $(C_6H_{10}O_5)_x$

$$(C_6H_{10}O_5)_x + C_6H_{11}O_5OPO_3^= \rightleftharpoons (C_6H_{10}O_5)_{x+1} + HPO_4^=$$
$$(C_6H_{10}O_5)_{x+1} + C_6H_{11}O_5OPO_3^= \rightleftharpoons (C_6H_{10}O_5)_{x+2} + HPO_4^=.$$

In the case of muscle phosphorylase the primers for formation of 1-4 maltosidic chains are the terminal groups of glycogen (9). Phosphorylase from potato can use primers of low molecular weight down to 4 glucose units (102). Posternak (86) found recently that phosphotetraose (the phosphate being esterified in the 6 position of the second or third glucose) can act as primer for potato phos-

TABLE 1

I *Disaccharides*

A) Phosphorylases:

   1) Sucrose phosphorylase, which is also a 1-2 trans-glucosidase
   2) Maltose phosphorylase

B) Trans-O-glycosidase:

   1) Amylomaltase
   2) Isomaltose transglucosidase
   3) Sucrose phosphorylase (cf. also IA)
   4) The sucrases (cf. also IIB)

C) Hydrolases and
  Transglycosidases:

   1) Invertase (Transfructosidase or Transglucosidase)
   2) Lactase
   3) β-glucosidase

II *Polysaccharides*

A) Phosphorylases:

   1) Amylophosphorylases
      Muscle Phosphorylase a and b
      Potato phosphorylase

B) Trans-O-glycosidases:
  1) linkage 1, 2 to 1, 4

   Amylosucrase
   Sucrose phosphorylase as transglycosidase (cf. also IA & IB)

  2) linkage 1, 2 to 1, 6
     (or 1, 2 to 2, 6)

   Dextran sucrase
   Levan sucrase

  3) linkage 1, 4 to 1, 4

   Rearrangement in the distribution of glycosyl units
   Amylomaltase (cf. also IB)
   Opening of cyclic dextrines with lengthening and redistribution of low molecular dextrines

  3a) linkage 1, 2 to 1, 2
    4) linkage 1, 4 to 1, 6

   Inulin transfructosidase
   Branching enzymes (branching factor in muscle; Q enzyme, R-factor in plants) Isomaltose transglycosidase (cf. also IB)
   Dextran dextrinase

C) Specific Hydrolases:

   Amylo-1-6-glucosidase

III *N-Ribosides*

A) Phosphorylases:

   1) Purine riboside phosphorylase

     (incl. probably $\overset{+}{N}$-nicotinamide riboside phosphorylase)
   2) Pyrimidine riboside phosphorylase

   3) Purine deoxyriboside phosphorylase
   4) Pyrimidine deoxyriboside phosphorylase

         in various microorg. different from 1) and 2)

   5) Specific Purine-Pyrimidine deoxyribosidephosphorylase from *E. coli*

B) Trans-N-glycosidases:
 1) Purine-Pyrimidine deoxyribose trans-N-glucosidase of *Lactobacillus helveticus* and related microorganisms
 2) Specific Pyrimidine-Purine deoxyribose trans-N-glucosidase of *E. coli*
 3) Specific Pyrimidine-Pyrimidine deoxyribose trans-N-glucosidase of *E. coli*

C) Hydrolases:
 1) Purine riboside hydrolase of *L. helveticus* and related microorganisms
 2) Pyrimidine riboside hydrolase (from yeast)

IV *N-ribotides*

 A) Phosphorylases:
  1) 5-adenylic phosphorylase
  2) 5-inosinic phosphorylase

 B) Trans-N-glycosidases:
  UDPGlucuronide in glucuronide synthesis

 C) Transglycosidases and Hydrolases:
  N-ribosyl transglucosidase of DPN

phorylase. It was found that the amylose synthesized contained a concentration of phosphorus which depended upon the ratio between phosphotetraose and glucose-1-phosphate used. The higher the former in relation to the latter, the shorter are the chains and the higher the phosphorus content. Posternak emphasized that these observations are a direct demonstration of the function of the primer, which is a molecule that serves as the first basis on which the new glucose units are built up. The polysaccharide phosphorylases are strictly specific for 1-4 maltosidic linkages. Since glycogen has a branched structure in which the glucose unit at the branch point carries, besides the ordinary 1, 4 linkage as linear chains, a 1, 6 linkage (which Cori and Larner (18) designated as the side chain), the enzymic phosphorolysis of glycogen is not as simple as the corresponding process in an unbranched starch (amylose). Fig. 1 shows an illustration of the process as revealed by the studies of Cori and Larner (18). The sidebranch is attacked completely down to the first glucose residue, which is hooked on by the 1, 6 linkage to the main branch (Fig. 1). The outer so-called main branch is also broken down in the direction of the branch point (and in the direction of the reducing group R) but the breakdown does not proceed nearly as close to the branch point. Hestrin (47) found that the limit dextrin obtained by action of phosphorylase (phosphorylase LD) contained an average of about 1 maltose residue per branch. This residue could be removed by addition of β-amylase. The discovery by Cori and Larner of the 1, 6 amylo-glycosidase, which specifically hydrolyzes the 1, 6 linkage of the side chain, enabled them, among other things, to make a much closer study of the specificity and mode of action of glycogen phosphorylase. In order for the amylo α-1, 6-glucosidase from muscle to hydrolyze the α-1, 6 bond, the glucose unit having this linkage must first be exposed by the action of phosphorylase. This is in contrast to some recently

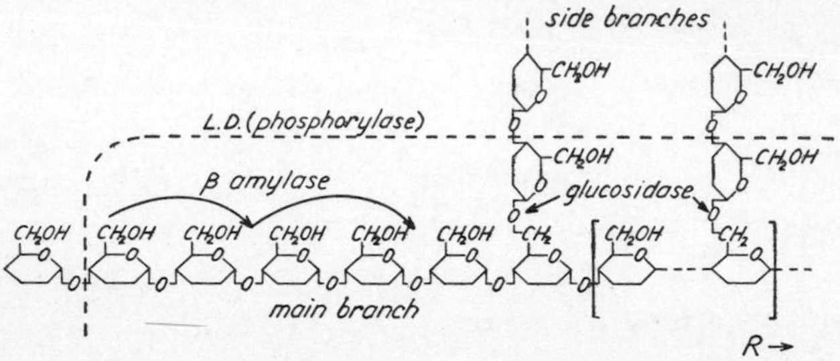

Fig. 1. Topography of limit dextrin (phosphorylase endproduct). (After Cori and Larner, 18)

described 1, 6 glucosidases in plants (Hobson, Whelan, and Peat, 49; Maruo and Kobayashi, 74) which seem to be able to " chip off " the whole branch. In the case of the glucosidase of muscle glycogen, however, all glucose units in α-1, 4 linkage must be split off from one of the outer branches before the glucose at the branch point is liberated as free glucose. Since the side chain is degraded down to the branching point, whereas all the 4 to 5 glucose units are left in the main branch (see Fig. 1), the distribution of the 1 to 2 maltose units as a residue per branch left in " phosphorylase LD " must be completely unequal.

One possible explanation for the unequal attack of phosphorylase is deduced from Fischer-Hirschfelder models of maltose and brachiose. These models have revealed that the α-1, 6 link is much more mobile than the α-1, 4 link because in the former case the link involves a carbon atom outside the pyranose ring. Cori and Larner find it conceivable that the greater mobility of the side branch permits its complete degradation by phosphorylase.

A closer understanding of the biological synthesis of glycogen was achieved by the discovery of enzymes which specifically catalyze branching (Cori, 19; Haworth et al., 42; Nussenbaum and Hassid, 82). Larner (66) has recently shown by means of carbon-labelled glucose-1-phosphate how this branching enzyme operates in muscle and liver. "Phosphorylase LD" was built up with ^{14}C-labelled glucose-1-phosphate in the presence of crystalline muscle phosphorylase to yield long straight chains. This long-chained ^{14}C polysaccharide was isolated and subsequently exposed to the action of the branching enzyme. The modified polysaccharide was isolated and subjected to enzymatic analysis by means of crystalline muscle phosphorylase and α-1, 6 amyloglucosidase. Larner found by this procedure that ^{14}C glucose-1-phosphate as well as free ^{14}C glucose could be isolated, demonstrating directly that straight chains were converted into branched. The branching enzyme from muscle and liver works on branches of a length between 6 and 11 residues. The Q enzyme from potato operates similarly, with the sole difference that it requires chain lengths with an average of 14 glucose residues before it will bring about a branching. A chain length of 14 residues in the outer chain is the average chain length of amylopectin. With the discoveries of α-glucose-1-phosphate, phosphorylase, the primers, and finally the branching enzyme, the course of biosynthesis of cellular glycogen can be accounted for in a truly elegant way.

Dextran dextrinase is an enzyme discovered in the medium from cultures of *Acetobacter capsularum* (Hehre, 44). This enzyme seems to catalyze, as a basic reaction step, the transfer of an α-D-glucopyranosyl radical from a terminal position in an appropriate linear dextrin molecule to a terminal position in a growing dextran molecule, as illustrated in Fig. 2. Repetition of this basic step could then lead to the simultaneous degradation of a dextrin molecule and growth of a dextran molecule, viz.,

$$\text{dextrin}_x + \text{dextran}_y \rightleftharpoons \text{dextrin}_{x-1} + \text{dextrin}_{y+1} \rightleftharpoons \text{dextrin}_{x-2} + \text{dextran}_{y+2},$$
$$\text{etc.,}$$

where the subscripts represent degrees of polymerization. For such a repetitive process to occur, the catalytic agent must have affinity for a range of dextrins as glucosyl group donors as well as for a range of dextrans as glucosyl acceptors, and Hehre believes that the *Acetobacter* enzyme has such affinity. The range of suitable dextrin substrates extends from materials that give some purple color with iodine down to 3- or 4-unit amylosaccharides, many of which would be required for the formation of an individual macromolecule of dextran. That is, n molecules of a particular dextrin with x transferable glucose units (or n molecules of various sized dextrins with an average of x transferable units) would be converted into a dextran polymer of nx units plus n units of a residual saccharide, which in the case of conversion of linear dextrins may possibly be maltose or maltotriose.

The large unhydrolyzed starch components or glycogens are not

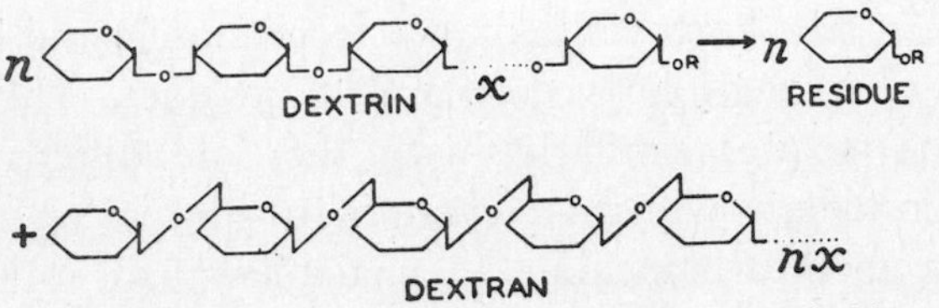

Concept of the over-all action of *Acetobacter* dextran-dextrinase

Fig. 2.

converted to serologically detectable dextran in the presence of the acetobacter enzyme, nor do they retard the enzymic conversion of dextrin to dextran.

Amylomaltase (97, 25). This enzyme, which is formed in a mutant of *Escherichia coli*, operates independent of phosphate according to the equation:

$$n \text{ maltose} \rightleftharpoons n \text{ glucose} + \alpha\text{-}1, 4 \text{ polysaccharide } (n).$$

If glucose is removed as it is formed (for instance, by addition of glucose oxidase), the polysaccharide produced gives, like starch, a blue complex with iodine. If the glucose is allowed to accumulate, the product formed does not give a blue color with iodine, but is a dextrin-like polysaccharide composed, on the average, of 4 to 6 glucose units. The formation of different products, depending on the glucose concentration, was shown to be due to the reversibility of the reaction, presumably according to the following scheme:

$$(C_6H_{10}O_5)_n + m\, C_6H_{12}O_6 \rightleftharpoons (C_5H_{10}O_5)_{n-m} + (C_{12}H_{22}O_{11})_m.$$

Maltose was isolated as the result of addition of glucose to the digest. In the assay glucose-1-phosphate was always added, since the bacterial preparations contain phosphorylase which would otherwise phosphorolyze the $(C_6H_{10}O_5)_n$ formed, and subsequently, due to the presence of phosphoglucomutase in the preparations, convert the glucosyl units to hexose-6-phosphate. The equilibrium constant is not known. In general, it seems reasonable that a conversion of 1, 4 linkage from a disaccharide to a polysaccharide can be turned in the opposite direction.

Sucrose phosphorylase. During a study of the metabolism of *Pseudomonas saccharophila* Doudoroff found that this strain was unable to use free glucose or free fructose, if added from outside, but that sucrose was utilized very efficiently. It is well-known that the outcome of this study was, among other things, the isolation of sucrose phosphorylase (26), an enzyme which catalyzes the following reaction:

sucrose + phosphate $\rightleftharpoons$ α-D-glucose-1-phosphate + fructose (furanose form)

$\Updownarrow$

(pyranose form)

The reaction is reversible, the phosphorolysis predominating (see section on thermodynamics).

The substrate specificity of the sucrose phosphorylase from *Pseudomonas saccharophila* has been worked out in detail, and some common steric requirements can be deduced from these studies. The specificity with regard to the glucose portion is absolute, i. e., so far α-D-glucopyranose-1-phosphate is the only ester which will react. The enzyme can combine this ester with another component provided it conforms to certain spatial requirements. Gottschalk, who has studied this problem, states the requirements as follows: " R, the glucose acceptor, must possess adjacent to the glucosidic oxygen an OH group, *cis* disposed and co-directional with the OH group of C_2 of the α-D-glucopyranosyl residue." Besides, the spatial requirements shown in Fig. 3 of the other groups of the monosaccharide have to be fulfilled. That L-arabinopyranose is able to react because it fulfills the requirements can be seen if it is written in the way in

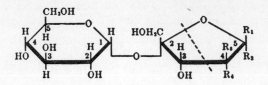

		R_1	R_2	R_3	R_4
a.	α-D-Glucopyranosyl-β-D-fructofuranoside (*i.e.*, sucrose)	H	CH_2OH	OH	H
b.	α-D-Glucopyranosyl-α-L-sorbofuranoside	CH_2OH	H	OH	H
c.	α-D-Glucopyranosyl-β-D-xyloketofuranoside	H	H	OH	H
d.	α-D-Glucopyranosyl-β-L-arabinoketofuranoside	H	H	H	OH

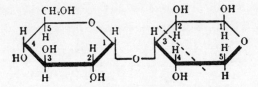

3-α-D-Glucopyranosyl-L-arabinopyranose

FIG. 3.   Steric specificities of sucrose phosphorylase.
(After Hassid, 40)

which Hassid presents it (40). Hassid and Gottschalk have pointed out that the reason why the phosphate ion can replace the sugar could be due to the fact that the length of the P–O bond of the tetrahedral phosphate ion is practically equal to the length of C–O and C–C bonds in sugars.

Maltose phosphorylase. The discovery of this interesting enzyme also stems back to work on utilization of sugars by a particular bacterial species, *Neisseria meningitidis*. It was found that maltose is utilized much more rapidly than glucose. Bacterial extracts bring about a phosphorolysis of maltose (Fitting and Doudoroff, 31). The ester formed was shown by enzymatic assays not to be α-D-glucose-1-phosphate. Fitting and Doudoroff purified the ester formed and a comparison of it with the synthetic β-D-glucose-1-phosphate (Wolfrom et al., 105) strongly indicated their identity. No other phosphoric esters or glucosyl compounds can replace β-D-glucose-1-phosphate as glycosyl donor in the reaction, catalyzed by the maltose phosphorylase. As to the glucosyl acceptors, glucose is the most active and the equilibrium can be formulated as follows:

maltose (α-1, 4) + phosphate $\rightleftharpoons$ β-D-glucose-1-phosphate + glucose.

Galactose, ribose, or maltose will not serve as glucosyl acceptors. Interestingly enough, D-xylose seems to be one of the few sugars which will liberate phosphate from β-glucose-1-phosphate in the presence of the enzyme; a disaccharide containing xylose, presumably α-D-glucosido-xylose, was detected. Fitting and Doudoroff successfully pursued other problems concerned with this new phosphorylase. Some of them it will be better to discuss under the sections dealing with thermodynamic aspects of enzyme mechanisms.

SUCRASES

Amylosucrase. The 1, 2 linkage of sucrose can be used to form either 1, 4 or 1, 6 linkages.

An example of enzymatic transformation of sucrose into a 1, 4 glucoside is the enzymatic conversion of sucrose into a glycogen-like 1, 4 polysaccharide. The enzyme which was extracted from a Gram-positive coccus, *Neisseria perflava*, was called amylosucrase by Hehre (48). The reaction can be expressed as follows:

$$n(C_{12}H_{22}O_{11}) \longrightarrow (C_6H_{10}O_5)_n + n(C_6H_{12}O_6)$$

$$\text{sucrose} \qquad \text{polyglucoside} \qquad \text{fructose}$$
$$(\alpha\text{-1, 4})$$

The polyglycoside formed gives a brown color with iodine and is broken down by amylases.

Dextran sucrase is an enzyme excreted by *Leuconostoc mesen-*

teroides. It forms from sucrose a dextran, α-1, 6 glucosidic poly-saccharide, (Hehre and Sugg, 43), which is precipitable by alcohol (see Chapter III).

$$n(C_{12}H_{22}O_{11}) \xrightarrow{\text{dextransucrase}} (C_6H_{10}O_5)_n + n \text{ fructose}$$

$$\begin{array}{cc} n \text{ sucrose} & \text{dextran} \\ (\alpha, 1\text{-}2) & (\alpha, 1\text{-}6) \end{array}$$

It is known that some dextrans have branches (presumably extra 1, 4 linkages) and they must therefore be formed as the result of action by at least two enzymes.

Levan sucrase is an enzyme which can be demonstrated in extracts from autolyzed bacteria of the strain *Aerobacter levanicum* (Hestrin and Avineri-Shapiro, 48). It catalyzes the following reaction:

$$n(C_{12}H_{22}O_{11}) \longrightarrow (C_6H_{10}O_5)_n + n(C_6H_{12}O_6)$$

$$\begin{array}{ccc} \text{sucrose} & \text{levan} & \text{glucose} \\ (\alpha\text{-}1, 2) & (\alpha\text{-}2, 6) \end{array}$$

This is a transformation of α-1,2 disaccharides into an α-2, 6 fructosidic polydisaccharide. The equilibrium is far towards the right, but there is evidence for reversibility from the fact that extra additions of invertase and glucose bring about a faster breakdown of levan than could be achieved with either component alone.

Other trans-O-glucosidases. Culture filtrates of *Aspergillus oryzae* contain a transglucosidase which converts maltose to isomaltose (6-(α-D-glucosyl) glucose) and to 6-(α-D-glucosyl) maltose, 6-(α-D-glucosyl) isomaltose, and an unidentified tetrasaccharide (85).* The products were identified by paper chromatography. The enzyme is inactive on glucose and glucose-1-phosphate. Incubation of the enzyme with maltose and a small amount of C^{14} glucose results in the formation of radioactive isomaltose and 6-(α-D-glucosyl) iso-

---

* These may be represented schematically in the following manner:

$$G^{py} \underset{1 \quad 4}{\overset{\alpha}{\rule{1.5cm}{0.4pt}}} G^{py} \text{ (maltose)}; \quad G^{py} \underset{1 \quad 6}{\overset{\alpha}{\rule{1.5cm}{0.4pt}}} G^{py} \text{ (isomaltose)}; \quad G^{py} \underset{1 \quad 6}{\overset{\alpha}{\rule{1.5cm}{0.4pt}}} G^{py} \underset{1 \quad 4}{\overset{\alpha}{\rule{1.5cm}{0.4pt}}} G^{py};$$

$$G^{py} \underset{1 \quad 6}{\overset{\alpha}{\rule{1.5cm}{0.4pt}}} G^{py} \underset{1 \quad 6}{\overset{\alpha}{\rule{1.5cm}{0.4pt}}} G^{py}, \text{ respectively.}$$

maltose along with nonradioactive 6-(α-D-glucosyl) maltose. The enzyme appears to transfer a 1, 4-linked glucosyl unit of maltose to the 6-position of glucose so as to yield isomaltose, which in turn can accept another residue to form 6-(α-D-glucosyl) isomaltose.

Transfructosidation. Bacon and Edelman (3) and Blanchard and Albon (6) independently observed that oligosaccharides containing fructose and glucose were formed during the action of yeast invertase preparations on sucrose and suggested that the enzyme may also act as transfructosidase. One of the oligosaccharides was tentatively identified as a trisaccharide containing fructose and glucose in the proportion 2 : 1. When yeast invertase preparations act on sucrose, in the presence of methanol, ethanol, n-propanol, or benzyl-alcohol, the corresponding fructosides seem to be formed as the sucrose is hydrolyzed (2). The product formed in the presence of methanol was isolated, partially purified, and tentatively identified as the β-methylfructofuranoside. It is important that the partner, i. e., the fructose acceptor, be present in rather high concentrations.

Whelan and Jones (76) have shown that incubation of high concentrations of β-methylfructofuranosyl and glucose with invertase brings about a formation of a disaccharide by transfructosylation. The disaccharide was identified as 6-[β-D-fructofuranosyl]-D-glucose i. e., $G \dfrac{\beta\text{-fu}}{2 \quad 6} F$.

Further evidence for the occurrence of transfructosidation has been presented by Edelman and Bacon with enzyme preparations from artichoke tubers (30). These preparations catalyze the transfer of fructose residues from inulin (a polysaccharide containing fructofuranosyl units linked through β-1, 2 bonds) to sucrose, so as to form a trisaccharide as well as higher oligosaccharides. The trisaccharide contains fructose and glucose in the ratio 2 : 1, like the one formed in the sucrose invertase reaction. The artichoke enzymes also catalyze the transfer of fructofuranosyl residues to raffinose, melizitose, and free fructose, but not to maltose, lactose, trehalose, or glucose. Thus the acceptor must be either fructose itself or a fructose-containing oligosaccharide. The preparations contain inulase, and the question arises again whether the hydrolytic and group-transfer reactions are catalyzed by the same enzyme.

Invertase from honey seems to be able to catalyze a trans-O-glucosidation instead of a trans-O-fructosidation (33).

Transgalactosidation. Wallenfels (99) found that extracts of various fungi contain a lactase which can also act as a transgalactosidase. One of the more important oligosaccharides formed by it is presumably galactosido-lactose. *Lactase* from *Saccharomyces fragilis* or *E. coli* can also catalyze the formation of oligosaccharides (1). The following combinations of disaccharides can be formed: Galactose-glucose; galactose-galactose; and the trisaccharide galactose-glucose 2 : 1. These findings show that transgalactosidation to glucose, galactose, and lactose, respectively, takes place. Other molecules, such as xylose and glycerol, also appear to serve as acceptors. It is possible that this type of transgalactosidation may play a role in *Lactobacillus bulgaricus Sarles*, which requires β-galactosides as growth factors (94).

Nucleoside phosphorylases. These enzymes are found in animal tissue as well as in many microorganisms. There is at least one group of enzymes which is specific for purine nucleosides and another group specific for pyrimidine nucleosides. Presumably there is one enzyme catalyzing the fission of ribosides and another for the fission of deoxyribosides. The phosphorolytic fission of inosine, for instance, can be formulated as follows:

$$\text{ribofuranose-1-hypoxanthine (inosine)} + \text{phosphate} \xrightleftharpoons[]{\text{nucleoside phosphorylase}} \text{ribofuranose-1-phosphate} + \text{hypoxanthine}$$

The 1-ester can be obtained in large amounts if the hypoxanthine formed is removed again by addition of xanthine oxidase, which oxidizes it to uric acid. The corresponding 1-ester of deoxyribose has been obtained by the same procedure, starting with hypoxanthine deoxyriboside. If the phosphopentosyl compounds are incubated with hypoxanthine or guanine and purine nucleoside phosphorylase, the purine ribosides are resynthesized and inorganic phosphate is liberated (56, 32). In the corresponding enzymic resynthesis of hypoxanthine deoxyriboside, it was shown that the product had high growth factor activity towards *Thermobacterium acidophilus* R26, which is a deoxyribosyl-requiring lactic acid bacterium (50). The enzymic equilibrium is towards purine incorporation both when studied with ribosyl phosphate and with deoxyribosyl phosphate (see Fig. 4). The addition of arsenate to nucleoside phosphorylase in the presence of deoxyribosides yields free deoxyribose (76).

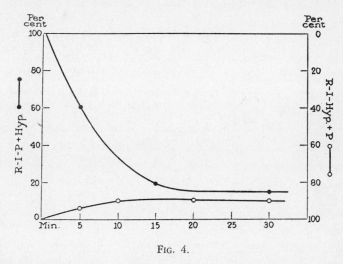

FIG. 4.

Graphic illustration of the equilibrium, ribose-1-phosphate (R-1-P) + hypoxanthine (Hyp.) ⇌ ribose-1-hypoxanthine (R-1-Hyp.) + phosphate (P). Abscissa, incubation time in minutes; ordinate, concentration of substrate mixture in percentage of initial concentration. The ordinate at the left applies to the mixture R-1-P + Hyp. (●); the ordinate at the right to the mixture R-1-Hyp. + P (O).

Properties of pentosyl phosphates. The two pentose-1-phosphoric esters are highly acid-labile, especially deoxyribose-1-phosphate, which is 50 per cent dephosphorylated at 20° within 15 minutes at pH 4 (33), and thus it is an example of one of the most acid-labile compounds of this type hitherto described. Ribofuranose-1-phosphate is fairly stable at pH 4 but highly acid-labile in strong mineral acid (in 0.5 N sulfuric acid at 20° it is hydrolyzed to the extent of 50 per cent within 2.5 minutes (71)). Ribose-1-phosphate is therefore stable under the conditions of the Lowry-Lopez phosphate determination method (71). The properties of the pentose-1-phosphates and of other phosphoglycosyl compounds are summarized in Table 2. Although the pentose-1-phosphates are formed from β-nucleosides (72), it is nevertheless difficult to make any suggestions with regard to the configuration of the phosphopentosyl compounds.

TABLE 2

STABILITY OF SOME ALDOSE–1–PHOSPHATE ESTERS

	neutral and weak alkaline react.	acetate buffer pH 4.0	0.5(N) H_2SO_4		cofactor in phosphosugar mutase
	20°	20°	20°	100°	
a glucopyranose-1-phosphate	stable	stable	stable	labile	0
β glucopyranose-1-phosphate	stable	stable	stable	labile	0
a glucopyranose-1, 6-diphosphate *	stable	stable	stable	labile	+
ribofuranose-1-phosphate	stable	stable	labile 50% in 2.5′		0
ribopyranose-1-phosphate **	stable	stable	labile 50% in 90′		0
ribose-1, 5-diphosphate	stable	stable	labile 50% in 5′		+
deoxyribofuranose-1-phosphate	stable	labile 50% in 15′	extr. labile		0

* Synthetic preparation (courtesy Prof. Posternak).
** Synthetic preparation (courtesy Prof. A. R. Todd).

Enzymic phosphorolytic fission of the 1, 4-a-glycosidic linkages of glycogen and starch yields a-glucose-1-phosphate, as does the corresponding fission of sucrose (20, 27). In contrast, the a-1, 4 glycosidic linkage of maltose yields β-glucose-1-phosphate (31). Whether there may be a single inversion, a double inversion, or no inversion at all, in the phosphorolysis of β-nucleosides, is at the present stage impossible to predict (see section on mechanism).

Specificity of the nitrogenous bases. The fact that the phosphorolysis of the purine and pyrimidine nucleosides is not catalyzed by the same enzyme has been established beyond any doubt (Deutsch and Laser, 24; Klein, 58; Manson and Lampen, 76). Paege and Schlenck (85) have described a pyrimidine nucleoside phosphorylase present in *E. coli* and specific for uridine. As to the question whether the same enzyme can catalyze the phosphorolysis of ribosides and deoxyribosides, or whether two enzymes are required, nothing definite can be stated. Studies on rat liver purine nucleoside phosphorylase indicate a common enzyme for the two pentoses (32), but in the bacteria the behavior indicated that two independent enzymes may be operating (55, 34).

The specificity of the liver purine nucleoside phosphorylase with respect to the nitrogenous aglycone is very unpredictable. Hypoxanthine and guanine ribosides or deoxyribosides are swiftly phosphorylized. The corresponding xanthine compounds react very slowly, however, and the rate of synthesis of the corresponding ribosides is of the same order of magnitude.

Surprisingly enough, adenine is not an active participant in the nucleoside phosphorylation reaction; correspondingly a direct phosphorolytic fission of adenosine does not occur, and the attack on this compound is preceded by a deamination of adenosine to inosine. An exception to these observations has recently been reported. *E. coli* apparently contains an enzyme which specifically catalyzed the phosphorolysis of adenosine (64).

Purine derivatives as antigrowth factors and mutagens and their relation to nucleoside phosphorylase. Among the many unpredictable facts concerning the specificity of this enzyme is the finding by Friedkin (35) that 8-azoguanine, incubated with ribose-1-phosphate or deoxyribose-1-phosphate in the presence of liver nucleoside phosphorylase, gives excellent yields of the corresponding azoguanine nucleosides. According to Kidder (57), 8-azoguanine is a strong antigrowth factor for *Tetrahymena geleii*, a microorganism which requires guanine as a growth factor. Also certain tumors are inhibited by azoguanine (57). Friedkin's findings raise the problem as to whether the participation of azoguanine in nucleoside (or nucleotide) metabolism can account for the suppression of growth. The enzymatically formed azoguanine ribosides were assayed by Kidder for growth inhibition on *Tetrahymena geleii* and were found to exert, on a molar basis, half the inhibitory effect of free azoguanine. A detailed study of the incorporation of azoguanine into nucleotides and nucleic acids (bypassing of nucleosides?) has not yet been performed, but experiments using isotopically labelled azoguanine (78) lend support to the theory (57) that this substance can give rise to the formation of abnormal nucleotides and nucleic acids. The author of the present review is, however, more inclined to bring up another aspect which might help to interpret the data collected on the effect of azoguanine on the growth of certain mammary carcinomas in mice. Friedkin's experiments show that azoguanine forms ribosyl or deoxyribosyl compounds very effectively. This might imply that under certain conditions (types of tumors where the availability or the rate of formation of ribosyl, especially deoxy-ribosyl, is such as barely to suffice for rapid growth) a side-tracking by azoguanine will manifest itself biologically. The conditions hinted at could be rapid expansive growth, during which the rate of biosynthesis of pentosyl in general becomes a limiting factor. If azoguanine acts like a ribosyl or deoxyribosyl trap it would greatly inhibit growth under such circumstances. The same type of effect may play a role in the antimutagenic effect of guanosine, inosine, and adenosine (Novick and Szilard, 81), as these compounds are able to reverse the mutagenic action of dimethylxanthine, azoguanine, and other purine derivatives (36). If ribosides, which are potential ribosyl phosphate producers, can incorporate some of the mutagenic purine derivatives, the latter will not appear in the deoxyribonucleic acids, which might again imply that they are accordingly barred from producing mutations. In this case the ribosyl compounds may function as a trap of mutagenic purines like azoguanine or 1, 3-dimethyl xanthine. The fact that the nucleosides also suppress the normal or " spontaneous " mutation rate adds to the interest of the whole phenomenon.

Phosphorolysis of pyridinium nucleosides. Rowen and Kornberg (89) have found that nicotinamide riboside (pyridinium ($\overset{+}{N}$) riboside) undergoes a phosphorolysis catalyzed by a liver enzyme which seems to be identical with the purine nucleoside phosphorylase. The reaction is reversible. These observations are particularly surprising because the pyridinium $(\overset{+}{N})$ riboside linkage does not have the typical properties of a substituted glycosidic linkage. It is, for instance, more labile towards alkali than towards acid (100). The reduced nicotinamide riboside (monohydro-pyridine riboside) is much more labile towards acids than towards alkali (100), i.e., it behaves like a typical glycoside; yet the reduced form is inert towards the enzyme. These problems will be discussed further in later sections.

Trans-N-glycosidases. During a study of the enzymes of *Lactobacillus helveticus* MacNutt (73) discovered this group of enzymes, which catalyzes the following type of reaction:

purine deoxyriboside + pyrimidine ⇌ purine + pyrimidine deoxyriboside.

TABLE 3

FORMATION OF DEOXYRIBOSIDES

adenine	+
guanine	+
hypoxanthine	+
xanthine	+
aminoglyoxaline-5-carbonamide	+
formamido malonamidine HCl	0
uric acid	0
2.6 diamino purine	0
thymine	+
uracil	+
5-methyl cytosine	+
4: 5: 6: triaminopyrimidine	0
methyl uracil	0

The reaction could also take place between two purines—even molecules of the same purine (54)—or between two pyrimidines. Table 3 lists purines and pyrimidines which could be incorporated in deoxyribosyl linkage by this enzyme, with a few examples of inert nitrogenous bases.

Of special interest is the fact that an incomplete purine structure like 4-amino glyoxaline 5-carbonamide (4-amino imidazole carboxamide) can be incorporated enzymatically in deoxyribosyl linkage. It seems that purine precursors can also be incorporated in ribosyl linkage (especially of ribose-5-phosphate). The riboside formed takes up formic acid, presumably to give hypoxanthine ribose-5-phosphate. The active participation of 5-methyl cytosine is also of interest. The trans-N-glycosidases of deoxyribosides were found in abundance in extracts from a number of lactic acid bacteria which under various conditions required either deoxyribosides or vitamin B_{12} as growth factors. Extracts from the same group of bacteria contained no detectable amounts of nucleoside (or deoxynucleoside) phosphorylase, and deoxyribose-1-phosphate was consequently found to be inactive. Ribosides may also exchange their bases by means of such an enzyme. However, this has so far not been possible to assay because dialyzed extracts from L. helveticus, L. delbrückii, and other B_{12}-requiring strains contain a very strong ribosidase which catalyzes the hydrolysis of the nucleosides to the free bases and free ribose (53). The occurrence of such a ribosidase has also been described in other organisms (11). Trans-N-glycosidases of deoxyribosides have since been described in E. coli (64). The specificity is more restricted here, i. e., there seems to be one enzyme catalyzing pyrimidine exchange and one for purine exchange.

Nucleotide transglycosidases. Although very few details are available yet, there is reason to think that the coenzyme of glucuronide synthesis operates as a glycosyl donor. According to Dutton and Storey (29), this coenzyme is a uridine diphosphoglucuronide and it is a reasonable assumption that the glucuronide acceptor (for instance, a phenol) reacts with the combined nucleotide to yield a glucuronide compound and UDP (see below).

The (DPN$^+$)-N-transglycosidase. The nucleosidase of DPN which liberates free nicotinamide and ADP-ribose (75, 39) has been studied recently by Zatman, Kaplan, and Colowick (108). They found that the well-known inhibition of the liberation of the pyridine base by nicotinamide was a typical competitive inhibition in the case of nucleosidase from *Neurospora.* However, the seemingly corresponding enzyme from spleen which is more strongly "inhibited" by nicotinamide than the neurospora enzyme, behaves differently. The inhibition is not competitive. By using ^{14}C-labelled nicotinamide, it was found that the spleen enzyme readily incorporates the radio-active base into DPN, whereas the neurospora enzyme is not able to catalyze such a synthesis. Several other aspects of this study will be discussed later. It suffices to state here that the spleen enzyme offers a particularly striking example of a hydrolase which can also act as a transglycosidase. The inability of the corresponding neuro-spora enzyme to bring about a synthesis makes the matter so much the more interesting. The possibility that the spleen enzyme can exchange nicotinamide for another base, for instance, an ordinary amine or a purine, is under investigation (108). The mode of action of this enzyme may be analogous to that of thiaminase (Woolley, 107).

The incorporation of nitrogenous bases in general may take place not only at the nucleoside or nucleotide stage but into more complex compounds like DPN (or ADP-ribose) or like some of the dinucleo-tides isolated from ribonucleic acid (Merrifield and Woolley, 77). In the latter case it was shown that uracil-requiring micro-organisms cannot be satisfied by uridine or uridylic acids (3 or 5) but respond particularly well to cytidylic acid dinucleotides.

Role of ribose-1, 5-*diphosphate in nucleotide formation and in the biosynthesis of purines.* The consideration of alternative pathways of ribose-1-phosphate metabolism is crucial to the understanding of the problem of nucleotide synthesis. Two independent investigators studying hypoxanthine synthesis in pigeon liver have found evidence for ribose-5-phosphate as the carrier of both incomplete purine precursors and complete purines. Greenberg (38) found that ^{14}C-labelled formic acid added to pigeon liver extract appeared in the hypoxanthine of 5-inosinic acid (hypoxanthine-ribose-5-phosphate) in markedly higher concentration than in that of inosine and of free hypoxanthine. Inosine had a conspicuously low isotope concentra-tion, and Greenberg was therefore led to believe that in the synthesis of purine nucleotides the nucleosides were bypassed. The nucleosides were considered to be breakdown products from nucleic acids and nucleotides and not steps on the biosynthetic pathway to the latter compounds. Such a bypassing of nucleosides was also indicated in some studies on nicotinamide nucleotide synthesis in hemolysates (67). A third observation of importance was the stimulation of inosinic acid synthesis in pigeon liver extract by the combined action of adenosine triphosphate and ribose-5-phosphate (Buchanan, 7).

It will be noticed that the studies performed on unfractionated extracts of tissues have given, in general, some extra information about nucleotide metabolism and have given hints about the existence of reactions which have so far not been detected in more fractionated systems. Consequently, studies on more or less intact or unfractionated liver preparations (4) were initiated. Bennett and I injected 8-^{14}C adenine into a perfused rabbit liver and found that the adenine had largely disappeared from the blood within 5 minutes. A large proportion was found in the adenylpyrophosphate (ADP, ATP) fraction (4). Goldwasser studied the purine metabolism of liver slices and homogenates and found that a marked incorporation of adenine into nucleotide took place (37). Homogenates of pigeon liver turned out, as on so many previous occasions, to be the most reproducible cell-free system. The supernatant obtained from spinning at 100,000 g was practically free of microsomes and possessed all the activity. The adenine was incorporated into 5-adenylic acid or adenosine diphosphate (37). Saffran and Scarano (90) have recently found that the particle-free extract is completely inactivated by dialysis, but can be completely reactivated by adding ribose-5-phosphate and ATP. The ribose-5-phosphate can be replaced by ribose-1-phosphate, but ribose-2-phosphate, ribose-3-phosphate, deoxyribose-1-phosphate, or ribose are not active (Table 4).

In contrast to the original extract, the dialyzed preparation incorporates adenine mostly into AMP. ATP could be shown to react with ribose-5-phosphate. The ATP-dependent enzyme is destroyed by heating at 65° for 5 minutes; preincubation of ribose-5-phosphate and ATP with the dialyzed extract, followed by heating at 65°, and then a further incubation with ^{14}C adenine, yielded ^{14}C-AMP, but there was no incorporation when the ribose-5-phosphate and

ATP were added only after the heating step (90). The adenine-incorporating enzyme is therefore stable in contrast to the enzyme which catalyzes the reaction of ATP with ribose monophosphate.

These observations were very close to a previous one made by the Buchanan group (7) namely, that an enhancement of inosinic acid formation occurs in pigeon liver by a combined action of ATP and ribose-5-phosphate. The obvious question was whether ATP phosphorylated ribose monophosphate (1 or 5-ester) to ribose-1, 5-

TABLE 4

FORMATION OF C^{14}–AMP FROM C^{14}–ADENINE BY A DIALYZED
PIGEON-LIVER EXTRACT

Dialyzed extract + C^{14}-adenine	cts/min in 5-AMP
	15
+ R-5-P + ATP	1868
+ R-1-P + ATP	2550
+ R-2 or 3-P + ATP	53
+ DR-1-P + ATP	30
+ ribose + ATP	90
+ ATP alone	22
+ R-1-P alone	82
+ α-G-1, 6-P$_2$ + R-1-P + Phosphoglucomutase	1840
+ R-1-P + phosphoglucomutase *	1110

* Spectrophotometric assay showed the presence of G-1,6-P$_2$ in the phosphoglucomutase preparation.

From Saffron and Scarano (90).

diphosphate. Here Saffran and Scarano were able to benefit from Klenow's demonstration that this ester is formed as the result of an interaction between ribose-5-phosphate and glucose-1, 6-diphosphate (60). It is necessary at this point to make a few remarks about phosphoribomutase.

The significance of phosphoribomutase in analogy with phosphoglucomutase (96) was first clearly recognized by Schlenck (92). Manson and Lampen found that deoxyribosides can be converted to deoxyribose-5-phosphate. Klenow and Larsen found that phosphoribomutase from muscle and yeast (60) can be activated by small amounts of synthetic α-D-glucose-1, 6-diphosphate. It should be added that the muscle phosphoribomutase requires an activator only in the presence of 8-hydroxyquinoline. A clue to the understanding of the nature of activation of phosphoribomutase was given by the following type of reaction:

ribose-1-phosphate + α-D-glucose-1, 6-diphosphate ⇌
ribose-1, 5-diphosphate + glucose-6-phosphate

This reaction, which is analogous to Leloir's reaction between α-D-glucose-1, 6-diphosphate and mannose-1-phosphate (69), can be pushed toward the right (and demonstrated optically) by addition of " Zwischenferment " and triphosphopyridine nucleotide (TPN), in the presence of which the glucose-6-phosphate is oxidized (100). The new diester which was isolated by means of chromatography on a Dowex 1 column has a strong cofactor activity in the phosphoribomutase test. Table 2 lists some of the properties of ribose-1, 5-diphosphate. It will be noticed that although the 1-ester phosphate is acid-labile it is not so labile as ribose-1-monophosphate.

With this knowledge about the formation and properties of ribose-1, 5-diphosphate, Saffran and Scarano were in a position to furnish further evidence for ribose-1, 5-diphosphate as the ester which reacts with radioactive adenine to yield 5-adenylic acid. First of all, they showed that incorporation of adenine can be increased just as much by preincubation with ribose-1-phosphate and glucose-1, 6-diphosphate (synthetic, (87)) as with the former and ATP.

Secondly, the ribose ester formed after these preincubations possesses the properties described by Klenow. It remains to study the reaction between ribose-1, 5-diphosphate and adenine in more detail in order to prove that we are here in fact dealing with a simple nucleotide glycosylphosphorylase.

Scarano (91) has recently succeeded in separating the enzyme which catalyzes the phosphorylation of ribose phosphate from a number of other metabolic enzymes. The fraction which Scarano obtained was freed from phosphoribo (or gluco)mutase and the reaction was shown to be a phosphorylation of ribose-5-phosphate in the 1-position by adenosine triphosphate (ATP + R-5-P → ADP + R-1, 5-P). The ribose diphosphate formed in this reaction was active as a cofactor in the phosphoribomutase test and greatly increased the rate of incorporation of adenine into 5-adenylic acid in the heat-stable liver fractions containing nucleotide phosphorylase.

The role of ribose-1, 5-diphosphate is probably not limited to its functions as a co-phosphoribomutase and as an exchange substance for adenine and hypoxanthine. It may also be the substance which reacts with nicotinamide (cf. Leder and Handler, 67), and perhaps it can, in general, serve as a " ribotyl " (5-phospho-ribosyl) unit for precursors of purines and pyrimidines.

THERMODYNAMICAL CONSIDERATIONS

Equilibrium data for reactions catalyzed by glycosyl transferases permit calculation of free energy data for the various types of glycosyl linkages. The studies on enzymic glycogen synthesis contain more interesting data than any other investigations in this field and will therefore be treated in greater detail, so much the more since several recent reviews have not given the later studies on muscle phosphorylase the attention they really deserve.

Glycogen phosphorylase. It was mentioned earlier that muscle phosphorylases build up 1, 4 polysaccharide chains by lengthening the branches of an already existing glycogen molecule. The equilibrium constant could be expressed as

$$K = \frac{[\text{terminal maltosidic linkage}] \times [\text{phosphate}]}{[\text{terminal glucose}] \times [\text{glucose-1-phosphate}]} \qquad (21)$$

By varying the glycogen concentration between 20 mg. per cent and 500 mg. per cent the Coris found that the equilibrium constant K is entirely determined by the ratio

$$\frac{[\text{phosphate}]}{[\text{glucose-1-phosphate}]}$$

i. e., the equilibrium of the reaction is independent of the glycogen concentration. The reason why the value of this ratio at a given pH is independent of the concentration of polysaccharide (within wide limits) must be attributed to the fact that the terminal glucose units (within a wide range) are equally active as glucosyl donors (terminal maltosidic linkage) and glucosyl acceptors (terminal glucose). Therefore, by adding more glycogen, the concentration of glucosyl donors and glycosyl acceptors is increased equally. Hence:

$$K = \frac{[\text{glucosyl donor}] \times [\text{phosphate}]}{[\text{glucosyl acceptor}] \times [\text{glucose-1-phosphate}]}$$

is equal to

$$\frac{[\text{phosphate}]}{[\text{glucose-1-phosphate}]}.$$

The variation of the ratio $\frac{[\text{phosphate}]}{[\text{glucose-1-phosphate}]}\left(\frac{P}{\text{G-1-P}}\right)$ with pH can be calculated by determining the value of the ratio for any pH, provided the pK values of the partners are known. The ratio $\left(\frac{P}{\text{G-1-P}}\right)$ has been found to be 2 at pH 8, at which pH both compounds are fully dissociated. If $A^=_P$ signifies the amount of phosphate present as divalent anion, and $A^=_{\text{G-1-P}}$ the amount of glucose-1-phosphate present as divalent anion, the ratio $\frac{P}{\text{G-1-P}}$ at pH 6 can be calculated from the following equation (Krebs, 62):

$$\frac{P}{\text{G-1-P}} = \frac{A^{--}_P}{A^{--}_{\text{G-1-P}}} \times \frac{K_2^{\text{GP}}([H^+] + K_2^P)}{K_2^P([H^+] + K_2^{\text{GP}})},$$

in which K_2^{GP} is the second dissociation constant for glucose-1-phosphate (7.76×10^{-7}) and K_2^P the corresponding constant for phosphate (1.5×10^{-7}). Since $\frac{A^{--}_P}{A^{--}_{\text{G-1-P}}}$ was found to be ca. 2, one has at pH 6:

$$\frac{P}{\text{G-1-P}} = 2 \times \frac{7.76 \times 10^{-7}(10^{-6} + 1.5 \times 10^{-7})}{1.5 \times 10^{-7}(10^{-6} + 7.76 \times 10^{-7})} = 6.8.$$

Hestrin has studied the border case in which the terminal groups of the polysaccharide can act solely as glucosyl acceptors, that is with a limit dextrin, obtained by the action of phosphorylase on glycogen. This type of limit dextrin, which was discussed on p. 679 (see Fig. 1), has the branches cut down to the minimum and therefore, if present in a molar excess over glucose-1-phosphate, cannot play the role of a glucosyl donor. It is clear that in this border case the limit dextrin will behave like any other glucosyl acceptor (for instance, like fructose or a purine) and the equilibrium constant must include the dextrin concentration.

In the expression:

$$K = \frac{[\text{terminal maltosidic linkage}] \times [\text{phosphate}]}{[\text{terminal glucose}] \times [\text{glucose-1-phosphate}]},$$

the concentration of terminal maltosidic linkages formed is equal to the consumption of glucose-1-phosphate (Δ glucose-1-phosphate) for the formation of one additional unit on the acceptors (limit dextrin in molar excess). The concentration of terminal glucose is proportional to the concentration of limit dextrin, which is supposed to contain ca. 14 per cent of terminal glucose. Expressed in directly measurable terms, we have:

$$K = \frac{[\Delta \text{ glucose-1-phosphate}] \times [\text{phosphate}]}{0.14 \times [\text{limit dextrin}] \times [\text{glucose-1-phosphate}]}.$$

To the formation of 1, 4 glycosidic chains added on the terminal groups of glycogen we have $K = \dfrac{[\text{phosphate}]}{[\text{glucose-1-phosphate}]}$, in which, K is independent of the polysaccharide concentration.

As will appear from Table 5, in the analogous reaction starting from the limit dextrin phosphorylase product, K has become dependent on the initial saccharide concentration and is smaller than the K found for the chain building from glycogen. This is illustrated in Table 5.

The kinetics of the formation of maltosidic linear chains on glycogen has been studied by Cori, Cori, and Green (22). They found that at constant pH and temperature and at a concentration of glucose-1-phosphate of 16×10^{-3} mol (the Michaelis constant being 5.7×10^{-3} mol) and a glycogen concentration, expressed in terms of the molarity of terminal groups, of 5.5×10^{-3} mol (the Michaelis constant being 1.2×10^{-4} mol), the reaction behaved kinetically like that of a reversible first order reaction.

Inasmuch as the formation of maltosidic linkages is a reaction between terminal glucose units and glucose-1-phosphate, one would expect the reaction to behave like a second order reaction. However, granted that the enzyme is almost saturated with respect to the reactants (compare the above mentioned concentrations as compared

TABLE 5

SUMMARIZED FROM HESTRIN (47)

μmols LD terminal groups (G_{LD})	μmols inorg. P	μmols. G–1–P	μmols G–1–P	$\dfrac{P}{G–1–P}$
at start	at equil.	at equil.	from start to equil.	at equil.
8	13	1.36	1.0	9.6
4	3.7	0.44	0.6	8.4
2	3.2	0.53	0.5	6.1

$\dfrac{[P]}{[G–1–P]}$ of glycogen at same pH (pH 7.3) $= 4.3$.

$$K_E = \frac{[G–1–P] \times [P]}{[G_{LD}] \times [G–1–P]} = \frac{1 \times 13}{7 \times 1.36} = \frac{0.5 \times 3.22}{1.5 \times 0.53} = 1.6.$$

with the Michaelis constants), the very peculiar dual nature of the end-group units, serving as glycosyl donors as well as acceptors, implies that the concentration of one of the partners remains constant during the course of the reaction. We have so far been confronted with very few examples of such concealed bimolecular reactions in enzyme chemistry. Let me mention another example which probably belongs to this category: Leloir's phosphoglucomutase reaction between diphospho-sugars and monoesters (69, 96).

The corresponding reaction between limit dextrin, phosphate and glucose-1-phosphate should follow a second order reaction. No data are available yet.

Interestingly enough, addition of free glucose acts as an inhibitor of glycogen phosphorylase in the following way. If

$$\left(\frac{1}{\text{glucose-1-phosphate}} \right)^2$$

is plotted against the reciprocal velocity, the glucose effect can be described as competitive inhibition. Also, a marked decrease of the glycogen concentration brings about an alteration in the time course of the process, approaching a second order reaction. Since a decrease in the concentration of terminal units in comparison with glucose-1·phosphate will give rise to the formation of long branches, the lengths of the branches may approach the border case in which the terminal groups function preferentially as glucosyl donors.

The thermodynamic data for transglycosidases and phosphorylases are of considerable interest for the understanding of many features of glycosyl metabolism. The equilibrium constant:

$$K = \frac{[\text{sucrose}] \times [\text{phosphate}]}{[a\text{-glucose-1-phosphate}] \times [\text{fructose}]}$$

was found to be 0.05 at a pH about 7 (41). For each mol sucrose (a-D-glucopyranosyl-2-fructofuranoside), i. e., $G^{py}\frac{\alpha}{1\ 2}F^{fu}$, formed from a-glucose-1-phosphate, between 1700 and 1800 cal. have to be furnished.

Doudoroff has proposed the idea that the sucrose formed in vivo is subsequently phosphorylated in the fructose moiety by ATP. This hypothesis, which is supported by experiments on *Pseudomonas putrefaciens* (Klein, 59), using ^{14}C-labelled fructose, is able to explain why the fructose moiety of sucrose can be utilized by the intact cell, whereas free fructose cannot. Formation of sucrose phosphate would also help to explain the enormous accumulation of sucrose in certain plants.

Since the equilibrium of the reaction catalyzed by sucrose phosphorylase greatly favors fission, it would be necessary in order to obtain sucrose phosphate to add some extra energy (phosphorylation from ATP?). A subsequent dephosphorylation of such an ester to free sucrose could give it a reasonable chance to accumulate in large amounts. A sucrose phosphate has recently been detected in the leaves of the sugar beet (8a). The possible role of uridine diphosphoglucose (UDPG) in the sucrose phosphorylase reaction will be discussed under the section dealing with mechanisms.

Some inconsistencies of equilibrium studies with thermal data.
Burton and Krebs (10) have called attention to the fact that thermal
data of changes in free energy by hydrolysis of disaccharides give
values which are much higher than those obtained from the calculation of the ester phosphate-bond energy and equilibrium studies.
For sucrose, ΔF is 10.8 Kcal. as compared with 6.6 Kcal. from
equilibrium studies. For the splitting of maltose the inconsistencies
of the energy data are truly grotesque: 23 Kcal. from thermal data
and 4.2 Kcal. from equilibrium studies. The reliability of the thermal
data for sucrose is fairly well guaranteed. One wonders whether
the thermal data for maltose do not need a revised recalculation.
Anyway, I hesitate to begin to revise our concepts of phosphate-bond
energy.

In the case of maltose phosphorylase, energy is released by forming
maltose from β-glucose-1-phosphate.

$$K = \frac{[\text{maltose}][\text{phosphate}]}{[\beta\text{-glucose-1-phosphate}][\text{glucose}]}$$

at pH 7 was found to be 4.4 (31). Since this equilibrium constant
is close to 100 times as great as that for sucrose formation, the bond
energy level of the maltose ($G^{py} \dfrac{\alpha}{1\ \ 4} G^{py}$) linkage is about 2700
cal. lower than that of sucrose ($G^{py} \dfrac{\alpha}{1\ \ 2} F^{fu}$), a relation which again
implies that close to 1000 cal. are released when 1 mol of β-glucose-
1-phosphate is converted into maltose. This is provided the bond
energy of the phospho-glycosyl is not essentially influenced by an
α-β inversion. Estimating the bond energy of the C–O–P–1– ester
as approximately 4800 cal., the bond energy of the sucrose glycosyl
linkage must be approximately 6600 cal. and that of maltose consequently close to 4000 cal. The bond energy of the 1, 6 glycosyl
linkage in dextran or isomaltose is probably distinctly lower than that
of the 1, 4 linkage. This is especially borne out by studies performed
on the transglycosidase from *Aspergillus oryzae*. This enzyme con-
verts maltose into isomaltose and panose ($G^{py} \dfrac{\alpha}{1\ \ 6} G^{py} \dfrac{\alpha}{1\ \ 4} G^{py}$).
Carbon-14-labelled glucose was readily incorporated into isomaltosyl

compounds, but not into maltose (85). Some recent studies indicate that the reaction:

$$2 \text{ maltose} \rightleftharpoons 1 \text{ glucose} + 1 \text{ panose}$$

is reversible. The trend seems to be the same with dextran dextrinase (44), i. e., from dextrins to dextrans. The bond energy of 1, 6 linkages may very well be below 2000 cal., and this would mean that it should be possible to demonstrate that amylo-1, 6 glucosidases (18, 49) can catalyze the formation of $(G^{py} \frac{\alpha}{1 \ 6} G^{py})$ linkages. The limit dextrin (phosphorylase-product) might be the best substrate for such studies.

The equilibrium constants for the reactions catalyzed by nucleoside phosphorylase

$$K = \frac{[\text{purine riboside}] \times [\text{P}]}{[\text{ribose-1-phosphate}] \times [\text{purine}]}$$

are of the order of 15, and for a purine like 8-azoguanine, which is an active partner in this reaction, K may be considerably larger. This may be of interest in connection with the problem whether ribosyl or deoxyribosyl are trapping agents for 8-azoguanine or, vice versa, whether the latter is trapping the former (51).

Theophylline (1, 3 dimethylxanthine) has greatly restricted resonance and tautomeric possibilities as compared with unsubstituted hydroxy or amino purines. One would therefore expect that in a reaction with ribose-1-phosphate (or ribose-1, 5-diphosphate) the equilibrium would be overwhelmingly toward the side of the formation of theophylline riboside (or ribotide). These considerations may bear on the observations that ribosides which can form ribose-1-phosphate, such as guanosine and inosine, are antimutagens toward theophylline and azoguanine, which are mutagens (81, 36).

A particularly interesting case is afforded by the data on the equilibrium constant

$$K_{eq} = \frac{[\text{N}^+_{\text{nic.}}\text{-riboside}] \times [\text{P}]}{[\text{N}_{\text{nic.}}] \times [\text{ribose-1-phosphate}] \times [\text{H}^+]},$$

which was reported to be around 10 at a pH of 7.4 (89). The

pyridinium N^+ glycosidic bond seemed therefore to have a bond energy essentially of the same order of magnitude as that of the purine N^+ glycosidic bond.

However, as pointed out by Zatman, Kaplan, and Colowick (108), the fact that the concentrations were expressed in μmol per ml. instead of mmol per ml. is a factor of importance in the case of K_{eq}, since using mmol instead of μmol would make K_{eq} bigger by a factor of 10^3.

$$K' = \frac{[N^+_{nic.}\text{-riboside}] \times [P]}{[N_{nic.}] \times [\text{ribose-1-P}]},$$

being uninfluenced by the selection of dimensions, would have been a more instructive expression to use in order to get an idea of the size of the bond energy at a specified pH. Using Rowen and Kornberg's experimental measurements, K' is 10^{-3} at pH 7 and 10^{-4} at pH 8. This means that at pH 7 (and 25°) approximately 4200 cal. are released by the phosphorolysis of the N^+ ribosidic bond under liberation of one H^+, and at pH 8 the same process releases ca. 5600 cal. A phosphorolysis of an ordinary N-ribosidic linkage would have consumed close to 1000 cal., this figure being dependent on pH to a limited degree only. It is actually difficult to compare bond energies of the two linkages, inasmuch as a large proportion of the energy release by phosphorolysis (or hydrolysis) of the N^+-ribosidic linkage has to do with the fact that the primary reaction product $\overset{\diagdown N^+ \diagup}{H}$ can be described as an acid which immediately repels the hydrogen as H^+. Since it is known that pyridine has a pK^{acid} of 5 and consequently a pK^{base} of 9, the process can be split up in two steps. Since at pH 7 $N^+_{nic.} \times 10^{-5} = N_{nic.} \times 10^{-7}$ we have $N^+_{nic.} = N_{nic.} \times 10^{-2}$.

The equilibrium constant for the pure phosphorolysis,

$$\overset{\diagdown N^+ \diagup}{\underset{R}{|}} + HOPO_3^{--} \rightleftharpoons \overset{\diagdown N^+ \diagup}{\underset{H}{|}} \quad R\text{-O-}PO_3^{--}$$

at pH 7 would be:

$$\frac{[(N^+H)_{nic.}] \times [\text{ribose-1-P}]}{[N^+_{nic.}\text{-riboside}] \times [P]} = 10^3 \times 10^{-2} = 10.$$

That is to say, the phosphorolysis proper at pH 7 releases approximately 1400 cal. (the hydrolysis at the same pH releases 1400 + 4800 = 6200 cal.). The remainder of the energy at this pH stems from the dissociation, $\overset{\diagdown\ N^+\ \diagup}{\underset{H}{\big|}} \rightleftharpoons N + H^+$ and corresponds to $RT \log \dfrac{10^{-5}}{10^{-7}}$ = approximately 2800 cal. Total sum for the Rowen-Kornberg phosphorolysis at pH 7 is therefore 4200 cal., and for the hydrolysis, 9000 cal.

The ΔF of hydrolysis of the NH-riboside linkage is only 4000 cal. and since the pK^{acid} of the hypoxanthine-N number 7 is probably 8 or more, the 5000 cal. difference between the ΔF of the fission of $N^+_{nic.}$-riboside and $N_{hypox.}$-riboside could largely be accounted for by the difference in pK^{acid} (or pK^{base}) values of the two types of free nitrogenous bases (e. g., $N^+_{nic.}$ and $NH_{hypox.}$).

One might therefore also illustrate the difference between the fission of the two types of compounds as follows. In both cases the thermodynamical stability of the N base is greatly increased by improved resonance and other factors. This release of free energy is, however, compensated in the $N_{hypox.}$-ribosidic fission by a concentration reaction by which H^+ and OH^- of the aqueous solvent are incorporated into the aglucone and the glycosyl radical respectively. In the $N^+_{nic.}$-riboside fission, however, the nitrogenous compound has no affinity for H^+, the concentration work of incorporating OH^- into the glycosyl moiety being the only energy-requiring factor.

The difference between the two types of N-glycosyls in the concentration work at pH 7, if we assume a pK^{acid} of 5 for $N^+_{nic.}$ and of 9 for $N_{hypox.}H$ can be calculated from the following equations. Since $\Delta F = RT(pK-pH)$, we have at pH 7:

For $N^+_{nic.}H$: $\Delta F = RT(5\text{-}7)$ — approx. — 2800 cal.;
i.e., a release of free energy.

For $N^+_{hypox.}$: $\Delta F = RT(9\text{-}7)$ = approx. + 2800 cal.;
i. e., a consumption of free energy.

The difference is 2×2800 cal., i. e., 5600 cal., a value which is a little higher than the 5000 cal. found. The pK^{acid} for $N_{hypox.}H$ may therefore rather be about 8.5. It should be added that one can equally well express the difference between $N^+_{nic.}H$ and $NH_{hypox.}$ by stating that the former is a relatively strong base ($pK^{base} = 5$).

MECHANISM

It was pointed out in the introduction that the transglycosidic and especially phosphorolytic fission of glycosyl linkages takes place between the carbon no. 1 and the oxygen, and not between the oxygen and phosphorus atoms. This is borne out partly by the fact that in the case of "N phosphorylases" glycosyl phosphates can exchange with nitrogenous bases, forming direct carbon-nitrogen linkages (nucleoside phosphorylase reactions), and also by means of some simple and ingenious isotope studies of "O-phosphorylase" (14).

The isotope employed was ^{18}O, and this was introduced into

$$\begin{array}{cc} O & O \\ | & | \\ \text{inorganic orthophosphate to make } O-P-O^{18} \text{ or } O-P-O, \text{ etc.} \\ || & || \\ O & O^{18} \end{array}$$

If this

^{18}O-enriched phosphate is added to a mixture of glycogen and crystalline muscle phosphorylase, the phosphate cleaves the glycosyl linkage, and glucose-1-phosphate is formed. This is again subjected to fission by the hydroxyl groups at carbon-4 of the terminal groups of the polysaccharide, and so on. Suppose that the fission of the glycosyl bond was a true phosphorylation. This would mean that a sort of phosphate anhydride reacted with the OH group of the carbon 1, thus losing one molecule of water with the statistical chance of one to four of one molecule losing an ^{18}O to the very much larger water pool. In a short time, therefore, the phosphate would lose most of its ^{18}O to the water. Since Mildred Cohn found that the ^{18}O concentration of phosphate remained unaltered in glucose-1-phosphate at the end of the experiment, it was concluded that the glycogen phosphorylase reaction was a catalytic transfer of glycosyl groups (see formula in introduction p. 675).

With sucrose phosphorylase it is also possible to perform the experiment with ^{18}O-enriched inorganic phosphate and glucose-1-phosphate, since, as will be discussed in this chapter, the sucrose phosphorylase catalyses such an exchange. In this case the ^{18}O concentration at the end of the experiment was found to be equally distributed between inorganic phosphate and glucose-1-phosphate and the total pool of phosphate and 1-ester phosphate had retained all the ^{18}O. The fission therefore takes place at the C–O bond in this case as well.

The problem of a possible α-β inversion will be discussed later.

Mildred Cohn also found that acid hydrolysis of glucose-1-phosphate performed in the presence of ^{18}O-enriched water did not give rise to the formation of ^{18}O-enriched phosphate. This was a clear indication that acid hydrolysis brought about a fission of the C–O bond, presumably according to the following type of reaction

$$\underset{\overset{\displaystyle |}{O^-}}{\overset{\overset{\displaystyle OH}{\displaystyle |}}{HO-P^+-O-R}} + H^+ \rightleftharpoons \underset{\overset{\displaystyle |}{OH}}{\overset{\overset{\displaystyle OH}{\displaystyle |}}{HO-P^+-O}}\text{——}R \rightarrow \underset{\overset{\displaystyle |}{OH}}{\overset{\overset{\displaystyle OH}{\displaystyle |}}{HO-P^+-O^-}} + R^+$$

$$R^+ + H_2O \rightarrow R-OH + H$$

in which R signifies the glycosyl moiety.

The fact that acid hydrolysis takes place at the glycosyl bond is also important in view of the recent finding that acid hydrolysis of lactose yields significant amounts of oligosaccharides (1). It should be added that the acid hydrolysis of glycosyl compounds, including phosphoric esters, yields a mixture of α and β glucose.

Addition of phosphatases to glucose-1-phosphate dissolved in ^{18}O-enriched water yields ^{18}O-enriched phosphate, and this reaction must therefore take place by a fission between O and P.

The theory of glycosyl enzyme complexes. Doudoroff and his coworkers found that addition of ^{32}P-phosphate to α-glucose-1-phosphate in the presence of sucrose phosphorylase but in the absence of fructose brought about a rapid exchange of phosphate, yielding ^{32}P-glucose-1-phosphate. The addition of fructose inhibited this exchange. This interesting fact, together with the observation that the sucrose phosphorylase can also act as a transglycosidase, prompted Doudoroff, Barker, and Hassid (28) to propose a theory by which a group in the enzyme combines with the glycosyl moiety to form a " glycosyl-enzyme," according to the following equation:

glucose-1-phosphate $+$ enzyme $\rightleftharpoons$ glucose-1-enzyme $+$ phosphate

glucose-1-enzyme $+$ ^{32}P-phosphate $\rightleftharpoons$ glucose-1-^{32}P $+$ enzyme.

Radioactive sucrose with " tagged " fructose was prepared by allowing radioactive fructose to exchange for fructose in the inactive sucrose molecule in the presence of an enzymatic extract from *Pseudomonas saccharophila*, according to the reaction (106):

glucose-1-fructoside $+$ enzyme $\rightleftharpoons$ glucose-enzyme $+$ fructose.

As pointed out by Zatman, Kaplan, and Colowick (108), this is a revival of the old Langenbeck theory (65) about substrate-ferment complexes through " Hauptvalenzen " according to the equations:

$$AB + X \rightleftharpoons AX + B$$
$$AX \rightarrow A + X$$

in which X signifies the catalyst.

The application of this concept to the present problems has been immensely fruitful, but perhaps not so much in explaining a mechanism like the exchange of glycosyl phosphate. To my mind, at least, the problem has just been switched to the question of how the formation of an obscure complex, the glucose-X, takes place. Is the hemiacetal linkage preserved? Or is it temporarily broken, with formation of a 1, 1′ substituted glycosyl group (see below)? Is there a double inversion or not? What is the nature of the enzyme group?

Sucrose phosphorylase manifests a different behavior with respect to the exchange of the glycosyl phosphate in the absence or presence of the other glycosyl partner, as compared with the other phosphorylases. Table 6 gives a survey of some of the most important observations on exchange reactions catalyzed by phosphorylases, concerning the phosphate-phosphate, phosphate-other glycosyl part-ner, or phosphate-arsenate partner.

The arsenate ester undergoes instantaneous hydrolysis in water (28). This peculiar phenomenon, which goes right back to the discovery by Harden and Young of the enhancing effect of catalytic amounts of arsenate on fermentations, was first clearly recognized by Warburg and Christian (101). They assumed that an arsenate

TABLE 6

phosphorylase	^{32}P exchange of 1–ester		rate of arsenate fission		inver-sion
	absence of R *	presence of R	abs. of R	pres. of R	
sucrose phos-phorylase	rapid	rapid	rapid	rapid	no
maltose phos-phorylase	0	rapid	slow	rapid	yes
polysaccharide phosphorylase	0	rapid	no	rapid	no
ribonucleoside phosphorylase	slow	rapid	no		?
desoxyribo-nucleoside phosphorylase	0	rapid		rapid	?

* R, other glycosyl partner.

analogue of the acyl phosphate of phosphoglyceric acid was formed and instantaneously hydrolyzed again. The reason why arsenate esters have such a short lifetime in water is still obscure. It would also be of interest to know at which place in the supposed arsenate ester the secondary fission takes place. This would be another interesting application of the ^{18}O isotope. Doudoroff's ideas about a possible mechanism and sequence of enzymic glycosyl transfer in disaccharide phosphorylases are outlined in Fig. 5.

With regard to the polysaccharide phosphorylase from muscle it can be added that in the absence of polysaccharide there is no exchange between the glucose part of glucose-1-phosphate and free glucose labelled with carbon-14 isotope.

The question of α-β inversions in connection with phosphorylase or trans-glycosidases has been widely discussed. The formation of

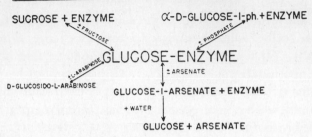

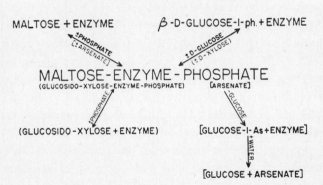

Fig. 5.   Doudoroff's interpretation of the mode of action of sucrose and maltose phosphorylases.
(After Fitting and Doudoroff, 31)

β-glucose-1-phosphate from the α glucoside linkage of maltose catalyzed by maltose phosphorylase is the first example of a clear-cut α-β-inversion brought about by this class of enzymes. In the case of sucrose phosphorylase or polysaccharide phosphorylase it has been suggested that a double inversion might take place i. e. α-glycosyl linkage yields a β-glycosyl-enzyme complex which again yields an α-glucose-1-phosphate (61). This reasoning may be fully justified for the α-glucosides where we are dealing with glycosides of the *cis* type. However, if we try to discuss the problem of inversion or no inversion in the phosphorolysis of the β-ribosides, which are glycosyls of the *trans* type, we must take cognizance of the recent studies by Hudson and his group (80) showing that benzoylated glycosyl bromides of the *trans* type upon addition of alcohols, do not give any α-β-inversion (e. g. the α-anomer of the bromide yields the α-mannoside and likewise with respect to the β-isomers of glucosides). There is offhand no reason why this could not happen with the riboside enzyme complexes. Our uncertainties have actually been increased and although we know that nucleosides are of the β-configuration we cannot predict whether the enzymatically formed ribo or deoxyribofuranose-1-phosphates are α- or β-esters.

The possibility of special prosthetic groups in the phosphorylase. The first indication that the phosphorylases may contain prosthetic groups stems back to the early work of the Cori group which showed that muscle phosphorylase requires 5-adenylic acid in trace amounts for activity (22). It was later found by the same group that muscle phosphorylase exists in two forms: " a " (which is comparatively easy to obtain in a crystalline form) and " b." Form "a" acts in the absence of 5-adenylic acid but addition of small amounts of this nucleotide brings about an enhancement in activity. If the activity per mg. enzyme protein in the presence of the maximum concentration of 5-adenylic acid (50 per cent of maximum stimulation is given by a concentration of 1.5×10^{-6} M) is called 100 per cent, then the activity of the same enzyme in the absence of 5-adenylic acid is 70 per cent (22).

Phosphorylase " b " can be obtained from muscles extracted after a prolonged tetanus. Skeletal muscle contains also an enzyme (" PR " enzyme) which converts " a " to " b." The " b " phosphorylase is completely inactive in the absence of 5-adenylic acid. A concentration of 4.5×10^{-5} M of the latter gives 50 per cent of maximum activity (22). It should be added that 5-adenylic acid does not exchange its phosphorus with P^{32} labelled inorganic phosphate in the presence of phosphorylase "b," glycogen and α-glucose-1-phosphate (15).

What is known about the nature of the prosthetic group of phosphorylase "a" as well as the mechanism of the conversion of "a" to "b" and its activation by 5-adenylic acid has until now remained very fragmentary, but the problems are so much the more fascinating. Crystalline trypsin is able to bring about a conversion of "a" to "b" (23); it probably acts by splitting off a fragment. In electrophoresis "a" moves faster as an anion than does "b" (23). There is an indication from U.V. spectra that "a" contains a purine or pyrimidine. The base is not adenine. It has not been possible to detect ribose. There are, however, distinct amounts of organic phosphorus (0.7 μg P per mg protein).* According to a recent report, recrystallized muscle phosphorylase contains 5-uridylic acid and naphthoquinone (9). I shall refrain from commenting on the finding of the latter constituent but cannot resist the temptation to discuss the possible importance of uridyl nucleotides for O or N phosphorylases and O and N transglycosidases in general. Even if the role of 5-uridylic acid in glycogen phosphorylase is uncertain there are examples of glycosyl transferring systems in which 5-uridyl compounds play a role.

The role of uridyl phosphoglycosyl compound in glycosyl transport. A few years ago Leloir and his group (12) succeeded in isolating the coenzyme of the so-called galacto-Waldenase (i. e. the enzyme which catalyzes the conversion of α-galactose-1-phosphate into α-glucose-1-phosphate) and he proved the structure to be 5-uridylic acid and α-glucose-1-phosphate linked together in a pyrophosphate linkage (uridinediphosphoglucose, UDPG, uridyl phos-

---

* It seems of interest here to mention a paper by Kritskii (63), which, although experimental details are scanty, poses some important problems concerning enzyme mechanism. He has found that crystalline muscle phosphorylase contains labile and stable phosphates. The labile P is a) released as inorganic phosphate by denaturation of the enzyme in trichloroacetic acid and b) it exchanges with inorganic phosphate added to the medium. It is of course a problem how specific the exchange with phosphate really is. It seems to be independent of the presence of polysaccharides or glucose-1-phosphate and might therefore be an adsorption. It is not excluded, however, that a phosphate-enzyme or labile ester complex exists and plays an essential role in phosphorylase reactions.

pho-1-glucose). UDPG undergoes a conversion to UDP-galactose by a very interesting reaction not as yet fully understood (the galacto-Waldenase (68).

In order to place emphasis on the fact that the phosphate is tied to the the 1 position of the hexose, I have suggested as a common term of classification, the name " uridylphosphoglycosyl " compounds. We have been interested in seeing whether nucleoside phosphorylase was somehow tied up with uridinediphosphate (UDP) in such a way that the nucleoside (or ribose-1-phosphate) was functioning as a glycosyl donor and UDP as acceptor. Calvin and his colleagues who have found UDP-glucose containing ^{14}C glucose as a product of photosynthesis (8) have also advocated such a view. They have given it the following formulation:

UDPG + fructose-6-phosphate $\rightleftharpoons$ UDP + sucrose phosphate.

The increased bond energy in a substituted glycosyl phosphate (see later) might be important for sucrose synthesis. They proposed that UDP in general might serve as glycosyl acceptor and UDPG as glycosyl-donor. It is known that the glycosyl part of UDPG can be glucose, galactose, N-acetyl glucosamine and β-glucuronic acid. The latter analogue, UDP-glucuronic acid has very recently been found to be the coenzyme of glucuronide synthesis (29). Free β-glucuronic acid-1-phosphate is inactive. There are strong indications that this process is an example in which a UDPG compound serves as a glycosyl donor and therefore undergoes fission at the O–C bond of the glycosyl linkage (see formula Fig. 6). Further studies, especially employing isotopes, will undoubtedly fully clarify this point.

If UDP-glucuronic acid is a glycosyl donor the problem arises whether polysaccharides like hyaluronic acid can serve as glycosyl donors for UDP, thus regenerating UDP-glucuronic acid. This is very well possible. An analogous situation would be the formation of 1-4 maltosidic linkages or of α-glucose-1-phosphate from UDP-glucose in the presence of polysaccharide phosphorylase. We have conducted studies, using crystalline phosphorylase " a " and found UDP-glucose inactive as an activator. We must, however, bear in mind that a specific β-form of UDP-glucose might be required here if the postulated double inversion occurs. We have also been unable to detect UDPG formation from glycogen and UDP. I feel that these negative observations do not necessarily invalidate the theory that UDPG somehow can act as a glycosyl donor and UDP as acceptor. Quite apart from the question of α and β glycosyl linkages we must also keep the question of the values of bond energies in mind. According to the rules of structural chemistry the type of linkage that we find in UDPG might make the glycosyl phosphate bond thermodynamically more unstable than that in glucose-1-phosphate and therefore increase the bond energy. If the bond

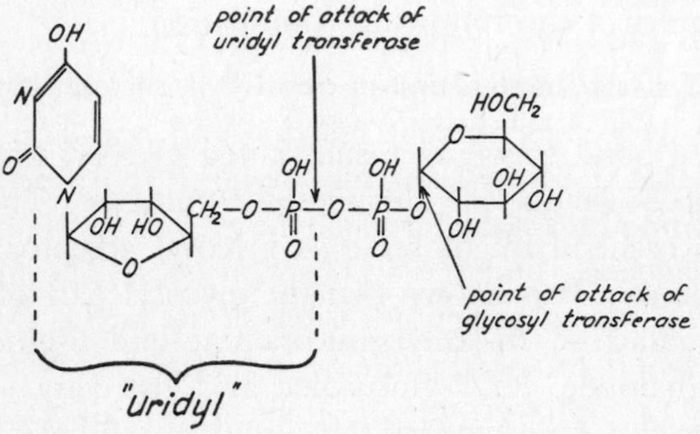

FIG. 6.   Uridinediphosphoglucose (UDPG, uridylphosphoglucosyl).

energy is greatly increased by this substitution it would make a UDPG formation from glucose-1-phosphate (or even from the more "energy rich" sucrose bond) and UDP very difficult, if not impossible. There are, however, other alternatives. We have found an enzyme which can make UDP-glucose from α-glucose-1-phosphate and uridinetriphosphate (UTP). This enzyme, which is abundant in Zwischenferment preparations (79) and in nuclei from liver cells (93), can work in both directions (79). I have classified it as belonging to a group of enzymes which one could call "uridyl transferases" because the fission takes place as shown in Fig. 6.

We have found two other uridyl transferases. One enzyme was found in galactose-adapted *Saccharomyces fragilis* and catalyzes the reaction between α-galactose-1-phosphate and UTP, forming Leloir's UDP-galactose ("Co-Waldenase") (68) and the other, in liver nuclei, involves the N-acetyl glucosamine analogue (70). Quite apart from the possible role of uridyl transferases in the formation of nucleic acid linkages I think that they may also play a role in regenerating UDP to UDPG through UTP. In forming the latter we know that ATP is needed (98, 5).

We might finish this topic by stating that at the present time we have only one example of a UDP compound serving as a glycosyl donor and even this example needs further elaboration.

Possibility of other glycosyl acceptors in enzymes. Since this symposium is liberal towards speculations provided they are constructive I venture to add a few remarks to the previously discussed enzymatic phosphorolysis of the pyridinium riboside bond. This type of reaction strikes one as a very peculiar reaction and one wonders about the possibility that a ribose-1-enzyme complex is formed in which an ordinary amino or amide group of the enzyme protein partakes and which subsequently undergoes phosphorolysis. The first step of the reaction, e. g., from pyrimidine riboside to ribose-1-enzyme, might then correspond to the thiaminase reaction (cf. Woolley's formulation (107)). The N^+ onium compound "alkylates" an amino group in the enzyme and this is subsequently subjected to a phosphorolysis according to the "ordinary" inosine phosphorylase model.

Kritskii (63) has presented evidence for a transribosidic reaction between guanosine and hypoxanthine forming guanine and inosine. The formation of the latter was not described but suspected on the basis of a demonstration of the appearance of guanine (determined as ammonia after deamination by guanase). Guanosine in the absence of hypoxanthine does not liberate guanine. The author is of the opinion that the reaction goes through a phosphorolysis step and that the enzyme bound phosphate is a partner. It is not as yet possible to decide whether the enzyme bound phosphate reacts as orthophosphate or as a phosphate ester with the enzyme.

Kritskii (63) ventures the assumption that the transglycosidic reaction of sucrose phosphorylase is a phosphorolytic reaction with enzyme-bound phosphate. However, there is much more evidence for the assumption that the sucrose phosphorylase is also a true transglycosidase. The rate of phosphate liberation from glucose brought about by sorbose depends on the concentration of the glucose-1-ester. In the " phosphate free " medium the rate of formation of glucosidosorboside is many times higher than the rate of the corresponding reaction could possibly be with traces of 1-ester (Doudoroff, Barker and Hassid (28)).

The possibility of 1, 1′ disubstitution as a step in transglycosidations. As mentioned before, the idea of an interposition of a glycosyl-enzyme complex does not tell us anything about the mechanism of exchange of glycosyl partners. As to the sequence of steps involved in such an exchange one might for instance with some justification raise the question of whether a formation of 1, 1′ compound with a temporary fission of the semiacetal linkage would not be the logical intermediary compound formed.

Subsequently there would now be a more or less equal statistical chance that the semiacetal linkage would be reconstructed by sacrificing either A or A′. In the case of deoxyriboside phosphorylase or trans-N-glycosidase there may be a chance of putting such a hypothesis to an experimental test. Deoxyribosyl compounds do not react with borate. If 1, 1′ deoxyribosyl compound were formed by sacrificing the 1-4 furanoid bond there would be a possibility that a 3, 4 borate complex could be formed and, if sufficiently stable, it would accumulate.

Mechanism of transglycosidation in hydrolytic enzymes. Although we are very far from an understanding of the enzymic glycosyl exchange the hypothesis of the glycosyl-enzyme formation has contributed to clarify the situation in one other respect, namely, that a number of hydrolases can also serve as transglycosidases. Take for example the ribosidase of DPN^+ which catalyzes the hydrolytic splitting of the pyridinium riboside bond. As mentioned previously an enzyme from spleen acts both as a hydrolase and transglycosidase; the transglycosidase becomes very marked by increasing the concentration of free nicotinamide to about 5-fold that of the DPN concentration (108). It is assumed that an ADP-ribosyl enzyme complex is formed and that this complex can react with H_2O or with another molecule of nicotinamide (unlabelled or labelled). Since the equilibrium is greatly in favor of H_2O as reactant (ΔF hydrolysis $= 9000$ cal at pH 7) the fact that nicotinamide reacts with a probability far beyond that of the simple thermodynamical equilibrium must be due to special conditions. The three main possibilities are (i) the active H_2O concentration at the surface of the enzyme is greatly reduced thus making the actual ΔF of hydrolysis much smaller. This factor might be of some importance; an increase in the nicotinamide concentration correspondingly favors the trans-N-glycosidic reaction (just as an increase in the fructose concentration enhances transfructosidation, 3). Because of the huge energy difference involved it is difficult to imagine, however, that this factor can contribute much. (ii) The enzyme suppresses the hydrogen ion dissociation from the liberated (" N^+H ")$_{nic.}$. This would lower the ΔF of hydrolysis very considerably although probably not sufficiently. (iii) The kinetics with H_2O and nicotinamide as reactants might be the essential factor. If the activation energy for fission by H_2O is lowered slightly by the enzyme (e. g., high activation energy) whereas the activation energy for the enzymic N-fission is lowered much more, one would over a limited but fairly long period of time observe an appreciable formation of the N-ribosyl compound. This possibility might be pursued experimentally by trying to measure the proportion of the hydrolytic and the transglycosidic reaction over a wide temperature range. One would expect to find that at low temperatures a relatively lower fraction of the turnover is attributed to hydrolysis and a relatively higher proportion to trans-N-glycosidic fission as compared with the distribution between the two types of fission at higher temperature. The relation could be illustrated as follows (Fig. 7).

A number of other transglycosidic reactions especially involving formation of the so-called oligosaccharides can be formulated with a glycosyl enzyme complex as an intermediary substance. For instance:

Transfructosidation (cf. (5)) for instance;

a)　sucrose $+$ enzyme$_1$ $\rightleftharpoons$ fructosyl-enzyme$_1$ $+$ glucose
((or a') (n) fructosan $+$ enzyme$_2$ $\rightleftharpoons$ fructosyl-enzyme$_2$
$\qquad\qquad$ $+$ $(n-1)$ fructosan)

b)　n fructosyl-enzyme $+$ sucrose $\rightleftharpoons$ β polyfructoside $+$ enzyme

Transglucosidation converting α, 1-4 to α, 1-6 linkages

a)　maltose $+$ enzyme $\rightarrow$ glucosyl-enzyme $+$ glucose

b)　glucosyl-enzyme $+$ ^{14}C glucose $\rightleftharpoons$ enzyme $+$ ^{14}C isomaltose

b')　glucosyl-enzyme $+$ ^{14}C isomaltose $\rightleftharpoons$ enzyme $+$ ^{14}C-6-
$\quad$ -(α-D-glucosyl) isomaltose or 6-(α-D-glucosyl) maltose-^{14}C.

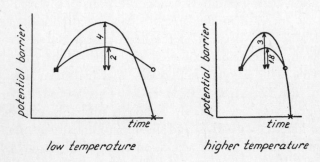

FIG. 7. Scheme to show the change in the relative amount of turnover attributable to the hydrolytic (upper curve) and transglycosidic (lower curve) reactions at low and higher temperatures.

Transgalactosidation. This can be expressed as follows:

a)　lactose (β, 1-4) $+$ enzyme $\rightleftharpoons$ galactosyl-enzyme $+$ glucose

b)　galactosyl-enzyme $+$ glucose $\rightleftharpoons$ allolactose (β, 1-6) (?) $+$ enzyme.

Aronson (1) has found that lactase from *Saccharomyces fragilis* can also catalyze the formation of 2 or 3 types of oligosaccharides. The fact that lactase can work as a transgalactosidase makes one speculate on the possibility of UDP-galactose being involved in the biosynthesis of lactose and other β-galactosides. The UDPG compounds should be considered as key substances, "organizers" (13), formed from inductors in the formation of adaptive β-galactosidase.

The formation of oligosaccharides in the acid hydrolysis of lactose may not require any special explanation. The concentration of lactose used was very high and if the glycosyl " radical " formed had a chance of reacting either with the 3, 4 or 6 hydroxyl group one would find that in Aronson's experiment the average molar concentration would be as high as 15 per cent of that of the water. If the average glycosyl-hydroxyl bond energy under standard conditions (1 Mol/L or an " activity " of 1 of the reactants) was 2700 cal., 1 per cent of the constituents should be present as $(C_6H_{10}O_5)_n$.

RECAPITULATION AND GENERAL CONSIDERATIONS

Enzymic transfer of glycosyl groups occurs as a common biological reaction. The glycosyl donors include not only monosaccharides but also polysaccharides and sugar-phosphoric esters. The glycosyl acceptors comprise many different classes of compounds: the hydroxyl of a sugar, inorganic phosphate, or the nitrogen of a series of nitrogenous bases.

In the synthesis of branched polysaccharides like glycogen there is an interesting interplay between the formation of α-1, 4 glucoside linkages, producing straight chains, and the formation of α-1, 6 glucosidic linkages, forming the basis for a new side-chain. The branching factor acts independently of the phosphorylase. The bond energy of glucosyl linkages varies. It seems to be largest in the 1, 2 linkage of sucrose, lower in the 1, 4 linkage, and lowest in the 1, 6 linkage. In the pentosyl series the $\overset{+}{N}$-ribosyl linkage of DPN has a considerably higher bond energy at pH 7 and at more alkaline reactions than N-ribosyl linkages of pyrimidine or purine ribosides.

There is no reason, however, to assume that the bond energies of the α-glucose-1-phosphate Cori-ester and that of β-glucose-1-phosphate are essentially different. Both types of phosphoglycosyl linkages can form maltosidic units. The α-esters form maltosidic linkages $(G^{py} \frac{a}{1 \quad 4} G^{py})$ in a polysaccharide, whereas the β-ester has recently been shown to play a role in the formation of free maltose.

Leloir and his coworkers have discovered two new types of 1-phosphoglucosyl compound, viz., α-glucose-, 6-diphosphate and uridinediphosphoglucose (UDPGlucosyl). It is not known whether the bond energy of the phosphoglucosyl linkage of a-glucose-1,6-diphosphate is substantially higher than that of a-glucose-1-phosphate. In the case of the analogous ribose-1-phosphate and ribose-1, 5-diphosphate it may be possible to compare the bond energies, since it has been possible to isolate enzymes which catalyse the incorporation of purines in lieu of the 1-phosphate group of both types of esters. The first type of enzyme is called a nucleoside phosphorylase, the second type a nucleotide phosphorylase. Both types of enzymes catalyse the incorporation of hypoxanthine, giving rise to the formation of inosine and 5-inosinic acid, respectively. The nucleotide phosphorylase catalyses also the incorporation of adenine, yielding 5-adenylic acid.

The a-phosphoglucosyl linkage of UDPG may have a considerably higher bond energy than that of free a-glucose-1-phosphate, due to the fact that the phosphate is tied up in a pyrophosphate linkage with the phosphate of 5-uridylic acid. It has been proposed (8) that uridine diphosphate (UDP) plays a role as a transfer substance of glycosyl groups, i. e., that the UDP might accept a glycosyl group from a polysaccharide, for instance, and donate it to another glycosyl acceptor.

If, however, the 1-ester bond of UDP-glucose has a significant larger $+ \Delta F$ of formation than that of the free Cori-ester, it may be doubtful whether UDP would function effectively as a transfer compound of glycosyl groups. In this case the cycle might rather be as follows:

(a)   UDP-Glycosyl $+$ Acceptor $A \rightleftharpoons$ UDP $+$ A-Glycosyl

(b)   UDP $+$ ATP $\rightleftharpoons$ UTP $+$ ADP

(c)   UTP $+$ P-Glycosyl $\rightleftharpoons$ UDP-Glycosyl $+$ P–P (pyrophosphate).

Reaction (a) may be the formation of a glucuronide or the addition of an extra glycosyl linkage in a polysaccharide. Reaction (b) is catalysed by an enzyme which has been described recently by Berg and Joklik (5). The enzyme, which might be called nucleoside polyphosphate transphosphorylase, is an acid-stable protein present in yeast and muscle. Reaction (c) is the uridyltransferase described in this paper.

The class of UDP-glycosyl (uridylphosphoglycosyl) compounds of the type discovered by Leloir and Park undoubtedly have many diverse functions. One possibility which should be looked into is the capacity to induce enzyme formation on an adaptive or even on a constitutive basis. The existence of intermediary substances operating between the so-called inducing substances and the enzyme formation, " organisateurs " as Monod calls them, are apparently formed gradually, probably under the consumption of energy. Monod and Cohn have found that some α-galactosides can induce formation of β-galactosidase although they are neither substrates nor inhibitors of the enzyme. It is not too unreasonable to turn one's attention once more to UDP-glucose and related substances and try to plan experiments which might reveal one more function exercised by this interesting class of nucleotides.

REFERENCES

1. Aronson, M. 1953. Transgalactosidation during lactose hydrolysis. *Arch. Biochem. and Biophys.*, **39**, 370-378.
2. Bacon, J. S. D. 1952. Transfructosidation by a yeast invertase preparation. *Biochem. J.*, **50**, XVIII.
3. Bacon, J. D. S., and J. Edelman. 1950. The action of invertase preparations. *Arch. Biochem.*, **28**, 467-468.
4. Bennett, E., and H. M. Kalckar. 1952. Unpub.
5. Berg, P., and W. Joklik. 1953. Transphosphorylation between nucleoside polyphosphates. *Nature*, in press.
6. Blanchard, P. H., and N. Albon. 1951. The inversion of sucrose, a complication. *Arch. Biochem.*, **29**, 220-222.
7. Buchanan, J. M. 1952. Studies on the biosynthesis of purines in vitro. In *Phosphorus Metabolism*, II (W. D. McElroy and B. Glass, eds.), 406-422, Johns Hopkins Press, Baltimore.
8. Buchanan, J. G., J. A. Bassham, A. A. Benson, D. F. Brodlay, M. Calvin, L. L. Daus, M. Goodman, P. M. Hayes, V. H. Lynch, L. T. Norris, and A. T. Wilson. 1952. The role of phosphate in the metabolism of photosynthetic and chemoautotrophic organisms. In *A Symposium on Phosphorus Metabolism*, Vol. II (W. D. McElroy and B. Glass, eds.), pp. 440-466. The Johns Hopkins Press, Baltimore.
8a. Buchanan, J. G. 1953. Sucrose phosphate in leaves from sugar beets. *Arch. Biochem. Biophys.*, **44**, 140.
9. Buell, M. V. 1952. The non-protein moiety of phosphorylase. *Federation Proc.*, **11**, 192.
10. Burton, K., and H. A. Krebs. 1953. The free-energy changes associated with the individual steps etc. *Biochem. J.*, **54**, 94-107.

11. Carter, C. E. 1951. Partial purification of a non-phosphorylytic uridine nucleotidase from yeast. *J. Amer. Chem. Soc.*, 73, 1508-1513.

12. Caputto, R., L. F. Leloir, C. E. Cardini, and A. C. Paladini. 1950. Isolation of the coenzyme of the galactose phosphate-glucose phosphate transformation. *J. Biol. Chem.*, 184, 333-350.

13. Cohn, M., and J. Monod. 1953. Specific induction and inhibition of enzyme biosynthesis, *Symposium, Soc. Gen. Microbiol., London*, April, 1953.

14. Cohn, M. 1949. Mechanisms of cleavage of glucose-1-phosphate. *J. Biol. Chem.*, 180, 771-781.

15. Cohn, M., and G. T. Cori. 1948. On the mechanism of action of muscle and potato phosphorylase. *J. Biol. Chem.*, 175, 89-93.

16. Cori, C. F., and G. T. Cori. 1936. Mechanism of formation of hexose-monophosphate in muscle and isolation of a new phosphate ester. *Proc. Soc. Exp. Biol. Med.*, 34, 702-705.

17. Cori, C. F., and G. T. Cori. 1947. Polysaccharide phosphorylase. *Les prix Nobel*, 216.

18. Cori, G. T., and J. Larner. 1951. Action of amylo-1, 6-glucosidase and phosphorylase on glycogen and amylopectin. *J. Biol. Chem.*, 188, 17-29.

19. Cori, G. T., and C. F. Cori. 1943. Crystalline Muscle Phosphorylase, IV. Formation of Glycogen. *J. Biol. Chem.*, 151, 57-63.

20. Cori, C. F., S. P. Colowick, and G. T. Cori. 1937. The isolation and synthesis of glucose-1-phosphoric acid. *J. Biol. Chem.*, 121, 465-477.

21. Cori, G. T., M. A. Swanson, and C. F. Cori. 1945. The mechanism of the formation of starch. *Federation Proc.*, 4, 234-241.

22. Cori, C. F., G. T. Cori, and A. A. Green. 1943. Crystalline muscle phosphorylase. III. Kinetics. *J. Biol. Chem.*, 151, 39-55.

23. Cori, G. T., and C. F. Cori. 1945. The enzymatic conversion of phosphorylase a to b. *J. Biol. Chem.*, 158, 321-332.

24. Deutsch, W., and R. Laser. 1929. Experimentelle Studien über den Nucleinstoffwechsel. *Hoppe-Seylers Z. physiol. Chem.*, 186, 1-10.

25. Doudoroff, M., W. Z. Hassid, E. W. Putnam, and A. L. Potter. 1949. Direct utilization of maltose by Escherichia coli. *J. Biol. Chem.*, 179, 921-934.

26. Doudoroff, M., N. Kaplan, and W. Z. Hassid. 1943. Phosphorolysis and synthesis of sucrose with a bacterial preparation. *J. Biol. Chem.*, 148, 67-75.

27. Doudoroff, M. 1943. Studies on the phosphorolysis of sucrose. *J. Biol. Chem.*, 151, 351-361.

28. Doudoroff, M., H. A. Barker, and W. Z. Hassid. 1947. Studies with bacterial sucrose phosphorylase I. The mechanism of action of sucrose phosphorylase as a glucose transferring enzyme. *J. Biol. Chem.*, 168, 725-732.

29. Dutton, G. J., and I. D. E. Storey. 1953. The isolation of a compound of uridine diphosphate and glucuronic acid from liver. *Proc. Biochem. Soc., Biochem. J.*, 53, XXXVII.

30. Edelman, J., and J. S. D. Bacon. 1951. Transfructosidation in extracts of the tubers of Heliantus tuberosus L. *Biochem. J.*, 49, 529-540.

31. Fitting, C., and M. Doudoroff. 1952. Phosphorolysis of maltose by enzyme preparations from Neisseria meningitidis. *J. Biol. Chem.*, 199, 153-163.

32. Friedkin, M., and H. M. Kalckar. 1950. Desoxyribose-1-phosphate I. The phosphorolysis of purine desoxyribose nucleoside. *J. Biol. Chem.*, 184, 437-448.

33. Friedkin, M. 1950. Desoxyribose-1-phosphate II. The isolation of crystalline desoxyribose-1-phosphate. *J. Biol. Chem.*, 184, 449-459.

34. Friedkin, M. 1952. Pers. com.

35. Friedkin, M. In *A Symposium on Phosphorus Metabolism*, I (W. D. McElroy and B. Glass, eds.), Johns Hopkins Press, Baltimore (1951).
36. Fries, N., and B. Kihlman. 1948. Fungal mutations obtained with methyl xanthines. *Nature*, 162, 573.
37. Goldwasser, E. 1953. Formation of adenine nucleotides from adenine by pigeon liver homogenates. *Nature*, 171, 126.
38. Greenberg, G. R. 1951. De Novo synthesis of hypoxanthine via inosine-5-phosphate and inosine. *J. Biol. Chem.*, 190, 611-631.
39. Handler, P., and J. R. Klein. 1942. The inactivation of pyridine nucleotides by animal tissues, in vitro. *J. Biol. Chem.*, 143, 49-57.
40. Hassid, W. Z. 1951. Metabolism of polysaccharides and disaccharides. In *A Symposium on Phosphorus Metabolism*, I (W. D. McElroy and B. Glass, eds.), 11-42. Johns Hopkins Press, Baltimore (1951).
41. Hassid, W. Z., and M. Doudoroff. 1950. Synthesis of disaccharides with bacterial enzymes. *Advances in Enzymol.*, 10, 123-143.
42. Haworth, W. N., S. Peat, and E. J. Bourne. 1944. Synthesis of amylopectin. *Nature*, 154, 236-238.
43. Hehre, E. J., and J. Y. Sugg. 1942. Serologically reactive polysaccharides produced through the action of bacterial enzymes. I. Dextran of leuconostoc mesenteroides from sucrose. *J. Exp. Med.*, 75, 339-353.
44. Hehre, E. J. 1951. The biological synthesis of dextran from dextrins. *J. Biol. Chem.*, 192, 161-174.
45. Hehre, E. J. 1949. Synthesis of polysaccharide of the starch-glycogen class from sucrose by a cell-free, bacterial enzyme system (amylosucrase). *J. Biol. Chem.*, 177, 267-279.
46. Heppel, L. A., and R. J. Hillmoe. 1952. Phosphorolysis and hydrolysis of nucleosides by yeast enzymes. 121st. Meet. Milwaukee, 180.
47. Hestrin, S. 1949. Action pattern of crystalline muscle phosphorylase. *J. Biol. Chem.*, 179, 943-955.
48. Hestrin, S., and S. Avineri-Shapiro. 1944. The mechanism of polysaccharide production from sucrose. *Biochem. J.*, 38, 2-10.
49. Hobson, P. N., W. J. Whelan, and S. Peat. 1951. The enzymatic synthesis and degradation of starch. XII. The mechanism of synthesis of amylopectin. *J. Chem. Soc.*, 596-598.
50. Hoff-Jørgensen, E., M. Friedkin, and H. M. Kalckar. 1950. Desoxyribose-1-phosphate, III. *J. Biol. Chem.*, 184, 461-464.
51. Kalckar, H. M. 1953. The role of phosphoglycosyl compounds in the biosynthesis of nucleosides and nucleotides. *Biochim. et biophys. Acta,* in press.
52. Kalckar, H. M., and E. Cutolo. 1952. Enzymic pyrophosphorolysis of uridine-diphosphoglucosyl (UDPG). IIe *Congr. Internat. de Biochimie*. Paris, 1952. 260.
53. Kalckar, H. M. 1952. The enzymes of nucleoside metabolism. *Fortschr. Chem. org. Naturstoffe*, 9, 363-400.
54. Kalckar, H. M., W. S. MacNutt, and E. Hoff-Jørgensen. 1952. Trans-N-Glycosidase studied with radioactive adenine. *Biochem. J.*, 50, 397-400.
55. Kalckar, H. M. 1951. Biosynthetic aspects of nucleosides and nucleic acids. *Pubbl. staz. zool. Napoli*, XXIII, 87-103.
56. Kalckar, H. M. 1947. The enzymatic synthesis of purine ribosides. *J. Biol. Chem.*, 177, 477-486.
57. Kidder, G. W., V. C. Dewey, and R. E. Parks. Purine metabolism in tetrahymena and its relation to malignant cells in mice. *Science*, 109, 511-514.

58. Klein, W. 1935. Experimentelle studien über den nucleinstoffwechsel. XXXVII. Über nucleosidase. *Hoppe-Seylers Z. physiol. Chem.*, **231**, 125-148.

59. Klein, H. P. 1950. Studies on the metabolism of pseudomonas putrefaciens. Thesis, University Calif., Berkeley.

60. Klenow, H., and B. Larsen. 1952. The action of phosphoglucomutase preparations on ribose-1-phosphate. *Arch. Biochem.*, **37**, 488-490.

61. Koshland, D. E. 1951. The mechanism of the hydrolysis of acetyl phosphate and its relation to some enzymatic reactions. In *Phosphorus Metabolism*, I (W. D. McElroy and B. Glass, eds.), 536-546. Johns Hopkins Press, Baltimore.

62. Krebs, H. A. 1953. The equilibrium constants of the fumarase and aconitase systems. *Biochem. J.*, **54**, 78-82.

63. Kritskii, G. A. 1950. Mechanism of phosphorylase action. *Doklady Akad. Nauk S.S.S.R.*, LXX Nr. 4.

64. Lampen, J. O. 1952. Enzymatic studies on the metabolism of nucleotides and their components in microorganisms. *Symposium on Phosphorus Metabolism*, II (W. D. McElroy and B. Glass, eds.), Johns Hopkins Press, Baltimore, 363-380.

65. Langenbeck, W. 1933. Fermentmodelle. *Ergeb. Enzymforsch.*, **2**, 314-335.

66. Larner, J. 1953. The action of branching enzymes on outer chains of glycogen. *J. Biol. Chem.*, in press.

67. Leder, I. G., and P. Handler. 1951. The synthesis of nicotinamide mononucleotide by human erythrocytes in vitro. *J. Biol. Chem.*, **189**, 889-899.

68. Leloir, L. F. 1951. The enzymatic transformation of uridine diphosphate glucose into a galactose derivative. *Arch. Biochem.*, **33**, 186-190.

69. Leloir, L. F. 1951. The metabolism of hexosephosphates. In *Phosphorus Metabolism*, I (W. D. McElroy and B. Glass, eds.), 67-93. Johns Hopkins Press, Baltimore.

70. Leloir, L. F., unpub.

71. Lowry, O. H., and J. A. Lopez. 1946. The determination of inorganic phosphate in the presence of labile phosphate esters. *J. Biol. Chem.*, **162**, 421-428.

72. Lythgoe, B., and A. R. Todd. 1947. Structure and Synthesis of Nucleotides. *Symposia Soc. Exptl. Biol.*, **I**, 15.

73. MacNutt, W. S. 1952. The enzymatically catalysed transfer of the desoxyribosyl group from one purine or pyrimidine to another. *Biochem. J.*, **50**, 384-397.

74. Maruo, B. and T. Kobayashi. 1951. Enzymatic scission of branch links in amylopectin. *Nature*, **167**, 606-607.

75. Mann, P. J. G., and J. H. Quastel. 1941. Nicotinamide, cozymase and tissue metabolism. *Biochem. J.*, **35**, 502-517.

76. Manson, L. A., and J. O. Lampen. 1951. The metabolism of desoxyribose nucleosides in Escherichia coli. *J. Biol. Chem.*, **193**, 539-547.

77. Merrifield, R. B., and D. W. Woolley, 1952. The relation of dinucleotides to the biochemistry of nucleic acids. *Symposium on phosphorus metabolism*, II. (W. D. McElroy and B. Glass, eds.), 354-358. Johns Hopkins Press, Baltimore.

78. Mitchell, J. H., H. D. Skipper, and L. L. Bennett. 1950. Investigation of the nucleic acids of viscera and tumor tissue from animals injected with radioactive 8-azoguanine. *Cancer Research*, **10**, 647.

79. Munch-Petersen, A., H. M. Kalckar, E. Cutolo, and E. E. B. Smith. 1953. *Nature*, in press.

80. Ness, R. K. H. G. Fletscher, and C. S. Hudson. 1951. New tribenzoyl-D-

ribopyranosyl halides and their reactions with methanol. *J. Am. Chem. Soc.*, 73, 959-963.

81. Nowick, A. A., and L. Szilard. 1952. Antimutagens. *Nature*, 170, 926.
82. Nussenbaum, S., and W. Z. Hassid. 1951. Enzymatic synthesis of amylopectin. *J. Biol. Chem.*, 190, 673-683.
83. Ochoa, S., and J. R. Stern. 1952. Carbohydrate Metabolism. *Ann. Rev. Biochem.*, Vol. 21, 547-602.
84. Paege, L. M., and F. Schlenk, 1950. Pyrimidine riboside metabolism. *Arch. Biochem.*, 28, 348-358.
85. Pazur, J. H., and D. French. 1951. The Transglucosidase of Aspergillus oryzae. *J. Am. Chem. Soc.*, 73, 3536.
86. Posternak, T. 1951. On the phosphorus of potato starch. *J. Biol. Chem.*, 188, 317-325.
87. Posternak, T. 1949. The synthesis of α- and β-glucose-1, 6-diphosphate. *J. Biol. Chem.*, 180, 1269-1278.
88. Rabaté, M. J. 1935. Contribution a l'étude biochemique des salicacées. *Bull. soc. chim. biol.*, 17, 572-654.
89. Rowen, J. W., and A. Kornberg. 1951. The phosphorolysis of nicotinamide riboside. *J. Biol. Chem.*, 193, 497-507.
90. Saffran, M., and E. Scarano. 1953, unpub.
91. Scarano, E. 1953, unpub.
92. Schlenk, F., and M. J. Waldvogel. 1946. Note on the metabolism of some ribose derivatives. *Arch. Biochem.*, 9, 455-456.
93. Smith, E. E. B., and A. Munch-Petersen. 1953. *Nature*, in press.
94. Snell, E. E., E. Kitag, and E. Hoff-Jørgensen. Carbohydrate utilization by a strain of lactobacillus bulgaricus. *Arch. Biochem.*, 18, 495-510.
95. Sutherland, E. W., S. P. Colowick, and C. F. Cori. 1941. The enzymatic conversion of glucose-6-phosphate to glycogen. *J. Biol. Chem.*, 140, 309-310.
96. Sutherland, E. W., M. Cohn, T. Posternak, and C. F. Cori. 1949. The mechanism of the phosphoglucomutase reaction. *J. Biol. Chem.*, 180, 1285-1295.
97. Torriani, A. M., and J. Monod. 1949. Sur la reversibilité de la réaction catalysée par l'amylomaltose. *Compt. rend.*, 228, 718-720.
98. Trucco, R. E. 1951. Enzymatic synthesis of uridine diphosphate glucose. *Arch. Biochem. and Biophys.*, 34, 482.
99. Wallenfels, K. 1951. Enzymatische synthese von oligosacchariden aus disacchariden. *Naturwissenschaften*, 38, 306-307.
100. Warburg, O., W. Christian, and A. Griese. 1935. Wasserstofübertragendes Co-ferment, seine zusammensetzung und wirkungsweise. *Biochem. Z.*, 282, 157-205.
101. Warburg, O., and W. Christian. 1939. Isolierung und Kristallisation des oxydierenden gärungsferments. *Biochem. Z.*, 303, 40-68.
102. Weibull, C., and A. Tiselius. 1945. A study of the starch phosphorylase of potato. *Arkiv. Kemi, Mineral., Geol.*, 19A, No. 1.
103. Whelan, W. J., and D. M. Jones. 1953. β-methyl fructoside as a substrate in transfructosylation. Abst. of *Biochem. J.*, 318. Meet., p. 8.
104. White, J. W., and J. Maher. 1953. Transglucosidation by honey invertase. *Arch. Biochem. and Biophys.*, 42, 360-367.
105. Wolfrom, M. L., C. S. Smith, D. E. Pletcher, and A. Brown. 1942. The β-form of the Cori-ester (d-glucopyranose-1-phosphate). *J. Am. Chem. Soc.*, 64, 23.
106. Wolochow, H., E. W. Putnam, M. Doudoroff, W. Z. Hassid, and H. A. Barker.

1949. Preparation of sucrose labeled with C^{14} in the glucose and fructose components. *J. Biol. Chem.*, **180**, 1237-1242.

107. Woolley, D. W. 1953. Biosynthesis and energy transport by enzymic reduction of "onium" salts. *Nature*, **171**, 323-328.

108. Zatman, L. J., N. O. Kaplan, and S. P. Colowick. 1953. Inhibition of spleen diphospho-pyridine-nucleotidase by nicotinamide, an exchange reaction. *J. Biol. Chem.*, **200**, 197-212.

DISCUSSION

DR. LIPMANN: This very fine talk is now open for discussion.

DR. DOUDOROFF: I would like to inquire a little bit more. As you may have noticed, in two of our papers we gave different equilibrium constants for maltose phosphorolysis. The second time we thought it was a little better, but we had to use tricks to get it. These equilibrium constants are not too good, due to the side reactions (such as the hydrolytic reaction, which I mentioned today), and also due to the extreme slowness of the reaction in the case of maltose phosphorylase; but I don't understand this big difference between our two approaches—that is, between the thermal data and the equilibrium data. It seems unreasonable. Another thing is this other type of complication, taking into consideration that the fructose in the sucrose is in a different form than in solution. Now, we get this apparent equilibrium constant, which doesn't really mean anything, since it is for the over-all reaction—that is, for the reaction of sucrose as you get it out of a bottle and put it into water. And, if one would want the energy of the bond itself, one would have to know the actual concentration of the furanose form of the fructose, and that we don't know except by various guesses. This was one of my comments. I wonder if Dr. Lipmann or Dr. Kalckar will take it up. The other thing I want to bring up is the interesting case of dextran-dextrinase. I remember we were bothered very much when Dr. Hehre's first paper came out. There was a transformation, apparently, from dextrans into dextrins and the other way around, which was demonstrated by actually separating the two forms. In other words, there seemed to be two different species of molecules. They were not mixed dextran-dextrins. It has just occurred to me that perhaps the case is one in which the two molecules have separate slots in the enzyme—that is, it isn't a matter of accepting the glucose and donating it indiscriminately to form dextran or dextrin units, but possibly a case in which the two polysaccharide molecules would lie side by side. The glucose residues that go from one to the other always must go from 1, 4 to 1, 6 or from 1, 6 to 1, 4. In that way you could build up chains of 1, 6 linkages and chains of 1, 4 linkages.

Dr. Calvin: I wonder if we could get Dr. Kalckar to write the equations on the blackboard in which this discrepancy of 6 and 23 calories applied.

Dr. Lipmann: Can we first ask about this value of 23 calories? For example, if that is the difference between two large figures for combustion values for sucrose on the one hand and glucose and fructose on the other hand, then it wouldn't be very reliable.

Dr. Calvin: I would really like to find out what the equation for the reaction is in the case of the 6 calories and in the case of the 23 calories.

Dr. Kalckar: The value of −10.8 Kcal is for the inversion of sucrose. This value of −23 is supposedly for the hydrolysis of the aqueous disaccharide.

Dr. Calvin: But where did you get the 23?

Dr. Kalckar: Well, this is from the recent paper of Burton and Krebs.

Dr. Calvin: Is this the heat of hydrolysis of sucrose?

Dr. Kalckar: No; this is free energy of hydrolysis of the disaccharide.

Dr. Calvin: Then this is the free energy of hydrolysis of sucrose into glucose and fructose at one molar concentrations?

Dr. Kalckar: Yes, under standard conditions. The discrepancy seems to be more reasonable in the case of sucrose, where you have 10.8 and 6.7. Of course, the calculation from equilibrium data is based on the bond energy of the ordinary esters as determined from equilibrium constants of phosphoric esters in the presence of phosphatases and phospho-mutases. We have to go way back to find whether the former were calculated under standard conditions or not, because there you don't have the same number of reacting molecules on both sides of the equation. For example, when you have glycerol-phosphate + water giving glycerol + phosphate, the water doesn't come into the calculations here. Whether or not the water concentration is included might affect the calculation to a large extent. I cannot recall the details of these "ancient" studies.

Dr. Lipmann: Well, if you consider the reaction in the appropriate standard states you don't have this trouble with the water concentration.

Dr. Calvin: I rather suspect that the value of 23 is based on heats of combustion data and that the free energy or entropy of formation of water has been omitted by mistake in this calculation.

Dr. Kalckar: It is a matter of subtracting one large number from the other; it rather looks like the federal budget.

Dr. Calvin: So I wouldn't be too disturbed about this.

Dr. Kalckar: My point was not to hide it.

Dr. Colowick: I would just like to get this straight. The large discrepancy was for maltose, wasn't it?

DR. KALCKAR: Yes. With sucrose the discrepancy is much smaller.

DR. LIPMANN: Now let me also get this straight. Are these free energy values?

DR. KALCKAR: They are obtained from thermal data.

DR. LIPMANN: If they are from thermal data, then they are heats of combustion?

DR. KALCKAR: Yes; but heat capacity measurements and entropy calculations are also included, so that the values are actually for free energy.

DR. CALVIN: Free energy of what? Of what reaction?

DR. KALCKAR: For the hydrolysis of disaccharides.

DR. CALVIN: I rather suspect that the direct equilibrium measurements are better and more reliable. Could I ask one question?

DR. LIPMANN: Certainly.

DR. CALVIN: You didn't say what the other product was in the reaction where you form UDPG by reaction of UTP with glucose-1-phosphate.

DR. KALCKAR: Oh, I'm sorry. The other product is inorganic pyrophosphate. We pushed the reaction by adding purified inorganic pyrophosphatase. Actually, we have in this case just been trying to get some equilibrium data for this reaction.

DR. LIPMANN: In the exchange reactions here, was that ribose-1-phosphate that you used?

DR. KALCKAR: The exchange reactions were carried out with desoxyribose-1-phosphate by Friedkin and we used ribose-1-phosphate, both in the presence of nucleoside phosphorylase.

DR. LIPMANN: Is that a slow exchange?

DR. KALCKAR: The reactions of both 1-phosphates were very slow in the absence of purines or pyrimidines. In the case of ribose-1-phosphate alone there was some exchange, however. I can say that everything, including the enzyme, was treated with norite, so that I wouldn't expect appreciable concentrations of the purine bases to be present. I have been contemplating the possibility that the nicotinamide riboside phosphorylase may act as a glycoside transfer enzyme. There is the possibility that it may be both a transglycosidase and a phosphorylase, but this is speculation.

DR. LIPMANN: What enzyme did you use for this?

DR. KALCKAR: This was a rat liver enzyme.

DR. NAJJAR: Dr. Kalckar mentioned that the conversion of ribose-1-phosphate to ribose-5-phosphate was effected by the action of phosphoglucomutase without the necessity of the coenzyme glucose-1, 6-diphosphate. Was that crystalline mutase?

Dr. Kalckar: It was carried to the most purified stage.

Dr. Najjar: During the past year Dr. L. Rosenberg and I have been studying an enzyme from rabbit muscle extract that catalyzes the formation of glucose-1, 6-phosphate from glucose-1-phosphate similar to that described in bacteria (Leloir, L. F., Trucco, R. E., Cardini, C. E., Paladini, A. C. and Caputto, R., *Arch. Biochem.* **24**: 65 (1949)). This enzyme differs from the glucose-1-phosphate kinase (Paladini, A. C., Caputto, R., Leloir, L. F., Trucco, R. E., and Cardini, C. E., *Arch. Biochem.* **23**: 55 (1949)) in the following characteristics:

(1) It needs no ATP. (2) Its pH optimum is at 8.0 instead of 6.8. (3) It has a different distribution pattern in ammonium sulfate fractions.

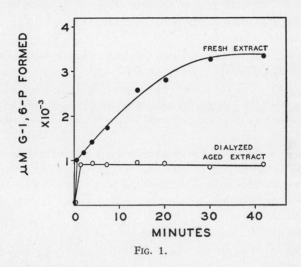

Fig. 1.

(4) It is very unstable and is completely inactivated by prolonged dialysis over 48 hrs. at 4° C. or aging over 4-5 days at 4° C. It is this last characteristic that made the following observation possible.

While studying the rate of synthesis of the glucose diphosphate by this enzyme, we observed that there occurred an explosive formation of a relatively large amount of the diphosphate within a few seconds following the addition of glucose-1-phosphate. The rate then proceeded rather slowly with a different slope as seen in the graph. We noticed further that when the enzyme was destroyed by aging or prolonged dialysis the initial formation of glucose-1, 6-phosphate was still present but that no increased synthesis took place with time as depicted in the lower curve of the graph. The magnitude of this explosive synthesis was not increased by the addition of ATP to the dialyzed extract, or boiled fresh muscle extract or by increasing the quantity of glucose-1-phosphate from 2-20 μM. It was, however, definitely dependent on the amount of enzyme used.

The foregoing facts indicated that this phenomenon was unrelated to the glucose-1-phosphate kinase or to the enzyme under study. In these extracts, therefore, glucose-1-phosphate was being phosphorylated to form the diphosphate yet neither ATP nor glucose-1-phosphate could act as the phosphate donor. The possibility that a phosphorylated enzyme might act as a phosphate donor was suggested by the explosive nature of the synthesis, its dependence only on the quantity of enzyme used and its self-limited nature.

Since the two transphosphorylation reactions referred to earlier were ruled out, the possibility of a phosphorylated phosphoglucomutase (PGM-phosphate) was considered and the following mechanism formulated:

(1)   PGM-phosphate $+$ Glucose-1-phosphate

$\rightleftarrows$ glucose-1, 6-phosphate $+$ PGM

(2)   Glucose-1, 6-phosphate $+$ PGM

$\rightleftarrows$ glucose-6-phosphate $+$ PGM-phosphate

Dr. M. Pullman and I have since tested a number of preparations of crystalline phosphoglucomutase (Najjar, V. A., *J. Biol. Chem.* **175**: 280 (1948)) with varying degrees of purity. The glucose-1, 6-phosphate synthesized by these preparations of crystalline mutase closely paralleled the mutase content as estimated by activity measurements. Experiments with pure crystalline enzyme corresponding to the highest activity obtained with electrophoretically homogeneous preparations (*ibid.*) are also included in the table. The molecular weight of the enzyme was taken as 77,700 g. (Cori, C. F., Personal Communication). The glucose-1, 6-phosphate was measured mainly by the magnitude of activation of a standardized muscle phosphoglucomutase preparation as used by previous workers (Cardini, C. E., Paladini, A. C., Caputto, R., Leloir, L. F., and Trucco, R. E., *Arch. Biochem.* **22**: 87, 1949) and also by measuring glucose-6-phosphate using the spectrophotometric method of Racker (Racker, E., *J. Biol. Chem.* **167**: 843 (1947)) after hydrolysis in 0.1 N HCl.

The mechanism postulated above shows that the PGM-phosphate is regenerated in reaction (2) and can now react as in (1), the net result being a conversion of glucose-1-phosphate to glucose-6-phosphate. The peculiarity of this reaction is that glucose-1, 6-diphosphate behaves as two substrates: in one instance transferring its 1-phosphate to the enzyme as in the forward reaction of (2) and in the other transferring its 6-phosphate to the enzyme as in the reverse reaction of (1). The above formulation also implies that the phosphorylated mutase reacts with either glucose-1-phosphate or glucose-6-phosphate to form the glucose-1, 6-phosphate. The data in the table are in accord with this formulation. Furthermore, we have shown that glucose-1, 6-phosphate reacts with dephosphorylated mutase (PGM) to yield glucose-6-phosphate as identified by the Zwischenferment.

The identification of the glucose-1, 6-phosphate synthesized from PGM-phosphate and hexose rests on the following facts. (a) the maximal stimulation of phosphoglucomutase activity in the presence of all cofactors except

THE FORMATION OF GLUCOSE-1, 6-PHOSPHATE FROM HEXOSE PHOSPHATE AND CRYSTALLINE PHOSPHOGLUCOMUTASE.

Enzyme Purity Per Cent	Enzyme μM added	Glucose-1-phosphate μM added	Glucose-6-phosphate μM added	Glucose-1, 6-phosphate formed μM $\times 10^{-3}$
100	0.015	0.02		6.4 (4.8)
"	0.018	0.01		4.6
"	"	0.02		6.3
"	"	0.04		6.4
"	"	0.20		9.3 (9.6)
"	"	2.00		9.1 (9.6)
36	0.0034	2.00		2.5
33	0.0035	2.00		2.4
"	"		1.8	3.1 (3.6)
"	"		1.8	3.5
"	0.004		2.0	4.5
"	"	2.0		3.0
20	0.0023	2.0		2.0
"	"	0.2		1.4
"	"	0.02		1.2

The enzyme mixture consisted of PGM, Hexose phosphate, Cysteine 0.5 molar and MgSO4 1×10^{-3} molar. Temperature 30° C. The values in brackets are repeat determinations of the coenzyme.

the coenzyme glucose-1, 6-phosphate, and the lack of further stimulation by added coenzyme. (b) This activation is completely destroyed by heating at 100° C. in 0.1 N HCl for 10 minutes. (c) The product of such a hydrolysis is glucose 6-phosphate. Preliminary measurements of the equilibrium constant of reactions (1) and (2) place the energy level of the mutase phosphate bond between 2000-3000 calories.

The possible existence of a phosphorylated PGM was suggested earlier (Jagannathan, V., and Luck, J. M., *J. Biol. Chem.* 179: 569 (1949)) and would adequately answer the question raised by Dr. Kalckar's observations that the crystalline mutase was able to convert ribose-1-phosphate to ribose-

5-phosphate without the need of adding glucose-1, 6-phosphate. The possibility that glucose-1, 6-phosphate is present in the enzyme as a contaminant or adsorbed in a specific manner is ruled out, since we have not been able to detect the presence of the coenzyme in any of our crystalline preparations after the enzyme is denatured and extracted by heating at 100° C. for 3-5 minutes at pH 5.0. However, using this procedure we were able to recover any added coenzyme to the native enzyme protein. (This work was supported by a research grant PHS, G-3289 from the Division of Research grants, National Institutes of Health, Public Health Service.)

DR. KALCKAR: I know that Dr. Saffran will be very much interested in this phenomenon and will be greatly relieved. We were a little worried about this strong effect of mutase plus ribose-1-phosphate on the formation of ribose diphosphate without extra additions of glucose-1, 6-diphosphate.

DR. ZATMAN: Dr. Kalckar has just referred to the exchange reaction catalysed by beef spleen DPNase and I think the results of our more recent experiments with DPNases will be of interest.

Our earlier results (Zatman, Kaplan and Colowick, *J. Biol. Chem.*, **200**, 197 (1953)) showed that the DPNase of beef spleen catalyses an exchange reaction between the nicotinamide moiety of DPN and C^{14}-labelled nicotinamide and this was cited as evidence in support of a mode of action of the DPNase which involved the reversible formation of an intermediary ARPPR-Enzyme complex:

$$\text{ARPPR}\overset{+}{\text{N}} + \text{Enz.} \rightleftharpoons \text{ARPPR} - \overset{+}{\text{Enz.}} + \text{N}$$

$$\downarrow \text{H}_2\text{O}$$

$$\text{ARP}\overset{+}{\text{P}}\text{R} + \text{Enz.} + \text{H}^+$$

As this reaction can be visualized as being a transfer of an ARPPR moiety from one nicotinamide molecule (bound in DPN) to another (free), it was early speculated that the enzyme might similarly catalyse the transfer of ARPPR from the nicotinamide of DPN to an acceptor which is structurally related to nicotinamide, resulting in the synthesis of a DPN analogue.

Our attention at this stage was turned toward the pyridine derivative isonicotinic acid hydrazide (INH) which was showing promising clinical results in the treatment of tuberculosis. Its structural relationship to nicotinamide stimulated our testing it in the beef spleen DPNase system and the results indeed indicated that it was ten times as potent an inhibitor as was nicotinamide. More extensive studies however, revealed a curious species specificity amongst the animal DPNases (Zatman, Colowick, Kaplan and Ciotti, *Bull. Johns Hopkins Hosp.*, **91**, 211 (1952)). Thus whilst the enzymes of ruminants and birds, *viz.* beef, sheep, goat, duck and pigeon, were sensitive to the INH (*ca.* 50 per cent inhibition at 10^{-4} M), those of the rat, mouse, rabbit, frog, pig, horse and man were relatively insensitive (little effect at 2×10^{-2} M). The *Neurospora* enzyme was also insensitive to the INH.

Our attempts to detect the predicted analogue using the "sensitive" beef spleen enzyme proved fruitless. The investigation of the "insensitive" enzymes however, was more successful after our initial observation of the production of a yellow colour, with an absorption maximum at about 390 mμ, which occurred on raising the pH of the system to 10.0 at the end of the incubation period. It is of interest to note that whilst INH shows only minor spectral changes at 390 mμ on raising the pH, N^1-methyl-INH immediately turns yellow and shows a peak absorption at 380 mμ.

We have since been able to isolate the yellow compound in a relatively pure form from a pig brain enzyme system (Zatman, Kaplan, Colowick and Ciotti, *J. A. C. S.*, **75**, 3293 (1953)). In neutral or acidic aqueous solution it has a single absorption peak at 260 mμ, a second peak appearing at 385 mμ when the pH is raised. Analysis for the ribose, P, INH, and 5'-adenylic acid moieties yielded values which are in reasonable agreement with the structure $\overset{+}{\text{ARPPR}}(\text{INH})$ for the analogue.

The isolation of the INH-analogue of DPN confirms the idea that certain animal DPNases can function as "ARPPR-transferases" and the following scheme satisfies all the experimental data obtained thus far with the pig brain enzyme:

$$\overset{+}{\text{ARPPRN}} + \text{Enz.}$$

$$+ \text{N} \quad \Big|\Big| \quad - \text{N}$$

$$\boxed{\text{ARPPR}-\overset{+}{\text{Enz.}}} \quad \xrightarrow{\text{H}_2\text{O}} \quad \text{ARPPR} + \text{Enz.} + \text{H}^+$$

$$- \text{INH} \quad \Big|\Big| \quad + \text{INH}$$

$$\overset{+}{\text{ARPPR}}(\text{INH}) + \text{Enz.}$$

This scheme demands that incubation of the analogue with enzyme and nicotinamide should result in the synthesis of DPN and in such an experiment about 50 per cent of the analogue was indeed converted to DPN.

When tested with the "sensitive" beef spleen enzyme, the analogue was found to be at least twice as potent an inhibitor as the free INH. On the other hand it appears to be inactive in the DPN-requiring dehydrogenase systems in which it has been tested so far.

Summarizing briefly then, certain DPNases have been shown to exhibit "ARPPR-transferase" activity and an analogue of DPN containing INH in place of the nicotinamide has been isolated. It is conceivable that such incorporation of drugs into essential coenzymes may be important in explaining the clinical activity of such compounds.

DR. LIPMANN: Dr. Zatman, does this analogue of DPN act as an inhibitor in DPN-catalyzed reactions?

DR. ZATMAN: We have tested it on yeast and liver alcohol dehydrogenases, lactic dehydrogenase and pyridine nucleotide transhydrogenase. On none of these enzymes does it have any effect.

DR. COLOWICK: But it does inhibit the DPNase.

DR. ZATMAN: Yes, it does inhibit the sensitive DPNase.

DR. LIPMANN: Did you find any other bases which would exchange with nicotinamide? I doubt that this enzyme is really a hydrolytic enzyme. I think that the last experiment you demonstrated, in which you get a synthesis of DPN, indicates what the enzyme actually does in the cell.

DR. ZATMAN: As far as the exchange with other bases is concerned, thus far we have observed analogue formation with the isopropyl derivative of isonicotinic acid hydrazide (substituted on the hydrazide N), and strangely enough, this is formed by the pig brain enzyme but not by the human prostate. Experiments with such compounds as nicotinic acid are in progress but we have no positive results to report as yet. In terms of DPN synthesis, we were thinking that the synthesis of DPN synthesized by this enzyme could only come from a precursor in which some group X was attached to the ribose in the position normally occupied by nicotinamide. Then this compound could react with nicotinamide in the presence of the enzyme to form DPN and X.

DR. LIPMANN: Yes. This residue is rather frequently found available floating around.

DR. ZATMAN: We have been speculating on the possibility that ribose-1, 5-diphosphate might react with ATP by a reaction analogous to that described by Kornberg to form pyrophosphate plus a DPN analogue in which a phosphate group is now in the position normally occupied by the nicotinamide. Such a compound could conceivably, then, be the precursor in DPN synthesis by the DPNase although it would seem unlikely from an energetics point of view.

DR. LIPMANN: Isn't this reaction almost completely analogous to the thiaminase reaction?

DR. ZATMAN: Yes, it appears to be.

DR. STROMINGER: I would like to come back to the uridyl transfer. I have recently found that compounds of the type which Dr. Park originally isolated from bacteria occur in many animal tissues also. Uridine pyrophosphate acetylamino sugar compounds are present in rather large amounts in some animal tissues — something of the order of 25 or 50 milligrams per cent. Hen's oviduct, which is the richest source that I have found, has been fractionated, and we have been able to obtain at least four different compounds. I would like to ask Dr. Kalckar whether the UDPX which he mentioned is really one compound or whether it's more than one compound, and whether the enzyme (which, interestingly enough, he describes from an animal tissue —liver nuclei) will react with all of the UDPX or with only part of it.

DR. KALCKAR: I can say only that the Park substance obtained from *Staphylococcus aureus* (grown in the presence of penicillin) and of which Dr. Park sent us samples is not attacked by the yeast enzyme. With respect to UDPX, in a letter I received from Dr. Leloir last March he told me that he had found that in the UDPX from yeast the X is identical with N-acetyl glucosamine. That is all we know at the present time. It is very interesting and very encouraging that UDPX is present in large amounts in so many different tissues. Dr. Evelyn Smith is continuing her studies on the pyrophosphorolysis of UDPX.

DR. STROMINGER: I would like to ask whether you have been able to measure the equilibrium constant for the reaction between ATP and UDP.

DR. KALCKAR: We don't know exactly, but according to my colleague Dr. Munch–Peterson the equilibrium is very close to 50:50.

DR. COLOWICK: I would like to hear what Dr. Calvin thinks of Dr. Kalckar's suggestion that the glucose-1-phosphate link in UDPG might be a more energy-rich link than that in free glucose-1-phosphate.

DR. CALVIN: I haven't thought about it, but the fact is that UDPG is more readily hydrolyzed than glucose-1-phosphate. That is the thing that identified it for us in the first place. So I would say that we would expect there to be a somewhat higher energy content in the UDPG than in the glucose-1-phosphate. The glucose-1-phosphate group is also right next door to a pyrophosphate group in the UDPG, and this might increase the energy content of the glucose-1-phosphate bond.

DR. COLOWICK: The rate of hydrolysis doesn't seem to have much relationship to the free energy of hydrolysis in some cases—for example, if you compare phospho-enol pyruvate with glucose-1-phosphate, the phospho-enol pyruvate is hydrolyzed in acid much more slowly but has a much higher free energy of hydrolysis than glucose-1-phosphate.

DR. CALVIN: That is true, but in this case we are making a comparison of UDPG with glucose-1-phosphate, in which case the bonding is the same in both compounds, and when you have a series of similar compounds it appears to be justified to draw conclusions concerning free energy of hydrolysis from rate measurements—provided, of course, that the mechanisms of hydrolysis are the same for the different members of the group.

DR. KOSHLAND: I don't quite agree with you, Dr. Calvin, because if you look at the rate of hydrolysis of phosphate esters at different pH values you find a great variation with pH even when you are dealing with the cleavage of a single compound. In these cases the change you make by varying pH may be analogous to adding a substituent. However, there is the correlation of triesters of phosphoric acid which are better phosphorylating agents than monoesters.

DR. CALVIN: The only analogy that Dr. Colowick was making was that in the case of phospho-enol pyruvate the bond which is involved is an enol linkage. The bond that is involved from carbon to oxygen to phosphorus is different from that in glucose-1-phosphate, since the adjacent groupings on the carbon are different in the two cases. On the other hand, when you compare UDPG and glucose-1-phosphate, in both cases you are hydrolyzing a bond in which the other substituents on the carbon are similar; so I think that a comparison of UDPG with glucose-1-phosphate is legitimate, whereas a comparison of glucose-1-phosphate with phosphate-enol pyruvate is not legitimate.

DR. KOSHLAND: What I am saying is that the change on going from glucose-1-phosphate at pH 7, where it exists as glucose-$OPO_3^=$, to UDPG at pH 7, which can be written as glucose-OPO_3R^-, may in reality be like going from glucose-1-phosphate at pH 7 to glucose-1-phosphate at pH 4 where it exists as glucose-OPO_3H^-. This would support Dr. Colowick's point: that the rate is not necessarily related to the equilibrium constant.

DR. KALCKAR: I wonder what Dr. Calvin would think of an attempt to attribute a role of the adjacent pyrophosphate linkage to the predicted increase in energy content of the glucose-1-phosphate linkage in UDPG. I don't know quite how to express it, but perhaps somehow the shift in electrons might cause a change in bond distances between phosphorus and oxygen in such a way as to change the energy content of the bond. These considerations are the result of discussions with my colleagues Drs. Rosenberg and Kofoed, physical chemists at the University in Copenhagen. There may be some complicating factors here worth bearing in mind.

DR. KOSHLAND: I think that anyone who talks about the energy of phosphate compounds has to be very humble about saying anything, particularly when you consider the problem of the energy content of inorganic metaphosphate as compared to ATP. We know there is a high free energy of hydrolysis of ATP, and yet the energy of hydrolysis of metaphosphate is low. Knowing these facts, it's pretty hard to say what is going on.

Note on Kalckar

While this survey was in print, an article by Gillespie and co-workers (R. J. Gillespie, G. A. Maw and C. A. Vernon (1953), The Concept of Phosphate Bond Energy, Nature 171, 1147-49) appeared. They voice strong objections against the common abuse of the word, Bond, as used in the now almost popular term " energy rich and energy poor bonds." In the physico-chemical sense and hence also in a biological sense a term like " bond " signifies a formation of electron pairs from atoms furnishing their electrons and thus giving rise to formation of molecules with a release of huge amounts of energy. Obviously, the breaking of molecular bonds, forming atoms, consumes large amounts of energy. When we biologists talk about the release of energy by splitting of a bond we mean something entirely different, namely, a redistribution of electron pairs (in special cases of odd electrons) and the energy differences involved in this reaction are compared, usually with reference to a redistribution brought about by hydrolysis. As an attempt to try to meet Gillespie's justified request for unambiguity in terminology the author of this review has decided to put the word bond, used to so frivolous a degree in biological literature, in future in the form " bond," the quotation marks being a modest token of recognition of the above request. Other points in Dr. Gillespie's appeal we cannot meet with the same unanimous approval. More and more, enzyme chemists are engaged in a kinetic approach with regard to phosphorylations and oxidations; an appeal for such an approach may therefore seem superfluous. I do not think that the laborious attempts to determine a few thermodynamical parameters such as oxidation-reduction potentials, ΔH of reactions, equilibrium constants and, if possible, calculations from thermal data are in any way sterile in spite of discouraging and perplexing inconsistencies. On the contrary, if they are used without too much prejudice, the knowledge of such constants and of their variations with the environment can direct the spotlight to a certain type of reaction as being better suited to perform coupled syntheses than some other. Gillespie and his colleagues are surely citing examples in which calculations may have been carried too far or in which an author may even have been carried away. Yet, in spite of inevitable mistakes made during attempts at basic orientation, it is hard to predict where we would be without such endeavors. Obviously, one should take care not to imply that these endeavors are worthless. The great importance of specific structures and " gearing " mechanisms has not invalidated the significance of energy relationships. Indeed, why draw a line of separation between kinetics and thermodynamics in a wider sense?

A SUMMARY OF THE SYMPOSIUM ON THE MECHANISM OF ENZYME ACTION

BENTLEY GLASS

Department of Biology,
The Johns Hopkins University

IN PREVIOUS SYMPOSIA of this series the fundamental question of the mechanism (or mechanisms) whereby enzymes catalyze biological reactions has been raised on numerous occasions. Observations that the activation energy of certain reactions is lowered by the appropriate enzymes and evidence that enzymes and substrates form intermediate complexes as predicted by Michaelis and Menten have led to the proposal of improved theories of enzyme action.

The relation of the configuration of the protein to its catalytic action necessitates a consideration of the forces and factors that determine and affect the sizes and shapes of molecules. Studies of steric relations, of the nature and number of essential groups, and of the changes that take place in the activation or denaturation of enzymes offer insight into the mode of enzyme action. The functions of metal ions in forming chelates with substrate and enzyme have recently become clearer. Finally, recent developments in the understanding of mechanisms of hydrogen and electron transport and of group transfers have been brought in the present discussions to a focus on the general problem of the mode of enzyme action.

PROTEIN CONFIGURATION AND BIOLOGICAL ACTIVITY

The first session was devoted to papers and discussion of the relation between protein structure and enzymatic functions.

Interprotein Forces. After summarizing the various kinds of forces which operate between interacting protein molecules, and between them and the other solute molecules which may be present, Kirkwood discussed in particular the theory of interprotein forces, such as those involved in the interaction of enzyme and protein substrate or of antigen and antibody. He adopted the hypothesis that the forces of major importance are the electrostatic forces and the repulsive forces, due to quantum mechanical exchange, that determine the size and shape of the protein molecules. The special features of protein molecules in this respect relate (a) to the structural pattern responsible for the specificity of interaction, and (b) to the mobility of the charges responsible for the electrostatic interaction. To the latter, especially because it has not been previously stressed in such discussions, Kirkwood devoted most attention.

The interaction of molecules with permanent electric multipoles can describe only the simplest cases. Proteins, which carry a large number of neutral and negatively charged basic groups to which protons become attached, have as a rule, except in very acid solutions, more such basic groups than protons attached to them. This means that a vast number of shifting configurations of the protons may exist. Hence the molecules acquire fluctuating charges and fluctuating multipole moments. A long-range attractive force results, diminishing with distance as $1/R^2$ where R is the distance between the protein molecules. With screening of this force by the statistical space charge of an electrolyte environment, the force is reduced by a factor depending upon the ionic strength through $\mathcal{H}$, the Debye-Hückel parameter. Of course, bound ions other than protons also produce fluctuations in the charge and its configuration and contribute to the intermolecular force.

Kirkwood presents equations for the potential of the fluctuating force between two protein molecules as a function of the intermolecular distance; and for the fluctuations of charge of two interacting molecules, quantities which enter into the previous relation. He illustrates the influence of the fluctuating force on the thermodynamic properties of a solution of a single protein (at the isoelectric point in an aqueous electrolyte solution large in total ionic strength compared to the protein) by showing its contribution to the osmotic pressure. At ionic strengths of the order of 10^{-3}, the fluctuation term is of predominant importance, and the strong intermolecular attraction is thus reflected in a coefficient of osmotic pressure substantially less than unity at protein concentrations of several per cent.

The assumptions used in the previous derivations ignored the non-randomness of the distribution of basic groups over the surface of the protein molecule—and hence ignored any specificity in the interactions. If one introduces the concept of complementary patterns, the fluctuation of charge would clearly provoke highly specific interactions. Steric matching of the complementary configuration of the basic groups on one protein with those on another protein might lead to a redistribution of protons and result in a strong specific interaction that would depend upon local details of the complementary configuration. In any case, the existence of the fluctuation force makes it imperative to consider the mobility of the charges and the shifting character of the charge distributions in estimating the interactions between protein molecules in solution. Relatively distant groups might affect the local interactions between complementary sites by serving as foci or reservoirs of mobile charges supplied to or withdrawn from the interacting sites.

The Essential Groups of Enzymes. The problem of the nature of the structures that confer upon certain proteins the enzymatic properties they possess has been investigated through the isolation of precursors as well as through the purification of the enzymes themselves. Studies of the formation of active enzyme from proenzyme and determination of the conditions upon which this change depends, studies of substrate analogues which may substitute for the normal substrate or act as inhibitors, and the use of specific enzymes to modify the protein structure of other enzymes have alike thrown light on the nature of enzymatic action. Herriott has used the work with two particular enzymes, chymotrypsin and pepsin, to illustrate advancing knowledge in this field.

The work with chymotrypsinogen shows that it is transformed into π-chymotrypsin (through the action of trypsin) without liberation of any nitrogenous fragments. Although trypsin also cleaves ester bonds, it is reasonably certain from Neurath's analyses (see below) that a peptide bond is cleaved in this case. Peptide bonds are also broken in the formation of δ- and α-chymotrypsins, which are degradative products of π-chymotrypsin. Both precursor and enzyme can bind a single molecule of N-acetyl-3,5-dibromotyrosine; but only the active enzyme will catalyze the exchange of O between water and the carboxyl group of this or related compounds (as determined by using H_2O^{18}). This suggests that the over-all action of the enzyme has two structural requirements: one possessed by both precursor and enzyme, and needed for substrate binding; and a second possessed only by the enzyme and needed for activating or labilizing the C-O bond. Diisopropylfluorophosphate (DFP), on the other hand, is bound only by the enzyme. It has been isolated in combination with the hydroxyl group of serine, but might have shifted to that site from its original binding, say with an imidazole structure. Implication of the latter in the enzyme's activity is indirect, and comes from photo-oxidation experiments and the pH activity curve. Ionization of only a few groups—probably just one—in the pH region 5 to 7 is necessary for enzyme activity, and this is the pK region for the imidazole structure of histidine. For the present it appears unlikely that the imidazole group is the one liberated when the enzyme is formed from its precursor, even though it may be important in binding the substrate.

Neurath and his colleagues have used the enzyme carboxypeptidase to analyze the end-groups of chymotrypsinogen and chymotrypsin. Carboxypeptidase hydrolyzes specific peptide bonds at the C-terminal ends of open polypeptide chains, only proline, hydroxyproline, cystine, cysteine, and possibly glutamine being unobtained as reaction products. α-Chymotrypsin has two N-terminal groups (isoleucine and alanine) and two C-terminal groups (tentatively, tyrosine and leucine). Since carboxypeptidase fails to release any free amino acids from chymotrypsinogen, the precursor is probably formed of one or more cyclic polypeptide chains. Presumably it has one peptide bond opened during its activation to π-chymotrypsin, and this liberates one basic C-terminal group (arginine or lysine), which is split off in further change to the α-form, as part of a basic peptide found to consist of 8 or 9 amino acids and with a molecular weight between 1000 and 1500 (Fig. 1).

A similar study on the activation of trypsinogen to trypsin showed first that carboxypeptidase has no effect on either the enzyme or its precursor in the native form, which is known to carry one free N-terminal group per molecule. It seems that the carboxyl end of the polypeptide chain must be closed in a ring or be sterically inaccessible, and that it is unaffected during activation. The action of

ACTIVATION SCHEME OF CHYMOTRYPSINOGEN (HYPOTHETICAL)

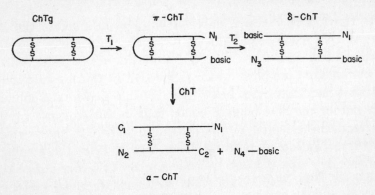

$N_{1,2}$-terminal A.A. (Desnuelle): Ileu, Ala

$C_{1,2}$-terminal A.A. (this work): Leu, Tyr.

Fig. 1. Hypothetical scheme of the activation process of chymotrypsinogen. *ChTg*, chymotrypsinogen, *ChT*, chymotrypsin; *Ileu*, isoleucine; *Ala*, alanine; *Leu*, leucine; *Tyr*, tyrosine. (From Neurath, Gladner, and Davis).

carboxypeptidase on the compound formed between trypsin and trypsin-soybean-inhibitor also demonstrated that trypsin has no free C-terminal group. After acid denaturation, trypsin liberates much more lysine than does trypsinogen when acted on by carboxypeptidase. At the N-terminal end trypsinogen has valine, trypsin has isoleucine. In the activation a peptide is therefore split off from the N-terminal end of the zymogen. It has been found to contain the three amino acids (valine, aspartic acid, and lysine), in the ratio 1: 5 (or 6): 1.

Neurath concludes that the available evidence indicates that formation of an enzyme from a zymogen by the action of a proteolytic enzyme is brought about by splitting off a peptide from the polypeptide chains of the protein. The peptide liberated is split off from the free amino end of the polypeptide chain in the case of trypsinogen, whereas during the activation of chymotrypsinogen a peptide is split off from the carboxyl end of one of the two polypeptide chains opened up by chymotryptic action, after the preliminary tryptic action has first opened one end of the cyclic structure.

As Herriott has shown, peptides are also split off in the autocatalytic conversion of pepsinogen to pepsin. Pepsinogen is a single peptide chain. It is first changed, by splitting off peptides, into the pepsin-inhibitor complex, which is inactive in clotting milk at pH 5.4, but which dissociates below that pH into pepsin and inhibitor. Only one of the nine peptide bonds split in this sequence of steps may really be essential to the activation. There is thus evidence that the activation of proteases may depend upon the freeing of certain end-groups through the opening up of a ring-structure or the splitting off of peptides from either a C-terminal end or an N-terminal end of a polypeptide chain.

Chemical studies with respect to the nature of the active groups essential for the activity of pepsin show that the primary amino groups, two disulfide bonds, and the phosphate ester can be altered without measurably changing the catalytic power of the enzyme. Various reactions that involve the tyrosine residues do, on the other hand, lower the enzymatic activity. Similarly, esterification of the free carboxyl groups with sulfur mustard results in a logarithmic decrease in activity as binding of the reactive residues increases. Thus carboxyl and tyrosine phenol groups appear important to peptic activity. As Herriott further indicates, external conditions such as the presence of cofactors may modify protease specificity considerably, as in the example where peptides resistant to papain are made susceptible by adding to the system certain other peptides.

Denaturation. Another approach to the study of the mechanism of enzyme action, that which was discussed by Kauzmann, shifts attention from the primary peptide bonds to the rupture of the secondary intramolecular bonds which maintain the gross structural pattern of the folded protein—in other words, to denaturation by physical, chemical, or biological agents. The types of bonds which maintain the protein in a folded state are (1) hydrogen bonds; (2) "hydrophobic" bonds representing the tendency of the more hydrophobic amino acid residues to avoid the aqueous phase and stick together—often, but inappropriately, called "van der Waals bonds"; (3) salt bridges—ionic bonds between oppositely charged amino acid residues; (4) London dispersion forces—true van der Waals forces; and (5) intramolecular chemical bonds, especially the cystine disulfide bond. Urea, for example, being a pure peptide linkage, forms hydrogen bonds itself. Hence it denatures proteins by breaking the interpeptide hydrogen bonds, of which there must be a great many (several hundred in even a small protein molecule) in order to confer stability, inasmuch as the energy required to rupture a single interpeptide hydrogen bond is quite small, perhaps as little as 100 calories. Heat probably exerts at least a part of its denaturation effect by increasing the power of water to break the same kind of interpeptide hydrogen bonds. Organic solvents, detergents, and surfaces should act by rupturing the "hydrophobic" bonds. As to acid and alkali denaturation, Kauzmann holds that it acts by virtue of "the very large electrostatic repulsion which exists within typical protein molecules at extremes of pH," and he has developed a quantitative theory on this basis, the primary assumption being that when a molecule becomes denatured it swells, and this reduces the electrostatic repulsion energy previously present. It would follow that those species with the largest charge would be expected to become denatured most rapidly. No more than an 8 per cent "swelling" of the activated complex of ovalbumin, compared with the native form, is needed to account for the observed effect of pH on the denaturation rate of ovalbumin. Support for the theory is to be seen in the behavior of pepsin, which is unusual in having a low charge at acid pH and a high charge at neutral pH. It denatures rapidly at neutral pH, unlike most proteins.

The denaturation effects of pressure, radiation, and proteolytic enzymes, and the inhibition of denaturation by various agents are considered briefly. Kauzmann concludes that denaturation is a complex phenomenon. One might suppose that some of the folding was stabilized by one type of bond and some of the folding by another, in which case the agents that bring about denaturation might act quite independently. Or, on the other hand, one could suppose that all the protein-folding was stabilized in a single way, by bonds of different kinds working together, so that, whatever type of bond was ruptured, the remainder would not be strong enough to maintain the structure. In this case a mutual aid of denaturants, or even an all-or-none type of denaturation, would be expected. This seems to hold true for ovalbumin, but not necessarily for other proteins.

As Wu pointed out in 1931, disorganization seems to be the most important aspect of denaturation. This can be visualized as either an unfolding of the peptide chain, or dissociation of the " molecule " into smaller units. The former is exemplified by the urea denaturation of ovalbumin, the latter by urea denaturation of tobacco mosaic virus. The action of urea is probably no different in the two cases. Whether the protein unfolds or dissociates when the intramolecular hydrogen bonds are broken depends on the continuity of the poly-peptide chain. In the virus, the molecule must be composed of non-chemically-linked subunits; in the ovalbumin molecule, of continuous chains.

The shapes of the proteins which unfold have been studied by Kauzmann through viscosity changes. The intrinsic viscosities of high polymers such as polystyrene closely resemble those of ovalbumin and serum albumin when the latter are dissolved in a solvent such as urea, in which different parts of the molecule do not tend to stick to one another. From these observations Kauzmann arrives at a picture of the denatured unfolded protein as a random coil rather than a rigid ellipsoid. [The results of flow birefringence studies on urea-denatured ovalbumin are inconsistent with the random-coil picture, and indicate a rod 500 to 600 Å in length; but these studies (Foster and Samsa) were made in a rather " poor " solvent and may not be comparable.] Kauzmann also presents reasons why the idea that denaturation is an aggregation of unaltered native molecules is inadequate. Denaturation, according to the evidence from optical rotation and x-ray diffraction, is accompanied by an internal reorganization. Hence "the elements that aggregate must have a different structure from that of the native protein." Aggregation, if it occurs, must then be secondary.

A summary of the thermodynamic data for protein denaturation leads to the conclusion that the large positive values of ΔH found must be more than balanced by the increase in the entropy (ΔS). In those examples which have been measured this has been found to be so. Trypsin, soybean trypsin-inhibitor, and chymotrypsinogen show positive values of ΔS about 10 times those observed in ordinary chemical reactions. Since entropy represents disorganization, this validates the description of denaturation previously given. For trypsin and chymotrypsinogen, this entropy increase takes place within the protein molecule, presumably by unfolding. The magnitude of the entropy change per mole, though large, is sufficiently accounted for by the theory that denaturation consists of unfolding into a more or less randomly coiled molecule. The large entropy change is nevertheless only a third or less of what it would be if the polypeptide chains were free to twist fully about each bond.

Five aspects of the kinetics of denaturation are considered by Kauzmann. First, the temperature coefficient of heat denaturation is remarkably large in many cases, e. g., for ovalbumin the Q_{10} is several hundred. This is a measure of the large activation energy of the process. Second, in the urea denaturation of ovalbumin the reaction is of a very high order with respect to the urea concentration, implying that the folds of the polypeptide cannot be opened unless several hydrogen bonds are broken at the same time. This further implies that the ends of the polypeptide chains must be inaccessible, or else the structure could be unfolded one hydrogen bond at a time, zipper-fashion. Instead, the *coiled* folds have to be attacked in the middle, and about 8 bonds must be broken simultaneously, until a single loop of one fold has been pried loose (Fig. 2, B). The high optical rotation attained in urea implies the existence of steric restrictions on the freedom of orientation about the bonds in the polypeptide chain, just as the study of the entropy change also seemed to show that the chain in the denatured protein is not fully flexible. Third, although for most proteins denaturation is a first-order reaction with respect to the protein concentration, the half-time of denaturation does vary with protein concentration in two cases, the urea denaturation of tobacco mosaic virus and the alkali denaturation of pepsin. In these cases an inhibitor or activator

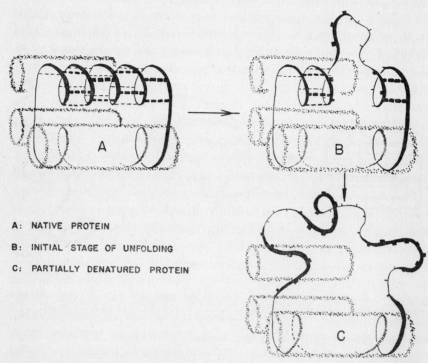

A: NATIVE PROTEIN

B: INITIAL STAGE OF UNFOLDING

C: PARTIALLY DENATURED PROTEIN

FIG. 2. Scheme for the unfolding of a protein molecule such as ovalbumin. *A*, the native protein, with no exposed ends of polypeptide chains. *B*, one loop pried loose by simultaneous breakage of about 8 hydrogen bonds. *C*, further unfolding to the stage of partial denaturation. (From Kauzmann).

of denaturation may be present. Fourth, certain observations, such as the much greater rate of change of optical rotation during the denaturation of serum albumin than of ovalbumin, tell us that one globular protein (the serum albumin) must be much less firmly coiled than another (the ovalbumin). The capacity of proteins to adsorb dyes may be related to the ease of unfolding, for serum albumin stands in a class by itself in this respect. Perhaps the looseness of folding of the native protein is related to the high adsorption of dyes as well as to the rapidity of unfolding. Fifth, a question still unsettled, is the relation between the irreversibly denatured state and the still reversible state. The latter may be intermediate, or may represent a different, " protected " state (Fig. 3).

During denaturation there is often an increased reactivity of sulfhydryl and disulfide groups. In urea solutions of serum albumin or ovalbumin, as Huggins and his coworkers have shown, gelation can

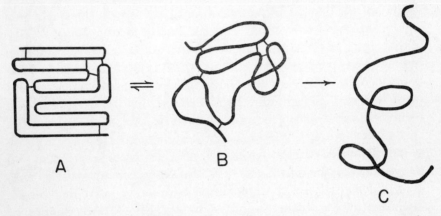

Fɪɢ. 3. Stages in the unfolding of a protein molecule with cystine cross-links. Change from *A* to *B*, reversible; from *B* to *C*, irreversible. (From Kauzmann).

be prevented by blocking the sulfhydryl groups. Probably intramolecular -S-S- bonds are exchanged for intermolecular ones during gelling. This view, Kauzmann points out, is supported by the evidence that an agent which combines with or destroys the sulfhydryl groups of ovalbumin also eliminates the change in viscosity normally found in this protein after the optical rotation has ceased to change. The effects of the same reagents on serum albumin resemble those on ovalbumin, except for differences due to the very low cysteine concentration in the former, and its greater cross-linkage by disulfide groups. These linkages in serum albumin are very likely of considerable importance in permitting its reversible denaturation. So long as they remain unbroken, they can prevent complete unfolding of the molecule in urea solution, and upon dilution of the urea the protein can revert to its native state, or nearly that (Fig. 3). If the cross-links place a constraint on the folding, then the less-folded serum albumin could unfold more rapidly and would be a less stable configuration than the more-folded ovalbumin, which has only two cross-linkages. How far these relations can be generalized remains to be seen.

In this connection Anfinsen reported an interesting preliminary study of the changes that occur during the " denaturation " of ribonuclease, which is a very small protein molecule comprised of a single polypeptide chain that makes only five convolutions held in a rigid conformation by four disulfide bonds. Upon being treated with pepsin, ribonuclease loses its enzymatic activity very rapidly, but, up to the point of loss of about 70 per cent of the activity, there is no increase either in the number of free terminal amino groups or of liberated -SH groups. The " denaturation " thus appears not to involve any splitting of peptide linkages, but instead, from the change seen in light-scattering properties, there is a rapid *aggregation* of the ribonuclease units up to a molecular weight of several hundred thousand. It is therefore clear that loss of enzymatic activity and, ergo, " denaturation " do not always involve an unfolding of the molecule, as Kauzmann suggested on the basis of the studies of serum albumin and ovalbumin.

The same problem has been approached by Schackman through a new method, involving the use of a synthetic boundary ultracentrifuge cell. Schackman undertook to study the attack upon insulin by chymotrypsin and the attack upon desoxyribose nucleic acid (DNA) by desoxyribonuclease. It was found that insulin is very rapidly torn apart by chymotrypsin, so that besides insulin itself only very small peptides of a molecular weight of 800 to 1000 are observable. But with DNA the opposite picture is presented. There is a gradual decrease in molecular weight, as if the bonds of a polymer were being attacked at random so as to produce a variety of molecules of different molecular weights. It may be concluded that, even if the general understanding of the changes that occur with loss of enzymatic activity and denaturation is not yet complete, at least the same type of behavior clearly does not obtain in all cases.

The Kinetics of Enzyme-Catalyzed Reactions. The structure of globular proteins may, according to Eyring, be subsumed as a primary structure, the amino acid sequence; a secondary structure, the spiral coiling; and a tertiary structure, the packing of the spiral " pencils " into compact, low-energy micelles. In slight contrast to the picture visualized by Kauzmann, Eyring sees reversible denaturation and enzyme inactivation as associated with the " melting " of the tertiary structure alone. The smallest protein molecules, such as ribonuclease and lysozyme, with molecular weights of about 15,000 to 18,000, may be depicted on this basis as a central spiral surrounded by six others, each spiral containing 24 amino acids of molecular weight averaging 100. This would make a barrel-shaped molecule of weight 16,800.

Molecules will be so packed as to avoid unnecessary cavities, for the energy required to volatilize a single molecule, leaving a hole behind, is double the average energy per molecule required to volatilize the entire liquid or solid, i. e., the heat of vaporization. To leave a hole the size of a water molecule would, Eyring calculates, cost 10,000 calories per mole in heat of vaporization; and, if this is uncompensated by any increase of entropy, the probability of getting such a hole is only one in 50 million. Smaller holes would of course be more likely to occur. A hole one-eighth the size of a water molecule would have a chance of occurring of one in ten. To use the colorful language of Eyring's oral presentation, holes produced by " molecular misfits " tend to be filled by anything handy, from wandering protons to old shoes. To be stable, a structure must not only avoid cavities, but opposing surfaces must also be compatible, like an oil-protein interface. Since a mole of ethyl alcohol dissolved in water has an interfacial surface energy of 9000 calories, then if the alcohol molecules can dip into the oily part of a protein, the free energy of the system will be lowered by 9000 calories, and be equivalent to a bond between alcohol and protein of that strength. Enzymes or membrane proteins give up their native structure to make these hydrophobic bonds, a phenomenon at the basis of much narcotic action.

Activated complexes possess fractional bonds, with some bonds breaking as others are forming. The important fractional bonds are 10 per cent over-extended, and any process that will extend a bond by 10 per cent will unsaturate it and make it reactive. Such processes, according to Eyring, include (a) the action of secondary electrostatic bonds that pull or push the electron pair of the primary bond toward the anion, (b) the addition to the molecule of groups that labilize a bond by pushing or pulling charge out of it by induction or resonance, and (c) the mechanical strain connected with steric types of distortion of the bond.

Among various kinds of activated complexes is what Eyring calls the " rack." In this configuration, atoms of the substrate molecule on both sides of the bond to be broken are bound strongly to the enzymes. The strength of the bond is thus sapped by strain and by leaching away of its electron pairs.

An enzyme lessens the free energy of activation of the activated complex, which cannot be much above 20 kcal., and is usually less. In a sense, the enzyme's efficiency as a catalyst is because of this relatively low energy of activation. From this relation it follows that no structure can be important in biological reactions which differs very much in free energy from known, stable structures. Upon this point, which he calls the " Principle of Similitude," Eyring lays great stress. Activated complexes, which live only about 10^{-13} sec., must be like some of the intermediates which can be isolated, inasmuch as 20 kcal. " will buy only a little stretching and distorting of the reacting bonds." Hence Eyring looks to the low-energy tertiary structure, rather than the primary or secondary, as the site of the special structural arrangements that characterize the activated complex formed of enzyme and substrate, and are analogous to antigen-antibody reactions. Eyring concluded this part of his discussion with a brief consideration of protein synthesis, on which he thinks the principle of similitude may throw considerable light.

The absolute rate theory discussed by Eyring is a refinement of simple collision theory, so as to apply to reactions of all orders.

The potential energy involved is a function of the configuration of the molecules, to plot which requires additional dimensions. It is convenient to think in terms of an analogy, a landscape in which energy is represented by altitude. Basins and valleys then correspond to compounds, the passes between valleys to activated complexes, and the course of a reaction a path from one valley, representing the reactants, up and over a pass into another valley, representing the products.

In practice, reaction rate theory is used exactly like equilibrium theory. When the Michaelis-Menten equation applies, several specific rate constants are seen to enter into the over-all rate of a reaction. These rate constants may have a simple dependence on temperature, or an " extremely fancy " one, e. g., decreasing on both sides of a maximum. Taking the behavior of oxidative enzymes such as luci-ferase as an example, Eyring points out that the reactants exist in a variety of isomeric states, combinations with one another, and com-binations with inhibitors. Thus total enzyme, $E_o = E + E_d + ES + E_dS + EY_3$, etc., where E is active enzyme, E_d denatured or inactive enzyme, ES and E_dS are enzyme-substrate complexes, and EY_3 an enzyme-inhibitor complex, etc. All of these must be included in the mathematical analysis, as Bull also points out (see below).

The kinetics of the enzyme-catalyzed reaction and the role of the enzyme-substrate complex as an intermediate in the reaction were further developed by Bull, who directed attention toward the need to derive an appropriate measure of the rate of activation of sub-strate by enzyme, and the need for an unambiguous measure of the affinity between enzyme and substrate. In order to measure the rate of activation truly, a standard reference state is required. The condition, saturation of enzyme by substrate, is commonly taken or implied. The maximum velocity of the reaction may then be calculated by rearrangement of the Michaelis-Menten equations. However, the use of the first-order constant as a measure of the rate of enzymatic reaction is unsuitable; and the maximum velocity as estimated from the Michaelis-Menten equation is under most conditions an erroneous expression of the rate of activation of the substrate by the enzyme.

The most meaningful standard reference state for an enzyme, according to Bull, is the state in which not only is the enzyme completely activated and saturated with substrate, but in addition the latter has no inhibiting effect on the enzyme, so that substrate is being activated at maximum rate at the given temperature. The specification of such a state requires more consideration of the theory of activation of enzymes, which has been strangely neglected.

Bull presents a consideration of the simpler and more probable equilibria in terms of enzyme concentration, substrate concentration, and activator concentration in their various states and combinations. Total enzyme, free and combined, is expressed in terms of the concentration of the active complex, concentrations of activator and substrate, and 8 dissociation constants; and this equation is combined with that for the rate of decomposition of the active complex to form the reaction products, so as to yield an equation for the reciprocal of the rate $(1/V)$. It is shown that data on the decomposition of urea by urease at $30°$ C. and pH 6.6 agree very closely with the curve plotted from this equation. In the absence of any inhibiting effect by the substrate on the enzyme, the equation becomes an expression of the maximum velocity of activation in the standard reference state. Another equation is derived to describe the situation in which the maximum velocity of the enzymatic reaction is a function of the activator concentration, as in the examples of trypsin and chymotrypsin. It is shown that data on the action of histidase on histidine as a function of pH agree satisfactorily with the curve plotted from the equation. Further equations are derived to yield the standard reference state of the enzyme in respect to both substrate and activator (in this instance, hydrogen ions); and in the case where excess activator concentration does not inhibit. The curve for the latter equation is fitted very well by data on the peptic hydrolysis of egg albumin as a function of pH. It should be noted that under the specified conditions (zero-order kinetics), the pH maximum has nothing to do with affinity between enzyme and substrate as a function of pH. It is a function of the dissociation of the proton-donating group of the enzyme.

From Bull's analysis, it follows that activators can be classified into two sorts, rate activators and affinity activators. The latter do not alter the maximum rate of reaction under zero-order kinetics, but do increase the rate of reaction up to the substrate concentration where zero-order kinetics begin to apply. Such activators increase the affinity of enzyme for substrate. In contrast, rate activators increase the rate of reaction at both high and low concentrations of substrate. They must enter into combination with the enzyme-substrate complex in the final step before its decomposition into the reaction products. Hydrogen ions can act in either or both capacities at once. Analogously, one could speak of enzyme inhibitors as rate inhibitors (non-competitive) or affinity inhibitors (competitive).

The ambiguity which attaches to the Michaelis-Menten dissociation constant for the enzyme-substrate complex, because the latter can decompose into either free enzyme and substrate or into reaction products and free enzyme, applies also to the calculated values for the dissociation constants in the above-mentioned equations. To obtain a measure of the affinity of enzyme for substrate independent of the kinetic data, a method must be developed for determining the concentration of the enzyme-substrate complex itself. This may be done from absorption spectra if the complex has significant absorption characteristics. That is not likely among the hydrolyzing enzymes, but might be possible with certain oxidation-reduction enzymes.

Bull suggests that further examination of enzyme-substrate affinities might profitably be focussed on the relation to the proportion of substrate existing as monovalent ion over the pH range, as in the binding of N-acetyl-3,5-dibromotyrosine by chymotrypsin; and on the binding of substrate by enzyme outside of the pH range delimiting the enzymatic activity. As an example of the latter, he reports data on the concentration of the enzyme-substrate complex formed between pepsin and egg albumin at pH 4.0. Maximum precipitation was at a mole to mole ratio, and from light-scattering measurements the association constant was calculated to be 1.46×10^7 ml. per mole. This compares with an association constant of 0.14×10^7 ml. per mole calculated from previous kinetic studies.

The discrepancy could be due to several causes, but the approach seems worth investigating.

Workers in this field will no doubt be very grateful for the further development and application of the Michaelis-Menten theory by Friedenwald and Maengwyn-Davies. The expansion of this theory has hitherto been largely ad hoc and directed to specific problems, as these authors say, and they have therefore undertaken to make certain simplifications, apply the theory in new areas, and in particular to give guidance in applying the theory to experimental data and in reaching valid conclusions.

Their first approach has been to develop first-order theory [i. e., cases in which only one molecule each of substrate (S), activator (A), or inhibitor (I) combine with each active locus of the enzyme, so as to include any number of dissociation constants]. Previous analyses of substrate-inhibitor interactions have been mainly restricted to a consideration of competitive or non-competitive inhibition. Yet there is evidence that intermediate and even "anti-competitive" relations may occur. Friedenwald and Maengwyn-Davies reduce all these types of inhibition to a single equation by including an association factor, a, which may vary from zero to infinity. When $a = 1$ the inhibition is non-competitive, when $a = \infty$ it is competitive, and when $a = 0$ it is "anti-competitive," or "coupling." A similar equation is developed to describe the interaction between substrate and activator. It includes, as special cases, "coupling" and "non-coupling" activation. Of the former, two types are distinguished, "depending on whether substrate is coupled to enzyme by the activator, or activator is coupled to the enzyme by the substrate." A graphical analysis of the Lineweaver-Burk type, which gives a straight line when $1/V$ is plotted against $1/[S]$, $[I]$, or $1/[A]$, is developed as an aid.

They then undertake a systematic analysis of second-order enzyme kinetics, which is defined as the situation when it is possible for two molecules of the same substance to be bound per active locus of the enzyme. The theory is applied to the well-known cases of inhibition by excess substrate and inhibition by excess activator. In the former instance, it turns out that possession by the active locus of two attracting groups is not a necessary condition. In the case of a substance that can act both as activator and inhibitor, it is possible to distinguish between the four cases of coupling and non-coupling activation, competitive and non-competitive inhibition. The graphic method is further developed for second-order cases, so as to provide a method for testing the applicability of second-order theory and for determining the various constants in the equations.

The third portion of the presentation by Friedenwald and Maen-gwyn-Davies is particularly interesting because of its independent discussion and solution of questions raised by Bull. It deals with the influence of pH on the kinetic theory of enzymatic reactions. The development of the Michaelis-Menten theory to include a consideration of the numerous ionic species of enzyme, substrate, activator, and inhibitor that may be simultaneously present in a solution shows that there is no need to assume that hydrogen-ion associations differ qualitatively from those involving other activators or inhibitors. Over a considerable range of data enzymatic catalysis appears to be an all-or-none phenomenon, that is to say, all potentially active ionic enzyme species act on a particular substrate at the same rate, and all others are inactive. The chief effect of hydrogen-ion association seems to be that of non-coupling activation, non-competitive inhibition. This implies merely that the state of dissociation of the charged groups at the active locus does not vary materially within the pH range of enzymatic activity. Good agreement between experimental findings and second-order theory is reported for many enzyme systems. In such cases, as Bull also noted, the maximum rate of reaction at optimal pH and with saturation of the enzyme with substrate is not identical with the activity that would obtain if all enzyme molecules were active. The relation between the hypothetical maximum (V_m) and the maximum obtainable (V_o) is equal to $1 + 2k$, the constant k usually falling between 0.1 and 0.01. Hence the error in assuming that $V_m = V_o$ is not great; but for higher order reactions this would not be true.

The Function of Metals in Enzyme Catalysis

The Relation of Chelation to Catalysis. Metal ions form complex compounds with a wide variety of ligands, i. e., atoms or groups of atoms which donate electrons to the metal atom to form a more or less homopolar bond rather than a coulombic type of bond. When ligands donating to the same metal atom are themselves united, the resulting compound is a chelate. In the classification Calvin adopts, compounds may be distinguished as monodentate, bidentate, or tridentate, according to the number of ligands that coordinate a single molecule with the metal atom. The monodentate type is an ordinary compound, such as a metal-ammonia; the bidentate type has two coordinating groups in a single chelate ring, as in metal-ethylene-diamine; the tridentate has three groups and forms two rings; etc.

Calvin has dealt particularly with the stability of the metal-chelate compounds. The stability constants are influenced by a number of factors, some of which are related to the stability of complex compounds in general, such as, for the metal, its charge, radius, and available orbitals, and for the complexing group, its polarizability, size (steric repulsion), and basicity. Of more concern in the present connection are those factors which are characteristic of chelate compounds and are limited to them, namely, steric effects, entropy effects, and resonance effects.

A fundamental property of the metal atom's electron configuration, and one that effects the stability of its chelates, is the ionization potential required to remove the last electron in the formation of a specific ion. The greater this energy, the greater the stability of the chelate compound. Thus a plot of the electronegativity of the metals against the logarithm of the chelation constant gives a linear relation.

The steric and entropy effects peculiar to chelate compounds involve changes in the translational, rotational, and vibrational energies of the chelate group. The steric effect is exemplified by the metal-binding of polymethylenediaminetetraacetic acid homologues, for which Schwarzenbach showed that the stability constants vary with the size of the ring. The larger the ring, the less the binding. This steric requirement of the chelating groups holds for calcium and other alkaline earth metals, but it does not apply to the binding of hydrogen ions, to which one would expect the ligand similarly to donate electrons. Thus chelation introduces certain additional factors over and above those that affect hydrogen-ion-binding, and these factors may be evaluated by comparing the chelation constants for chelate groups of the same acid dissociation constant.

Another example cited by Calvin is the stronger binding by a silver ion of two ammonia molecules than of a single ethylenediamine molecule. The feeble chelation in the latter case is presumably a steric effect due to bond angles, since silver tends to form linear bonds (180°), and the chelate cannot readily form a linear complex.

A sharp contrast is exhibited by the binding of nickel with the same two groupings. If the steric effect alone controlled the result, one would expect nickel, like silver, to bind ammonia more readily than ethylenediamine; but the opposite is the case. In aqueous solution, three ethylenediamine molecules will displace six ammonia molecules from attachment to the nickel atom. This is explained by Calvin in the following way. In the binding of six ammonias to nickel, ΔH is -19 kcal. and ΔS is -22 entropy units. In the binding of three ethylenediamines in aqueous solution to nickel, ΔH is -25 kcal. and ΔS is + 2 e.u. Combining these two reactions, it is clear why the three ethylenediamines will exchange for the six ammonias on the nickel. For, although ΔH is small (-6 kcal.), there is a very great entropy increase (+ 24 e.u.) that drives the reaction. Similarly, in all those cases in which the temperature coefficients of the equilibrium constant K could be measured, the differences in chelating power of related groups were found to be attributable almost entirely to the difference in the ΔS component of the free-energy change, rather than to a difference in the ΔH portion. This type of effect is therefore called the entropy effect by Calvin.

A similar example is offered by the binding of zinc for nitrogen, although in this case the equilibrium constant has not been studied as a function of temperature, and only log K at a single temperature is available. Nevertheless, the increase in log K with the ligation of the nitrogen atoms is indicative of a strong entropy effect. For when zinc binds four nitrogens separately, log K is 9.5; binding them in ligated pairs, it is 11; and binding them all in a single ligand, it goes up to nearly 15.

The resonance effect characteristic of some chelated complexes includes changes in electronic energy in addition to the translational, vibrational, and rotational effects. In acetylacetonate-Cu and salicyl-aldehyde-Cu chelate rings, a direct electronic interaction between two O atoms, or between an O and a N atom, is possible through the coordinated system. The acetylacetone derivative binds the copper much more strongly, probably because there is nothing to interfere with the –C=C– double bond adjacent to the anionic oxygen; whereas in the salicylaldehyde the bond is part of a resonating benzene ring, and so is double only half the time. Calvin suggests that in the binding an electron pair may actually move over to form a double bond with the copper, making a benzenoid type of ring involving the copper atom.

Mildred Cohn has described, in the discussion of Calvin's paper, an extremely delicate new method for the study of metal complexes, namely, the paramagnetic resonance absorption method. Although limited to the study of ions and molecules which are paramagnetic— such as, par excellence, the manganous ion—it can measure directly and rapidly the concentration of the free metal ion in solution or without disturbing the equilibrium state. With the manganous ion in solution in dilute crystals, one can obtain a superfine absorption spectrum with six distinct peaks, instead of the single absorption spectrum peak obtained by other and cruder current methods. The paramagnetic absorption method can also be used to follow the rate of a reaction. The formation of complexes in some cases causes a loss of the hyperfine structure, in others it does not, depending respectively upon whether the bonding is covalent or ionic. So far, it has not proved possible to detect the paramagnetic resonance spectrum of any complex itself, probably because of the great breadth of the absorption peaks in such cases.

Coming to the question how chelate compounds exercise catalytic functions, Calvin has proposed the idea that the chelate rings which arise primarily from entropy effects will act by means of changes in translational, vibrational, and rotational degrees of freedom; and that those involving electronic changes will act by shifting electrons so as to weaken bonds and form unstable intermediates. An example of the first sort is perhaps the action upon phosphate-transfer systems of magnesium and of manganese, a chelating function that brings together the coenzyme and enzyme through a double chelate ring involving the pyrophosphate group of the coenzyme. An intermediate type of catalytic action, with probably both entropy and electronic effects, is the alkylation of an amide of a β-keto acid (the diethyl amide of acetoacetic acid), using the copper salt. The copper forms a relatively stable chelate with the O and N atoms, exposes the *amide* carbonyl and permits its alkylation. This is quite different from the result of ordinary alkylation of the *ketonic* carbonyl of such a compound, as observed when the sodium salt is used.

The purely electronic type of catalysis is exemplified in the decarboxylation of oxaloacetic and oxalosuccinic acids, with copper forming a chelate ring between the carbonyl and α-carboxyl groups. Electrons shift from the β-carboxyl group toward the carbonyl, CO_2 is liberated, and thus an unstable intermediate which loses copper is formed. A spectacular example of this type of chelate is the Cu or Ni chelate of salicylaldehyde, which forms a Schiff base with an α-amino acid ester, and then performs a variety of reactions virtually unobtainable except in the chelate compound, e. g., racemization, oxidative deamination, or ester exchange. A final example given by Calvin is the action of copper chelate compounds of pyridoxal in transaminations.

Molecular Properties of Metal-Protein Complexes. Klotz has raised three main questions for consideration: (1) which groups on the protein molecules form the ligands? (2) which metals form complexes and what determines their affinities? (3) which of the observed modes of interaction between metals and proteins are biologically significant, especially in enzymatic catalysis?

In the protein, it must be the polar side-chains that provide the ligands, since the carboxyl and α-amino groups are linked in peptide bonds. Of the side-chains, only the guanidinium, aliphatic hydroxyl, and amide groups appear not to enter into metal complexes, a fact which emphasizes the importance of the competition of hydrogen ions in the complexing process, for each of these three groups, when dissociated, is so strong a base that protons cannot be displaced from the acid by metal ions, except at very high pH. Ligand groups may be investigated by four general categories of method, stoichiometric analyses, chemical modification, pH dependence, and optical methods. In the stoichiometric analysis there is often a sharp break in the number of metal ions bound as the unbound cation concentration increases. A correspondence between the number of free groups of a given type and the uptake of metal ions then provides strong indications of the involvement of the specific side-chain. For example, in the interaction of the sulfhydryl group of serum albumin with metals there is a sharp break in the binding of mercurial ions at one mole of metal ion. Silver behaves similarly. With other evidence, it may be concluded that Ag^+ and Hg^{++} are bound in a 1: 1 complex with -SH groups, of which there is a single one per molecule of serum albumin. For proteins with higher stoichiometric ratios, the uncertainty will increase regarding what particular groups have the greater affinity for the metal.

Exposure of the protein to chemical agents that react only with a particular kind of group is informative, although once again the method is reliable only when the particular side-chain tested is low in proportion. In copper-albumin reactions it has been shown by the use of Hg^{++}, Ag^+, or salyrganic acid, that the single -SH group of albumin is involved in the complex. Failure of deamination of gelatin to affect the uptake of Ca^{++} seems to exclude the amino side-chains in calcium-binding; it is presumably attracted predominantly to the carboxyl groups. There is evidence of this type for the binding of Zn^{++} by histidine residues of serum albumin and of chromium by the carboxyl groups of collagen.

Binding in a particular pH range corresponding to the ionization of certain groups may be indicative of their participation. Thus conalbumin takes up iron or copper in the pH ranges of lysine and tyrosine ionization. Many metals are bound by serum albumin only above the isoelectric point, pH 5, which corresponds to the ionization of the imidazolium groups—this implicates histidine in the binding of zinc, cadmium, and lead. But pH profiles may be quite mis-leading—calcium and copper are also bound above pH 5 by this protein, although not by histidine residues. One must recall that many proteins change from a positive to a negative net charge in this pH region, and this fact may in part account for the metal binding.

Spectroscopic methods are excellent, but limited in applicability. Copper-albumin complexes have been studied by this means, since the $COO..Cu^{++}$ linkages have maxima near 700 mμ and the $N..Cu^{++}$ ones near 600 mμ. The latter, at pH 9, are implicated. Similarly, the copper-conalbumin complex has been shown to involve phenolic side-chains; and indirectly, Fe^{++}, Zn^{++}, Pb^{++}, and Cd^{++} are demonstrated to form mercaptides with serum albumin.

The order of affinity of metals for certain proteins with relatively few sites of high affinity has been determined. Conalbumin binds the series $Fe^{+++} > Cu^{++} > Zn^{++}$; and the sulfhydryl group of serum albumin binds the series $Hg^{++} > Ag^{+} > Pb^{++} > Cd^{++} > Zn^{++} > Ca^{++}, Mg^{++}$. The large number of side-chains with carboxyl and basic nitrogen groups present in most proteins produces, on the other hand, a less specific type of binding. The metals Cu^{++}, Ni^{++}, Co^{++}, Zn^{++}, Cd^{++}, Pb^{++} bind in approximately that order, much as they combine with amino acids. The alkaline earth metals stand a grade lower in affinity. The alkali metals (Na^{+} and K^{+}) give little sign of any binding.

That metals may serve as bridges in the formation of ternary complexes is shown by the formation of a pepsin-zinc-azopyridine dye compound. Hg^{++}, Cu^{++}, Ag^{+}, Ni^{++}, Co^{++}, and Mn^{++} will also function in forming this particular bridge. The order of relative efficiency observed ($Cu^{++} > Co^{++} > Zn^{++} > Mn^{++}$) is the same as the order of the chelate stability constants of metal with the azopyridine dye, so that the affinity of the metal ions for the protein is here of less importance than their affinity for the small molecule. The anomalous behavior of copper and mercury in some of these reactions brings to mind their great divergence from other metals in regard to their hydrolytic equilibria, which are marked by a strong affinity for the hydroxyl ion.

Klotz discusses the effects of the metal-protein interaction on enzymatic activity under three heads. First is the effect of the complexing on the properties of the metal. This is best illustrated by the iron and copper oxidation-reduction enzymes. In the case of the copper enzymes, a function of the protein is clearly to keep the copper in solution at physiological pH's. Yet the unique behavior of the copper enzyme must be sought in some further effect, for prepared complexes of water-soluble cuprous and cupric serum albumin exhibit no unusual oxidative properties.

Second is the effect of the complexing on the protein. Obviously the electrostatic charges are shifted, and this may alter the affinity of the enzyme for the substrate. Also, dissociation curves are shifted along the pH axis. Again, the electrostatic effect may influence the equilibrium between the monomeric and dimeric states of an enzyme. The configuration of the protein may be changed, as in the formation of mercaptides in cases where the thiol group is involved in the enzymatic action. It is especially interesting that, as Riggs has recently shown, the metal may influence an enzymatic site at a considerable distance on the molecular scale—for blocking the thiol group on the protein part of hemoglobin by means of a mercurial compound had a marked effect on the oxygenation of hemoglobin, that is, on the combination of the Fe atom of heme with oxygen. Finally, a metal may activate an enzyme by removing an inhibitor, as in the reversal of beryllium inhibition of alkaline phosphatase by Mn^{++}, Co^{++}, or Ni^{++}.

The third aspect of the effect of a bound metal on the protein Klotz terms " cooperative effects." The bridge formation mentioned above offers one example of this. A real question to be answered here is why Mn^{++} and Mg^{++}, which are lowest in chelating ability, are nevertheless the most common activators of enzymes. A somewhat similar difficulty is that the products of peptide hydrolyses are commonly better chelating agents than the reactants. Furthermore, the formation of a chelate would be expected to stabilize the ground state of a complex rather than the activated state. One of Klotz' most interesting points is that the metals most active in forming chelates with substrates were not found to be necessarily the most effective in forming bridges to the protein, probably because their complexing ability favored competing reactions.

Klotz has therefore developed a scheme which discounts the chelating ability of the cation, and instead emphasizes the activated, intermediate state in the process. If the mechanism of hydrolysis of simple esters may be carried over to amides and peptides, one can

suppose an intermediate of the form
$$\begin{array}{c} \text{OH} \\ | \\ \text{R--C--NHR}' \\ | \\ \text{O}^- \end{array}$$
produced by addition of OH^-. A cationic metal on a suitable protein could favor the

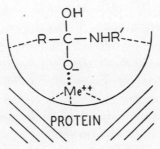

Fig. 4. Formation of an active protein-metal-substrate intermediate, as proposed by Klotz. (From Klotz).

formation of such an activated intermediate either by increasing the local concentration of OH^-, or by stabilizing the transition state through the formation of a complex (Fig. 4). Klotz would have the R and R' groups that determine the specificity of the substrate for the enzyme interact directly with the apoenzyme. From this standpoint it is easier to understand the roles of Mg^{++} and Mn^{++} as the common activators of enzymes. Being among the weakest of coordinators, they still retain open coordination bonds. Because they react weakly with OH^- ions, they are in a state to stabilize the intermediate by forming a link with the negatively charged C–O$^-$ group of the substrate. Klotz, extending the ideas of Hellerman, develops this mechanism to explain the behavior of the arginase system, where the sensitive bond is of the same type as in amides and esters. Here the metal would facilitate the opening of the C=NH bond and the simultaneous introduction of the OH⁻ ion. Finally, in the activity of the phosphatases, Mn^{++} and Mg^{++} again might stabilize an intermediate in an analogous way.

This radical departure from accepted views of the role of a metal in enzyme activation will hardly be accepted at once by workers in the field, but that it is stimulating and will provoke new lines of experimentation can scarcely be doubted.

Specificity and Mode of Action of Metal-Enzyme Complexes. The contribution by Emil Smith and his coworkers likewise suggests that the side-chains of the substrates interact with the protein portion of the enzyme, by van der Waals forces, and that the metal ion serves to form a coordination complex with substrate and enzyme. This view, advanced several years ago on the basis of preliminary work with intracellular peptidases, is now supported by experiments with preparations of high purity. The work on two of these enzymes is summarized here.

Prolidase, discovered by Bergman and Fruton in 1937, is an enzyme that hydrolyzes glycyl-L-proline, and is unique in being the only known enzyme that will attack a peptide bond involving the imino nitrogen of proline or hydroxyproline. It does not attack the more usual type of peptide bond. Prolidase is specifically activated by Mn^{++}. Using swine kidney as a source, prolidase has been purified about 12,000-fold, but few new aspects of its behavior have emerged as a result. The enzyme is also stabilized by sulfhydryl compounds, and strongly inhibited by p-chloromercuribenzoate, an inhibition reversed by the addition of glutathione or cysteine. These facts suggest the presence of an essential -SH group on the enzyme. Iodoacetamide inhibits the enzyme if added before Mn^{++} activation, but does not do so if added afterwards. This implies that the Mn^{++} is bound to the sulfhydryl group and protects it from iodoacetamide, although not from the other inhibitor. A number of other facts indicate also that the metal is bound directly to the protein. As in the case of other metal enzymes, the simple mass-law relation expected for one metal ion per active center on the enzyme appears to hold, namely, [active-enzyme]/[metal][inactive enzyme] = K. Prolidase activity is limited to activity upon dipeptides. Because of the tendency of Mn^{++}, like other metal ions, to form chelates with five-atom rings, together with the evidence that the uncharged amino and the ionized carboxyl groups are essential points of attachment, Smith arrives at the picture of the complex formed by substrate, metal, and enzyme shown in Fig. 5.

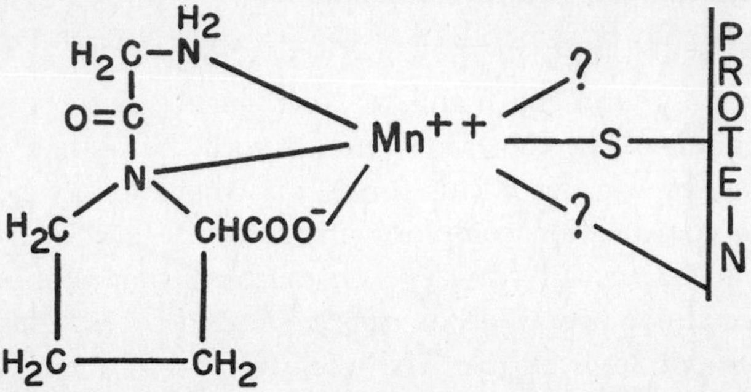

FIG. 5. Coordination of glycyl-L-proline with prolidase, as postulated by Smith et al. (From Smith, Davis, Adams, and Spackman).

Because of steric interference of the hydroxyl group with the formation of the complex, glycylhydroxy-L-proline is only about one-tenth as reactive as glycyl-L-proline. Activity is increased if glycyl-allohydroxy-L-proline, which has its carboxyl and hydroxyl groups in cis instead of trans position, is substituted. Thence it is concluded that the pyrrolidine ring of the substrate must interact directly with the surface of the enzyme, by a van der Waals force, the binding of the polar groups of the substrate by the metal ion being insufficient to explain the specificity of the enzyme for the substrate. This conclusion is further supported by the weak action of the enzyme on glycylsarcosine, a dipeptide with an imide bond but no pyrrolidine ring.

Smith postulates that the enzyme action comes about through combination of the metal with the nitrogen atom of the peptide bond. Electrons would then be displaced from the peptide carbonyl carbon to the nitrogen; the former would become more electropositive and would strongly attract hydroxyl ions. Catalysis would then occur through the usual type of hydroxyl-ion attack.

The second metal-enzyme studied extensively by Smith and his group is leucine aminopeptidase, which hydrolyzes many amino acid amides and peptides, and is strongly activated by Mn^{++}, more weakly by Mg^{++}. It has been purified from swine kidney about 850-fold. The stability of the enzyme is decreased by Mn^{++}, but increased by Mg^{++}. The rate of hydrolysis of the various amino acid amides tested, which may be symbolized by the structure $R_1CHNH_2CONH_2$,

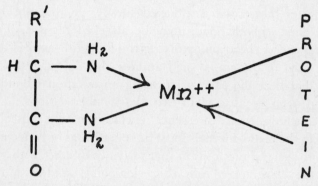

FIG. 6. Coordination of L-leucinamide with leucine aminopeptidase, as postulated by Smith et al. (From Smith, Davis, Adams, and Spackman).

is a function of the nature of the side-chain R_1. Branching at the β-carbon slows down the rate of hydrolysis, a fact which suggests that a steric factor is involved. Parallelism in this respect between the enzymatic hydrolysis and acid or alkaline hydrolysis provides evidence that the attack on the peptide bond of the substrate when it is bound in the enzyme-substrate complex is mediated by ionic catalysis in the usual way. The slow action on amides of the aromatic amino acids also indicates that the side-chains of the substrate molecules are involved in binding to the protein. The picture of the complex that emerges (Fig. 6) is that of coordination between the metal ion and the free amino group and the peptide (or amide) nitrogen of the substrate. The metal ion must also be bound to at least two sites on the enzyme. This binding is, however, pH-labile, and the activity curve may be fitted by an un-ionized imidazole group and an un-ionized terminal α-amino group, or by two imidazole groups of different pK values.

In acting on dipeptides, the aminopeptidase must be supplied with a substrate in which the residue bearing the R_1 group is of the L-configuration. The possibility of binding to the carboxyl group of a dipeptide in which both residues are of the L-configuration cannot be ruled out, although the more likely binding is such as that postulated for the amide. The attack on glycyl-L-leucinamide is interesting, in that one bond is hydrolyzed rapidly, to liberate NH_3, and thereafter the second is attacked slowly. In the case of other dipeptide amides, both bonds may be attacked rapidly. There is, then, some type of chelation involving the dipeptide amides different than that seen in the amino acid amides and dipeptides. It seems probable that here the Mn^{++} is forming an additional bond to the peptide nitrogen, so as to yield two five-membered rings.

Smith concludes that " in essence, chelation of the substrate with the metal in the metal-enzymes must be regarded as only one example of the more general proposition that enzymes interact with multiple sites on the substrate. From this viewpoint, studies of enzyme specificity are studies of the number and kinds of interactions involved in the formation of enzyme-substrate complexes." As Smith notes, this is a reaffirmation of Bergman's polyaffinity theory.

THE MECHANISM OF ELECTRON AND HYDROGEN TRANSPORT

One-Electron and Two-Electron Transfers. For more than twenty years the hypothesis that oxidation-reduction reactions necessarily proceed in steps of one-electron transfer, a hypothesis starting from Haber and Willstätter and rendered definitive by Michaelis, has dominated our thinking about the mechanism of such reactions. The distinction between one-electron and two-electron transfers is of course in part a matter of definition; and hence Westheimer, in proceeding to reconsider present evidence in support of the existence of two-electron transfers in inorganic and organic chemistry, has first defined what he would consider a two-electron transfer, namely, a reaction in which no species is produced having an odd number of electrons and a half-life during the reaction of more than 10^{-11} seconds. This means that any "free-radical intermediate, to be considered, must survive long enough to break out of the 'solvent cage' in which it is formed, so that it may react with some compound other than those surrounding it at the moment of its creation."

Westheimer has selected examples of one-electron and two-electron oxidation-reduction reactions, both inorganic and organic in nature, for consideration and comparison. From inorganic chemistry he takes simple exchange reactions, detected by radioactive tracers, between ferricyanide and ferrocyanide ions, between cobaltous and cobaltic ethylenediamine complexes, or between the ammonia complexes of cobalt, as good examples of one-electron transfers. These range from reactions too fast to measure, in the first case, to reactions very slow, in the case last mentioned. The high energy of activation in the slow reactions may be due to a combination of factors, such as electrostatic repulsion between ions of like sign, a high degree of solvation dependent upon a high charge on the central ion, and the charge of the coordinating agent (e. g., ammonia shields cobaltous and cobaltic ions better than ethylenediamine does). Further examples of inorganic one-electron transfers are found in chain reactions involving free radicals; but Westheimer points out that Shaffer's principle of equi-valence changes, according to which single reactions between two-electron donors and acceptors, or between one-electron donors and acceptors, will be fast, whereas single reactions between two-electron donors and one-electron acceptors, or the converse, will be slow, does not hold in all cases.

In organic chemistry the formation and destruction of stable free radicals, such as the triphenylmethyl radical in the reaction between hexaphenyl ethane and iodine, or semiquinone radicals in the oxidation-reduction reactions of quinones, represent obvious examples of one-electron transfers. There are also numerous well-known free-radical chain processes of this character, such as the oxidation of tetralin by O_2.

Yet if the evidence that one-electron transfers occur in both inorganic and organic reactions is well established, the like may also be said of two-electron transfers. Thus, in the inorganic realm, the oxidation of iodine by hydrogen peroxide must, from the kinetic equation and from other evidence which rules out the participation of free iodine atoms, involve the formation of hypoiodite (IOH) by transfer of an oxygen *atom* from H_2O_2 to an iodide ion. For the oxidation of sulfite by ClO_3^- or by hydrogen peroxide, and for the oxidation of arsenite by chromic acid, similar arguments for the occurrence of two-electron transfers may be made. In organic reactions, the addition of molecular bromine to transstilbene appears to be a polar reaction without formation of a free-radical intermediate, and therefore a type of two-electron oxidation. Other examples of oxidation-reduction reactions without the formation of free-radical intermediates are the oxidation of an aldehyde to an acid (via the oxime) by hydroxylamine, the oxidation of isopropyl alcohol to acetone by aqueous chromic acid, reductions of organic compounds by inorganic reagents such as lithium aluminum hydride by way of the transfer of a hydrogen atom with its electron pair (hydride ion transfer), and other hydride ion processes.

In biochemistry itself, Michaelis' hypothesis of obligatory one-electron transfers has not yet been either proved or disproved. The exact nature of the enzymatic mechanism must be settled here by the same kind of rigorous studies as for comparable reactions in inorganic and organic chemistry. In particular, the reactions involving the pyridine nucleotides are unclear. The experiments using deuterium as a tracer, Westheimer points out, leave it quite uncertain whether a deuterium atom or a deuteride ion is transferred. In the discussion, studies by Yarmolinsky and Colowick were described that eliminate a part of the supposed evidence for the occurrence of a free-radical intermediate during the reduction of DPN to DPNH by dithionite. The yellow compound known to occur as a transitory intermediate in this reaction was shown to be, not a free radical, but an addition compound. This is probably the sulfoxylate (–OSOH), which then by hydrolysis yields DPNH.

Chance and Fergusson have considered the relative probability of one-electron and two-electron reactions in catalase and peroxidase reactions. Four analogous enzyme-substrate complexes have been identified in each of these reactions by means of spectroscopic and magnetometric methods. These complexes are designated from I to IV in the order of their formation, but not all of them are actually concerned in the reaction sequence. Only complex I is rate-limiting and highly active in the catalase reactions; in the peroxidase reactions complex II is rate-limiting, and both complexes I and II are highly active. The peroxidase complex II retains only one oxidizing equivalent of the two oxidizing equivalents possessed by complex I. No evidence of any free radical occurring in the reaction could be found. The kinetic data indicate that both peroxidase and catalase reactions start alike, with formation of complex I, which then reacts with an electron donor. In the case of catalase, in which at least one type of single-electron donor, the hydroxyl radical, has been ruled out, it therefore appears that both reducing equivalents (electrons, hydrogen atoms) of a donor such as alcohol or H_2O_2 are transferred to complex I virtually simultaneously (in less than 10^{-7} sec.). In the case of peroxidase, both one-electron and two-electron donors may function, although the latter are much more common. With either one-electron or two-electron donors, successive collisions with two donor molecules will account for the kinetic data. That is, even with a two-electron donor, once complex II is formed, it must collide with yet another donor molecule to free the enzyme. The formation of complex I, its transition to complex II, and the liberation of enzyme from complex II in the peroxidase reaction are all independent of pH. If complex I is a simple addition complex, $Fe^{+3}(H_2O_2)$, reaction with a donor molecule AH_2 might, so Chance and Fergusson think, produce complex II in the form of $Fe^{+3}(OH\cdot)$, along with water and a half-oxidized donor molecule $AH\cdot$ which remains entirely hypothetical for the present.

Direct Hydrogen Transport and Steric Specificity in Reactions Catalyzed by the Pyridine Nucleotide Dehydrogenases. Although it has become conventional to think of the mechanism of oxidation-reduction reactions in terms of electron transfer alone, evidence has recently been provided by Vennesland and her coworkers at the University of Chicago that in some of the pyridine nucleotide dehydrogenase reactions there is an actual transfer of hydrogen atoms between substrate and coenzyme. This demonstration was rendered possible by using deuterium as a tracer in the study of two enzyme systems, alcohol dehydrogenase from yeast and lactic dehydrogenase from heart muscle. Both reactions are alike in being oxidations of an alcohol (primary or secondary), but nevertheless differ in certain respects such as sensitivity to sulfhydryl reagents. It was clearly shown that in both systems all of the hydrogen transferred to DPN$^+$ when it is reduced to DPNH is derived from the substrate and not from the aqueous medium. Moreover, when enzymatically reduced DPND is reoxidized enzymatically with acetaldehyde, all of the deuterium is removed; but if chemically reduced DPND is used, only somewhat more than half of the deuterium is removed. Clearly, the enzymatically reduced DPND consists of only one of the two diastereomers at position 4 of the pyridine ring, whereas the chemically reduced DPND consists of a mixture of both. [In the discussion Colowick reported the evidence obtained with Pullman and San Pietro that reduction of DPN is actually at the para position, rather than at an ortho position, as formerly thought.] The same was observed if lactic dehydrogenase was used instead of alcohol dehydrogenase, and pyruvate as substrate instead of acetaldehyde. The results show that both enzymes transfer hydrogen directly from the coenzyme to the substrate, both show stereospecificity for DPN, and both transfer the hydrogen to and from the same side of the pyridine ring of the nucleotide.

A survey of the pyridine nucleotide dehydrogenases which have been sufficiently examined also shows that all of them are likewise stereospecific for their substrates: lactic dehydrogenase for L(+)-lactic acid; an *l*-β-hydroxybutyric acid dehydrogenase and also a *d*-β-hydroxybutyric acid dehydrogenase; *d*-isocitric dehydrogenase; and a β-hydroxysteroid dehydrogenase. It therefore seemed likely that the reduction of acetaldehyde to ethanol by alcohol dehydrogenase might also be stereospecific, and this possibility was investigated by Vennesland and Westheimer, by preparing the two enantiomorphs of deuteroethanol and then observing the products of their enzymatic reoxidation. When deuteroethanol (CH_3CD_2OH) was prepared from ordinary acetaldehyde and DPND, then upon reoxidation all of the deuterium was recovered in DPND and none in the acetaldehyde. No racemization occurred. But when deuteroacetaldehyde (CH_3CDO) and DPNH were used to prepare deuteroethanol, the deuterium was recovered entirely in the acetaldehyde upon reoxidation, and none was found in the pyridine nucleotide.

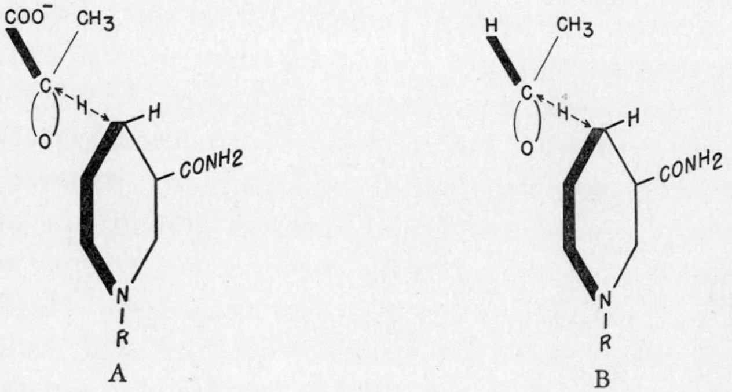

Fig. 7. A scheme to illustrate the stereochemical specificity in direct hydrogen transfer between coenzyme (DPN) and substrate. *A*, the lactic dehydrogenase reaction. *B*, the alcohol dehydrogenase reaction. (From Vennesland and Westheimer).

If confirmation of the stereospecificity of the enzymatic reaction is needed, it is supplied by the further demonstration that following conversion of one of the enantiomorphs of deuteroethanol to the other by a Walden inversion, the opposite results were found. That is to say, monodeuteroethanol (CH_3CHDOH) prepared from deuteroacetaldehyde (CH_3CDO) and DPNH yielded, after inversion and enzymatic reoxidation, unlabelled acetaldehyde, and all of the deuterium was recovered in the pyridine nucleotide. Thus, just as in previously investigated displacement reactions of derivatives of secondary alcohols, in this case of an enzymatic displacement reaction resulting in the formation of a primary alcohol, the asymmetric carbon atom is attacked on the tetrahedral face opposite the carbon-oxygen bond (of a carbonyl group) which is broken. The reactions catalyzed by the two enzymes are pictured, for purposes of visualization and not with any intention of indicating an actual mechanism, in Fig. 7. Perhaps the necessary steric orientation is secured, in the case of the pyruvate substrate, by the binding of the highly polar carboxyl and carbonyl groups to particular sites on the enzyme; but it is difficult to account for the steric specificity of the acetaldehyde substrate in an analogous manner. Perhaps some steric repulsion for the methyl group forces it out of all but the proper orientation on the protein surface. At any rate, it would be hard to account for the stereospecificity for the substrate without formation of an enzyme-substrate complex. The findings for the lactic and alcohol dehydrogenases suggest that other oxidations of alcohols and aldehydes by pyridine nucleotide dehydrogenases may likewise involve a direct hydrogen transfer with stereospecificity.

Kaplan, in discussion, suggested another mechanism for the direct hydrogen transfer. Hydroxylamine acts as a competitive inhibitor of ethanol in the liver alcohol dehydrogenase system. In the presence of the enzyme, DPN, and hydroxylamine a complex is formed, but only in the presence of all three. The compound appears to have the properties of a DPN-hydroxylamine addition compound. If this is so, possibly the enzyme acts similarly on the normal substrate, so as to form an alcohol-DPN addition compound that is then split to acetaldehyde and DPNH.

In the discussion, San Pietro reported on work of the McCollum-Pratt group in which it was shown that the transhydrogenase enzyme of *Pseudomonas fluorescens* offers a further example of direct hydrogen transfer, between various oxidized and reduced pyridine nucleotides. In this case, however, a deuterium experiment analogous to Vennesland's revealed no stereospecificity in the reaction TPND + DPN → DPND + TPN.

Studies of Enzyme Mechanisms in Vivo. The delicate spectroscopic measurements by Britton Chance of the reaction kinetics of catalase, peroxidase, and alcohol dehydrogenase enzyme-substrate complexes in aerobic cultures of *Micrococcus lysodeikticus* and bakers' yeast have opened new vistas into the nature of enzyme mechanisms in living cells. It has proved possible not only to identify the inter-mediate complexes but also to determine the sequence of their formation and disappearance and to identify the rate-limiting, or " Michaelis," complex for a given set of conditions.

The catalase reaction involves two steps. First, catalase unites with hydrogen peroxide generated in the cell, and forms a catalase-H_2O_2 complex. For the second step, two alternatives exist. Either the complex reacts with a second molecule of hydrogen peroxide (a catalatic reaction) ; or it reacts with some other hydrogen donor, such as alcohol, formic acid, or nitrous acid (a peroxidatic reaction). The biological function of catalase is thus broader than simply that of a scavenger of excess H_2O_2. In the steady-state, 1.6 catalase hematins out of the total of 4 are bound by H_2O_2. The fact that methyl hydrogen peroxide will bind all four catalase hematin groups has been used to identify the intracellular peroxide as truly hydrogen peroxide and not an organic peroxide. The change in optical density that takes place when formate is used as donor in step two, above, is clearly that to be expected if hydrogen peroxide rather than an organic peroxide is the physiological substrate. In bacterial cells of *M. lysodeikticus* the catalase–hydrogen-peroxide complex can be seen spectrophotometrically to disappear slowly as the metabolism be-comes anaerobic. The turnover is .07 per sec. The free hydrogen peroxide concentration existing in cells in the steady state can be calculated to be 10^{-8} M, a level at which the catalatic and peroxidatic actions of catalase are roughly equal.

In yeast cells the use of exogenous peroxide by peroxidase is rapidly increased as cellular respiration is initiated by glucose. The amount of peroxide used is double that of the oxygen used in aerobic respiration, and is even higher in anaerobic respiration. Formation of the active peroxidase complex II requires, as has already been said, the participation of a hydrogen donor. This donor appears to be (ferro-)cytochrome c, for the latter may be observed spectro-scopically to become oxidized when peroxide is added, and antimycin-a, which blocks the reduction of cytochrome c, also eliminates the rapid utilization of peroxide in the presence of glucose. Cytochrome a cannot be ruled out as an additional donor by the present evidence. The ability of peroxidase to function in oxidizing reduced cytochromes is not altered by agents such as carbon monoxide or azide. This fact leaves it still uncertain to what extent peroxide is normally supplied to peroxidase during respiration. From the lifetime of complex II Chance has calculated that the turnover of peroxidase is 2 per sec. in the starved aerobic cell and as high as 200 per sec. during rapid respiration.

Efforts have also been made to quantify the reaction kinetics of the cytochrome system (cytochrome b, Slater's factor, and cytochromes c, a, and a_3), a system which is of especial interest because the cytochromes are attached to the mitochondria and are insoluble under physiological conditions. Ordinary collision theory would therefore scarcely be expected to apply to them; yet velocity constants of the same order of magnitude as those for catalase and peroxidase reactions will adequately account for the action of the cytochrome system if collision is restricted but some sort of sequential arrangement of the enzymes on the mitochondria exists in the living cell. Using a succinic oxidase system from heart muscle homogenates, Chance finds that a steady-state of the cytochrome system is reached when the substrate is added in excess. During the steady state the intensity of catalytic action of the cytochromes can be read from the differences in optical density spectra at two characteristic wavelengths, cytochrome a being evaluated at 605-630 mμ, cytochrome b at 562-575 mμ, cytochrome c at 551-541 mμ, cytochrome a_3 at 444-470 mμ. The percentage of each in the reduced state indicates that cytochrome a_3 is most fully oxidized in this system, and cytochromes a and b least. There are roughly equal concentrations of all four in the system. The turnover numbers, relative to concentration, range from 22 to 56 per sec. The calculated velocity constants derived from turnover numbers and percentages of each component in the oxidized and reduced forms, for the five reactions succinate $\rightarrow$ succinic dehydrogenase (including Slater's factor) $\rightarrow$ cytochrome c $\rightarrow$ cytochrome a $\rightarrow$ cytochrome a_3 $\rightarrow$ O_2, are respectively 0.1, 100, 230, 40, and 10×10^6 per mole per sec. But if the cytochromes are so arranged on the particles that their effective concentrations are greatly increased, because of proximity, the larger velocity constants would be greatly decreased. It is conceivable that, since the concentrations of the cytochromes are about equal in the particles, they are arranged in assemblies containing one each of the necessary enzymes. Although proof of this is lacking, it is suggestive that very small particles obtained from *Acetobacter vinelandii* contain a complete bacterial succinic oxidase system.

In bakers' yeast in the analogous steady state reached in aerobic alcoholic respiration, the distinctive cytochrome is a pigment similar to cytochrome b and to the yeast peroxidase complex II, yet different from both. Chance holds that the peroxidase complex II is present and can participate actively in the respiration of the yeast cell. Stotz in discussion reported that in his laboratory a new cytochrome pigment, perhaps the same as Chance's " cytochrome b," had been found. Absorbing at 552 mμ, this cytochrome seems to stand between cytochrome b and cytochrome c in the succinate system and to be necessary for the reduction of cytochrome c.

The spectrophotometric method has also been used by Chance to study the nature of DPNH-enzyme and DPN-enzyme compounds, in the cases of alcohol, lactic, and triose phosphate dehydrogenases. The general findings are that binding of the coenzyme by the protein can occur without any detectable shift in the DPN and DPNH spectra; that when a shift does occur it does not appear to be caused by binding of a sulfhydryl group; but that with either DPN or DPNH there are two spectrally distinct types of complexes (330 mμ and 360 mμ). The alcohol-dehydrogenase–DPNH–enzyme complex from horse liver, which *does* show a shift in spectrum of DPNH upon binding with the enzyme, permitted earlier kinetic data to be correlated with the equilibrium data. The disagreement of one order of magnitude which was obtained is not regarded by Chance as unsatisfactory, in view of the numerous errors possible in estimating the six velocity constants for the three successive reactions (bonding, oxidation, dissociation). The results show that a hypothetical aldehyde-enzyme complex simply breaks down at a rate exceeding 45 per sec. and an alcohol-enzyme complex at a rate exceeding 0.4 per sec., and neither is therefore rate-limiting.

The yeast triosephosphate-dehydrogenase–DPN complex has also been studied in vivo. Chance has estimated, on the basis of the molecular extinction coefficient of the complex, that 10 per cent of the total yeast protein is attributable to this enzyme. Krebs, in discussion, confirmed this astonishing figure with a report of the results of three additional and independent methods, which yielded enzyme to the amount of 30 per cent of the extractable protein from electrophoretic observation, 14 per cent from a comparison of the specific activity of yeast juice with crystalline enzyme, and, most accurately, 20 per cent by quantitative precipitation with an antiserum prepared against the crystalline enzyme.

In starved yeast cells in which respiration is suddenly initiated by addition of alcohol or glucose, the oxygen uptake reaches a maximal rate before the reduction of DPN becomes maximal. Furthermore, subsequent oxidation of DPNH does not slow down the respiration; and in the presence of iodoacetate the DPN-reducing enzyme is rendered inactive, whereas the DPNH-oxidizing enzyme exhibits even greater activity. It is therefore clear that since large fluctuations of the DPN–DPNH steady-state level in the respiring cell fail to produce changes in the respiratory rate, a cyclic reduction and reoxidation of the pyridine nucleotides must exist, under the control of separate enzymes. The DPN-reducing enzyme is identifiable with triose phosphate dehydrogenase, and in all likelihood the DPNH-oxidizing enzyme is α-glycerol phosphate dehydrogenase, which is the only known DPN enzyme with activity toward dihydroxyacetone phosphate that would balance the reducing action on DPN of the triose phosphate dehydrogenase. Chance thus conceives of a DPN cycle which is governed by the dehydrogenases and which controls the steady-state level of DPN/DPNH in respiring cells " to a considerably greater extent than do the respiratory enzymes."

Velick's quantitative studies of the alcohol dehydrogenase complement those of Chance and enable a comparison to be made between the enzyme derived from mammalian tissue and that derived from yeast. Neither is isolated as a DPN complex. The yeast enzyme has a molecular weight about twice that of the mammalian enzyme, 150,000 against 73,000. Both enzymes bind DPNH much more strongly than DPN, and the liver enzyme binds two moles of DPNH to one mole of enzyme. For the yeast enzyme, DPN and DPNH show competitive binding. The stronger binding of DPNH thus serves to inhibit the oxidation of ethanol, according to Velick the first direct quantitative evidence of the displacement of substrate (DPN) by an inhibitor (DPNH) from an intermediary complex. The dissociation constants have been measured for all four enzyme-coenzyme complexes, and are much higher for the yeast enzyme (Velick) than for the liver enzyme (Theorell and Chance). Direct binding measurements on the liver alcohol dehydrogenase/DPNH complex have shown, as also in the case of the glyceraldehyde-3-phosphate dehydrogenase/DPN complex, that the Michaelis constants depend strongly upon steady-state conditions and are not direct measures of the dissociation constants. The apparent equilibrium constant $\frac{[\text{DPNH}][\text{acetald.}]}{[\text{DPN}][\text{alc.}]} \cdot \frac{f_{\text{DPNH}}f_{\text{ald.}}}{f_{\text{DNP}}f_{\text{alc.}}}$, where f = fraction not bound to enzyme, shifts with increasing enzyme concentration. At high concentrations it is ten-fold as high as at low concentrations, for the yeast enzyme.

THE FUNCTION OF ENZYMES IN GROUP TRANSFER

Acyl and Carbonyl Complexes in Relation to Electron Transport and Group Transfer Reactions. Racker has reviewed in a comprehensive way the three main aspects of the roles of carbonyl and acyl complexes, namely, the formation of such complexes in oxidative processes, the degradation of acyl complexes, and transfer reactions involving acyl or carbonyl complexes. In reality, these three aspects can scarcely be considered apart. They have been studied most fully in the three systems, glyceraldehyde-3-phosphate dehydrogenase, pyruvic acid oxidase, and α-ketoglutaric acid oxidase.

In the first of these, it has proved possible to demonstrate that the enzyme catalyzes the transformation of the triose phosphate to

1, 3-diphosphoglyceric acid by means of two main steps, the first oxidative and resulting in the formation of an acyl-enzyme intermediate, the second phosphorolytic and resulting in production of the acyl phosphate. The formation of an acyl-enzyme intermediate in this reaction is analogous to the formation of the thio-ester linkage in acetyl-CoA, demonstrated by Lynen and Reichert. The existence of this intermediate was indicated by finding that DPN is reduced in the absence of inorganic phosphate or any other acyl acceptor save the enzyme itself (Boyer and Segal; Velick). Presence of the intermediate was demonstrated by Racker, using gram quantities of the enzyme with acetyl phosphate as substrate. The presence of a thio-ester was established by the hydroxylamine reaction, and small amounts of the thio-ester were isolated on paper chromatograms. It was also found, from studies of absorption spectra, that DPN forms a complex with the –SH groups of the enzyme, and that known acyl phosphates cause this complex to disappear. Racker has therefore concluded that the very first step is the formation of a DPN–S–enzyme complex which provides a mechanism for electron transfer, most likely by hydrogen transfer from the –SH group of the enzyme to DPN. Cleavage of the DPN–S–enzyme complex by the aldehyde ("aldehydolysis") would then follow, and would leave the DPN reduced and form the thio-ester. Boyer and Segal, however, hesitate to accept the view that this is the only mode of addition of the aldehyde to the enzyme, inasmuch as the substrate can protect two of the –SH groups on the enzyme from alkylation by iodoacetate whether the DPN is oxidized, reduced, or absent. In other words, sulfhydryl groups are protected even when not involved in a DPN–S–enzyme linkage. Furthermore, there is no exact equivalence between moles of DPN reduced and of substrate bound, as would be expected if the "aldehydolysis" postulated by Racker were the entire mechanism. Hence Boyer and Segal retain in their scheme an intermediate step in which the aldehyde forms an addition

$$\overset{\displaystyle H}{\underset{\displaystyle OH}{\text{compound with the enzyme complex } (R\text{–}C\text{–}S\text{–}E\text{–}DPN),} } \text{ following}$$

which hydrogen transfer to DPN takes place, leaving the same acyl intermediate postulated by Racker, namely, $R\text{–}\overset{\overset{\displaystyle O}{\parallel}}{C}\text{–}S\text{–}E\text{–}DPNH$. According to the estimates made by Boyer and Segal from the equilibrium data, the free energy of hydrolysis of the acyl-enzyme bond is of the order of 10 kcal. That is to say, it is definitely a " high-energy " bond.

The second part of the glyceraldehyde oxidation reaction is that in which the acyl-enzyme complex is cleaved. This involves the cleavage of the acyl–S bond by inorganic phosphate. According to Velick, the kinetic data suggest that the phosphate ion does not form an intermediate complex with the enzyme, but reacts directly with the acyl-enzyme complex upon collision. Whatever the exact details of the process may be, it is now quite clear that the long-sought 1,3-diphosphoglyceraldehyde, supposed to serve as an intermediate in triose phosphate oxidation, is purely mythical; and a quite different sort of mechanism, that of the formation of an acyl complex with a sulfhydryl-bearing enzyme, enables the oxidation and phosphorylation of the substrate to take place.

Studies by Velick and by Boyer and Segal of quantitative aspects of the enzyme glyceraldehyde-3-phosphate dehydrogenase have also thrown light on the mechanism of action of this enzyme. Velick has compared the enzyme obtained from two different sources, mammalian (rabbit) muscle and yeast. The molecular weights appear to be very similar, 120,000 for the former and 122,000 for the latter. The two enzymes are similar but not identical in amino acid constitution, and are serologically distinguishable. The mammalian enzyme, however, has two molecules of DPN per molecule of enzyme bound in a tight complex, whereas the yeast enzyme, although it has a strong binding power for DPN when that is added, has none bound to it initially. The dissociation constant of the yeast enzyme is about 5 to 10 times as large as that of the mammalian enzyme. In respect to reagents that oxidize thiol groups both forms of the enzyme react similarly. For example, two equivalents of *p*-chloromercuribenzoate completely inhibit the yeast enzyme, which may then be reactivated by cysteine; the yeast-inhibitor compound is incapable of binding DPN. Activity of the mammalian enzyme is lost upon reaction with three to four equivalents of the inhibitor, and in so doing the enzyme loses its bound DPN; it is also reactivated by cysteine. Boyer and Segal, who also have worked with the mammalian enzyme, find from its reaction at pH 4.6 with the same inhibitor, p-chloromercuribenzoate, that a total of 10.3 –SH groups can react per mole of enzyme. Various preparations range from 8 to 13.5. This compares with a value of 10.7 half-cystine residues per mole (Velick and Ronzoni). From these studies, evidently most of the cystine sulfur of the enzyme exists in the form of –SH groups in the crystalline muscle enzyme. The lack of stabilizing disulfide cross-linkages would help to account for the instability of the enzyme. The maximum turnover number of the enzyme with inorganic phosphate (60 per cent higher than with arsenate) is about 12,500 per min. at 28° C.

In the discussion, Astrachan described experiments with oxidized and reduced forms of the crystalline enzyme. The oxidized enzyme binds DPN, according to Astrachan, through the pyrophosphate group. When thus bound, the DPN is much more susceptible to attack by various enzymes than is DPN bound to the reduced enzyme. This suggests that in the active, reduced enzyme, DPN becomes less available to other enzymes by virtue of some new linkage formed between DPN and the essential –SH groups of triose phosphate dehydrogenase. The conclusion is in conformity with Racker's theory of the formation of a DPN–S–enzyme complex.

Great attention has recently become directed to the function of lipoic acid (6,8-dimercapto-octanoic acid), in the oxidative decarboxylation and dehydrogenation of keto acids such as pyruvate and α-ketoglutarate. From studies of this system in *Streptococcus faecalis*, *Escherichia coli*, and *Proteus vulgaris*, Gunsalus and his coworkers have disclosed the widespread group transfer functions of lipoic acid in the generation and transfer of acyl groups and in hydrogen transfer.

Lipoic acid occurs in disulfide, dimercapto, and mono–S–acyl/mono-mercapto forms, all of which are biologically active. Only the D-isomer, which corresponds to that isolated from tissues, seems to be active in pyruvate dehydrogenation and lipoic transacetylation. The oxidation-reduction potential of the disulfide/dimercapto lipoic acid pair of compounds is as low as that of DPN⁺/DPNH, and perhaps as low as that of the hydrogen electrode. It is not yet possible to state the form of the coenzyme definitively. The experiments of Reed and DeBusk indicate that it may be lipothiamide pyrophosphate (LTPP), but Gunsalus and Calvin (in discussion) are doubtful of the existence of any amide linkage. So far, the acetyl lipoic acid resulting from transacetylation has not been isolated or fully characterized, but it bears one acetyl group per mole of the dimercapto-lipoic acid.

In the oxidation of pyruvic acid it is necessary to account for the need for a considerable number of cofactors, namely, thiamin pyrophosphate, Mg^{++}, lipoic acid, coenzyme A, and DPN. Evidence summarized by Racker and Gunsalus is now sufficient to substantiate the occurrence of the oxidation by means of four steps: (1) decarboxylation, requiring the thiamin pyrophosphate and Mg^{++}, leads to formation of an active acetaldehyde which, since not set free, must remain bound in a carbonyl-enzyme or carbonyl-diphosphothiamin complex; (2) splitting of the –S–S– linkage of lipoic acid by the active aldehyde in an aldehydolysis that yields an acetyl lipoic compound, a thio-ester the presence of which has been demonstrated by the hydroxylamine reaction; (3) transfer of the acetyl group to CoA, leaving the completely reduced lipoic acid; (4) reduction of DPN by the reduced lipoic acid. The enzymatic oxidation of pyruvic acid is thus seen to be closely analogous to the oxidation of glyceraldehyde-3-phosphate, with aldehydolysis of an –S–S– bond substituted for aldehydolysis of an –S–C– bond.

The oxidation of α-ketoglutarate appears to be virtually identical to the mechanism just shown for pyruvate oxidation, as far as the point where an acyl-CoA compound is formed. In the first step, thiamin pyrophosphate and Mg^{++} are required, and an " active succinic semialdehyde " is formed through decarboxylation as a carbonyl-enzyme (or carbonyl-diphosphothiamin) complex. In step two, lipoic acid and coenzyme A are involved, and it is probable that, as in pyruvate oxidation, the active aldehyde splits the –S–S– linkage of lipoic acid to form a thio-ester, whereupon the succinyl group is transferred to CoA and the reduced lipoic acid is reoxidized by DPN.

The four steps described above are reduced by Gunsalus to the following equations:

$$
\overset{O\ O}{\underset{}{R'-\overset{\|}{C}:\overset{\|}{C}^-}} + DPT^+ \rightleftharpoons [R'-\overset{O}{\overset{\|}{C}}:DPT] + CO_2 \tag{1}
$$

$$
[R'-\overset{O}{\overset{\|}{C}}:DPT] + \ \underset{S-}{\overset{S-}{\Big\rangle}}\!\!\overset{R}{} \rightleftharpoons R'-\overset{O}{\overset{\|}{C}}:S-\underset{:S-}{\overset{R^-}{\Big\rangle}} + DPT^+ \tag{2}
$$

$$
R'-\overset{O}{\overset{\|}{C}}:S-\underset{:S-}{\overset{R^-}{\Big\rangle}} + CoASH \rightleftharpoons R'-\overset{O}{\overset{\|}{C}}:SCoA + \underset{:S-}{\overset{HS-}{\Big\rangle}}\!\!\overset{R^-}{} \tag{3}
$$

$$
\underset{:S-}{\overset{HS-}{\Big\rangle}}\!\!\overset{R^-}{} + DPN^+ \rightleftharpoons \underset{S-}{\overset{S-}{\Big\rangle}}\!\!\overset{R}{} + DPNH \tag{4}
$$

R′ = CH_3–, $HOOC(CH_2)_2$–, etc.

R = $(CH_2)_4COOH$

DPT = diphosphothiamin, thiamin pyrophosphate, cocarboxylase

From these equations it is seen that the cyclic disulfide form of lipoic acid acts as an acyl-group acceptor, the carbanion donor being a diphosphothiamin-"aldehyde." The initial DPT-reaction which forms the DPT-carbanion donor may be common to a number of other reactions, such as other keto acid decarboxylations, or oxidative reactions with electron acceptors that would liberate free acids. The second form of the lipoic acid coenzyme, the S-acyl derivative of the dimercapto form, in turn transfers the acyl group to coenzyme A, and thus becomes the simple dimercapto form of lipoic acid. Finally, by hydrogen transfer to DPN, the oxidized cyclic disulfide form is regenerated. Presumably, each of the four reactions in the over-all mechanism is catalyzed by a distinct enzyme.

In the studies on *E. coli*, the enzymes for the various steps in the oxidative decarboxylation of the alpha-keto-acids have been considerably purified. One fraction (" B ") has been found to contain a lipoic dehydrogenase, the enzyme required for reaction (4) above. Another fraction ("A") contains both a lipoic transacetylase, the enzyme that catalyzes the reversible transfer of acetyl groups between coenzyme A and lipoic acid (equation 3, above) and also a step dependent upon DPT, the latter being shown both by the CO_2 exchange and the DPT requirement for reaction with ferricyanide, 2, 6-dichlorophenolindophenol, or acetaldehyde. The units of lipoic transacetylase found in the "A" fraction are only half those necessary to account for the total dismutation of pyruvate, a discrepancy which Gunsalus suggests may be due to failure of the assay system in vitro to react at the rate of the true acyl-CoA-forming step of the keto-acid system.

In *Proteus vulgaris*, strain X19, there is a rather different keto-acid oxidation system, which bypasses acyl-lipoic generation and leads to acetate. Nevertheless, this organism also possesses an acyl-generating keto-acid system analogous to that in *E. coli*, and *E. coli* also possesses a soluble carboxylase which can be coupled to the acyl bypass mechanism of *Proteus*. Thus the mechanisms for keto-acid oxidation in the two organisms are not so distinct as it seemed at first.

Racker also discussed the role of acyl complexes, particularly thio-esters, in several other systems: bacterial aldehyde dehydrogenases, diacetyl oxidase, the oxidation-reduction of glyoxals, and fatty acid oxidation. To varying degrees the imperfect evidence implies the presence of analogous mechanisms in these systems, although the participation of lipoic acid in many of them has not yet been investigated. As for the role of thiol groups in the formation of acyl complexes, Velick warns that the mere presence of thiol groups in an enzyme need not imply that the enzymatic mechanism involves formation of a thiol bond with substrate or coenzyme. Many enzymes of diverse functions are known to possess essential thiol groups. In some cases inhibition of the enzyme action through substitution or oxidation of the thiol group might act through a steric effect, the catalytic activity being affected even though the thiol group was at some distance from the catalytic centers.

The degradation of acyl-enzyme complexes and the transfer of acyl and carbonyl complexes can scarcely be considered apart, inasmuch as the degradation of acyl complexes is commonly brought about by means of a transfer of the group except in the case of some direct hydrolyses. Thus several thio-esters of glutathione (e. g., acetyl- and lactyl-glutathione) are directly hydrolyzed by mammalian enzymes, and acetyl-CoA, succinyl-CoA, and acetoacetyl-CoA are hydrolyzed by enzymes known as deacylases.

Simplest of the acyl transfer reactions is the transfer of an acyl group to inorganic phosphate, as in the phosphorolysis of the acyl group of glyceraldehyde-3-phosphate, discussed above, and in the well-known phosphotransacetylase reaction of bacteria. In the latter reaction the acetyl group is transferred from CoA to phosphate, following which the acetyl phosphate may be broken down in two ways, either irreversibly by hydrolysis to acetate and inorganic phosphate by means of an acetyl phosphatase, or reversibly by transfer of the phosphate group to ADP by means of a bacterial kinase.

Another type of acyl transfer is the transfer from a thio-ester to a free acid by means of CoA, e. g., the CoA-transphorase reaction of *Clostridium kluyveri*, proceeding from acetyl-CoA and propionate to propionyl-CoA and acetate; or an analogous system found in mammalian tissues that transfers CoA from a succinyl group to an acetoacetate group. Ochoa, in the discussion, has suggested that enzyme-CoA complexes, rather than acyl-enzyme complexes, may be the true intermediates in these transfers. Lipmann further developed this concept by relating the results of recent experiments done in collaboration with Lynen on the acetate-activation reaction in yeast:

$$\text{ATP} + \text{CoA} + \text{acetate} \rightleftharpoons \text{AMP} + \text{acetyl} \sim \text{CoA} + \text{PP}$$

By using pyrophosphate marked with P^{32} and acetate marked with C^{14}, it proved possible to demonstrate a very rapid enzymatic equilibration of pyrophosphate with ATP and of acetate with acetyl-CoA. Lipmann postulates an exchange of AMP $\sim$ enzyme with AMP $\sim$ PP (i. e., ATP), or, in other words, that an energy-rich intermediate complex is formed between AMP and enzyme (E). The addition of CoA inhibits this exchange, so the CoA is to be regarded as competing with AMP for attachment to the enzyme. Furthermore, acetyl-CoA and acetate also interchange readily, although less rapidly than ATP and pyrophosphate. Lipmann therefore postulates a series of three reactions, as follows:

$$E + ATP \rightleftharpoons E \sim AMP + PP \qquad (1)$$

$$E \sim AMP + CoA \rightleftharpoons E \sim CoA + AMP \qquad (2)$$

$$E \sim CoA + acetate \rightleftharpoons E + acetyl \sim CoA \qquad (3)$$

Analogous to this reaction, and yet different in that AMP and pyrophosphate are replaced by ADP and inorganic phosphate, is the hydrolysis of succinyl-CoA in the over-all oxidation of ketoglutarate. This may possibly proceed by a similar mechanism.

Transfer from one thio-ester to another, with liberation of a free –SH group, is of importance in fatty acid metabolism, e. g.,

$$2 \text{ acetyl–CoA} \rightleftharpoons \text{acetoacetyl–CoA} + \text{CoA–SH}.$$

Acyl transfer from acetyl-CoA to choline or other amines, or to amino acids by way of acetyl-CoA, as well as the recently discovered transfer of the acyl group from acetyl-CoA to an imidazole group, form yet another category of acyl-transfer reactions. The acetyl-CoA transfer to imidazole formed the substance of a contribution to the symposium by Stadtman. In *Clostridium kluyveri* the acetyl-CoA system, already discussed, is combined with a system that transfers the acyl group from coenzyme A to imidazole, the enzyme being called imidazole acetylase. The transfer reaction is highly endergonic, rendering detection of a direct enzymatic acetylation of imidazole by acetyl-CoA in the absence of acetyl phosphate and phosphotransacetylase difficult. Substitution of acetyl glutathione for acetyl-CoA in a non-enzymatic system was studied more successfully. The acetylation of imidazole in this system reached equilibrium in 5 minutes. There is also a non-enzymatic decomposition of acetyl imidazole in the presence of inorganic phosphate, to yield acetyl phosphate; and the rate of acetylation is proportional to the concentration of monobasic phosphoric acid over a considerable range.

The equilibrium position of the acetyl-phosphate/acetyl-imidazole system was studied spectrophotometrically, and from the equilibrium constant thus obtained it was calculated that the ΔF_0 is about + 2,800 calories. Since acetyl phosphate has a free energy of hydrolysis of 12,000 to 15,000 calories, this puts the free energy of hydrolysis of acetyl imidazole in the range between 15,000 and 18,000 calories. The compound is thus definitely in the class of " energy-rich " substances. It is therefore tempting to speculate about its biological functions, in particular to suppose that the histidine residues in proteins may act as acyl group carriers in enzymatic transfer reactions. To date, however, no important imidazole derivatives, except for urocanic acid, have been found to substitute for imidazole in the reaction catalyzed by the *C. kluyveri* enzyme.

The final type of acyl transfer discussed by Racker was the exceptional condensation of acetyl-CoA with oxaloacetate to yield citrate. This reaction, catalyzed by the condensing enzyme, differs from all others in the participation of water and the release of a free carboxyl group:

$$\text{acetyl–CoA} + \text{oxaloacetate} + H_2O \rightleftharpoons \text{citrate} + \text{CoA}$$

or, in the reverse direction, in the unexpected reaction of the carboxyl group with the –SH group of coenzyme A.

Transfers of carbonyl groups are catalyzed by carboxylase, transketolase, and transaldolase enzymes. Carboxylase (from yeast or wheat germ), which decarboxylates pyruvic acid to acetaldehyde, also catalyzes the formation of acetoin from the condensation of free acetaldehyde with an " active aldehyde " which contributes preferentially to the carbonyl end of the acetoin molecule ($CH_3CO \cdot CHOHCH_3$). An analogous enzyme, pyruvic oxidase from pigeon breast muscle, decarboxylates both pyruvate and hydroxypyruvate, and performs the acyloin condensation without free acetaldehyde. In this case, as with " active acetate " (acetyl-CoA), the presence of an electron acceptor such as ferricyanide acts as an inhibitor by competing with the acceptor aldehyde for the active group. It thus appears that a single enzyme is able to form an active carbonyl-enzyme complex from pyruvate (or from free acetaldehyde in the case of wheat germ carboxylase), and can be condensed with another free aldehyde molecule to yield an acyloin by an "oriented condensation," such as Neuberg predicted over 30 years ago. The nature of the carbonyl complex is still unknown, but very likely thiamin pyrophosphate (cocarboxylase) participates in its formation, since it is the sole cofactor required in the double reaction of pyruvate (or hydroxypyruvate) decarboxylation and acyloin condensation catalyzed by the carboxylases. Another system is one in which pyruvate rather than free aldehyde participates in the condensation, yielding acetolactate, which in turn is decarboxylated to form acetoin (Krampitz).

Quite similar to the preceding enzymes in action is the transketolase enzyme of yeast, in that an active aldehyde-enzyme complex is formed, either by splitting ribulose-5-phosphate or by decarboxylating hydroxypyruvic acid. The active aldehyde group may then be transferred to an acceptor aldehyde, such as glycolaldehyde, glyceraldehyde, or ribose-5-phosphate, to yield in the last case the newly discovered, important sedoheptulose-7-phosphate. In the formation of this active aldehyde ("active glycolaldehyde," according to Horecker), cocarboxylase and Mg^{++} ion are essential, as in the carboxylase system (Horecker; Racker). Like the pigeon muscle pyruvic oxidase, the transketolase-ThPP-glycolaldehyde complex is not dissociable, thus differing from the typical carboxylase; but it also differs from the pyruvic oxidase in acting only on hydroxypyruvate, and not on pyruvate as well, and in failing to act with acetaldehyde as the acceptor aldehyde.

Yeast has also yielded a transaldolase enzyme, studied by Racker, Horecker, and their respective coworkers. This enzyme transfers a dihydroxyacetone group from sedoheptulose-7-phosphate to glyceraldehyde-3-phosphate so as to yield fructose-6-phosphate and a still-unidentified tetrose phosphate. In analogy with the foregoing mechanisms of transfer reactions, one can postulate here the formation of an "active alcohol" intermediate, i. e., an alcohol-enzyme complex. In the presence of muscle aldolase and hexose diphosphate as a source of glyceraldehyde-3-phosphate, the tetrose ester is converted to a new heptulose, which appears to be sedoheptulose-1, 7-diphosphate (Horecker).

Group Transfer as an Enzymatic Substitution Reaction. Koshland has presented enzymatic group transfers in terms of substitution reactions, according to the model system $B–X + Y \rightarrow B–Y + X$, where B is the transferred group, X the donor, and Y the acceptor molecule. From consideration of straight organic reactions in which such replacements occur, it may be deduced that the general mechanism of replacement of one group attached to a primary or secondary saturated carbon atom by another group is that (a) a reagent with an unshared pair of electrons makes a *nucleophilic* attack on the carbon atom by sharing its electrons with the latter, while (b) a second reagent makes an *electrophilic attack* on the departing group by attracting its electrons and thus weakening its attachment to the carbon atom. A consequence of this mechanism is that with the replacement an inversion of configuration occurs whenever the carbon atom involved is asymmetric. It seems likely that displacements on phosphorus atoms have the same fundamental character as those on carbon atoms.

Applying this model to enzymatic substitution reactions, Koshland suggests that three types of mechanism can occur. The first, and simplest, takes place when Y and $B–X$ react directly on the surface of the enzyme, which simply polarizes the electrons in the substrate molecules so as to make them more reactive. Basic groups would enhance the electron-sharing tendency of Y, and acidic groups would decrease the strength of the $B–X$ bond. The $Y–B$ bond begins to form while the $B–X$ bond is breaking. In this mechanism the attacking group Y must approach from the side opposite to X, i. e., the $Y–B–X$ angle is approximately $180°$. Koshland calls this a *single displacement mechanism.*

The second mechanism differs from the first in involving formation of an intermediate enzyme-B complex. A nucleophilic group on the enzyme first attacks and cleaves the $B–X$ bond, thus creating an enzyme-B complex. This is then attacked in a second step by Y to give the final product, $Y–B$. The two successive transfers of B

make this a *double displacement mechanism.* An example is the synthesis of sucrose by sucrose phosphorylase from glucose-1-phosphate and fructose. The glucose group is first transferred from phosphate to enzyme and then from enzyme to fructose.

The third mechanism is postulated to occur when the affinity of the enzyme for the X, B, and Y groups creates an acute angle between Y, B, and X, so that Y attacks the carbon atom of B from the "front" instead of the "back." This may be called a *" front-side displacement mechanism."*

The three mechanisms can to a certain degree be distinguished experimentally, for the single displacement mechanism should lead, if the B–X bond involves an asymmetric carbon atom, to an inversion of configuration. Of four known enzymatic reactions that result in inverted configurations, two certainly involve a single displacement mechanism. They are the hydrolysis of amylose by beta amylase, and the phosphorolysis of maltose. The same mechanism may obtain in the conversion of glucose to galactose, for inversion occurs in the transformation of uridine diphosphoglucose to uridine diphosphogalactose, as Leloir pointed out in a previous McCollum-Pratt Symposium.

Koshland lists eleven enzymatic reactions in which configuration is retained even when the bond to an asymmetric carbon atom is broken. For all of these the double displacement mechanism appears to be preferable as an explanation to front-side displacement. A detailed analysis of the sucrose phosphorylase reaction indicates the reasons. Sucrose phosphorylase can catalyze the exchange of inorganic phosphate with glucose-1-phosphate, as demonstrated by transfer of P^{32}. If an exchange reaction of this type $(B–Z + Z^* \rightarrow B–Z^* + Z)$ is to occur by a single displacement mechanism, the Z group must be able to occupy both the site normally occupied by X, the donor, and by Y, the acceptor. Maltose phosphorylase will not catalyze this exchange, and, as noted already, the inversion that occurs in the phosphorylation of maltose indicates a single displacement mechanism. The lack of extensive racemization in the phosphorylation of sucrose, and the retention of configuration, argue against the occurrence in that reaction of a single displacement mechanism. Additional specificity requirements rule out the front-side displacement mechanism. In addition to the exchange of inorganic phosphate with glucose-1-phosphate, sucrose phosphorylase catalyzes an exchange of fructose with sucrose. By the front-side displacement mechanism, this would mean that phosphate and fructose could each act at the sites normally occupied by the other, a supposition difficult to reconcile with the failure of other substances to react which are structurally much more similar to fructose than is phosphate. It is more reasonable, Koshland thinks, to suppose that the phosphate acts at one site and the fructose at a different site, but that the glucose-enzyme complex is quite stable kinetically. Muscle phosphorylase fails to catalyze the exchange between inorganic phosphate and glucose-1-phosphate, although stereochemically it is very like sucrose phosphorylase. This difference can be explained if, instead of a stable enzyme-glucose intermediate, the muscle phosphorylase produces a transient one. There is ample evidence from chemical studies that the inverted intermediates formed in double displacement reactions may vary from the stability of fully formed covalent bonds to the transient character of a loose sharing of electrons. Or it may be that the muscle phosphorylase fails to carry out the exchange because the geometric conditions for reaction require both $B–X$ and Y groups to be present on the enzyme surface, and certain groups present in muscle phosphorylase (but not in sucrose phosphorylase) prevent this. Although failure to observe exchange between $B–Z$ and Z^* is evidence against the occurrence of a stable B-enzyme intermediate which does not require activation by the acceptor Y (in this case, fructose), it does not exclude the formation of a transitory intermediate or one which does not require activation by the acceptor.

The mechanism of the hydrolysis of acetylcholine by acetylcholinesterase came in for further consideration. Nachmansohn and Wilson have presented evidence from experiments with inhibitors and pH data to support a mechanism involving the formation of an acyl-enzyme intermediate; and in the present symposium Wilson developed this theory of mechanism in terms of the forces of interaction contributing to the stability of the enzyme-substrate complex, and the nature of the hydrolytic process and the regeneration of free enzyme. Studies with the action of the inhibitors prostigmine and eserine as a function of pH revealed a marked preference in the binding of the cationic form of eserine, a tertiary amine, in comparison with the quaternary amine prostigmine, the binding of which does not change with pH. The effect of electric charge is also seen with alternative substrates, such as dimethyl aminoethyl acetate, which is predominantly cationic below pH 8.3 and which below that pH reaches a hydrolytic rate, in comparison with acetylcholine, of 85 per cent, although at and above pH 9 the relative hydrolysis is only 30 per cent. It may be concluded that the enzyme has a negatively charged region important to the attraction, orientation, and fixation of the substrate upon the enzyme surface.

This *anionic* site upon the enzyme attracts the cationic portion $(CH_3)_3N^+-$ of the substrate molecule. Methylated competitive inhibitors inhibit with increasing potency up to *tri*alkyl inhibitors, but tetraalkyl inhibitors have no greater effect than the trialkyl ones, probably because the structure of the ammonium group prevents the enzyme from coming into close contact with more than three alkyl groups simultaneously. The enzyme must also have an *esteratic* site that reacts to form a covalent bond with the opposite, strongly polar, carbonyl end of the acetylcholine molecule, $-O-C^+-O^-$. Of

$$\underset{CH_3}{\overset{|}{}}$$

special importance is the electrophilic carbon atom in this group, for the more electrophilic the character of the species in a series of nicotinic acid derivatives, the more pronounced the inhibition of acetylcholinesterase; and similarly for various alternative substrates. Inasmuch as the enzymatic hydrolysis changes with pH, although the structure of acetylcholine itself does not, the alteration with pH must be attributed to change in the enzyme structure, such as dissociation of acidic and basic groups. The activity of the enzyme, at a maximum between pH 8 and pH 9, represents a state of dissociation capable of forming an enzyme-substrate complex. The decline of activity of the enzyme in acid media may be attributed to poorer binding caused by the addition of protons to the anionic and esteratic sites. The unimpaired binding of prostigmine by the enzyme in alkaline media, on the other hand, shows that the decline in the hydrolysis of acetylcholine with pH in the alkaline range is not due to poorer binding. It must then be due to some requirement for the acid group in the hydrolytic process. Only the undissociated acid molecules have the electrophilic carbon atom necessary for the formation of the enzyme-substrate complex.

Wilson postulates a two-step hydrolytic process: (a) simultaneous acylation of the enzyme and internal elimination of a small molecule, followed by (b) deacylation of the enzyme. The prediction, made on the basis of this proposed mechanism, that the enzyme should catalyze an exchange of oxygen between acids and water has been realized experimentally. Using thioacetic acid, H_2S is evolved. It is interesting that the small cationic inhibitor, a trimethyl ammonium ion, bound at the anionic site, does not interfere seriously with the thioacetate reaction at the neighboring esteratic site—a fine illustration of the spatial and functional independence of the two sites.

Specificity of the enzyme toward its substrates may derive either from the formation of the enzyme-substrate complex or from the hydrolytic process that follows. The former acts at low substrate concentrations, the latter at maximum velocity. The maximum velocity of an enzymatic reaction will depend on the free energy of activation, which contains both an energy and an entropy term. The cleavage of two ester bonds, such as those of ethyl acetate and acetylcholine, should have approximately the same energies of activation (although bonds more difficult to transform, such as amide bonds, would have higher energies of activation and therefore lower maximum rates). Hence the tenfold faster maximum rate found for acetylcholine than for ethyl acetate must reside in the entropy term. Wilson suggests that the critical complex which is formed would have much less freedom of orientation in the case of a substrate like acetylcholine, bound at two or more points, than in the case of a simple substrate like ethyl acetate. The change from the enzyme-substrate complex to the critical complex would therefore involve a greater entropy of activation for acetylcholine than for ethyl acetate, and a correspondingly greater maximum velocity. In this concept of enzyme mechanism, the protein " forms a matrix for the multipolar attraction of substrates and orients the substrate in a manner which is easily distorted into the critical complex."

Koshland, like Wilson, takes the reaction with acetylcholinesterase of phosphate esters, such as diisopropylfluorophosphate, to indicate that a basic group on the enzyme makes a nucleophilic attack on either the carbon atom of the acetylcholine or the phosphorus atom of the phosphate inhibitor, so as to form in the first case an acyl-enzyme intermediate which hydrolyzes readily, or in the second a phosphoryl-enzyme intermediate that is more stable. But Koshland points out that data are not yet sufficient to enable an unequivocal choice to be made between the formation, on the one hand, of an acyl-enzyme intermediate implying a double displacement mechanism, as postulated by Nachmansohn and Wilson, and a single displacement mechanism, on the other.

A consideration of the cleavage point of the substitution enzymes leads to an interesting distinction between the three phosphorylases (muscle, sucrose, maltose), which cleave the glucosyl-OPO_3 bond, and the phosphatases (acid, alkaline, acetyl, ATP), which cleave the bond between the phosphorus and O atom. The correlation of specificity with cleavage point extends to the degree at which the same two reactants may yield the same two products by means of different cleavage points. Thus sucrose and water react to give glucose and fructose when catalyzed by either invertase or maltase, but in the first case the fructose-oxygen bond is cleaved, and in the second case the glucose-oxygen bond. In these two cases the chemical nature of the split bonds is, of course, equivalent. Two general rules have by now become apparent: (a) that if chemical reactions show that one bond (R–O) is broken much more easily than an alternative one (Q–O), then enzymatic cleavage also splits the R–O bond; and (b) if the enzyme exhibits strict specificity for a group being transferred (R) and wide tolerance of variation in another (Q), then R–O cleavage occurs. To illustrate the first rule: in chemical hydrolysis of acetylcholine, the acyl-oxygen bond is readily split, the methylene-oxygen bond with great difficulty; in enzymatic cleavage, it is also the acyl-oxygen bond that is split. It follows that, in general, esterases should cleave the acyl-oxygen bond, and that transglycosidases should cleave the bond between the oxygen atom of the bridge and the carbon atom of the transferred group. The second rule is illustrated in the transfructoside action of invertase, which permits only the slightest changes in the beta fructofuranoside ring but tolerates wide variations in the other. The cleavage occurs between the oxygen atom and the fructose ring.

The important phosphate group transfer reactions are those catalyzed by the kinases and the transphosphorylases, or as Boyer and Harrison insist both should be called, the phosphoferases. In the kinase ("phosphokinase") reactions, the terminal phosphate of ATP is transferred to a compound bearing a hydroxyl group. This probably takes place by a single displacement mechanism, with one P–O bond being broken and one P–O bond being formed. The kinase reaction with creatine, the hydrolysis of ATP by lobster muscle, the phosphoglycerate kinase reaction, the hexokinase reaction, the myokinase reaction, and among others the fructokinase, galactokinase, and phosphofructokinase reactions probably all involve a nucleophilic attack on the terminal phosphorus atom of the ATP. The mechanism in the reaction of nicotinic mononucleotide with ATP, which involves displacement on the innermost phosphorus atom of ATP, may be analogous. The transphosphorylases, which involve a donor other than ATP, can be interpreted on a similar basis, namely, a displacement on the phosphorus atom by either the final acceptor or by first the enzyme and then the final acceptor. Koshland points out that whether the reaction is exchange, hydrolysis, synthesis, or transphosphorylation depends only on the particular combination of the ultimate acceptor and the phosphate donor. Phosphokinases, transphosphorylases, and both acid and alkaline phosphatases are thus basically similar, for they all transfer a phosphate group from donor X to acceptor Y. Contrariwise, the phosphorylases act by a displacement on a carbon atom rather than a phosphorus atom. Hence the transferred group (B) is a glycoside, while the phosphate group from which it is displaced becomes the donor group (X) in the generalized scheme.

Studies by Boyer and Harrison on the mechanism of the pyruvate-

ADP phosphoferase (pyruvate kinase) reaction seem to rule out either formation of a diester as intermediate or the formation of an enzyme-phosphate intermediate. By using pyruvate labelled at carbon atom 2 with C^{14}, they looked for exchange with the pyruvate moiety of phosphopyruvate. In the absence of ATP none was found, although this exchange was steady in the presence of ATP. These results rule out the formation of an enzyme-phosphate intermediate in the absence of ADP. On the other hand, evidence against the diester mechanism was found by using O^{18} as a tracer in water and testing for its incorporation into the phosphate group when the latter was transferred to ADP. If one can assume that the P–O bond is split, the hydroxyl group of the acceptor should exchange with water, allowing the oxygen atom of water to be incorporated into the terminal phosphate group transferred to ATP. No exchange with water occurred. This is also true of the analogous reactions catalyzed by 3-phosphoglycerate phosphoferase and by hexokinase. Neither water as such nor hydroxyl ions participate in the mechanism. The attachment of the phosphate to the acceptor is by way of the O atom of the acceptor itself. In this reaction mechanism it is not necessary to postulate formation of a complex between the enzyme and the group transferred. If this mechanism is correct, then the positive charge on the phosphorus atom is of central importance, and factors which increase it should favor phosphate transfer. There is adequate evidence that this is so. The role of magnesium in this reaction mechanism can also be interpreted as bringing about an increase in the positive charge on the phosphorus atom, and thus making easier the attack by nucleophilic agents.

Koshland includes the transfer of methyl and methylene groups among the reactions that may be explained by a displacement mechanism. He concludes that on the basis of mechanism " the similarities between different subgroups may be greater than between different enzymes in the same subgroup. Thus, the shift from a phosphatase to a transphosphorylase or from a glycosidase to a transglycosidase may involve merely a change in specificity, whereas two phosphorylases may react through entirely different kinds of enzyme-substrate intermediates. . . . As in the case of their chemical analogs, a few

...hanisms may suffice to explain the mode of action of ...enzymes which catalyze the wide variety of substitution ...eactions."

The Mechanism of Transglycosidation. Kalckar's discussion of transglycosidation mechanisms related the action of transglycosidases to those of the phosphorylases. A lengthy list of enzymatic transfers of glycosyl groups can now be drawn up, including not only disaccharide donors but also polysaccharides and sugar-phosphate esters. Glycosyl acceptors include hydroxyl groups of sugars, inorganic phosphate, or the nitrogen of a purine, pyrimidine, or pyridine base. A major unsettled question is whether in such transfers a glycosyl-enzyme complex is formed, e. g., in transglucosidations, transfructosidations, and transgalactosidations.

From thermodynamic data, Kalckar points out that the bond energy of glucosyl linkages varies. It is highest in the α-1,2-glucose-fructose linkage of sucrose (approximately 6600 calories), is intermediate in the α-1,4-glucose-glucose linkage of maltose (4000 cal.), and is lowest in the α-1,6-glucose-glucose linkage found in isomaltose, dextran, and glycogen (2000 cal.). Among the pentosyl linkages, the N^+-ribosyl linkage of DPN has a total $-\Delta F$ of hydrolysis of 9000 cal., over twice that of the purine and pyrimidine ribosides (4000 cal.). The new types of 1-phosphoglycosyl compounds found by Leloir and his coworkers, namely, glucose-1,6-diphosphate and uridine diphosphoglucose, have unknown bond energies. Kalckar points out that it may be possible to determine the bond energies in the analogous pentosyl compounds, ribose-1-phosphate and ribose-1,5-diphosphate, because of the availability of enzymes (nucleoside and nucleotide phosphorylases, respectively) that substitute purines (viz., hypoxanthine) for the 1-phosphate groups of both esters. It is possible, as Calvin and his colleagues proposed in a former McCollum-Pratt Symposium, that uridine diphosphoglucose (UDPG), because of the pyrophosphate linkage it contains, has a higher bond energy than the free Cori ester, glucose-1-phosphate; and that therefore UDPG can play a transferring role for glycosyl groups. Kalckar emphasizes the thermodynamic difficulty which might block any such role if the 1-ester bond of UDPG has a considerably larger bond energy than that of the free ester; and instead he suggests a three-step mechanism for glycosyl transfer:

(a)   UDP-glycosyl + acceptor $A \rightleftharpoons$ UDP + A-glycosyl

(b)   UDP + ATP $\rightleftharpoons$ UTP + ADP

(c)   UTP + P-glycosyl $\rightleftharpoons$ UDP-glycosyl + PP

The recent discovery, by Berg and Joklik, of an enzyme (nucleoside polyphosphate transphosphorylase) that catalyzes reaction (b) lends strength to this suggested scheme, inasmuch as reaction (a) is exemplified by the already known UDP-glycosyl transfers in the synthesis of glucuronides, and possibly of polysaccharides; and reaction (c) has been found by Kalckar and his coworkers to be catalyzed by a group of uridyl transferases of which three have already been observed. One of these uridyl transferases makes UDP-glucose from α-glucose-1-phosphate and uridine triphosphate (UTP); a second makes UDP-galactose in an analogous reaction; and the third involves the N-acetyl glucosamine analogue.

Undoubtedly the UDP compounds discovered by Leloir and his collaborators and by Park and Johnson have a diversity of important functions, among which Kalckar mentions the possible formation of nucleic acid linkages and the capacity to induce the formation of enzymes adaptively, or even constitutively. The latter possibility grows out of the recent work of Monod and Cohn that has revealed the existence of intermediate compounds ("organisateurs") between the substrates and adaptively induced enzymes. Thus, certain α-galactosides induce the formation of β-galactosidase even though they are neither substrates nor inhibitors of the enzyme.

The hypothesis of a glycosyl-enzyme intermediate has in particular helped to clarify the mechanism of transglycosidation by hydrolytic enzymes. DPN-ribosidase acts as a hydrolase to set free nicotinamide from DPN, but it also acts as a transglycosidase for the ADP-ribosyl group by transferring it from the nicotinamide of DPN to free nicotinamide. Zatman has added very interesting new data that throw light on this reaction and its analogues. Isonicotinic acid hydrazide, which acts as a strong inhibitor of certain "sensitive"

es (from beef, sheep, goat, duck, and pigeon) but
ther "insensitive" DPN ribosidases (from *Neurospora*,
it, frog, pig, horse, and man), was tested to see whether it would
serve as an acceptor of the ADP-ribosyl group. From systems containing the "insensitive" type of DPN ribosidase, especially one
derived from pig brain, a yellow isonicotinic hydrazide analogue of
DPN was isolated. Its formation in this system proves that certain
animal DPN-ases can function as ADP-ribosyl transferases. Zatman
suggests the following scheme:

$$ADP-ribosyl-N^+ + enzyme$$

$$+ N \Big\Uparrow\Big\Downarrow - N$$

$$ADP-ribosyl-enzyme \xrightarrow{\;H_2O\;} ADP-ribose + enzyme + H^+$$

$$- INH \Big\Uparrow\Big\Downarrow + INH$$

$$ADP-ribosyl-IN^+H + enzyme.$$

The DPN analogue is twice as potent an inhibitor of the "sensitive"
DPN-ase systems as free isonicotinic hydrazide, but is quite inactive
in so far as DPN-requiring dehydrogenase systems are concerned. In
view of the great current interest in the effects obtained with
isonicotinic hydrazide in the treatment of tuberculosis, one cannot
overlook the possibility that by incorporating a certain drug into the
structure of an essential coenzyme a great deal of light may be
thrown on the clinical activity of the drug.

In contrast to the possibility of the formation of glycosyl-enzyme
compounds, Najjar has presented evidence for the formation in one
system of an enzyme--phosphate complex, as Jagannathan and Luck
had earlier suggested. An enzyme from rabbit muscle was identified
as phosphoglucomutase (PGM) and was found to form glucose-1,
6-diphosphate from glucose-1-phosphate without ATP in two steps:
(a) an explosive synthesis within a few seconds of mixing the
reactants, followed by (b) a more gradual synthesis over a period
of about 30 minutes, utilizing glucose-1-phosphate as phosphate
donor. The enzyme is quite unstable and is completely inactivated
by aging for 4 to 5 days. When aged enzyme is used, only the initial
burst of synthesis is present and there is no secondary formation of

glucose diphosphate. The initial burst does not increase with amount of ATP or glucose-1-phosphate but varies only with the concentration of enzyme. This suggested that still another phosphate donor must be present, and it was postulated to be a phosphorylated form of the enzyme itself. The two-part cyclic system was formulated as follows:

(a) PGM-phosphate $+$ glucose-1-phosphate $\rightleftharpoons$ glucose-1,6-diphosphate $+$ PGM

(b) glucose-1,6-diphosphate $+$ PGM $\rightleftharpoons$ glucose-6-phosphate $+$ PGM-phosphate.

With crystalline phosphoglucomutase (PGM) the formation of glucose-1,6-diphosphate was found to agree with the postulated scheme, showing that this system does not need to be primed with glucose-1,6-diphosphate as a coenzyme for the transphosphorylation. Similarly, the transphosphorylation of ribose-1-phosphate to ribose-5-phosphate without an addition of the diphosphate ester, a problem raised by Kalckar, may be explained.

Polypeptide Synthesis. Another type of enzyme-phosphate compound was found by Lipmann and Maas in their study of pantothenic acid synthesis. This reaction represents a model peptide synthesis. In this system, a pyrophosphate split of ATP initiates a peptide condensation of pantoic acid and β-alanine. However, when radioactive pyrophosphate was used as a tracer, it was found that the pyrophosphate did not equilibrate with ATP independently of the addition of pantoic acid, although the β-alanine was immaterial to the equilibration. This finding was interpreted in terms of a transfer of the pyrophosphoryl group from ATP to the enzyme, and in the second stage an exchange of the pyrophosphoryl on the enzyme with pantoate, yielding a pantoyl-enzyme compound. The lack of direct exchange between ATP and pyrophosphate is thus regarded as being due to the need of pantoate to liberate the bound pyrophosphate from the enzyme. The primary activation of the enzyme is hence by means of pyrophosphorylation, in place of the adenylation found in the ATP-CoA-acetate reaction. Coenzyme A is clearly not involved here. Most significant is the observation that the reaction requires activation of the *carboxyl* group in order to synthesize a peptide bond, since it is the pantoate and not the β-alanine that combines with the enzyme in the pyrophosphoryl exchange.

Looking into the future, this summary may well close with a consideration of the model for polypeptide synthesis suggested by Lipmann. Combining the mechanism for the pyrophosphoryl synthesis of a peptide bond, as just described, with the idea of a sequential arrangement of specific activation centers, along the lines proposed by Britton Chance as a basis for electron transfer between

PROTEIN SYNTHESIS.   MODEL CYCLE

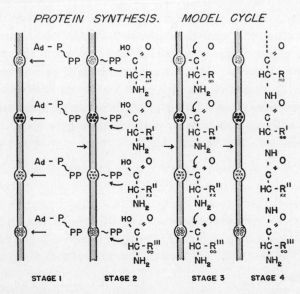

STAGE I   STAGE 2   STAGE 3   STAGE 4

FIG. 8. Model suggested for polypeptide synthesis by Lipmann. Stage 1, specific centers on the model are activated by a transfer to them of ∼ PP from ATP. Stage 2, exchange of pyrophosphoryl (or phosphoryl) groups for the carboxyl groups of specific amino acids. Stage 3, each carboxyl group, thus activated, unites in peptide linkage with the amino group of the adjacent amino acid. Stage 4, the finished polypeptide is split off. (From Lipmann).

the cytochromes, Lipmann has devised a brilliant scheme for explaining protein synthesis. One supposes, to start with, that an enzyme has the activation centers for specific amino acids lined up in a particular sequence. These each become activated by a combination with pyrophosphoryl groups transferred to the enzyme from ATP. Next these are exchanged with the carboxyl groups of the corresponding free amino acids, which are thus lined up with the α-amino group of each one adjacent to the now activated carboxyl group of the next. A condensation reaction then results in the formation of a free polypeptide chain having the same pattern as the sequence of specific activation centers on the enzyme. The complete polypeptide, freed from the enzyme, leaves the latter ready to repeat the cycle (Fig. 8).

Because the synthesis of a peptide bond requires less energy than that which is available from an energy-rich phosphate bond, the excess energy may be used in the concentration of the specific amino acids at the enzymatic sites, as Linderstrøm-Lang has proposed. This would be possible if the enzyme-carboxyl linkage yields only about half as many calories as does the energy-rich phosphoryl bond. The mechanism for directing specific amino acids to the right centers remains to be worked out, but even so the proposed mechanism has obvious value in explaining such phenomena as gene duplication, the genetic control of enzymes, and the formation of adaptive enzymes.

AUTHOR INDEX OF PARTICIPANTS

SUBJECT INDEX

A

Absolute rate theory: 123

Acetaldehyde as substrate for glyceraldehyde-3-phosphate dehydrogenase: 467

Acetate-requiring mutants: 472

Acetoin formation: 470, 483; synthesis, 605

Acetylation of amino acids: 480; of glutathione by acetyl-imidazole, 590, 592; of imidazole by acetyl-P, 589; of orthophosphate, non-enzymatic, 585

Acetylcholine, hydrolysis of: 624

Acetylcholinesterase: 624, 627, 642; inhibition of by eserine, 644; inhibition of by prostigmine, 644; interaction between active groups of and its substrate, 652

Acetyl-CoA: acetylation of amines by, 482; formation of, 471; formation from pyruvic acid, 606; pyrophosphate formation and, 474

Acetyl-CoA and oxalacetate, condensation of: 483

Acetyl glutathione: 467, 477

Acetyl-imidazole, equilibrium between Acetyl-P: 588; acetylation of glutathione, 590, 592; absorption spectrum of, 582; aminolysis of, 481; energy-rich nature of, 581–97; reaction with glutathione, 594; reaction with orthophosphate, 591; synthesis from acetyl phosphate and imidazole, 581

Acetyl-imidazole decomposition: influence of $H_2PO_4^-$, 588; spectrophotometric measurement of, 586

Acetyl-imidazole hydrolysis, effects of pH on: 587

Acetyllipoic acid compound: 471

Acetyl lipoic acid formation, from acetyl phosphate: 567

Acetylmethylcarbinol: 472; formation of, 483

Acetylphosphatase: 476, 627

Acetyl phosphate: acetyl lipoic acid formation from, 567; and acetyl-imidazole, equilibrium between, 588; in acetylation of imidazole, 589; -imidazole reaction, components of, 583; as substrate for glyceraldehyde-3-phosphate dehydrogenase, 467; transacetylase, acylation of DL-6, 8-dimercaptooctanoate, 567

Activated complexes: 10; structure of, 131

Active aldehyde: 470

Active glycoaldehyde: 543

Active succinic semialdehyde: 475

Acyl and carbonyl complexes, formation of in oxidative processes: 465

Acyl complexes: degradation of, 476; transfer of, 480

Acyl-enzyme complex: 467, 468, 476; hydroxamic acid formation, 468

Acyl enzyme formation: 520–32

Acyl group formation: 475

Acyl imidazoles: 595

Acylimidazole linkage, ΔF of: 483

Acyl phosphatase reaction, inhibition by glutathione: 535

Acyl-transfer reactions: 481; chemical, 480; CoA transfer from thiolester to a free acid, 481; from one thiolester to another, 481; thiolester to choline, amino acids, amines or imidazole, 481; thiolester to inorganic phosphate, 481; thiolester to oxaloacetate, 481

Acylation of DL-6, 8-dimercapto-octanoate, acetyl PO_4-transacetylase: 567

Adenine: 618, 693; formation of adenylic acid, 697

Adenosinetriphosphatase: 627; reaction mechanisms for, 664

Adenosyl methionine: 635

5-Adenylic phosphorylase: 679

Alanine racemase: 616

Alcohol dehydrogenase: acetaldehyde dissociation constant, 500; binding of DPN, yeast, 496, 497; comparison of constants for yeast and mammalian, 514; concentration, effect on equilibrium, 499; deuterium transfer with, 358, 359; horse liver, 439; mammalian, 495; ternary complex, as a reactive intermediate, 513; yeast, 439, 496

809